LENIN

LENIN

THE NOVEL

ALAN BRIEN

WILLIAM MORROW AND COMPANY, INC.

NEW YORK

First published in England,1987, by Martin Secker & Warburg Limited,
54 Poland Street, London W1V3DF.

Library of Congress Cataloging-in-Publication Data

Brien, Alan.
  Lenin: the novel / Alan Brien.
    p. cm.
  ISBN 0-688-07944-X
  1. Lenin, Vladimir Il'ich, 1870–1924—Fiction. 2. Soviet Union—
History—20th century—Fiction. I. Title.
PR6052.R44315L4 1988
823'.914—dc19   88-1908
                                                CIP

Printed in the United States of America

First U.S. Edition

1 2 3 4 5 6 7 8 9 10

BOOK DESIGN BY JAYE ZIMET

FOR JILL, WHO THOUGHT I'D NEVER BEGIN
AND THEN I'D NEVER END

CONTENTS

LENIN

SIMBIRSK

1 8 8 6 - 1 8 8 7

I

JANUARY 13   SIMBIRSK   1886

Father is dead. Inside my head, the fact sticks like a clot of blood on the walls of the skull. It is as if I had just had a—what's the word? Sasha would know—hemorrhage is it? A small part of my brain seems to have gone numb. There's a blind spot, a bare patch, a little bit of desert I can no longer grow anything on.

The day before yesterday Father was finishing off his Annual Report. With him in his study, checking the figures, was Anna. Now she tells us that she stopped reading out statistics because he became delirious. Started muttering nonsense. She persuaded him to go off to bed. True, she is the eldest. She and father have a strange relationship, close but somehow formal. The Confidential Clerk, Sasha calls her. But why didn't she tell the rest of us? After all, Father *delirious*! As easy to imagine as—what?—the Tsar reading a book? Ha!

Yesterday, he did not have dinner with us at noon. How could I not have noticed? Mother says he approached the dining room door and just nosed in—"as though he had come to say good-bye."

About five o'clock, Mother summoned Anna and me to his study where he lay on his sofa. As we three watched, he shuddered and grew stiff. He was nearly fifty-five. *Father is dead.*

JANUARY 14   SIMBIRSK   1886

Each morning, from a list tucked into the edge of the mirror, I memorize five new words. A week ago I could have sworn I was not conscious that the word "hemorrhage" existed, let alone being able to spell it and apply it to myself. Now it has killed father. I wonder—is it hereditary? Like the dreadful "honors" that descended on all of us when I was three or so and Father became a State Councillor. (I should include here a diagram of the three ladders of our hierarchy, Court, Military and Civil, and its thirteen horizontal degrees of human worth. State Councillor is on level number eight, counting from the Tsar downward that is.) I had just got used to filling in the word "Noble" in the box marked "Rank" on forms when Father was moved up a rung to Actual State Councillor. At the age of twelve, this seemed to me a bit comic. Still does, to be honest. Not Pretend Councillor, you see, or Supposed, or Rumoured, or So-Called, but *Actual*. It also meant the Order of Vladimir (Third Class) since he became the equivalent of Major-General.

Standing in as oldest male in absence of Sasha—still in St. Petersburg—I could hardly put all this guff down on the official burial documents without, I am sorry to say, an occasional snigger. That isn't really like me. But then Anna says I've changed *overnight*, becoming (would you believe it?) rude, aggressive, callous, given to nasty jokes and jeers.

Perhaps older sisters are always like that.

Will she ever stop droning on about how appalling I was as a child? How *backward* I was, *she* feared even possibly *retarded*! Only learned to walk at the same time as Olya who is a year and a half younger! Toppled over all the time, falling on my big, fat head, *she* worried was far too heavy for my body! *She* christened me *Kubyshka*, or Little Wooden Block, meaning, I suppose, that I was as boringly indestructible as an educational toy.

Talking of toys, Anna also spreads the story that I deliberately broke all of mine, and many of theirs, pulling them to pieces behind the nursery door under the pretense that I wanted to know how they were made.

"Kubyshka!" For a diminutive, "Volodya" is bad enough. Though "Vladimir" (even *first-class*!) does not suit me much better. I prefer "Ilyich" because that is how I address myself inside my head.

Perhaps a death, and a funeral (day after tomorrow), in a family that was always so close and so somehow *ordered,* brings up these silly tales of childhood. Or is it that my mind is buzzing about like a locked-in fly, anything rather than settle on the dominating object in the house—our dead father?

I have never tried a diary before. But I can see that, though I complain about the things people say about me, I must really like them or I wouldn't note them down. How pathetic! How self-indulgent! From now on, I will try to make this a record of truth.

In future, no more sentimentality! No more romance! After all, everybody dies.

JANUARY 15   SIMBIRSK   1886

The day before the funeral. Father laid out in open coffin on the living room table. This morning, before anyone was up, I went in there.

What I saw could have been a waxwork model of me. Me dressed up, made up, to look like a middle-aged state functionary, your typical ennobled civil servant. Since I have pledged to get everything right, I also felt he looked—well, a bit lower-class. More like somebody's bailiff or head clerk. If we are really so alike, as Anna says everybody notices, then I am examining myself at fifty-four. Let's be scientific, and Sasha-like.

Brow. A filing cupboard. I have always had this feeling that if Father had a knob up there, he'd have been able to sit down and slide out the card index on which he recorded all that mass of detail, the vast collection of facts, he had amassed as school inspector.

Eyes. Like a mask cut out of paper worn a bit too often at family charades. Yet with lids closed, metallic as Tatar face armor. Someone who laughed a lot or stared hard at the sun. If the slanting lids were open—dare I? YES—my own, tiny cinnamon eyes.

Nose. A bit snouty with a dash of the animal. What?—fox or weasel. Some questing, burrowing, hunting creature.

Hair. Almost totally bald. What's left, like mine, foxy red. My hair going too—at fifteen! A long farewell to those blond curls, like Christmas party streamers.

Complexion. Gray. Not corpse gray, but the gray of his, and so far my, everyday life. Gray of somebody who makes wild forays into the light, but prefers watching, with lined brow, from the shadows.

Build. Mine. Stocky, chubby, mulish shoulders. Deep, broad chest. The set of a chucker-out, possibly a stevedore. Even dead, retaining muscular bulge, india-rubber bounce.

This is how I should look, embalmed and put on show. Ha!

I touched my father. The deep, deep cold of his flesh, as if he had been already buried for decades, sunk in a glacier. Even now, twelve hours later, the chill steels my fingertips.

JANUARY 16   SIMBIRSK   1886

The funeral ... Everything you would expect from our noble
Orthodox Church. I was one of the coffin bearers so I observed
it all, close-up. I cannot say it impressed me much as a farewell to
this world of the flesh and the Devil. Instead, the presence of all
too living humanity soon grew overpowering. I seemed to be
hemmed in by walls of sense impressions.

By smells of oils—holy oil and hair oil; oil from olives, from
nuts, from sweat glands, from skins; oil for lamps, for guns and
swords, for leather and wood, for carriages, for machinery; oil of
the cook and the embalmer; oil of church and state: anything and
everything unctuous, oleaginous.

By smells of smokes, clouds and vapors—the smoke of incense,
of cigars, of turf fires; the smoke of pea soup with ham, of fresh
tea, of altar candles; the smoke of pollen rising from shaken wreaths,
of steaming horse shit, of mouths chewing unheard words in the
frosty air; the smoke of damp skirts and soaked greatcoats, of
steaming horse piss, of atomy flakes from snow-sculptured bushes:
anything and everything redolent, reeky, crepuscular.

By smells of powders, spores and grains—the ice-creamy vanilla sweetness of female cosmetics; the breakfasty nuttiness of new
sawdust; the hot ash of snuff; the dead dankness of gravestone
grit; the floury patina of baker's sugar on the funeral cakes; the
dry, artificial dustiness of that handful of baked earth, ordered in
advance to scatter on the coffin, "saving your honors' fingers" the
pollution of real, staining soil; the tepid, stale comfort of the cathedral air, dancing with dyed motes, as the winter sunlight radiates its spokes through the stained glass: anything and everything
that is carried by the atmosphere, blown on the breeze.

I was hounded by sounds—bells upon bells, peal after peal
falling from the belfry onto the churchyard as brazen hoops from
on high, pancakes piling up on a plate; hymn upon hymn, boys'
soprano so clean and pure it slices through your temples like an
ice-pudding headache, men's bass so subterranean and slow it vi-
brates toward you under the floor and shakes your crotch like a
hand on your balls; tongues of mourners clacking away like sewing
machines, no meanings, only background noise. Every item picked
out by the ear as too loud, too shrill, too repetitive, unhuman,
barely animal, basically mechanical.

I was haunted by visions—"details," as in our new Art Appreciation primers at school, abstracted from the overall official picture of the funeral. All of them curiously chosen for their "earthiness," their emphasis on the body, on physical functions. A pretty woman, confident she is last in line, giving a searching probe with right-hand forefinger at her bum. A trio of merchants ("Foxes" in our family argot) too absorbed to care who sees them, counting and recounting a grubby deck of rubles as they pass the grave. An ancient aristo (what we call "Apes" or "Peacocks") ablaze with medals, whose nostrils sprout bristles like shaving brushes. A young couple, entwined like twin octopuses who cross in front of the hearse without seeing we exist, would swear in court no funeral occurred in that place on that day.

A pigeon with one leg, earlier blundering about like a drunken cripple, which rests its blackened stump on the scalloped fringe of a grave just in time to stand at attention, in dignity, as the cortege passes.

A stain of wine on Father's copy of the *Simbirsk Gazette,* still unread, lying on the study desk.

I turned queasy, back home for baked meats. Heard myself beginning to growl and snarl like a wild beast in a pet shop. Who were all these ludicrous forked creatures, done up in clothes and ornaments as in a nursery rhyme, billeted in my lair? What sort of person was Father that his funeral would attract such hybrid monsters?

The noises I was making started to be audible even to me— it was like being woken by your own snoring—and I was glad that someone took me by the arm and led me away from the concourse of caricatures.

"Why don't you go upstairs and be on your own? You've had a trying time and deserve a rest. Anna and I can manage." It was old Quince-Face, Kerensky, our headmaster. Father had appointed him our guardian.

I allowed myself to be conducted to the private staircase that leads only to the double attic shared by Sasha and me. I even forgave Q.F. for his ghastly child, Alexander, that five- or six-year-old police spy who has been going around telling everybody that I shoot kittens and tear the wings off blackbirds.

But it is beneath me to deny such calumnies. In principle, I would kill kittens, tear wings off birds, for a higher cause. What must be done must be done. So I contented myself with taking no action, except giving him a real boot up the backside the last time I saw him out of sight of any adults.

JANUARY 17   SIMBIRSK   1886

Woke this morning early, snow-light on the ceiling like the reflection from a giant moon, snow-silence all around, a world buried in cotton wool. I felt—what?—bleached. No, newborn, new-*laid*, like a fresh-dropped egg. Like I used to feel at Easter in the old days, when life could start again, purged and scoured of all the old rusts and scabs. At the funeral I must have had some sort of attack, a kind of epilepsy, *petit mal* Anna calls it. All I know is that it felt as if I were being sucked down into another dimension.

Nobody but Q.F. noticed so far as I could tell. No one said anything, anyway, according to Anna. She was far more concerned to ensure that we all realized how distinguished and admired Father must have been to attract such a turnout. All the top Apes and Peacocks were there, though even she had to admit typically odious in their admiration of their own condescension, exuding vague benevolence, telling children standing between their parents that they must be brave about the loss of their father, and making a fair crack at getting right the name of the deceased. "He was a good, sound fellow, er, Nikolai Ilyich, sound and, er, responsible." Most of the middling sort, she reported, government functionaries, professional pensioners, superfluous gentlefolk, also appeared, though careful not to be seen to be too close to the dead man, after all you never know. "Decent sort, Ilya, er, Nikolaevich, but never quite one of us." These are the Parrots (sit on the same perch saying the same thing) and the Rabbits (say nothing, keep on the move). I think I'll stay here today on my iron bed and read. In my (slightly smaller) half of our annex there is plenty to choose from.

I have not got very far with Goethe and Heine and Schiller that represent Mother's heritage from her Germanic family. School books I nevertheless enjoy—Ovid, Xenophon, Homer, Suetonius, and my favorite, Cicero. Hugo, Molière, Balzac, I suppose from Father's student days. I moved them all up from the living room on my fifteenth birthday. (What a different person I was then!) Then my own Russians—Turgenev most of all, Tolstoy almost as much, Goncharov's *Oblomov* read how many times?

Sasha's room is mainly given over to scientific textbooks, or hefty reference books (Darwin, Huxley, Spencer, Mill) as well as the inevitable sets of flasks, beakers and test tubes. There is, I'm sure, only one piece of fiction. N. Chernyshevsky's *What Is to Be Done?* or *Stories about New People.*

S. has (twice) urged me to read this but I can't seem to get into it. After *On the Eve, Fathers and Sons* and *Rudin,* it seems clumsily written and, especially for Sasha, very romantic.

Imagine! A rich, young Peacock gives away all his money and trains himself to be a revolutionary. He even does body-building exercises, eats raw meat, and sleeps on a bed of nails. Ha!

No one else ever comes up here, not even Olya, my favorite, my *almost* twin.

It is only just sinking in that Sasha was not at the funeral. A thousand miles away (correction: 935) in Petersburg, even his letter saying he would not be coming only arrived on the morning of the funeral. It was as laconic as he is. He writes that he is sorry to hear the news but that he has reached a critical point in his experiments on his annelid worms.

I thought Mother might be hurt. But supposing she were, who could tell? She is not a great one for expressing her emotions in words. Strangers have to take on faith her feelings for her platoon of a family—for me and Sasha and Anna and Olya and Marya and Dmitri as well as for the other little Olga who was born and died two years before I was born and little Nikolai who was born and died when I was three. You only begin to sense, when you know her, how much is banked down inside. Various Parrots are gossiping on about how she never wept, barely spoke, at the funeral, so Anna has heard.

Sitting in the dark alcove behind the stove I watched her, illuminated like a cathedral statue, under the white oil lamp with its tin reflector, opening Sasha's letter. Her face did not change. She took it and just brushed it with her lips.

Now, Sasha, of course, always spoke the absolute truth or kept his mouth shut. (Or so at least Anna was informing all the mourners who were willing to listen—not many.) I suppose I believe that. In a questionnaire in our family magazine, published usually at the end of the summer holidays, we were all asked: What are the two worst vices? He answered "Lying and cowardice." What did I answer? Need you ask? I answered "Lying and cowardice."

Until very recently, those four years between us made me his shadow, his echo.

Another of those damned family tales has me invariably replying "The same as Sasha" to every inquiry, even to Do you want cream or butter on your porridge? According to this version of the Ulyanov Saga, Volodya the toy breaker, the top-heavy box on legs, the raucous player of pratical jokes, only became the perfect pedant when he saw Sasha in his school uniform with the silver buttons, and cried out *"The same as Sasha!"*

Sasha, needless to say, and you don't need to be Sasha's favorite author (Dostoievksy) to work that out, looks not at all like me or Father. Sasha alone, I have to say, is almost as handsome as Mother, though in a weird sort of way it's hard to describe. I have nicknamed him over the years the Clown, the Ikon, the Idiot Prince—all quite funny if you know him. But none of them ever seemed to catch on.

His face is elongated, as if reflected in the back of a spoon, with a dropaway chin that you could only notice in profile. *His* skin isn't gray, oh no. It's white as frozen milk, and all his features are carefully carved. "A snowman by Cellini," I blush to recall I captioned a sketch of him by Olga, a year or so back.

But I swear people in the town who have never laid eyes on him before do bump into each other staring at him. Still, I suppose they would do the same if they met Quasimodo.

It is his eyes that most distract people. They are recessed deep in that bony skull, almost as if they were turned inward. The total effect is not helped toward the anonymity he seems to crave by black hair that stands out like a nest of snakes.

Sometimes I think he appears as—how would Father have put it in his lectures to us on religious history?—the apotheosis of Don Quixote. Other times I fancy he is more like Rosinante—the Horse with the Rueful Countenance. Anyway, well cast to be the tragic protagonist or the destined marytr. In that department, it's definitely *not* the-same-as-Sasha for me, thanks. I'd rather be Sancho Panza. When Father used to take us through Homer, line by line, I always identified with Odysseus, the crafty survivor, rather than any of the pious boneheads who were supposed to be the heroes. Still, how many people does one meet who can play a lethal game of billiards, meanwhile shouting out chess moves on a board carried in their head? Could Odysseus? Sasha can!

JANUARY 24   SIMBIRSK   1886

Sasha remains in Petersburg, from which he dispatches a typical taciturn communiqué informing us that he has been awarded a gold medal for whatever it is he does with his worms. Anna, who's also up there except during the holidays, says she rarely sees him.

He's always locked away in a cupboard off his bed-sitting room. Now we know why. And to think I'd been telling myself this story about him having joined that People's Will group, *Narodnaya Volya*, that blew Tsar Alexander II into pieces five years ago and become engaged in brewing up another bomb for Tsar Alexander III. Their slogan, repeated by Father in a whisper of fascinated horror, "Alexander after Alexander," seemed to me very much in Sasha's clipped, tombstone style.

But then, whatever he is doing or thinking, he never tells. He must have been about sixteen when he lost his faith in religion. But none of us heard anything about it until Father asked him casually one Sunday whether he had been to vespers. He answered "No!" in such a voice that even Father, who as superintendent of the public schools in the province was accustomed to making the most savage headmasters cringe, thought it best to say no more.

Anna ranges about the house, desperate for someone she can really talk to (at, more likely). She keeps sighing for Sasha, even though she must know he would not be much use as an audience to her. He'd listen all right but then remain totally silent at the end. Something compulsive chatterers and myth-knitters like Anna find particularly frustrating. They'd rather you didn't listen. (I think.)

Our Mitya at twelve and Marya (eight) are too young to appreciate the nuances of gossip. And my beloved Olya, her disloyalty in walking before her turn forgiven (but not forgotten), would rather spend her time with me. We go into retreat in the orchard, under a snow-thatched lattice of branches like a Tatar war tent, with a shared blanket and a couple of baked potatoes that double as hot-water bottles. Drunk with laughter, we dream up comic fantasies about friends and family.

So to find someone she can tell what is *really happening* in the *actual world* (her words) Anna has to catch me on the wing. Not easy, since I acquired this habit of entering and leaving the house by the windows—I don't know why—when I was very small.

JANUARY 30   SIMBIRSK   1886

The Petersburg term must be about to begin any time now. But Anna still here.

Imagine living in a town a thousand miles from the capital. Five hundred and sixty from your country's nearest big city, your country's only other true big city, Moscow. How can Europeans hope to understand us, or we understand them? Our nearest neighbors in spirit—no, not spirit, in mind—must be either China or America. Yet both of those could fit together within Russia's borders and still leave space over for Europe. But don't let me get started on what it means to be condemned to survive in the back-woods of Simbirsk!

When old Kerensky asked for an example of a paradox in the Rhetoric class I leaped up with one on Simbirsk. No one comes here by accident. No one comes here except by accident. Ha! Old K. stared at me, raised his eyes to heaven, puffed out his cheeks, strained and swallowed painfully, like someone forcing down an inedible piece of stale bread, Or perhaps someone expelling an undigested piece of tough crap. Either way, the expression would be the same. And I must say I seem to be able to trigger it more often than any other pupil.

I can't imagine why Anna would want to spend a minute longer here than she needs to. Of course, she pictures herself as supporting and comforting Mother in her bereavement. But, honestly, comforting Mother would be like taking buckets of water to Lake Baikal, or sending a ton of chocolate to that great, fat lump, the Tsar. She radiates affection, concern, care, devotion, dedica-tion, sacrifice, like a stove. Like a stove on wheels, she moves around on tiny, invisible castors, red-hot with love. And any piece of love *you* brought to *her*, hoping to pop it inside the glowing mouth and feed that hourglass, faintly potbellied kiln, would catch fire and burn to ash on the palm of your hand before you got within touching distance.

As a furnace of family feeling, she is self-feeding, a perpetual source of life-giving energy. Like the sun. And like the sun, it is unthinkable to imagine a day she will not have risen before us to warm our world. She is extraordinary. Far more unusual, and unrepeatable, than Father. We do not appreciate her. Yet she can also be somehow comical.

We thought Father was a slave driver. Mother, far from eman-cipating us serfs, or ameliorating our conditions a little, has re-doubled the pace. She positively worships Sasha for sticking with his Petersburg worms instead of returning to see Father handed over to the Simbirsk ones (not funny, Ilyich. Sorry, Old Man). I think she may even have a faint contempt for Anna for not staying there with him.

FEBRUARY 7   SIMBIRSK   1886

Anna left this morning. As I write this, I cannot help glancing back at some of the earlier pages. Never having kept a diary I only now realize how often what was correct then, only a few weeks ago, may now seem wrong. Whatever you put down looks so permanent. A historian or a biographer could easily be persuaded that some entry summed up what you felt most of your life, most of your youth, at least most of that year. Yet I know, rereading what I have written about Anna, that nothing need be really true except at the moment of putting it on paper.

From what I've left behind as evidence, even I would easily imagine it was impossible for us to have become quite intimate in this last week. Whatever subject was raised, we found we were talking about Father. Now that he had gone, it was as if we were seeing him for the first time. Perhaps his afterimage was more powerful than his presence. Or was it that his presence had been too powerful? So that it was easier to examine his memory, like his photograph, than his real live face, to autopsy his reputation instead of his person. Anyway, these were the sort of themes we found we could share. We did have something in common—Ilya Nikolaevich Ulyanov.

We pooled our information, only to find it did not always agree. We asked each other questions but did not arrive at any certain conclusions. Had Father been a success or a failure? We did not even know that for sure.

Professionally, well, yes-and-no. A snakes-and-ladders career. Depending on how you look at it.

No doubt, he had climbed a long way up from plebby beginnings in what seems to have been a rather squalid area of Astrakhan, that half-Tatar Volga port on the Caspian.

Anna says that Father sent for her just before she left for college to tell her *his* father had been a poor tailor who died when he was seven. His elder brother put him through grammar school and university (Kazan, actually—top-rank provincial, good enough for Father and Tolstoy, and probably me next year, though not Sasha and Anna).

No wonder his children have inherited this overwhelming desire to study, this painful sense of duty, this admiration for persistence, self-denial and self-improvement. Certainly he tried hard

to raise a dynasty that was distinctly un-Russian. No mess, no laziness, no daydreaming, no slug-a-bedism, no Oblomovs, in this
household.

At first, Father appeared to be rising irresistibly. Academic
records—Anna has been through his desk—show he always won
top marks. Like Sasha. Like me. He became the protégé of his
maths prof, Lobashevsky (never heard of him). Anna says Sasha
has assured her Lob was a genius, the founder of non-Euclidean
geometry. Would have been world-famous—if only he had not
had the bad luck to be a Russian. Oh, *that* Lobashevsky!

After graduation (Physics, Maths), Lob fixed for him the post
of director of the Meteorological Station at Penza. She says it was
a characteristic Russian government job: prestigious, demanding,
thankless, and, of course, unpaid. To support himself he taught
his subjects at the Institute of the Nobility in Penza.

Six years later, aged thirty-three (all this is written out, and
filed away, like a curriculum vitae intended to be presented to St.
Peter when he arrives at the pearly gates), he marries, moves on,
and becomes a schoolmaster in Nizhni-Novgorod. NN is, I hear,
quite a place. Cafés, theaters, newspapers, libraries, politics, a hotbed
of intelligentsia, the full life of a city. Here Anna, then Sasha, then
the first Olga, were born. Here too, I imagine, Father discovered
his philosophy of life, his attitude to God, the Tsar and, well, what
else is there for a good state servant? All his books have "Nizhni-
Novgorod" written after his name inside the cover.

In 1869, the year before I was born, he was given what must
have seemed a dubious promotion. He became one of the first
inspectors of primary schools anywhere. And was posted to Simbirsk province.

According to Anna, who has read up on these things, it was
a good time to start a career in education. Alexander II was encouraging expansion of learning, the transfer of knowledge to the
people. (We have discovered a timetable for progress, based on
government projections, which Father preserved. It gives 1922 as
the Year of Total Literacy. I must keep it—should be worth a
fortune as a curio in 1923.) In 1874, he became superintendent
of primary schools. That Annual Report, unfinished at his death,
contains the information that in his seventeen years he had "caused
to be built four hundred and fifty schools, doubling pupil attendance for the province."

Everyone agrees he worked like a Titan. As we recall together
those wonderful homecomings, little Christmases, we begin to realize how often he must have been away. We had had a childhood

more like that of the family of a deep-sea sailor than a school official.

We checked the entries in his diary, bare notes of places and travel times, means of transport, reason for journey, expenses, and confirmed that he was on the road most of the year, often for weeks on end, in every season, in any weather.

No wonder he wrote down all the readings he collated from barometer and thermometer, records of wind speed and direction, soil temperature, moisture content of atmosphere, average rainfall and then made his forecast. He also, stickler for accuracy, registered how often he was wrong in his calculations and Mother was right in her guesses. He did not mention—did he know?—that her prophecies were based on whether the hens were facing east or west, how late the sheep slept, and whether the bees were humming high or low.

Of course, he used to tell us bits about his journeys. But it was only flipping through these bare jottings that I suddenly saw him, in a flash, on horseback wading the floods of spring along roads more like rivers; juddering by wagon across the iron-ribbed mud of autumn where blocked ruts had to be cleared with a sledgehammer; sliding by sled over a winter countryside so eider-downed with snow that all traces of human habitation had vanished and he steered by compass and the stars.

Father had a short temper. Like me, I fear. But I hope I also grow to such a man, hardened by cheerful obstinacy, who can get on with anybody, whoever they are, on terms of equality. Unlike his city-bound colleagues, he prided himself on operating more like a trapper than a pen-pusher.

He would turn up unexpectedly on many a rural official's doorstep, willing to sleep the night on the floor of a hut, or among animals in the barn.

Yet despite this devotion to duty, his entire career almost foundered when it should have been at its peak. He was forcibly retired at fifty-one, and only taken back by an administrative fluke. In the last few years of his life, he was to see (so we read from documents in his desk) much of his life's work destroyed by the reaction against popular education that followed the assassination of Alexander II in 1881.

He also kept clippings from liberal newspapers we never saw in the house which mildly protest against the Statute of 1884 ordering the dismissal of progressive academics, the expulsion of unreliable students.

We never heard, or overheard, a word from him in sympathy

with those who suffered. I was specially interested in one cutting which has the Minister of Education announcing that schooling should never be provided for "the children of cooks." What about the children, and grandchildren, of Mongol tailors?

The case of Ilya Nikolaevich Ulyanov remains temporarily unsolved. Anna opts for secret radicalism. Did he not sing the verses of the subversive poet, Pleshcheyev, when walking with us children in the woods where we would not encounter eavesdroppers? Don't ask me—my mind must have been on other things. It is true old Quince-Face once called him, in my presence, "the Liberal." But I took this to be some kind of common-room nickname referring to his open, straightforward, direct manner, already mentioned.

I see him as a good-hearted, generous conformist. If anything, he did too much for the system, for what Sasha calls "Tsar-ism"? (I cannot wait for him to come home for summer when I will compel him to give his assessment.) Mother has had letters every day from old pupils, now teachers, even inspectors, some even well known. All tell how he gave them extra tuition after hours, or at weekends. (Free, of course!) After he became the top man in the province, the superintendent, he would still take the classes of teachers who were ill, or away for personal reasons, without ever letting the authorities know.

MARCH 12   SIMBIRSK   1886

Winter is over—official! In Simbirsk, it happens almost as quickly as you can say it. My regime since Anna left has been severe and unchanging. Up before dawn, jobs around the house, hour of homework, school and more school, three hours of homework, until at last, in the fullness of the night, skating along the river. I'm going to get my gold medal from the Grammar (same as Sasha!).

From today, alas, no more winter pleasures. Spring has arrived. Continuous noise of gunfire along the Volga as the ice floes crack, tilt up and start to ride downstream on each other's backs, like bones through a mincer. Another sound too invades the whole town. Soft, hissing whisper, like water trickling down the back of a cave, as the snows melt. The sun, which has been at best coldly distant, pale and metallic, for months on end, now breathes warmly on the periwigged trees, the padded houses, the glassy streets.

Already, the winter white has almost vanished from the canvas.

I have studied our snow very closely day and night. Life here encourages great attention to small matters. While the sun shines, it is the flattest, most bleached, most blank white, like a pattern of paper cutouts on paper. It has no shades or tints, no perspective, no detail. It absorbs rather than reflects light. After a while, it produces a kind of blindness as if the pupils of your eyes had been frozen out. It can send you mad. Under the moon, it is much more fascinating. Everything seems handmade under the moon, which is why night is so dangerous. Then the snow is silvered, massy and ornate, a precious ore, set off by the sepia of cloud shadows. This can also send you mad in another direction, into a world of make-believe, opera and ballet, Greek epics and Nordic sagas.

What spring does—I'm not inventing this, you can read testimonies to it in Pushkin who visited here, Goncharov who was born here—is turn the place into a giant cone, a huge bouquet, a pyramid, of colors. The entire slope becomes one tumbling orchard pouring down from the cliffs of the high right-hand bank in a waterfall of flowers, mainly a velvety white, but speckled with yellows and blues, and riding on a bed of bright green leaves. These are the blossoms of the sharp, sweet-sour, little golden Volga apple, of the fat, blowsy, purply transparent grape and the dried-blood-red cherry with the tough skin and the dark, spurting juice. The air is thick with perfumes so that you half swim as you walk through them, toes just touching the grass. The nightingales sing. For a couple of weeks, Simbirsk can claim the title of the most beautiful town in all Russia, a kind of paradise, or rather, to be exact, garden of Eden.

APRIL 10   SIMBIRSK   1886

My birthday. At last. How long I have had to wait for my official age to creep up to my real age. Inside, I seem to have been sixteen since I was about six. (Well, *eleven,* at the latest.) All this time I have felt like a child impersonator, an actor put into a schoolboy costume for a farcical scene and forgotten by the manager.

I have loyally spoken the lines I have been given but I have been conscious that there were things I could not say, subjects I could not explore, thoughts I could not think, because they would be out of character and attract unwelcome attention. But now, at sixteen, I can begin to be as much a grown-up outside as I have been within.

After all, down the slope among the Foxes, not to mention the Oxen (the laborers) and the Wolves (the semi-criminals), I would already be married now, or as good, or bad, as. I would have been earning a living, making money anyway for somebody, these five or six years. Up on the Crown, of course, you stay younger longer than anywhere except Purgatory. There, Apes of thirty, even forty, go on being gay young blades, the rising generation, until their fathers die and they inherit the title and the money. I have overheard the old Peacocks, up in the Nobles' Tea-Shop, or along the Nobles' Parade, complaining about these overgrown delinquents of theirs fighting duels, gambling away villages, debauching peasant girls, knocking down respectable Rabbits with racing carriages, and then muttering, with an indulgent laugh, "Boys will be boys."

Take this diary, for instance. I am quite aware of its "literary" pretensions, its overwriting, its near-plagiarisms, its adoption of attitudes, its sensationalizing. Yet I know that if I showed it to anybody around here (except Oly who hears it as a monologue from time to time) they would find it hard to believe I wrote it. Certainly Sasha, probably Anna, both still think of me as a slow learner, an awkward pupil, who must plod on round the clock just to keep up. None of them has any idea of how much goes on inside my head, how well I have primed and oiled the thinking machine. I can write a page of this in the time it takes most people to get through the first sentence of the first paragraph of a novel. I can read at the speed that most people think, and I can remember whatever I punch with the tag—*"remember!"*

Old Q. F. Kerensky thinks I have the making of a "superb" Latin scholar (he told Father but, of course, not me) because I can translate on sight any unseen passage from Latin to Russian and vice versa. Nobody realizes I love Latin and read and write it for pleasure. If I were asked the two worst vices today, I should not say "Lying and cowardice." They do not tempt me. I should say "Skating and Latin." They are what distract me from my chosen goal.

Unfortunately, I have not got a chosen goal. When Father died, I felt as if a log had moved in the river jam. But others are still locked there. What they are, I do not know. And where the flow might take me, who can tell?

MAY 10   SIMBIRSK   1886

I see now Mother growing paler and more saintly; no time for the occasional glass of wine and biscuits with a neighbor; the samovar barely used from day to day; our food gradually less in meat and more in beans; the oil lamp in the living room lit later and put out earlier. We are on the rocks. Something must be done!

I asked her if I could help. She looked at me for a while with that distant yet critical scrutiny that has often unnerved even the Foxiest of shopkeepers on the Old Crown. It turned out that she had been (as I guessed) worrying about money and unable to decide in her mind how to address the authorities for assistance due to a service widow. Having passed the inspection (head up, eyes front, thumbs along seam of trousers) I was allowed to collaborate on a letter. My draft was much better than hers.

Or did she allow me to think so? Anyway, we agreed that the final document was a most artistic begging letter, which even had Mother laughing as I dictated it to her.

I insisted on laying the titles on thick—"Your High Noble Supreme Excellence, Most Honorable and Gracious Trustee"—it being better to invent a few than miss a real one.

She requested permission to plead that she now had no way to "preserve myself in the manner of the widow of a hereditary noble, to pay back the money borrowed to meet the costs of the funeral of Actual State Counsellor I.N.U., to keep a daughter who is studying at the Pedagogical Institute in Petersburg and an older son who had graduated from Simbirsk Grammar with a gold medal and is now in his third year at the Petersburg Science Faculty where he has been highly praised and just been awarded another gold medal for his thesis on . . ." (Mother wants to say just "worms" but I explain that Noble Supreme Excellent Parrots do not live in a world where "worms" are named, so instead I put) . . . "The Segmentary and Reproductive Organs of Fresh-Water Annelids."

"I hope that with God's help, he will in future become a support for me and his younger brothers and sisters but for the present he and the other children still need my support and without an income I cannot provide this."

MAY 31   SIMBIRSK   1886

A reply today from the Kazan Parrot of Parrots. Mother is to get a pension—1,200 rubles. How much *is* that?

How pathetic to know so little of Anna's "real world" that I hardly understand what things cost. Why should I? All I have ever needed has been bought for me by Mother. She has always said "Do not bother your head, Volodya. Time enough to worry about all that when you are at University and have to look after yourself."

But this gives me a unit of measurement. I remember now when Anna went up to Peter (as they all call it) to join Sasha, Father gave each of them an allowance of 80 rubles a month. The figure sticks in my mind because after Anna's first year, Sasha came home and handed Father back half the money. He had been living, to help the family finances, on 40 rubles a month but said nothing until the year was over in order not to put pressure on Anna to do the same. Typical Sasha! (What *does* he spend his allowance on now? He has never handed any rubles back since.)

So the pair of them need the allowance for nine months of the year; $2 \times 80 \times 9 = 1,440$ rubles. Subtract 1,200 pension. We have an annual income of 240 rubles *less* than we need just to maintain the two eldest in the family.

I suggest another letter along more sensational lines—the stars are shining through the hole in the attic roof under which my poor kiddies sleep . . . young Volodya walks to school barefoot so that his boots may be worn every Sunday to the Cathedral . . . after school, he tramps the streets collecting horse manure for sale to rich peasants . . . my eldest son at University has won a diamond cross for his thesis on the segmentary and reproductive organs of Parrots . . . my eldest daughter plays the piano in a disreputable café frequented by student anarchists . . ."

She did not laugh.

"I have already made arrangements that will provide enough for you all," she said. "All I ask is that *you* particularly do not be rude and disrespectful to the lodgers."

JUNE 7   SIMBIRSK   1886

The lodgers arrived yesterday. Nothing to say about them except that all three (one m. two f.) are peculiar-looking, strange-smelling and possessed of ludicrous habits.

I said as much, determined not to be shamed by poverty, to my only close school friend, Pavel Yakovelevich.

"Old Man," he said, "in your long life, so eloquently written on your wizened physog, have you not learned that *all* lodgers are peculiar-looking, strange-smelling and of ludicrous habits? More to the point, would you care to join in a small wager I have with Andrei Petrovich—to wit, he taking the affirmative, I the negative, as to whether you will be bald by Christmas?"

What I often thought in other households to be eccentric and demanding relatives were also lodgers. I am learning about the real world.

JUNE 8   SIMBIRSK   1886

The Spring Miracle having started as usual on March 12 and ended a fortnight later, the floods began. Gouts of browny water welled up all over the great green plain that lies to the east of the Volga. From the other side, at the top of Simbirsk on the Ural mountains, it would look as if the land as far as the horizon has been scattered with pieces of broken mirror.

Now with June comes the summer, our worst season. The days pass by like strings of barges through baking heat. Every last cup of moisture hidden between the toes of trees in the heart of the forest dries up. The dust, brown as coffee grounds, covers everything and everybody.

JUNE 29   SIMBIRSK   1886

Tomorrow we shall get out of Simbirsk. Father will no longer be with us, but then he rarely was on our holidays. Would he recognize me? Two radical changes. I no longer have any religion. I think it left me, like a long, bad cold in the head, during that nervous attack I had at his funeral. Its going was quite painless. I do not believe in a God any more than I do in the Wood Demon, or in Zeus, or in Odin. What freedom! It is like emerging from a locked room where you have spent your life. Now I see it all for the first time.

Also, I gradually begin to sense what Tsar-ism must be. Oddly enough, it started to flood in on me as I was thinking about our sled rides.

Simbirsk is segregated the way Russian society is segregated. It might almost be a three-dimensional diagram—Nobles, Bureaucrats, Merchants, Peasants and Plebs. I do not quite understand all their relationships but perhaps I can work them out with Sasha and Anna. Apes, Peacocks, Parrots, Rabbits, Foxes, Wolves, Oxen really are treated like different species.

And then the whole history of Simbirsk seems designed to teach a lesson. Leafing through our family mag, I see that we have drawn up an indictment without realizing it. Simbirsk is not an old town. It was founded around 1650 when the Great Russians were "pacifying" the aborigines, the Tatars, the Chuvash, the Mongols, driving them eastward and seizing their lands. It must have been very much like the Frontier in America, the "Wild West" of our cheap cartoon magazines.

Here gathered runaway serfs, deserting soldiers, criminals and outlaws. They formed into gangs of highwaymen and bandits, soon indistinguishable from rebel armies. In the seventeenth century Stenka Razin led an uprising "to wipe out the notables and the boyars." For five years, he ruled the Volga. Only one town held out. A hundred years later the Don Cossack Pugachev stormed through the same lands with his rebel bands seizing the river towns. Again only one held out.

And this was . . . ? You there at the back of the class. Simbirsk, of course! The epitome of loyalty to the Tsar. Here, both folk heroes were defeated, dragged off in chains to be drawn and quartered in Moscow.

And yet, I begin to wonder what the masses of the people of Simbirsk province were fighting *for*.

The latest figures (1885) show that less than 7 percent of our region's population live in anything resembling a town. One-third of our million peasants are classified as "horseless"—poorest of the poor, no transport but own feet, no power but own hands. Absolute paupers, yet the original owners of the territory (like the

Red Indians) were the Mongols, Chuvash, Tatars, etc. Seventy-three percent of prime land belongs to large landlords. Out of 4 million acres of forest (more than half already property of Tsar's family) one-third belongs nobles; one-fiftieth left to peasants who form 95 percent of population. No wonder we have been able to collect so many anti-tributes from native-born writers. "Not a town but a graveyard"—Goncharov.

In the whole region of Middle-Volga, only one spot stands out like Arcadia—Kokushkino. I hope that illusion at least is preserved.

JUNE 30　　　ON THE VOLGA　　　1886

This morning we left Simbirsk, 48 Moscow Street and the lodgers, on the steamer for Kazan, 150 miles up the Volga, against the current. It will take us until dawn tomorrow. So we spend the night aboard! One of the great treats in life.

The Volga paddle-boat, white as a swan, is a magnificent creation—a large mansion, or possibly small palace, gliding along as if on a magic carpet. Like most stately homes, like Simbirsk itself, it is divided into levels, each corresponding to a certain rank or degree of occupant. Though this is rather selfish, I must say I am glad that our hard-up family is still traveling first-class. (I suppose Mother's well-off brothers-in-law, our Kokushkino uncles, have stumped up for the tickets.)

We are once more on the top deck. Most of this is taken up with a spacious, cool, dark saloon, with curved cream and gold roof, always rustling with fresh, bubbly air, untouched by cooking smells from the galley or oily heat from the engine. The walls are inlaid with patterned mahogany and birch, lined with brassy, serpentine arms holding out oil lamps in the shape of torches. In the center, a Turkey-carpeted floor, a dozen tables, bolted down, always being laid and relaid as meals and drinks are served at every hour of day or night. Every dining chair upholstered and cushioned. Round the walls, deep stuffed sofas. Much more elegant and luxurious than home—ours, anyway.

Most of the first-class males spend their time here, eating and drinking, or lounging about as in a club "reading the papers"—i.e., sleeping. If they have paid the supplement for a cabin at the front, they usually leave that to the children and womenfolk. They only ever take any notice of the countryside when we dock at a landing—then they pace around the rear promenade, automatically glaring down on all new arrivals.

On the top deck, all is order, and (usually) quiet. The price of order, however, as we have found over the years, is an occasional bout of fury by one of the more important travelers, who will upbraid a steward or even beat a lesser minion. (One of Sasha's rare sayings pops up as I write—"If you want to know where you stand in Russia, simply find out who flogs whom.")

On the middle deck, things are more informal. Low, flat ceiling; bare floor where people dance, the crew often joining in; central hanging lamp; no tables—instead you bring your own food from a bar and eat it standing, from shelves along the walls. Here are the middling sort, and everybody is equal in a jolly way.

The bottom deck is just the deck. The people here look, as Father often said, "as if they had been rounded up in a police raid." They have nowhere to sit except on rope coils or crates of cargo. Nowhere to sleep except leaning back to back. Nothing to drink except what they bring or brew up on spirit stoves. Nothing to eat except what they carry in great, red, flowered gypsy handkerchiefs half the size of bedspreads.

Down here having paid your fare does not protect you from being given the boot or the elbow by the sailors if you get in their way. I once saw a drunken soldier thrown overboard by the stewards, and the ship's captain barely turned his head. Yet when they have been aboard for a day, the two sides get very friendly, sit about in the prow playing cards, singing songs and telling jokes.

Why then do I prefer to make the journey in boring old first-class? The answer is—only a first-class passenger has the *laissez-passer* to go anywhere on the ship (not that many, indeed any, do). On the other two decks, you are restricted to that deck. Especially at night, ever since our very first trip ten years ago, I have always yearned, and increasingly succeeded, in slipping away to explore.

The first time, I must have been about eleven, I had hidden myself at the stern in an empty tea chest that made a perfect cubbyhole. (I have always felt more comfortable, safe, at ease, in very small, dark places.) It turned out somebody else thought so too—the dishwashing boy, who slaved away from six in the morning until midnight, then slipped off to *read* by candlelight! Only two years older than I was, he was nearly a foot taller, though thin as a sapling.

We became immediate friends—unusual for me—and I

promised to bring him some books on our return trip. Though why he needed to read other people's stories when he told such marvelous ones of his own, I do not know. Some of his true tales—orphan, kicked out no older than I was then, flogged, robbed, exploited, starved and yet still a utopian idealist!—were worthy of Leskov or Gogol. (Really!) He had a way of describing what had happened to him that was very simple, yet extremely odd and absolutely unforgettable.

We only met, Alexei Maximovich and I, on two trips, Simbirsk—Kazan—Simbirsk, in 1881. Yet I see the picture, as if it were yesterday, of the two of us on the return journey hanging our legs over the stern into darkness. He pointed out shadowing us, like a wolf following a sleigh, what might have been a huge, floating coffin. It was a convict barge on tow. It had no lights, no windows, only a silvery flash as the moonlight caught the bayonets of the guards. Over the repetitive gurgle of the water, like the same phrase of music again and again, we could hear a rhythmic murmur from inside the barge. "They are saying their prayers," he said, "or their curses." He was paid seven rubles a month.

AUGUST 31   KOKUSHKINO   1886

The holidays are over. The coach, a hefty great *tarantass* (more suitable for a hearse) waits down below to take us to Kazan and the steamer to Simbirsk. I have not written a word here for two months. Happy people have no need of diaries. *Et in Oblomovka ego.*

As ever, a land of dreams, where time stands still. For weeks, the haloed sun has been stuck in the Virgin-Mary-blue sky from a children's painting. Not a cloud has floated by, hardly a breath of wind wrinkled the trees. All has been warm, soft, moist, balmy, *sickening* almost. Like a birthday treat drink that is too sweet, a bed that swallows you in a hot embrace.

Adults painted in, stuck on, figures in a landscape. Mother and her sisters, Anna and Lybov, with their jovial husbands, Yuri the Butler, the house servants, the peasants, none of them seemed to move. Even Anna and Sasha, entwined like lovers, made snaily progress from field of corn to grove of hazel trees, swimming pond to wading stream, picnic to picnic. The rest, Olya, Mitya, Marya and me, sometimes linked with, sometimes opposed to, our Kokushkino cousins, matching us age for age, sex for sex, ran in and out of the others as if they were statues in a square. It was all mindless, innocent and intoxicating.

This was a world too young for me. I know now it will never last until next summer. Was it wrong to think of no one but ourselves? I would have liked to join A. and S. in their talks. There was so much to ask, to tell. But they were as exclusive as a honeymoon couple. So I plunged into my final bath of youth as into a vat of trodden grapes. Six months until my grammar finals. Then I may arrest, possibly astonish, them with my thoughts. Ho! Ho!

JANUARY 1   SIMBIRSK   1887

New Year's Day and it's winter in Simbirsk. (Big news. It's winter all over Russia.) No, that's not as stupid as it sounds. Winter here out-winters winter anywhere except Siberia on this continent, possibly across the globe. If nothing happens in other places, *minus* nothing happens here. It is as if each day runs backward. Not only is everything you do dreary and pointless, but, as you do it, you have a distinct memory of having done it before in exactly the same way just a few hours ago. So the best you can do is to wait (vainly) for something to happen that has not happened before. This is not just my reaction. There is a celebrated affliction of the spirit, a kind of emotional catarrh, a constipation of the will, known all over middle Russia as the Simbirsk Flu. After all, Goncharov himself was born here, grew up here, worked as secretary to the governor here, and is still alive somewhere (lucky for him, *not* here). His novel, *Oblomov,* is about a man suffering from Simbirsk Flu who cannot even bring himself to leave his sofa and go out into the street. *Oblomov*-ism, I have heard Father say, this "moral sickness," is what is wrong with Russia today, and yesterday, and "tomorrow, and tomorrow, and tomorrow" (Shakespeare's *Hamlet,* I think). Anyway, by comparison with Oblomov, Hamlet is D'Artagnan!

But what can an individual do, alive but paralyzed, bundled up and cut off, like a bluebottle in a spider's web? It is now 1887, for Heaven's sake, and we still have no railway; telegraph for official messages only; hardly any roads (how Father used to thunder on that subject!). At the best of times, Simbirsk depends on one sluggish moving artery, the Volga. Now that is frozen over for four months.

JANUARY 12   SIMBIRSK   1887

First anniversary of Father's death. Mother does nothing to mark the occasion that I can see, so I do not mention it. She is almost as much a mystery as Sasha. She may speak nine languages, as old Kerensky once assured me, but she can be silent in them all. Her entire energy, mental, physical, emotional, is devoted to looking after those of us still at home. It is as if each one had been endowed with a personal lady-valet—the only escape from being looked after until your teeth ache is locking yourself in your room. The few other people she spends time with are those who have been equally devoted to the Simbirsk Family Ulyanov amd more or less live here—Solovyova, midwife to all of us children, and Kashkadamova, Anna's governess, who also tutored us boys for first school.

Neither Anna nor Sasha came for Christmas. I have given up skating to work longer hours at home. I have also given up chess—Mitya is not much of a challenge. He throws a fit when I refuse to allow him to change a move once he has touched the piece. "But it was a mistake, a mistake!" he howls. It does not help when I say: "Fine. Everyone makes a mistake. You must learn the only real lesson, do not make the same mistake twice." A trifle priggish? But true.

Otherwise, no news. And I expect none, hope for none, until the month of the examinations is over—May 5 to June 6. Nothing must stand in the way of a triumph there. What Mother wants from us, and for us, is far more than Father ever did. He would settle for success, she aims at FAME!!!

MARCH 3   SIMBIRSK   1887

When I got back from school at teatime today Kashkadamova was waiting for me just outside in the street. She had a letter in her hand that had been sent to her by one of Mother's relatives in Petersburg. They had asked her to break the news in it to Mother, but she said she had not got the courage. Her hand was shaking and the tears in her eyes were so huge they magnified the pupils to twice the size.

I was rather rude and offhand. These lovable old ladies are

often trembly and hysterical about nothing. I read it as I walked up the steps and into the porch, almost knocking over Mother who was hurrying out to see if there was anything I needed. I had just reached the statement that Sasha had been arrested on March 1 accused of leading a plot to kill the Tsar. I was thinking desperately how to phrase this, while my eyes raced ahead to make out what was said about Anna being also in the hands of the police, when Mother tore the pages roughly from my hands. It was almost as if she knew already what was written there and she was simply checking the grammar.

She went through it twice at speed, then folded it away, and began issuing orders. Kashka was set to packing Mother's clothes, chosen for warmth and hard wear, though with one set of best— for she intends to visit the magistrate, the police chief, the minister of justice, the Tsar, to protect her children. I was dispatched to find a horse on which she could begin the ride of eighty miles to Syzran, our nearest railway station. Olga was sent round the house collecting all the money she could find. Mother was determined to set off tonight. I persuaded her to wait until tomorrow.

We were glad of something to do. Whenever we passed each other, we told each other what we were up to, like children playing a game. I do not want to think about Sasha's action just yet—but I knew that if he had made the plot, then he could not have acted otherwise. I do not want to think just yet about his fate—it could end very badly, possibly with hanging, certainly with imprisonment or internal exile in Siberia. Later I will insist on learning exactly what happened, and why. Explore the mystery of this fearless, incorruptible brother, so silent and so dedicated, experimenter with chemicals and bombs, dissector of worms and emperors, the person who has influenced me more than any other and yet whom I obviously have never really known.

But tonight, action. I have booked a coach rather than a horse for dawn. But I could not find a single man, however "liberal" in his politics, however close a colleague of Father's, or a social inti-mate of Mother's, who would risk accompanying her on the jour-ney. The story of the arrest of Sasha and Anna is already all over town. Who dare even appear to assist the regicide family? Our hometown is living down to its reputation . . . "If you want to grow up to hate tsarism, arrange to be born in Simbirsk."

MARCH 4   SIMBIRSK   1887

Mother has gone. She would not let me see her off. I was determined to be up at dawn. But she was in my room, beside my bed,
before I awoke. The first thing I knew she was holding my hand
and talking. I had the feeling that she had been talking even while
I slept.

"I am going now, my darling," she said. "Sasha and Anna may
be sent who knows where if they are found guilty. And I will follow
them, wherever that is. If it is exile, I will share their hut. If it is
prison, I will camp outside the gate. It is upon you that the job of
looking after your brother and sisters will fall. I have no doubt
you can do it. You are the strongest of us all. But for this future,
whatever happens, you must be equipped with every advantage
we can win for you or you can win for us. You must do as brilliantly
now in your examinations as you would have done if your father
had not died and if Sasha were still free. Tell me you will not fail
or falter."

I could not help thinking how different—as ever—my mother
was proving from the mothers of my friends. No weeping, no
sentimental burblings about missing me or Olga, Marya and Mitya,
no question of owing any duty to the rest of her family . . . more
like a queen parting from an old retainer, a prima donna leaving
the provinces for a debut in the capital. At fifty-two, her new task
was more important than any that had faced her before. Being
Mother, she was rising to it. Splendid! *D'accord!* She was right, of
course.

It *was* the rational decision. That may not be why she had
made it. But it was the correct move given the state of the board.
What use would I be in Peter, a schoolboy, not even a student, a
nobody, under age, doubly suspicious to the authorities, with no
weight, no *gravitas,* no recognizable role to play. Whereas here, I
have no problems. We were all brought up to look after ourselves.
I am damned if I am going to be deprived of my gold medal with
all the embarrassment it would produce among them having to
honor the brother of a radical accused of plotting against the Tsar.

She was the right one to go. Tsars, ministers, police chiefs,
judges, even they understand about mothers. And she will be the
mother of mothers, out-monumenting any classical marble ma-
trons enduring tragic fate from Greece or Sparta.

Before I could answer, swear my oath or plight my troth or whatever the script called for me to do, she was gone. She left in a swirl of fur and a mist of veils, a discreet glitter of jewelry over a sincere sobriety of semi-mourning, her fingers cool as fresh-picked flowers on my cheek. It was clear mine had been a non-speaking part.

From my window, I watched her trundle off in the ramshackle hired coach—perhaps I had overdone her instructions to beat down the driver's price?—as I had so often watched father leave. We are a family accustomed to separations. The air was milky and alive as it is under a waterfall. The sun rose, quite small, rather distant, but very distinct. I had the silly feeling it had become a golden ruble and if I peered I would see the head of the Tsar amid his halo of admiring words. It was going to be the first of those over-hot spring days that come unpredictably, as burning as summer, giving the impression that nature is still fiddling with the controls and hasn't quite got them right for the year.

I looked around the rest of the house frontage, leaning out for a good view. In the window to my left, there were three faces, one medium, one small, one tiny. I haven't told them anything yet, except Sasha's ill and mother has gone to look after him—she would too. I only hope *that* will be all I will have to tell them.

Since I was up, I thought I might as well start reviewing for an hour or so before school.

APRIL 3   SIMBIRSK   1887

Heard from Mother. Her petition to the Tsar, made the day she arrived, delivered in person, has at last been acknowledged by him in writing. Alexander III grants permission, in his own hand, for her to visit her son. There is something about these feudal intimacies, between breeder of would-be assassin and intended sacrifice, imprisoned revolutionary and whimsical autocrat, Little Father and petitioning mother, that quite makes the flesh creep.

She saw him (she writes) in the Schlüsselburg prison on March 30, a month after his arrest. Kneeling before her, he clasped her knees and wept. She told him that friends in highish places had promised if he renounced his views and asked the Emperor to forgive him, his life would be spared, whatever the verdict and sentence of the court. Sasha said that was not possible. To do so he would have to name his comrades, recount all the details of the plot. He was determined to plead guilty and repeat that he was not sorry for planning to remove the Tsar. "It is you I am sorry for, Mamma," he said. "Forgive me."

Mother concludes—"After that, I did not insist and no longer tried to persuade him. I did not want to make it worse for him."

She also says she had been granted the privilege of attending the trial. It seems likely the authorities will accept that Anna knew nothing of the operation so the initial threat of five years in Siberia may be commuted to internal exile for a shorter period. Not too bad for the fearful crime of happening to call round to your brother's lodgings and walking into a web of secret policemen.

I cannot really picture the scene, and Mother does not supply much detail. Working hard for my exams at least keeps my mind occupied.

APRIL 10   SIMBIRSK   1887

My seventeenth birthday. The first without Mother, Sasha and Anna. The second without Father. No more news from Peter. So I give myself—or really the others—a party.

Oddly enough, I think it is the first I have really enjoyed. I hate having things organized around me. I like to be in charge. Ideally, I would like to do it all since no one else ever seems to me to get it—whatever "it" is—quite right. This is, I suppose, a character fault—"autocrat fantasy" Anna has started to call it. But I do not think she is correct. After all, autocrats love having others run around after them, wait upon them, plan ceremonies in honor of them. I would really rather everyone did their own jobs well and left me alone to get on with mine. More of a "major-domo fantasy." I have never wanted to be a prince. But, very likely, I would make a marvelous Dandini.

This evening, after school, I staged the treat I thought would give most pleasure to the three younger children. And I think it did. Mainly, "it" was eating.

We began with borscht made by Kashkadamova and left overnight in the garden icehouse. Then there was Olga's contribution (coincidentally her favorite?) of eggs in cream. Mother's recipe, carefully filed in a loose-leaf book on a cord behind the kitchen door, is for eight. Olga used the largest chafing dish for its half-pint of sour cream, its eight rings of lightly fried French bread crust, its eight eggs beaten with dill, between four.

My contribution was a *krendel,* or typical Volga-side birthday cake, a confection so doughy, so suffocatingly filling, it makes your teeth hum to think of it. It is my sole culinary achievement. Here's how I do it—definitely the best recipe there is, tried and tested.

Two ounces of yeast is mixed with some water and sugar, half a pint of warmed milk and half a pound of flour, into a dough and well beaten. Then it is covered with a damp cloth and left near to the stove until it is twice the size, and has rather disgusting bubbles plopping up.

Now eight egg yolks, half a pound of vanilla sugar, are stirred in, followed by as near half a pound of butter as you think your liver will stand, a handful of sultanas, and another half-pound of flour. It now has to be kneaded for longer than anyone under the age of seventeen can imagine, covered with that damp cloth, and once again allowed to double in amount.

More kneading (if you start after school, *krendel* will always, but only just, be ready by bedtime). Now roll into a long snake with flattened head at each end and loop into figure of eight. At least another half-hour, rising, rising, coat with some beaten egg, sprinkle lavishly with almonds, and cook for nearly an hour, or when no one can bear to wait another minute. Final garnish of icing sugar and eat while just still warm.

We went to bed in a daze, weighed down with ecstatic indigestion. I had managed for most of an evening to forget Mother, Anna and Sasha. I think we all had. Until Mitya turned at the top of the stairs, by his bedroom door, raised his candle and intoned —"*Po Tsarski.*" It was what Father always said after Christmas dinner, his greatest compliment—"Fit for a king."

APRIL 25   SIMBIRSK   1887

Another letter from Mother, only the second since she left nearly two months ago. She says Sasha told her something when she first saw him in prison that she had not told us. (I write "us" because I share all my news, all my feelings, with Oly. The two others know nothing.) Sasha, after asking her pardon, insisted: "You must resign yourself, Mamma, to the inevitable."

But our mother, as he should know, is not one for resignation. She accepts only the *fait accompli,* the finished deed. Then, finally, what is done is done. She turns to the future, without second thoughts, almost no regrets. Until then, she does not give up.

So she has been everywhere, knocking on every door, leaving cards with every doorman, buttonholing anyone who has influence on anyone who has influence. She has also seen Anna, and the two of them have infected and reinfected each other with that potent, dangerous bacillus, hope.

Her efforts resulted in her being given entry to the trial which began on April 19. Sasha (she writes with the pride of a parent with a child in the school play) had grown more manly in his six weeks in prison. In court, his voice had become deeper, more impressive. "How well he spoke—so convincingly, so eloquently!" His final speech in defense affected everyone who heard it. But she could not bear to sit through to the end—it was too moving.

The verdict is guilty. The sentence is death. She saw him once for a moment afterward and told him through the double grating only one word: "Courage!" Courage. The one virtue each has no need to recommend to the other.

MAY 4   SIMBIRSK   1887

Tomorrow the final examinations at the grammar school start. They do not end until June 6. One of my projects (self-chosen) was "Secondary Education in Europe." Nowhere could I find a system that placed such an emphasis upon one make-or-break hurdle for seventeen-year-olds.

Twenty-one days out of the next twenty-nine will be spent, two and a half hours morning and afternoon, locked in the high school hall, with its institutional green walls, windows beginning above head height, and Gothic, churchy beams. The desks are made more for praying rather than writing, lids steeply sloped, seats decoratively carved for maximum discomfort. Its pot inkwells are arranged so that they work loose to the rhythm of your writing hand, and release a probing root of poisonous, metallic blue that seeks out your paper toward the end of every session.

By the close of the first two weeks, a few of the entrants have always begun to drink the ink. They argue about its unique flavor with each other on the way home. No one quite knows why this happens. It is clearly a nervous, defensive reaction to the strain. Some say a reversion to childishness. Others a pretend attempt to produce a mild illness and earn a pass result on a doctor's certificate. If the latter, it is a very badly thought-out scheme. The examiners like nothing better than being presented with a malingerer for their inquisition. In Anna's year, a group of girls, one of whom had a doctor for a father, dosed themselves with some mild drug. They trusted to safety in numbers and hoped a minor epidemic would get the blame. Instead, the authorities sent for the professor of forensic medicine at Kazan, a man who had sniffed a hundred homemade poisons on a thousand dead lips. He took one gulp of their breath and instantly diagnosed the *materia medica* used. Sure enough, that same stuff turned out to have disappeared from the local doctor's cabinet.

The examination is taken with a savage seriousness by everyone. In the case of the desperate girls, they were not only failed, and expelled. There was a proposal that the ringleaders should be sent to a house of correction for female criminals. It was only old Kerensky's threat of resignation that quashed it. You are never allowed to forget that failure in only one subject makes it impossible for you to graduate. Or that nongraduates have absolutely no chance of getting a job even of the lowest status in the service—and what else is there for an educated person to do, outside the professions?

My own theory about the ink-drinkers is that those of them who in the final days go to incredible extremes, queuing up for refills throughout the session, are acting out a symbolic suicide. Psychological breakdowns are frequent, most often just before the exams start. Real suicides are not unknown. Once every two or three years, usually between the final sitting and the announcement of the results four days later. The last two fainthearts who killed themselves in shame at their failure had actually *passed* with above-average marks.

So it is no surprise that the neighbors, the teachers, and most fellow pupils, look at us strangely out of the corners of their eyes. I allow no sign to escape that I am aware of being studied. But, of course, I know what they are thinking: "How can he, and his sister, Olga, almost a pair of twins, carry on with such an examination now they know their elder brother has been sentenced to death?"

They say among themselves: "Are this pair exceptionally brave, or callous, or unimaginative, or self-centered, or stupid? These two have to be exceptionally *something*!" Olga and I have talked it over, briefly. As soon as we spoke, we found we thought exactly the same way. So there is no need for more discussion. We are doing what we are doing from basic, common-sense realism.

Whatever happens to Sasha—and I for one have no hope for his pardon—he will under no circumstances be allowed to walk away free. He will never complete his studies, earn a living, keep the rest of us until we are old enough to do so ourselves. Therefore, it is essential that we are equipped with all the weapons and armor needed to succeed in what old K. calls "Life's Tournament." And of these, the first, most basic, is a grammar-school diploma. So— we will each get the best we can. We hope that will be the best there is. Whatever happens to Sasha, the effect on him, if he is allowed to live, and upon us, who are determined to live, will be all the worse should we start collapsing, retreating, conceding victory to the world outside. At the moment, there is nothing any of our family can do to fight back except *pass our examinations*. It isn't much. But it is a start. So, backs straight, heads up, eyes glazed against penetration by glances hostile or even sympathetic, we march together, silent, through our schoolfellows. It will have to do. For the moment.

MAY 8   SIMBIRSK   1887

One minute to noon, today as usual, I was the first person at the door of the exam room, ready for the dinner break. I have made a point of this, even after papers about which I did not feel so secure as I do about my best subjects. I suppose I do it to show (1) the monitors; (2) any teachers who sit in from time to time; and (3) my competitors, that I have everything under control. I can see that my little performance works.

The first lot nod approval. By temperament and training, they like to see routine become ritual. Some young person must be head of the line. It is now reassuring that it is always this same person. It means that the examination must seem a fair test to one examinee. If this one can do it, why not the rest? This form of self-praise is necessary to them because of the exam's crucial nature. Every year, after the results, a wave of agitation and dissatisfaction rolls across the otherwise torpid provinces. Those whose offspring have not done as well as expected write to the papers, organize petitions, lobby relatives, complain to the governor, all denouncing the "scandal." There has never been a high-school graduation known that pleased more than a quarter of the parents of those taking part. Russia being Russia (I have not come across European parallels in my researches), at least half a dozen of the disappointed oldsters will arm themselves with axes, sabers or muzzle-loading blunderbusses and attempt to wipe out the family insult by attacking one of the overseers. Russia being Russia, mostly they grapple with the wrong man, get drunk and fall in the river, or are arrested by the police several leagues from the spot.

The second lot, the teachers, look rather awed. The third, our contemporaries, are increasingly unnerved and lose more confidence in themselves with each session. By stamping the image of the all-conquering, predestined victor upon them, I have also embossed it on myself. I feel lifted on an up-draft, a gliding eagle. I will be top in *everything*.

This assurance, like that which seemed so improbable when it buoyed up the classical heroes, is absolutely essential. For this noonday, the doors fell open that extra minute early, as never before, and Quince-Face clawed at me and began starting various sentences he couldn't finish. I understood immediately, but had to speak to him as to a child.

"Spit it out. Sasha? Yes. Executed? Of course. When, today? Yes, by hanging? Thank you. It was to be expected. How did you hear so quickly? Ah, by the telegraph. I see. Our masters in Peter are worried about something. Can it be another Ulyanov gold medal? Another *two* Ulyanov gold medals?"

Quincy-Kerensky went purple as the arse-hole of a costive horse. (Respectable grown-ups seem to think that "face like a horse's arse" is just cheap vulgarity. But there *are* such, exactly, all folds and bobbles, pendulous lips and protruding knobs, *exactly*, and not really unpleasant when you get used to them.) I see he is really a noble fellow, more so perhaps than Father who shook his head when his teachers were persecuted for their opinions, but did nothing anyone might notice.

"My son," he said. He'd never said *that* before. "My son, you, and Olga, will get the awa . . . awa . . . awards you merit. My life and reputation stands guaran . . . guarantee for that."

During the break, over our sausages and cheese, I told Oly about Sasha, holding her hand beneath her skirt so tight I could have snapped it into spare ribs. I hurt her, and I meant to hurt her, physical pain paralleling the anguish of emotions. She did not let me down. Apart from a slight flush of the cheek, a faint watery circuit of the eye, her expression never changed. All around looks were arrows, hitting us in shoals. Two St. Sebastians, we finished our food, folded away the greaseproof paper, and brushed down the crumbs, walking back into the examination without a wince or a limp, though wounded a hundred times.

In the afternoon, trig., and Thucydides into Russian. This session was also—I can say this only to my diary—a triumph. I seemed to, no I *did*, envision all the questions before I read them. I started writing down my answers without waiting to understand what was being asked. I was left with twenty-five minutes over after completing the last paper.

As a bonus to the faraway examiners (or possibly a kick in their *loco parentis?*) I took a passage I knew by heart from Turgenev and translated it into Greek. Brilliantly!

The glow of that, like old sunburn, still radiates a painful warmth after we have gone early to bed, as part of our examination routine. But underneath, the wound of Sasha's death cuts so deep I fear to look. I feel like a soldier in the midst of battle who dares not check that all his limbs are there in case he falls down and dies. We must fight on. That is the only immortality Sasha would hope for.

I count myself into sleep. Not sheep. But, foot by foot, down into oblivion, as in a sinking undersea boat, or a dropping lift in a mine. As I reach the level of darkness where the mind switches off, I hear a faint whirring, watery sound. It is Oly crying. She is crying for Sasha. But she is also crying for me.

MAY 12   SIMBIRSK   1887

Mother's letters about S.'s execution reached us today. Though on the spot in Peter, she learned that the sentence had been carried out after we did. Principal Kerensky, notified by telegram that midday, told me during the dinner break. Mother writes that she had made the long steamer trip up the Neva to the Schlüsselburg fortress on Lake Ladoga as usual that morning. She took along a requested volume of Heine's poems (*Memo*: must read him!) which the warder assured her would be passed on as soon as possible. She left, believing another day had been gained during which our S. still lived.

In the afternoon she went out to the shops and by chance happened to buy the *Government Herald* from a street-seller. Sasha's execution was the headline story. He had been hanged with four others at dawn in the courtyard of the prison. "Death of the Plotters!" shouted the newsboy as he ran on to the next customer. What a shitty system! Its very inefficiency is itself a kind of filthy insult, worse than many a deliberate punishment. What dregs masquerading as scum operate it. The turds! The crap! The ordure! The excrement! The feces! The droppings! Such dung as rule us do not deserve words. Someday I foresee, I feel in my hands and muscles, how I will shovel this refuse into the *cloaca maxima,* sprinkle it with lime, and slam the lid. They will vanish from the earth, burned and bleached away, with not even a bad smell to linger on in their memory. In mankind's history, they will be just a flush in the pan. Ha!

MAY 15   SIMBIRSK   1887

Mother is back. She did not send any message that she was on her way or ask to be met at Syzran station. She did not ring the bell, or knock. She came in quietly, unannounced, through the back door. Her hair is completely white.

I thought that only happened in sensational novelettes, or folktales. It makes her face look rosier, healthier, indeed much, much younger.

JUNE 6   SIMBIRSK   1887

Exams ended today. Anna is already in Kokushkino, soon to be our new family home. Though acquitted in the trial as expected, she is ordered to live in exile. We are due to leave Simbirsk, after settling a few little local matters, as soon as we can pack.

My thoughts return, as they have done increasingly over this last year and a half, to that recipe Sasha charcoaled on the wall above his bed in '85—"If you want to grow up to hate tsarism, arrange to be born in Simbirsk." It interested me originally because I couldn't understand it. And, at fifteen, I wasn't used to that. What anyone could write I assumed I would be able to read and digest. If I needed any help, there were all the dictionaries and encyclopedias in Father's reference library. Simbirsk seemed to me tedious but tolerable. It provided no reason to hate the Tsar—a gross, brutish figure, as thick as two Volga boatmen, but hardly an enemy of mankind. As to tsarism, it was a concept that didn't exist in any of the books around our house.

Now I wonder how I could have been so blindfolded. At Father's funeral, the town gathered to honor him. So, they were mainly hypocrites, I suppose. But if hypocrisy is the tribute vice pays to virtue, at least the tribute *was* paid. The virtue *was* recognized. In the desertion of the Ulyanovs after Sasha's arrest, the Simbirskians' real attitude to life was exposed—naked self-interest, open cowardice, total conformity. No more hypocrisy! And the system which supports the Tsar was revealed as organized oppression and exploitation. I leave my birthplace a dedicated hater of everything it represents. The same as Sasha! Good riddance to bad rubbish.

Even sprightly Olya, always happy wherever she is, caused a bit of a stir the New Year before Father died by inventing for her toast the dramatic line, "It's good to be on Moscow Street in Simbirsk but it will be even better on Simbirsk Street in Moscow." Father, amazingly, joined the chorus of opprobrium hurled at me—"Sit on him!" "Put him under the pump!" and the like— along with a hail of sugared almonds left over from Christmas when I returned from a quick check of his own gazetteers to inform them: "There is *no* Simbirsk Street in Moscow!"

JUNE 20   SIMBIRSK   1887

Last day in Simbirsk. At noon we leave on our final steamer trip upriver to Kokushkino. This is the moment, I feel, I have always looked forward to. And yet this morning, sitting on my trunk, waiting for a couple of mangy Wolves from the lower depths of town—the only people who will besmirch themselves by fetching and carrying for *us*!—I am impelled to write about some of the glowing experiences—"epiphanies," Father would have said—I have had here.

There was always the skating. Imagine—I'd forgotten the skating!

I liked it best at night. When the snow clouds had been rolled back and the sky glistened like a sugared pastille (prob. black-currant). Then the air was so cold, it passed into another element. I can't explain it quite. But it's as though it had turned into a liquid, compressed oxygen or something of that sort (Sasha would have known). As though humans had become flying fishes on the surface of the moon. Perhaps this is what chloroform feels like. I knew as soon as I sat down on the riverbank and tied on my skates I would become another person.

I always took to the ice alone and began to head downriver away from the groups larking about around the fires. I never remember having learned. I just began pumping arms and legs, as if dog-paddling. At first, it would appear I was putting out too much energy for too little result. I was running in a dream. And then—*ping!*—as though I had sliced through some invisible barrier, slid into a world behind the looking glass, I was now *flying* as in a dream.

The face becomes an iron mask. Your breath snakes in and out of the nostril holes like mercury. The bank ripples past in a blur of black and white. The blades ring out with the hissing, metallic music of sleigh bells under water.

And I, who cannot dance a step when the carpet is rolled back in the parlor, let alone in school halls, begin to leap and spin and pirouette and reverse like a silly creature in the ballet.

But that's all I miss. Except for . . . of course, except for sledding. The steamer hoots in the distance and still all our luggage is here on the step. Yes, the sledding.

When Sasha was back for the New Year's holiday, he and I used to take Anna and Olga to make up a family foursome down "The Slope." From the top of Simbirsk to the bottom.

Sasha built our sled himself according to the best scientific principles available (i.e., his own). The runners and the rails were made of *hollow* steel, something nobody (around here anyway) had ever thought of, to combine lightness and strength. And where others had wood, Sasha used leather. It was an admirable construct. I suppose quite attractive in its way, though I'm not much of a judge of these things. Anyway, Anna kept on referring to it as *chic*!

When we first got aboard the sled—me front, then Olya, then Anna, with Sasha crouched at the back—it sank as deep into the squeaky, scrunchy snow as into clay. It seemed impossible that this overloaded, stranded vehicle could ever move. Then Sasha strained and panted, almost on his knees, shoulders pushing low. He cried: "Damn Inertia!" and the spell was broken. The sled jerked forward as if pulled by horses. Sasha leaped up behind. We all cheered and whooped.

This must be what it feels like being shot out of the mouth of a cannon at the circus. Earth and atmosphere no longer put up any resistance—partly, Sasha used to claim, because of the bear grease he alone thought of smearing along the shiny, saber-blade edges of its runners.

We whistled along over a surface as polished as the inside of the barrel of a sportsman's rifle. ("It's like the seat of a civil servant's trousers," said Olya once, a witticism duly recorded in our mag. though Father frowned a little at the "vulgarity.") We appeared not to mark, scarcely to touch, the gloss, except when we needed to swerve round a corner or miss a frantic pedestrian scrabbling about like a spider in the bath. Then Sasha and I, who had been holding our feet out and up in readiness, drove our heels into the ice, scoring out ribbons of white apple peel, swinging the sled from side to side with alternate pressures as if shooting the rapids in a canoe.

We started at the top, the Crown it calls itself on the Volga in our "Nest of Gentlefolk." Here the townhouses of the aristocracy resemble country mansions, wrapped round with orchards, lapped by parkland, protected by high walls, with gatehouses like Spanish galleons. The roads are properly cobbled, the pavements thoroughly modern. The banks are built of granite and the shops possess glass fronts. The Cathedral, the headquarters of the various administrations of the province, plus the only really decent school, are all nearby. But just in case you should forget quite what part of Simbirsk you are in, there are everywhere the signs: "Noble Assembly Hall," "Noble Academy," "Noble Baths," "Noble Rooming House," even "Noble Conveniences and So On": the last, in embossed metal, Sasha and I will now never manage to purloin.

In winter little of this is to be seen, especially at night—the only time for skating and sledding. Then buildings are shrouded in snow like furniture under dust sheets. The manors, behind their stone and wrought iron, are solid, featureless blocks, citadels of the Troll King. We used to slide and slither by, at the speed of a runaway horse, through an empty town that seems as long abandoned as Atlantis. Then we would make a slight detour to hit the Old Crown, the "best section" of earlier days.

Nowadays this is the *quartier* of the new gentry, the nobles of the buff form in triplicate, the special permit, the report upon the report upon the report. Here congregate the aristocracy of the Service: civil and un-civil depending on whether you are above or below them. For despite all the intrigues, feuds and jostlings, what really counts in Simbirsk is your rank. This is clearly indicated by the gold braid on the cuff, collar and shoulder of your uniform. This decides how you are addressed, and whom you may address; which parties you are invited to; how near you stand to the governor on state occasions; how far back you are in the procession to the altar of the Cathedral on holy days.

This was one area I really liked—its toffee-colored walls, fretworked fringes of roofs, hand-carved posts along verandas, rows of shutters with holes shaped like flowers, funny turrets, domes, towers, arches, outside staircases, lean-tos and extensions anyone can add in a couple of days.

We must have lived in almost every bit of the Old Crown. I

was born shortly after we got here so I don't claim to remember much of that first place. But I could show the curious visitor the exact spot in which we took lodgings, a two-story villa on Streletsky Street.

What it looked like indoors, I doubt I ever noticed, but the green nearby stirs some emotions. Here poor families from the slummy, rag-and-twig hutches down by the docks used to climb on summer weekends to eat, drink, play games and (mainly, I suspect) sleep on the grass.

One picture I never forgot—the single central window in the long wall that faced our side door, just across the grass. This building was (and is) a prison. Every Sunday morning in summer I would see the barred space fill up with the heads of prisoners, gray-skinned and shaven-skulled, like turnips in a string bag. All day they would never move, just staring at the picnickers.

The third level of Simbirsk, gradually creeping up the slope, belongs to the Merchants. The buildings here are for use, not ornament. The owners often live on top of their businesses. Cranes peer out of sentry boxes, lined up along the roofs, like wooden birds from the cuckoo clock. There are great apertures from which funnels pour out grain, minerals or even vegetables. But at the ground level, the most important thing is a heavy door with a really big lock.

The squares, on the flat near the quays, are dull and ordinary except when full of merchants buying and selling, quarreling with each other and only uniting if an opportunity presents itself to fleece the peasant or the gentleman.

By now our sledding impetus would be running down: St. Inertia, the patron virgin of Simbirsk, exerting her powers. We usually stopped in front of the first house that still showed a light. If you knocked long enough, the Foxes always answered. (It might be money, money, money.) When it turned out that it wasn't money, indeed the reverse, and they were going to have to offer some lemon tea, or a taste of black sherry, a few honey cakes, cracker biscuits, perhaps even a piece of preserved goose, to the hungry sledders from (almost) the crown of the town, they still hurried to oblige.

It was as if I were there on the sled. Sasha grunting, Anyuta singing under her breath, Olya holding me tight like a pillow, her little, hot tongue flicking at the back of my neck. That bit was real enough. In my nostalgic daze I had followed her down the hill from the house, up the gangplank, and onto the boat deck. My hands were on the stern rails and she was behind me once more, nuzzling my ear again.

The steam-horn hooted. Automatically, I hooted back.

"According to Anyuta," she said, "you've done that ever since you were three. Mother told you not to shout. You complained— 'But the boat shouted at me first!' "

There was a moment when we could just see, or always had persuaded ourselves we could just see, the chimney and gable of Moskovskaya Ulitsa. Mother had taken Mitya and little Manyasha up to the salon for icing cakes and strawberry cordial. We were the only passengers paying farewell to Simbirsk.

"So what's your best memory of Moscow Street?" demanded my sister. "Tell me *now*! Immediately!"

I thought I was going to remind her of the ride from the Crown to the docks, from the Peacocks to the Foxes. But instead I said: "I used to go out alone into the garden after midnight. All silence away from you noisy sleepers inside. I'd explore each of our childish realms. The Black Forest, all lined with lilac. The Yellow Forest of acacias. The Red Forest built of hawthorns. The Dirty Forest where old pans and bottles seemed to grow. I could see every detail, however dark the night. I felt I had an appointment with somebody. All I ever got were wet feet and a scratched face. Isn't that interesting now?"

But Olya was crying. The tears slid down inside my shirt.

I tried to cheer her up. "Cheer up," I said. "Rotten old Simbirsk! Soon we'll be in Kokushkino, the best place in the world."

She sniffed. "It's not Simbirsk. It's just I thought your best memory might include me. Will I never learn?"

It seems I have put my foot in it again.

The riverboat gave its last hoot. I hooted back.

PETERSBURG

1 8 8 7 - 1 8 9 5

Now we are settled in Kokushkino, Mother's family estate, our land of Cockaigne, I realize that for the last year Simbirsk had been like a constant headache, a fur hat too tight, a roof too low to allow you ever to stand up straight. The jack-in-the-box inside me has expanded, breathing a deeper breath for every steamer-mile north along the great flattened snake of the Volga.

The first thing I did—hang up grammar-school certificate 468. Already, it seems to be about another person in another world. Apparently, Vladimir Ilyich Ulyanov came top of his year in every subject he took, even Religion. Only in Logic did he get less than the fullest possible marks.

Anna made a face (how like Sasha she looks sometimes). "The wrong way round, surely, for a skeptic and an unbeliever?"

I did not answer. What did they know?

Oly intervened. "Not at all. If God had created the human race, he would be unknowable. But since it was humanity which invented the gods, to learn about ourselves we must learn about our religions. When the majority believe in something that is clearly not true, it behooves the unblinkered to examine this false doctrine and find out what it is and why mankind are fooling themselves."

"All right," said Anna, her voice betraying reined-back indig-nation at being educated by one of the "babes." "So. Religion must be dissected, analyzed. Why then neglect logic? Surely, your most useful tool?" This was getting more interesting, but Oly trod cov-ertly on my toe. She began to pace the room, fingers hooked through the shoulder straps of her dress, as through the armholes of a waistcoat, left eye screwed up. Quite an impersonation!

"Not so. Logic, true logic, so my Master Ilyich holds, must depend on closeness to reality, to facts, to propositions that can be tested in action. What is taught in our grammar schools is the mere juggling of words and phrases. A pedants' game, neither useful nor pleasurable. An inferior form of chess, the tiddly-winks of the intellect. Do I interpret your thesis correctly, Magister?"

I might have known. When arguing aloud to myself, using Oly as a sounding board, I had hardly noticed how much she was supporting me all the way. My diagnosis exactly. Indeed, rather improved by being trimmed and concentrated.

Anna too had been listening attentively. When Oly stopped and bowed, as in our school debating society, she applauded. *"Har-asho!* Splendid! *Brava!"* The two embraced.

What a family! Have we any need of teachers, colleagues, even friends, outside? I felt myself in danger of being invaded by silly, sentimental feelings. So I saluted them with a distant, solemn nod and exited into the garden through the window.

AUGUST 1   KOKUSHKINO   1887

The best place to see Kokushkino is from a punt moored mid-stream on the Ushna on an August morning. Here, I retire for "fishing"—that is, letting the carp slowly unpack my hook while I lie reading, half-buried under a ziggurat of books.

From here, Grandfather's white mansion, steps widening down to the landing, columned front inset with rows of shuttered windows, sides flanked by fretted verandas, could be an illustration from one of those sensational novels about the American Civil War the wives of our former serf-owners are all reading. (How they pity the poor black slaves and would love to adopt a family or two of them!)

Across the glistening, quicksilver-flecked surface, the Big House's façade, eye-blinding in the noonday glare, floats on that wooded hillside like a mirage. Uncanny even in broad daylight, the image is twinned with its upside-down replica, green-stippled and rippling, daubed on the river's canvas.

While we were tiny, the old boy added to it what he always described as "another wing." Actually a second, only slightly smaller, building, nearby but separate, hidden among its own evergreen, overgrown coppices. We children preferred this "Little House," not least for its enormous, grand salon, occupying more than half the ground floor, known as the Billiards Hall.

One by one, as soon as we could be relied upon not to poke holes in the baize, or fizz sticky liquids over the brass and mahogany fittings, we were authorized to amuse ourselves with the four huge tables. Even after we had learned to play billiards, passed the stage of having to kneel on library steps or be held up around the waist by servants, we continued to use the tables for our own games. As parade grounds for our toy soldiers. As jungles of dried flowers through which Noah roamed in search of hidden animals. As countrysides of baronial castles and peasant villages, built from candle boxes and stacked magazines, a blue scarf winding through as a river. Only Sasha spent much time actually handling cue and balls. And he could rarely find anyone to join him except the doddery old coachman, Roman. Even Sasha was not encouraged to come here in the evenings when the uncles drank, smoked and mused, to the leisurely click of the ivories.

Our great daytime treat was hiding, as many as a dozen cousins together, underneath the tables during those operatic, summer-day storms which are staged every five or six days throughout the heat of August. It was an odd thing. We did not retreat into their damp, slatey crevasses, between elephantine legs, because we were afraid. Surprised outside, when black-and-blue clouds filled up an empty sky, we would be exhilarated. Dancing, singing, doing cart-wheels and handsprings in the pelting rain, while the heavens roared and applauded. It was only *after* we had crushed ourselves into these dark, dusty, indoor tombs, that we enjoyed being ter-rified.

As Tolstoy might have said, all Russian winters are alike, but every Russian summer is different. Certainly, we felt our Kokush-kino summers were made only for us.

After the adventure of the steamer trip, Mother would some-times insist that we stop over in Kazan for a night with her sister and our Veretennikov cousins, so that we could "cool down." What we mostly preferred—Father, especially, the few times he was with us—was to discover that Aunt Anna and Uncle Nikolai had gone ahead. Then, we need not pause.

Our cousins would be waiting all day for us at the crossroads about two miles from the estate gates. It became their ritual. Up early, pack bottles of home-brewed licorice drink, a basket of *pi-rozhkis,* camp out with clotheshorses and sheets for makeshift tents on the grassy verge.

Some summers we might be hours, possibly days, late without being able to warn them. And when at last our overloaded *tarantass* did appear, bowling along those dried-up canals of roads like a ball of blown wool, we would know we were almost there because, above the squeak and jingle of the harness, the coconut-shell clack of horses' hooves, we could hear the chorus—"Here come the Ulyanovs! The Ulyanovs are here!"

In those days (only a summer ago) we often shared the three months' vacation not only with the Veretennikovs but also with Mother's other sisters and their families, the Zalezhskys and the Ardashevs. A third sister, Aunt Sophy, had married the richest landowner in Simbirsk Province while still in her teens, and gone to live on his enormous estate near Stavropol on the Volga, twenty times the size of Kokushkino. None of them had seen her since.

The most important resident, then as now, was the butler, Yuri, christened by Sasha and Anna *Jean Valjean*, or J.V., after Hugo's hero in *Les Misérables*. He ruled everybody, adults and children, servants and farmworkers, the peasants in "our" village. He had a filthy temper which would grow worse and worse the longer we stayed, as though we were unwanted guests eroding our reluctant welcome. Toward the end of the vacation, there would always be one evening meal when J.V. would enter the dining room waving above his villainously close-cropped head, impaled upon a carving knife the length of a saber, our roast joint. Then he would slam it on the table and shout—"Feed your mother-fucking selves!"

We youngsters rather enjoyed that spectacle. Though we shuddered along with the rest as the story of his life was retold for the umpteenth time. He was rumored to be a mass murderer, so drunk at the time of the crime that, instead of polishing off his own large family, he had stabbed to death the even larger family next door. When arrested, so the story ran, he said—"I blame myself. I ought to have remembered I didn't have any little buggers with red hair." Grandpa Blank, then police surgeon and medical superintendent of a madhouse, was so taken with this remark that he had Yuri released into his lifelong custody.

Yuri was always respectful toward mother, whom he continued to address as *Mamzelle Blanc* in a vairry-Frrrench accent. Father he ignored. Though sometimes he might pretend to mistake him for some visiting menial come to catch rats in the pantry or sharpen knives in the kitchen.

Mother, of course, arrived along with us in the same coach. Yuri would take her aside each time, in agitated fashion, whispering loudly, "Sorry, m'lady. But the Ulyanovs are here." The way he said it was a cross between "There are bugs in the beds" and "The bailiffs are in."

Now, there is *nobody* here but the Ulyanovs. And we are depleted by two. The three aunts have agreed that we can use the Little House for the time being, though none will be visiting us here. It is enough to have a blood relation rearing up an assassin—fortunately for them, they do not share our hated surname—without attracting the attention of the authorities by touching our hands or eating from the same plates.

AUGUST 25   KAZAN   1887

"Very talented, invariably diligent, prompt and reliable. First in all his classes. Upon graduation awarded a gold medal as the most meritorious pupil in achievement, development and behavior in the entire school. Not a single instance on record, in school or outside, of his invoking by word or deed any adverse opinion from the authorities or teachers. Guiding principles of his upbringing have been religion and rational discipline."

No surprise that such an official testimonial from the headmaster of Simbirsk Grammar should have resulted in the fortunate pupil becoming enrolled today as a student at Father's and (as Father always added) Tolstoy's alma mater, Kazan University.

What is surprising is that old K. should have written that about *me*. He knows, because I told him so in my graduation interview, that I totally reject religion. He knows, as one of Father's few intimates, a regular visitor to our house, that Mother is not a believer. He knows that Father never insisted upon any of us conforming, though himself conventionally pious, and a regular church attender. How can he have forgotten that, only a couple of years ago, I mounted a campaign of mockery and intimidation against poor old Monsieur Port, our French master? I used to imitate his appalling Russian to his face while the whole Upper School guffawed and jeered. It almost became a "pupil riot." (What a wigging Father gave me!)

What K. may not know is exactly what happened to Sasha's two gold medals, the one from Simbirsk and the one from Petersburg. Has anyone told him they were melted down to raise money to buy chemicals for the bomb that never went off?

I'm grateful for K's big white lies nevertheless. Without them, another Ulyanov would never have been authorized to enjoy higher education. He need not worry that I shall take Sasha's road. I intend to be as model an undergraduate as I was a schoolboy.

DECEMBER 6   KAZAN   1887

Hey ho! Well, that *was* a short university career! I'm writing this after two nights in the Kazan police cells. I'm a little lightheaded. Being carried off by the constabulary, and locked away incommunicado, is a traditional part of Russian higher education. Our equivalent of what in other nations' seats of higher learning would be a fine by the proctors. Even though your grossly overcrowded cell is grossly overcrowded with fellow scholars, all singing bawdy songs, improvising offensive chants, and generally competing to be the local Garibaldi, there are still moments after silence falls in the early hours when you can feel your heart thud. Then you start to wonder. Is this the first step on a road that will end with me chained to the wall of a dungeon for twenty years like Blanqui?

And to think—though I would die of shame to admit it anywhere else but here—I am almost totally innocent!

Once accepted into the forensic faculty—classes this first term in religion (universally required subject), the history of Russian and Roman contracts, and English—I was obliged to sign a declaration that I would not become a member of any societies, even authorized ones, without first obtaining permission from the "Student Inspector." This individual, unknown so far as I can discover in European colleges, is a cross between a colonel of gendarmes and your father confessor.

On September 2, I became a member of a society formed by students who shared in common a hometown in Simbirsk Province. Such groupings have been common in our universities for some time—Sasha and Anna both belonged to long-standing provincial clubs in Peter. We could not think of much to do when we met, so we decided to organize a student cafeteria (technically illegal, but never known to attract prosecution). Somehow or other I became the Simbirsk rep on the all-university council. And so, quite unaware, and unprepared for an involvement in politics, I attended an unpublicized meeting on December 1 to hear a report from Moscow students. How they had organized a peaceful demonstration against the University Discipline Act of 1884 (about which I remember even discreet Father had forwarded a mild protest to the minister). Also against the circular by the Min. of Pub. Ed. for June 18 this year, unnoticed by me in mid-exam, which barred lower-class children from going on to secondary and higher education. And how their demo had been brutally suppressed, many leaders expelled and imprisoned.

Probably nothing would have been emitted by us, except a froth of words, if the damned Student Inspector had not burst in and ordered us in the most florid and dictatorial fashion to disperse. Like his equivalent in Moscow, he found himself elbowed round the room, then thrown—actually lowered quite gently— out of the window.

It would now be an act of cowardice to obey.

We sat tight. As time passed, we composed a petition to the rector. The demands escalated hour by hour, agreed unanimously. All I did was not vote against.

In our preamble, we cited "the impossible conditions of Russian life in general and student life in particular." We declared our "desire to call the attention to society to these conditions." I realized that I knew little more about the former than I did about the latter.

Soon we ran out of the parochial propositions—cheaper meals, a second reading room, our own library, interest-free loans. It seemed logical to make wider demands—government of the university by the rector and a board of professors without interference by Petersburg through the governor; an undergraduate court to arbitrate all disputes and to award all scholarships and fellowships; every student who had been expelled from a university *anywhere in Russia* to be readmitted immediately; such regulations, rights and privileges to operate *throughout the land.*

In case these were not enough, and to give the Tsar a really bad night, we ended by denouncing the violence employed by the state in Moscow. And we instructed the authorities there to arrest those responsible, i.e., themselves.

Some of us were still arguing over the spelling of the more unusual words, when the doors (which we had forgotten to lock) burst open. In poured an unruly mob of policemen. At random, they arrested one hundred of us, about a tenth of the student body.

I think I would have been passed over. I was a freshman with an unfamiliar face. A police sergeant was pushing me, with a kind of avuncular roughness, down the stairs.

"Why get involved in this nonsense? Don't you realize you're banging your head against a brick wall?" And he playfully scraped mine against the bricks of the corridor.

I felt myself grow rigid at the indignity. I heard myself voicing, for the first time, a political slogan. "Yes, there is a wall. But it is a rotten one. A good kick will make it crumble."

I gave him a token hack on the shin.

Other fellows gathered round. They obviously liked the slogan. "Kick! Kick! Kick!" they began shouting. "Down with the wall, wall, wall!"

"Right, you young puppy. Where's your identity card? I'm taking you in."

I produced it, reluctantly. He took one look.

"Ulyanov! By God! Might have known. Back to the barracks, lads. This is the ringleader."

My fellow inmates now agree. They have convinced themselves I started it all, especially those who weren't there. Probably only Mother, who insisted on coming to university with me as a sort of female Figaro, realizes I was so taken by surprise I did nothing. She seems confident she can arrange that the authorities will impose no worse than rustication. I was beginning to get the feel of a city. "Rustication" will be a real punishment, even at Kokushkino.

I will just have to educate myself.

DECEMBER 20   KOKUSHKINO   1887

Since I was booted out of Kazan, all the family have been together, sharing the little rooms in the Little House. The Billiard Hall has remained firmly locked. But tonight, the door swung open as Oly and I passed.

Glasses and bottles, kitchen-made *kvass* and real Moscow lemonade; Portuguese port and Spanish sherry, both London-bottled. Plates and serving platters, some cold on beds of ice, others hot over spirit lamps, offering lots of *zakuski*—meat balls, fish balls, artichoke hearts with ham and cheese, salted herrings in sour cream, aubergine "caviar," and caviar.

And books, books of a kind unseen by us. Fat, falling-apart albums spliced with thick paperboard sepia photographs. Mostly plump, middle-aging ladies, more or less naked, reaching for high cupboards, bending over into awkward corners, sprawled uncomfortably ajar on sofas, and in a couple of instances rather ill-at-ease in the open air, pictured from below climbing apple trees.

Was somebody preparing us for an initiation, a rite of passage?

Oly hit on the correct response in her oblique fashion, leaving any eavesdropper unsure whether she quite appreciated what she was saying. She stared. She fiddled about. Then she remarked, terribly loudly, as on stage, giving a long swoop to my name: "Vol-*ooood*-ya, my dear. I fear this is what people mean by *a den of vice*."

There was a certain amount of spluttering behind screens. Then *Jean Valjean*, Yuri, the butler, appeared in front of us with a rattling tray.

Yuri's attitude to all the Ulyanovs, but especially to Oly and me, has changed spectacularly since we took over in July. As we sat there in the Billiard Hall, and were waited upon to our great pleasure, I felt I knew what had precipitated the change. Somehow his cracked old brain had registered that Sasha had been executed for an attempt on the life of the Tsar. Being close relatives of a would-be regicide relegated us to a class above him in the criminal hierarchy. At last we were worthy to employ him as a servant. The Ulyanovs are aristocrats of the underworld.

DECEMBER 21   KOKUSHKINO   1887

Last night, I heard Grandpa's English clock every time it chimed. It punctuated the same dream sequence again and again. Yuri's face floating in darkness, like a turnip lantern. His hands as big as serving salvers, piled high with food, lunging at me, forcing me to eat, though my mouth was already thumb-packed with un-swallowed food as a pipe with tobacco. Just when I began to choke, the lights were switched on. I was in a small bare room. The hands had become two faceless warders, glove puppets as big as men, who seized me and started dragging me toward the door. It was the door of Father's study in Simbirsk. Behind it, I knew, there was the gibbet on which I would be hanged.

At this point, each time, I woke up feeling the rope strangling. I would lie there, listening to the whirr the clock makes before it strikes. As it reached the last stroke, I would be in the dream again. By dawn, I was exhausted.

I had to get up and have a pee among the bushes. On the way back, I stopped by Oly's door. I couldn't resist. I opened it and slid into bed beside her, something I have not done for years. Not since before Father died. She enfolded me.

"What is it?

I told her.

"Heartburn," she said.

I said I thought that a bit callous. She groaned, and then chuckled. Then she spoke, for once almost solemn. "From the day Sasha was arrested, there has hardly been an hour when I have not thought—how must it feel to be taken out and hanged? I meditate on it the way a nun is expected to meditate on the crucifixion of Jesus. There is no step along our brother's way to execution I have not trodden. He was arrested on March first. Did you know that was two hundred and ninety-five days ago? After two hundred and ninety-five days, for the first time, and then in a dream, you, dear brother, finally begin to wonder how Sasha must have felt, murdered in cold blood. No, my dear Volodya. With you, it is heartburn."

I fell asleep in her bed. When I opened my eyes she was gone, leaving beside me the warm print of her pretty body like the form of a hare. She was right, of course. But she was also wrong. What use to the dead Jesus, or his Church, are a million nuns in their cells meditating on his crucifixion? What would have made his death worthwhile, and built a militant movement, would have been for Peter to cry "Down with the Romans!" and pick up a sword when the cock crew thrice. Then we might have started a Christian religion which fought for humanity to have a decent life here on earth instead of a pretend one in the sky.

JANUARY 2   KOKUSHKINO   1888

Still pondering over two quotations on half-burned scraps of paper (from the same letter or memo?) that Mother had found among rolled squills of paper in a jar on Sasha's desk. The others had nothing on them. All may have been intended only for lighting lamps, pipes, cigars. Anyway, the police in Peter missed them. Here they are, unmistakably in his handwriting: ". . . to engage in elaboration of theoretical principles would amount to surrender. Any philistine can theorize—the revolutionary has to fight . . ." And: ". . . it is suicidal to engage in any political activity before one has clarified the principles on which it should be based . . ."

JANUARY 20   KOKUSHKINO   1888

Some notes on the short, happy life of Alexander Ilyich Ulyanov. For I am sure—strange as it might sound to those who did not know him—his life *was* happy.

Sasha, even as a boy, never put any trust in comforting illusions, daydreams, reveries about what might have been. He always had a piercing sense of realism, of what was or was not practicable. He had no interest in any enterprise beyond his powers. When we were involved in some joint project, he would test each link of the chain in his head before we started. He was the least spontaneous person I have ever met. His aim was always to opt for certainty, or anyway ninety percent sureness. Yet failure never depressed him. It was only nature's way of telling him that he had not done his homework. If you know enough, then choice ceases to exist.

"Someday you will understand, Volodya," he used to say in those summer holidays when he still talked to me. "Freedom is the recognition of necessity."

It was a tough nut to crack. Anyway, I wasn't listening. While he was making some plan, I was always the one shouting: "Let's go, let's go, let's *go!*" Anywhere. So long as we were moving. Sasha, however, never made a journey without maps.

His was the biologist's philosophy: any creature that has adapted to its environment, achieved a balance and reconcilement of its needs and powers, must be fulfilling its evolutionary destiny. In other words, happy.

Sudden intuition—most unscientific. Did Sasha *intend* to fail in his attempt to assassinate the Tsar? Tsars have been killed before—the last only six years to the day. But nothing had changed. Except for the worse. This time, to be caught, to be tried, to make a speech from the dock, to proclaim the reason why the Tsar must go to his death, *that* (he may have argued to himself) would be a truer victory.

And yet, had he, I wonder, considered that although the authorities might let him address the court (the Tsar more than anybody wanted to hear the reason why) they might also forbid his speech being reported? I'm sure Sasha must have examined this option. Ah! Then he must also have counted on his words being secretly recorded, printed, distributed, discussed, spread like winged seeds of the sycamore to sprout among small, determined, radical groups across Russia? Alas, this is simply guesswork.

I can only be sure I have marked out his trial when I have actually trodden it myself in my own mind: read what he read, reasoned as he reasoned, faced what he faced. "Just like Sasha . . . ?" Perhaps. When I catch up, I may not feel obliged to imitate his actions. I too will say to myself: if we follow this line, then this will result . . . but if that, that. His necessity need not be mine.

JANUARY 25   KOKUSHKINO   1888

One of the sources of Sasha's philosophy—an underlined copy of Nechaev's *Revolutionary Catechism*. I have learned it by heart in the last couple of months. Sergei Genadievich was an enemy of tsarism whose ice-cold courage never melted. He appeared to have the personality of a giant hedgehog—everyone who touched him was somehow pricked and infected by his ideas. Sentenced to twenty years in Siberia, he still so frightened Alexander II that the Tsar insisted he be imprisoned under the royal nose in the Peter and Paul fortress. Despite being penned in a shallow cell, half the depth of its massive walls, his every gesture monitored and listed in a weekly report, he dominated his warders. Some he even converted to the cause.

When *Narodnaya Volya* wrote offering to devote all their energies to rescuing him, he wrote back instructing them that it was more important they remain dedicated to their principal aim— the assassination of the Tsar. When *Narodnaya Volya* blew up Alexander II less than nine years later, his successor, Alexander III, exacted his revenge on Nechaev. He lost all privileges. Every contact ceased with anyone beyond the solid steel door of Cell No. I, which slammed on him like the gate of a tomb. His name was never mentioned again. On December 3, 1882, "the prisoner in Cell No. I" died of "dropsy complicated by scurvy." But the news was never published. Only a short time before Sasha's attempt on Alexander III was there semi-official confirmation that the "Nechaev monster" who haunted Dostoievsky's notebooks and dominated that masterpiece of reactionary spite, *The Possessed*, was no longer alive.

He was a liar, a blackmailer, a thief, a forger, a seducer, finally a murderer. He was incapable of transmuting his theory and passion for overthrowing capitalist society into any kind of practical effect. He set up a fantasy network of conspirators, allegedly numbering four million but never counted as more than a couple of hundred, either by the Okhrana or rival plotters. His only concerted operation was the bungled killing of an innocent student, Ivan Ivanovich Ivanov. Nevertheless, the way Nechaev phrased his philosophy can still alarm both enemies and admirers like the beating of a drum, the sounding of a bugle. Once you have read his definitions, they remain embossed on the memory, a rubric that nothing can chisel away.

Sometimes my thoughts go out of focus, like the images on the glass in my camera. Then I can see lines from his *Catechism* outlined on the mind's epidiascope screen.

The revolutionary is a doomed man . . . no personal concerns, no occupation, no feelings, no attachments, no property, and no name.

Morality is everything that aids the victory of the revolution. Anything that obstructs the path is immoral and criminal.

The revolutionary can expect no mercy from the ruling class. . . . He must accustom himself to torture.

He is not a revolutionary if he has any sympathy with this world. He should not hesitate to destroy any thing, any belief, any person in this world.

Our task is absolute, terrible, universal and merciless destruction. . . . To forge the masses into a single, unbreakable, all-destroying force—that is our ambition, our conspiracy and our purpose for existing.

FEBRUARY 6   KOKUSHKINO   1888

Early in the New Year, I wrote a long letter to Pavel Yakovelevich, my closest, probably my only, friend from Simbirsk Grammar. It was a conscious piece of showing-off. He would know that as much I did, and relish it, even if it rubbed home that he was up to his neck in that backwater while I was striking sparks and firing off roman candles at university. So I made it a real performance, full of insults to the professors at university and the officials of the town. I listed those students (many of whom he knows) who were on the people's side, those few who supported the provincial tyrants. There were some really stinging phrases, some smarting insults, and I was congratulating myself on this talent for polemic.

Anyuta, however, had been watching me from a distance. She knew I almost never write letters. Then she asked what it was about.

I was delighted to read her the whole thing, walking up and down, waving an arm, turning dramatically as I reached the end of the paragraph and the end of the *salon*. There was no applause. After a silence, she reminded me that Sasha's conspiracy had been betrayed by just such a boastful, indiscreet letter from one of the gang to a school friend in Kharkov. It had been opened at random by the censorship and turned over to the police. Did I not remember I was under police watch, official and open? It certainly included reading my mail. I was risking my friends, myself, my family, all our futures, for a silly-clever exercise in egoism. I should tear it up now.

I refused. I felt an almost parental sense of ownership and pride in this effort.

It has lain there on the corner of the hall table for around thirty days. This morning I opened it, reread it, and tore it up. Anyuta was right. I feel better immediately. I shall not make that mistake again.

FEBRUARY 12   KOKUSHKINO   1888

From Mother's reports of her talks with Sasha, from the observation of Anna and her fiancé, Mark Elizarov, arrested with Sasha and now also in exile here, I put together this outline. When Sasha was first studying in Peter he cared for nothing but his work. Throughout three and a half years, that was all he thought about. He would go into the room within his room, the cupboard-kitchen he had fitted out as a one-man stand-up laboratory, and not emerge again for a day or a night, sometimes for a weekend. When he did, he was never sure how long he had been away from the world. It might feel like only a couple of hours. Yet here he was—parched, hungry, sleep-heavy, bristling with five o'clock shadow twice over. Friends urged him to get his nose out of science, take part in affecting the real world.

Occasionally, lured out to a late-night alehouse or an early-morning brasserie, he argued the case for pure research. He was amassing information that, so far as he knew, no one else possessed. Later, in a long life devoted to science, he would have time to extract meanings, advance theories, test hypotheses.

Walking the Volga woods with Father, he repeated his friends' arguments as his own. Father replied, as Sasha himself had done, with the case for scholarship as superior to politics. The next step ought to have been to reverse roles. To try out Father with the proposition that tsarist autocracy needed enlightened, organized opposition and challenge instead of disinterested, impartial experiments for the sake of experimentation. He could not tell Father how much he was growing to hate society as it was arranged for the benefit of the rich, the lazy, the selfish, the frivolous, the pompous, the self-satisfied. Father saw only the dangers—rustication, expulsion, exile . . . he let the three dots speak for the rest. He made the archetypal parents' plea—keep out of trouble, if not for yourself, at least for us. Think what disgrace and sorrow you could bring upon the family. When Sasha did venture out that Christmas with a few friends, he was shocked, then gradually more and more outraged, at how little it is permitted for almost anybody not a member of the Royal Family to do on the streets. The ordinary citizen is not even allowed to smoke!

The first venture he took part in was to mark the twenty-fifth anniversary of the Liberation of the Serfs on February 19, 1861. This was to be done by holding a communal mass in the Volkovo Cemetery in honor of the pioneers of the "great reform." This, then, was Sasha's first political act in public. He suggested circulating all of Peter's middle-class liberals inviting them to take part. They responded, in true, fearless liberal fashion, by not turning up. It would have never occurred to me that this was in any way a dangerous gesture, let alone an act of anti-government defiance. If a protest demo were needed, should it not have been *against* the "great reform" which all revolutionary writers and propagandists of the time (Chernyshevsky, Dobrolyubov and the rest whom I've just been reading) regarded as a fraud?

Are we now sliding down into the valley of reaction at such a speed that, looking back, both radicals and autocrats, police and rebels, begin to see even "February 19" as a huge, heroic attempt to alter society?

In the winter, he and his friends decided to stage another commemorative demonstration, this time with a mass in the cemetery honoring the twenty-fifth anniversary of the death of Dobrolyubov. This time around a thousand students paraded. This time the police *were* there. The gates of the Volkovo were locked, and permission for a mass refused. As they straggled in twos and threes back to Peter, they were rounded up like sheep by the trained hounds of tsarism, the Cossacks.

Sasha experienced the sense of impotence, a grown-up treated like a naughty child. He began to ask what sort of society this was. The mass of the students, warned against future protests even of this mild kind, melted away. From now on, it seemed to Sasha, there was only one weapon still available. It was the one used, or anyway advocated, by many of his new heroes from the past— *Terror!*

I think I have followed him, trailed him like a detective, without losing him. Can I now interpret, and paste in their right place, those two scraps of paper Mother found in his room? I think he could not have actually *wanted* to fail. That was a silly-clever solution. What is more likely is that it did not matter to him whether the Tsar was blown up or not—so long as the attempt was made, and known to the nation to have been made. (Anyone else might have thought that one difference might be the chances of his own survival. But I know, beyond doubt, that when Sasha decided on an enterprise, the question of his personal safety would not count on either side of the equation.)

So I deduce from the evidence of the notes that he is adjudicating at an internal debate. One side argues—the time to hit back is now. Only academic liberals, armchair rebels, stay indoors among books or test tubes while there is violence against the people on the streets. The terrorism of the state should be answered in its own language. The other rebuts—action should not precede theory. Do not use the means unless you have determined the end. To attack the Tsar without preparing the ground for a general protest would be suicidal. But then, is not suicide also a powerful weapon? The blood of the martyrs manures the seed of the Revolution.

But, above all (I try to reconstruct the moment inside his head), Sasha would have felt that there must always be a time when the philosophizing has to stop. What could it matter, in the long vista of history, whether this or that sortie failed? In the end, the war would be won, victory being the sum total of a thousand personal sacrifices.

For now Sasha was answering the question *What Is to Be Done?* with the answer: Anything, but *Something*. And that Thing must be direct, violent, sensational. Sasha had swallowed that fiery potion for which there is no relief, except a larger dose. I can imagine his moving logically from hermetic independence to practical involvement, step by step, laying each stone deliberately in front of him as he forded the stream.

In the absence of an organized party with a coherent philosophy, individual action was all that lay to hand. Terrorism! He became, in a phrase he used to Mother, "a human bomb." Few details appeared in the papers, because of the censorship. But

Mother had them all at her fingertips. What Sasha cooked up for his group—working on hints found in textbooks in the university library—was a most inhuman bomb. It still gives me a slight sweat when I think of it—an inner shell containing wired sticks of dynamite, a glass capsule of nitric acid as a trigger, and then, packed round in paper coffins, like liqueur chocolates, fifty hollowed-out shotgun pellets with soft centers of *strychnine*!

The police described the bombs as "amateurish" and "badly made." But then everything about the operation was amateurish and badly made. The leader, Pyotr Shevyrev, was already a loser. Fanatical, impulsive, scatterbrained, tubercular, believing himself, sometimes literally, to be a reincarnation of Nechaev, he concealed, from himself as much as from the rest, that he only had a few months to live.

Shevyrev was an even worse organizer than Nechaev. Intoxicated with a kind of messianic exultation, he rarely considered what happened in the shadowy city of flesh-and-blood. Security did not exist, except for Sasha. He refused to drop even a hint of his new philosophy to sister or brother. The rest gossiped, one of them even writing to an acquaintance halfway across Russia about his devotion to "Red Terror." Intercepted in a random check, it alerted the Okhrana.

His companions knew nothing about conspiracy, security, publicity, sedition, terrorism, insurrection. They had no funds, no escape routes, no proclamations to cover success or failure. They called themselves the "Terrorist Faction of the People's Will" (*Narodnaya Volya*). But they had no links with the real *Narodnaya Volya*, the group which had killed Tsar Alexander II on 1 March 1881. There was a good reason for this—*Narodnaya Volya* no longer existed. It and every other organized, underground opposition of the eighties had been hunted down and eliminated. They were alone, without any mass support, which could only come from peasants or industrial workers. They were bound to fail, fail even if they had succeeded in blowing up the Tsar. *That is not the way.*

What the way is, I am still not sure. I am reading hard. I am searching for companions of like mind. I am looking for those with experience of the various roads to a new society.

FEBRUARY 15   KOKUSHKINO   1888

Mother, having told us everything she knows about Sasha, does not want to talk any more about the past. She is keeping to her rule that remorse, regret, nostalgia for the might-have-been, are the most destructive of emotions. The peasant saying—"Not even God can increase last year's harvest."

Still no answer to my request to the minister of the interior asking permission to travel abroad to finish my studies. Perhaps I should have allowed Mother to go to Peter in person, as she suggested. But there is something rather embarrassing about a grown man (almost eighteen) being nursery-maided in his relations with his government.

SEPTEMBER 13   KAZAN   1888

Back in Kazan, the first time for nine months. Mother has a magic touch with authorities and bureaucrats. When they see her coming, the façade begins to shake and crumble. She epitomizes, with her sad, beautiful face and halo of white hair, the widow of the great man who has died penniless, the sole support of the brood of young geniuses, in some salon problem picture—"a story without words." They know they are going to have to break the rules from time to time, reveal a glimpse of the golden heart behind the steely front. Why not today?

I have been smoking ever since I reread *What Is to Be Done?* as an adult. Much taken with the hero Rakhmetov's dedication to cigars as stimulants to rational thought. I prefer their cheaper, more modern equivalent, the "gasper." Though not because of any great pleasure from the weed itself. It is more the whole performance, the ritual operation, which soothes my nerves.

The atmosphere of our discussion groups is veined with swirling scarves of chiffony smoke, layer upon layer of blue-streaked lawn. You can make an impressive attack on the other speaker simply by breathing out upon him. Frequently, one of our debates ends with just the dominant pair, two knights on a chessboard, pumping feathered plumes of defiance at each other down loftily uptilted noses. "Like cabhorses in winter," laughs Olga.

MAY 3   ALAKAEVKA   1889

Another move, this time from Kazan to Alakaevka, a village about
thirty miles west from Samara. Mother has contracted to buy an
estate, with a mill, of 225 acres. Kokushkino all over again. I had
no idea we could afford such a place—the price, after much bargaining, was settled at 7,500 rubles. A tidy sum, more than six
times her state pension. She must have got more for Moscow Street,
and for her inherited share of Kokushkino, than any of us thought.
Will we ever know? Mother prefers, like the gamblers on the Volga
boats, to keep her cards close to her bosom. It is like having your
own private Rothschild to run your affairs. Very reassuring!

MAY 7   ALAKAEVKA   1889

The trees around the house are loaded with the dead branches of
winter which should have been lopped off at the beginning of
spring. For the last two days, I have been cutting them back, piling
the old wood into a sizable mound. The trees look absurdly, even
cruelly, shorn. Mutilated soldiers on hospital parade. I always find
it hard, when first pruning, to believe that any living things will
not only survive, but be strengthened, grow bigger and tougher,
by being hacked back to juvenile stature. But once I convince
myself that it has to be done, I see it as preventive surgery. I can
cut and saw with confidence.

   Obviously, I could not expect on my own to trim and prepare
the whole orchard for late-summer fruiting. It looked as if it had
been too long neglected. All around the house, in every direction,
so far as the eye can penetrate, we are hemmed in by a gray army
of many-limbed zombies, decorated with a few green ribands which
alone suggest that deep down a few may still be alive.

   But as I got four or five trees deep, far enough to be invisible
from the porch or the verandas, I would come across an odd sight:
Over and over, I found a grove of well-pruned plums, apples or
cherries, all on its own, carefully tended and prepared for crop-
ping. What possible reason would anyone have for hiding these
little oases of living orchard away in a big, dead wilderness? Who
could that anyone be? I have been a countryman long enough now

to know there is only one answer—the kulak, the tight-fisted, cunning *petit-bourgeois* among peasants. The longer he and his cronies could discourage prospective buyers, the more seasons they could get firewood for nothing, poach the game, scrump the mushrooms, even camp out in the outhouses and sheds. All without altering the appearance of the place. Ah, but then how to raise their own crops of fruit without being seen by outsiders and passersby?

Of course! By protecting each cornucopia with a protective husk of unsellable, aging timber. Got them! I will now employ them as hired hands to reap the harvest they thought they had cornered for themselves.

My mood of confidence carried over into my bonfire-making. There were some obvious difficulties. It has been an exceptionally wet May. Everything that is to be burned is sopping, including a large, thick hall mat that has been left out so long it has grown a crop of watercress. The sensible approach would have been to leave the job until a day or two of breeze and sun had dried my tinder. Nevertheless I was determined to proceed against the odds, bending nature to my pyromaniacal skill.

I started by folding the mat round, like the base of a turret, leaving only one tiny way-in facing the prevailing wind. Then I ranged the branches on end in concentric circles inside, reaching as high as they could go, filling the gaps with smaller bits, finishing off what was now practically a tower with a carapace of overlapping leaves. I started the arson of this edifice by inserting a small dry faggot, crowned with a flaming ball of tar, into the servant's entrance at ground level.

For fully five minutes, no change occurred. Only I knew that inside the castle, down in the dungeon, a midget incendiary was at work.

Then the dark, scaly skin of this totem pole began to breathe out, through every joint, a rippling pearly layer of smoke which gradually clothed all the outside with a silky shift. The pile's smoke grew thicker and bluer, taking on the texture of an Assyrian emperor's beard. The thing began to tremble and hum. I widened the door a little, catching a glimpse of the dancing red hell inside. Within seconds, small flames in blue and yellow began to run up and down the outside. As the leaves dried, they flared out like a series of matches struck in succession. The branches gradually folded in.

But the ragged wigwam, such was the massy weight of soaked foliage tamped down inside, still crooned and shook without collapsing, more smoke than fire. After half an hour, most of it had

fallen inside the drum of the matting which still resisted like as-
bestos. Now great scarlet tongues leaped up, licking at the trees,
firing an occasional burning lance at the wooden wall of the house
from within this miniature steel-furnace. Then, with a pitchfork,
I lifted the mat and toasted it this side and that. After more than
an hour, I had managed to induce the great cylinder to consume itself, every piece, leaving behind only a clean, white deposit of ash.

A ridiculous sense of achievement. But I remember Herzen
—"There is always something revolutionary about a fire."

SEPTEMBER 2   ALAKAEVKA   1889

"Volodya," said Mother today in that sweet voice which makes the
listener at first believe he is about to listen to a recital of poetry.
"Volodya, my dear. I try never to worry you about money. But
you know how much we have. Though Anna is marrying, Olga is
preparing herself for university, and you are not allowed to earn
an income. We need every kopek we can get. Do you think it is
quite fair to spend some of what little we have on useless, harmful
cigarettes?"

I nipped in half the one I had in my hand. "Mamouchka," I
trumpeted, "I will never smoke again."

And I know I never shall. Even if I have to strain my willpower
to its utmost. After all, the mind has its own muscles. They too
develop more strength the more you force them to the limit.

SEPTEMBER 10   ALAKAEVKA   1889

I am going to have to tell Mother that I cannot run this farmstead.
Clearly, I see now, this is what she wanted, to get me away from
the temptations of conspiracy, student plotting, lecturing on subversive topics, writing inflammatory pamphlets. One martyr is
enough in the family. Yet we are all edging our way into underground opposition—not just Anna, already a marked woman, but
also her fiancé Mark; me newly dipped into revolutionary theory
and history; Olga my almost-twin, neck and neck; even Dmitri at
fifteen puzzling his slow way in our wake. Only Marya has not
caught the infection. But wait until next year when she's twelve!

Father would be astonished to see what a transformation has been wrought in his conventional, competitive, exam-passing, social-climbing family. Perhaps Mother is too, under her Niobe exterior. Who knows what hot, live feelings flicker beneath the marble or what plans are hatching behind the mask? I am sure my future is already being written into her next year's diary. Day by day, am I expected to slide myself into the role of country gent, enlightened farmer, little father to my band of people? Just like Grandfather Blank?

SEPTEMBER 30   ALAKAEVKA   1889

Today I told Mother I could no longer bear trying to treat the estate as a business proposition. It is not that I find this so difficult—I am no Oblomov! Indeed I have discovered that I have something of a talent for handling money. I am a born organizer. Once I analyzed, ordered, digested, selected ideas and facts when I was writing my essays. I perfected the technique of examination-passing. Now, I can analyze, order, digest and select the figures and totals presented to me, when I am managing this place, perfecting the technique of profiteering.

But I do not wish to do so. It is obvious to me studying the peasantry at close quarters that they are far more like embryo capitalists than primitive socialists. I have set out to discover how the rural economy works, who exploits whom, what is needed when, how the machine runs. So I do not instruct, I ask. I do not lecture, I listen.

What I cannot tolerate is becoming *myself* a cog, albeit a well-greased and oversized one, in the grinding down, pressing and decanting process. There is little I have not examined and categorized here. Our land, bought from a bankrupt, has no longer any tools, or hired hands to use them. If we wish to cultivate it, not just for ourselves but to produce a cash surplus, we can only do so by employing laborers from the miserable, blighted village of Alakaevka. I have carried out my own census. Thirty-four families in thirty shacks, nine without a single horse or cow. All with tiny plots barely capable of supporting a small dog or half a dozen flea-bitten hens. No school; but of course an alehouse. Two hundred souls from whom they proudly produce four boys who can read and write (after a fashion). They need Father!

The rest are totally illiterate, though the four or five kulaks have taught themselves to count. And these, though miserable enough by our standards, or those of almost any town-dwellers, wrench a slightly more rewarding living from exploiting their fellows. If we wish to be a going concern, we can only do so by operating through these kulaks.

As the son of the manor, small but self-contained, my relations with the peasants may have their strains and problems. But they are human strains and problems. If I begin a partnership with the kulaks, enriching myself and my family by a collusion to enslave the country people almost as much as if they were still serfs, then our relationship will become unnatural, abnormal, *obscene*.

OCTOBER 2   ALAKAEVKA   1889

I think I have reached the point Sasha was at when he stood in the Petersburg dock. The parting of the ways between Populism, the philosophy of the People's Will—*Narodnaya Volya*—and Marxism, the philosophy of the Liberation of Labour group.

In Europe, there are no longer any crossroads. They have more proletarians than peasants. Capitalism has overtaken and buried feudalism, the city sucked dry the countryside. The party of labor, of the industrial workers, the Social Democrats, exists legally everywhere, or at worst functions behind the thinnest disguise. These are mass movements, backed by trade unions, publishing newspapers which sell in their thousands. Autocracy, the bourgeois dictatorship, is tempered by parliamentary democracy. Workers' candidates stand for election, and enter the house of representatives. Whatever the people need, it is not undercover conspiracy, assassination, bomb-throwing—terror.

In Russia, we can still, must still, choose. Is Populism the authentic Russian way? It is tempting to believe so. It flatters the national vanity. In time of despair, it provides the alcohol, the oxygen, of hope. If we really are, so to speak, the Chosen People of Socialism, then maybe we *can* make the great leap forward, vault over several hurdles across the highway to revolution. Set an example to the torpid factory hands of Europe, possibly the world. Marx thought this quite likely. Engels came close to forecasting it.

If only we knew what Sasha himself had said in his speech from the dock . . . I was muttering something like this as I paced the corridors. Mother appeared, a beckoning ghost pointing to a cupboard under the main stairs. Here I found a pile of tin brief-cases marked "Annual Reports." Inside were the documents of the case, official and unofficial, press cuttings in several languages, letters from relatives of the other accused—an entire archive worthy of the Security Department of the Home Office. Even a desk, a candle, a pad of ruled paper, pen and ink. It had been waiting for me.

After a brief sorting, I abstracted the three hundred page transcript of the trial. It must have been made for the authorities, but someone had copied it (colossal task) and passed it on to Vladimir Burtsev. B. is a radical publicist sympathetic to the Narodniks, self-appointed historian of the revolutionary movements of Russia. He lives mainly abroad and is quite used to undercover operators dropping off on him the occasional secret state paper. Not everyone, I was told in Kazan, thinks this is such a marvelous idea. Burtsev's library in Paris is open to anyone with passable credentials on the left. Who knows how many police spies are among them, tracing back the sources? Certainly, the border police appear not to be overzealous in interrupting his flow of correspondence. He was able to forward this file, openly, to Mother (she kept the wrapping), from Simbrisk to Kazan to Kokushkino to Alakaevka, without difficulty.

A few minutes' examination satisfies me that the real *Narodnaya Volya*, already suppressed, had nothing to do with Sasha's little group. They took its name to cheer themselves up, frighten the authorities. I see also that Sasha never denied responsibility for the attempt. Indeed, he tried to persuade the police he was the prime, virtually the only, mover. So! There was a time for lies, was there, dear brother, after all?

The first words I read of Sasha's address to the court, page 289, held me rigid, barely blinking, a schoolboy suspended in time. For I heard Sasha's voice speaking aloud from the dead, as if through the trumpet of a medium.

> I do not dispute the facts. I attempted a crime. I exercise my right of defense only to explain my motives.
>
> From early youth I have gradually developed a distaste for our social system. Since I came to Petersburg, it has tainted everything I saw, heard, tasted, smelled. It was a bell ringing in my head, a stench in my nostrils.
>
> This led me to study the social and economic sciences as well as the biological and chemical ones. Sometimes I read until night

and day blurred. Soon I saw that vague, cloudy dreams of freedom and equality and brotherhood could only become solid creatures walking this earth by a scientific approach to change. My aim was socialism.

I asked myself the question—what method was most likely to achieve this goal? There is no doubt. The correct path is through rational propaganda, logical argument, mass education. Words, books, newspapers, lectures.

The judge could not contain himself. "Poisoned bullets are not the most elegant items in a civilized discussion, are they?"

I recognized exactly the chilly tone in which Sasha must have replied. I can see the wintry smile. The judge had fallen into his trap. The riposte would be like a handful of crushed ice being stuffed down the back of your neck.

There *is* no civilized discussion in Russia. *This* is the only place where such topics can be raised. On the steps of the gallows. You and your policemen have blanked out all intellectual life. Socialist propaganda? We can't even publish new poetry, circulate non-political magazines, stage plays in which people talk like real people.

Here it is impossible to undertake any scientific examination of anything!

You, up there, are all-powerful. We, the so-called intelligentsia, are few and feeble, gathered in a handful of cities. Your little finger cuts off our last pulse of free speech.

Perhaps this is why you could not appreciate that our tiny number nevertheless would never rest. We had minds that refused to stop working. For us, it was a necessity to think freely, to share our thoughts with others less privileged, less educated, than ourselves.

We have learned that it is only through terror, this century's great political invention, that we can defend, let alone extend, our inalienable rights. This is the weapon of the weak, of the physically feeble but the spiritually strong. It is our form of single combat against the big battalions of tyranny.

Let me warn you. Do not take comfort from the fact that there are only ten of us in this box. It will always be possible in this country to find ten people who care so much for their ideas that they are willing to sacrifice themselves and die for their cause. And we will always take some of you with us if we can. Nothing you can do will deter us.

I attempt no moral justification for my unfortunately failed crime. I realize it may have no political effect whatsoever. I just wish to explain that assassination, even the use of poisoned bullets, is the unavoidable consequence of conditions today. If you want to stop terror, you must listen to what I am saying here. That is all, thank you.

(Someone, presumably Burtsev, has transcribed comments by the Tsar himself, scribbled in the margins of the original. He writes: "Not just cracked, a complete idiot!" and "The essence of communism!" And so on. Finally, reluctantly, our Emperor concedes: "This honesty is quite touching.")

I have never felt so proud—*my* brother!

OCTOBER 11   SAMARA   1889

Mother has finally abandoned the idea of me becoming a manager of my own estates. We will use Alakaevka as our summer quarters, the way we did with Kokushkino, but winter in town. The town is Samara, thirty miles to the east. We moved today.

At first sight, not much of an improvement. Though its population is said to be 100,000, twice that of Simbirsk, it keeps the air of a dead-end backwater. "This used to be a one-horse town, but unfortunately the horse died." Typical local joke told by brother-in-law Mark's brother, a typical local rogue, known as "Ole Mustard" (*Gorcheeza*).

NOVEMBER 1   SAMARA   1889

Samara has never had nobles. Nor serfs. It was too far east in the steppes to attract the ones who needed the others. Therefore, no elegant parks, European pseudo-classical public buildings, Parisian statues, London squares. Instead of a nest of gentlefolk, more a corral of cattle barons, a granary of corn merchants. Effect: rather as if that lair of the foxy merchants in Simbirsk had crept uphill, swallowed the whole town.

When one of these super-kulaks manages to harvest more gold rubles than he can haul in a fleet of sack-filled carts, he will start to push up a massive, stone house. These could be modeled on the burial vaults of minor aristocrats. Tombs with every dimension mechanically multiplied by twenty—huge doors, windows, walls, a roof of ten-feet-thick piecrust. Then they throw round each one a picket fence, sit back on dwarf furniture amid the unheatable spaces, and wait. For what? For the dark people to revolt, overthrow the Tsar, set up a peasant republic where the money changers and wholesale-retailers rule? Meanwhile, they make no attempt to lay out these residences in avenues or *piazzas*, or even to establish a *quartier*. Each stands alone in a wilderness of vacant sites, tumbledown cottages, overgrown pathways, the odd undemolished chimney, jungly garden long gone to seed. Beyond these, little villas form a ring, marking a turnpike before you reach the slum villages of the semi-nomads, the barge-haulers, the landless peasants who have learned that when you are free nothing is free, the laborers who slave in the mills and warehouses.

Not likely to be much sympathetic companionship for us there, you would think. Add to which, no industry, not even a small-scale factory. So we are also cut off from the politically educated, economically alerted workingman. Then add to that no university. So we are also isolated from progressive, intellectually aware students and teachers.

However, just *because* this place is so philistine-ridden, so bereft of the usual radical agitation found among workshops and lecture halls, the tsarist authority has labeled it officially "a safe town."

And this means, I bump at every turn into revolutionaries who have served their term in Siberian exile and have been permitted to use Samara as a halfway house on the route back to the dangerous big cities. It means this is also a place to which suspected metropolitan persons, possible carriers of the germs of dissent, whom it is for some reason inconvenient for the authorities to prosecute in open court, can be summarily banished for a spell. They are all under police watch. But then so are we.

Living in Samara means that at last I can meet people who live and breathe the revolutionary doctrines about which I have only read. I can talk to those who may have talked to Nechaev and Tkachev, Chernyshevsky and Herzen, Zaichnevsky and Lavrov.

Samara will be *my* university!

MARCH 21   PETERSBURG   1891

Second visit to Peter. My three-day journey from Samara leaves
me feeling I have been knocked out, three nights in a row. But it
is essential I get my academic qualifications from the most impressive institution in the country—the University of St. Petersburg. Moscow, or even Kazan, would have been enough to permit
me to practice law, especially in the back of beyond like Samara.
But I foresee a career dedicated to better things than courtroom
disputes about the inheritance of pigsties or the rights of way
through middens. My ambition is to indict, and convict, and condemn to mass demolition, the criminal system of tsarism. For this,
I need to have the best possible degree? Yes. I cannot afford to
have anyone say that I aim to turn society upside down just because
I am a failure, a third-rate dunce, someone who could not compete,
and rise to the top (after all, as Father did), by my own abilities.

There are Social Democrats in Samara who classify this as
collaboration with the enemy. Opportunism, careerism. But I note
that they tend to be café-haunters, afternoon-sleepers, professional
failures. In a word, Oblomovs. How can they hope to lead our
people, to impress their colleagues, to frighten the authorities,
when none of them is even a hero to his valet?

This morning I handed over to the chairman of the Law
Examination Board my application (as arranged) to sit for an LL.B.
(upgraded to LL.M. when accompanied by a thesis) as an external
student. Here am I, concerned that the revolutionary should appear to be that Chernyshevskian figure, the salt of the salt of the
earth. Opposite is the embodiment of the state, Ch. L.E.B., more
ludicrous than a cartoon—eyes twin, weeping cysts, wattled nose
meeting warty chin, lips pursed as a turkey's rectum. Still, he accepts my papers, casting, so far as his dripping old orbs permit,
an interested eye over my essay which he reads (rather skips) in
my presence.

"The Law Examination Board recognizes the monograph by
Hereditary Nobleman Ulyanov. It congratulates him upon his theme
that the moral power of the law must rest upon a pyramid of
logical suppositions, tested in action, rather than on the duty, awe,
love, felt for the embodiment of the law in our Emperor, the Tsar,
important as that is. This also happens to be the interpretation of
the Law Examination Board's Chairman."

I allowed myself to show a gratified surprise I did not feel. Olga's friends in the Forensic Faculty had already warned me of his prejudices on my visit last August. I bowed, and retreated backward from the presence. Partly to flatter the old fool. Mainly to avoid revealing the weaknesses of the student uniform I had borrowed (also from Oly's friends). From the front, it had a sketchy conviction, so long as I breathed shallowly and kept half-crouched—from behind, the resemblance to a roasted beetle, splitting at the seams, would be unmistakable.

APRIL 10   PETERSBURG   1891

My twenty-first birthday. A weekend off in the middle of my pre-lims. I am able to celebrate at Oly's lodgings with her and a few of her lively, radical young friends. I say "young" but, of course, she and they are nineteen or twenty, some already in their second year, all caught up in the student politics of the capital city. And I am a self-taught hermit from the backwoods, only for the second time under a strange roof without my Mother in the next room. Yet I feel I am a generation ahead.

Excellent presents (packed and posted in Samara even before I left), portable, useful, inexpensive. After the others have gone, O. and I sit together on her little sofa and write home. Mine a brief bread-and-butter "thank you"—my pen has been scribbling page after page over the past four days. O.'s that regular police report Mother makes each of us send in on the others whenever we meet far from home. O. shows me her opening:

> I think, darling Mamouchka, that you need not worry that our Volodya is overexerting himself. Firstly, he is reason personified, and secondly, his examinations were very easy. He has already completed two of the seven subjects and received top marks, a 5, on each paper, according to the results, admirably quick! posted outside this morning. He is resting today, Saturday. He came here at noon for his birthday meal and told me he had spent the morning walking by the Neva. This evening, at sunset, he insists I come with him to the river to watch the ice breaking up.

This is *not* true. I have *not* seen the results of the papers so far. No bureaucrats could be that quick! Our birthday celebration was

early evening, *not* noon. I have *not* been walking by the Neva,
though I would like to see the ice booming and tobogganing by.

Oly laughs. "What did I write there? 'Reason personified.' You
are wedded to reality, poor old boy. I flirt with imagination. Letter-
writing is my form of art. Come, let us parade together along the
river. Then all you have to do is get top marks in your examinations, and my letter will be a prophecy become history. Move!"

MAY 8   PETERSBURG   1891

Oly is dead! Today of all days. Myself, I never count such anni-
versaries, indeed train myself to ignore them. But I had to cable
Mother at Alakaevka and I know that she, like Anna, and . . . of
course, Oly too, never forgot that May 8 was the day of Sasha's
execution. Exactly four years ago. Mother is on her way. Anna has
been refused permission to leave her place of exile.

Oly died from typhoid in a hospital so filthy I feared for my
own survival when I took her there. Last weekend, we had celebrated my actual results—top marks in seven subjects—by baking
a Volga cake. She was, now I think, not at her liveliest, a touch of
putty gray under the toy-soldier glow in the cheeks, a dull glaze
on the bright eyes. But still as gay and smart as anyone I've ever
known. Even now, an effigy stiff and white as a candle, coffined
on her sitting room table, I fancy I can see her breasts move under
the silky shroud.

I am having some problems keeping the coffin open for the
next three days. But I am determined Mother shall say the "good-
bye" she wants. The undertaker complains there is a health danger
and threatens calling the gendarmes under the Burial (Infectious
Diseases) Act 1880. I counter with two much older (and disgracefully partial) laws—the Special Rights and Inalienable Prerogatives
of the Nobility (1705) and Rites and Rituals of the Holy Russian
Orthodox Church as Embodied by Statute (1610).

I am winning. After all, my head is stuffed with the most law
it will ever contain. I try to throw a fence round Oly in my mind.
Outside, she is dead, and will soon be buried. Inside, she lives on,
dancing, singing, laughing, somewhere too far away for us to visit
her. Outer Mongolia, Siberia, Australia?

I must keep occupied until Mother arrives.

MAY 18   ON THE TRAIN   1891

Mother and I started off yesterday from Peter on our way home. Tomorrow we reach Samara, then the thirty-mile coach trip to Alakaevka. Curses on these Russian journeys, this one by our Slav standards quite short. For three days, we are to be shaken and tossed in our box, like dice being rattled by a giant ogre.

I have taken twin sleeping berths with private sitting room— damn the expense! But the comfort is more illusory than real. Not that it seems to bother Mother. She floats on her own, as equidistant from roof, walls and floor as a fish in a tank. She is the original vertical woman. Whichever direction she raises her eyes is up. As with Father, as with Sasha, so with Olga. They are already fossilized in the stony past. Only the future is fluid. So the rest of us—Anna, Dmitri, Marya and me—must be dosed, like sick children, with those extra helpings of attention, observation, concern and love, left over from the other three. We shall be, as hospitals say, in "intensive care" for as long as she is on earth.

Nevertheless I fear that this freak casualty—there wasn't even anything approaching an epidemic of typhoid—means that I must postdate some of the key stages in my life plan. I must stay longer in Samara, after I qualify as a lawyer, instead of moving briskly on to Peter. "I wasn't there" was all she said about Oly. We must be "there," so *she* can feel *we* are safe, for a longer time than I intended.

The first thing, though—get my degree! Back home, it must be work, work, work for the autumn finals in Peter this September. My marks were as good after Sasha's execution as before. They will be as good after Oly's departure as before. I swear.

NOVEMBER 11   PETERSBURG   1891

Horse-drawn sleighs are skimming along the glassy highway of the Neva, today the busiest thoroughfare in all Peter. They say there are no straight lines in nature. Could human ingenuity construct such a perfectly flat surface, stretching for miles, able to bear the weight of an army, in two or three days? With my skates on, I have been able to move from one end of the capital to the other at a speed that only a steam locomotive could exceed.

I box and bury thoughts of my last visit. Today, this is my own day of triumph. Over the past six weeks, I have sat eight exams, some lasting two or more days, in eleven subjects. (The Law Examination Board likes to make everything as complicated as possible, including its own regulations.) Whatever, I have achieved first place in *every* one, papers, exams, subjects, out of 124 candidates. I now only await the formality of my degree, due sometime in January next year, then the license to practice. Tonight I leave on the awful trip back to Samara. Within two years, say by November '93, I aim to be settled in Peter. And then we shall see what we shall see.

DECEMBER 10   SAMARA   1891

After Oly died, I found there were patches of my mind I no longer visited. They had become fenced off, painted over in a new color by an alien invader. Occupied territory. For a while, I considered them no great loss—mainly producing crops of jokes and anecdotes, quizzes, conundrums and teases, telling of old tales, swapping of new bright ideas. (*"You'll never guess what I saw, I did, I heard, I said, last Sunday . . . Have you ever wondered if . . . Did you know, believe it or not, that . . . If you ruled Russia . . . Suppose we were in Paris . . . In twenty years, will we still . . ."*) It was only lately I began to realize that without this small change of human intimacy many of our grander designs will grind to a halt, unoiled.

I had never sought out a companion. Until I was twenty-one, there was always that special one to hand. Even when she was in Peter and I was in Samara, only a few months, we saved up our scraps and remnants to pin on each other when next we met. Who could ever replace Oly?

I think that Maria Ivanovna Yasneva may be the answer to that question I never knew I was asking. She is the liveliest, noisiest, most radical exile in town. She will not refuse a challenge. Indeed, is renowned for rarely saying "no" to any invitation to anything— to drink a toast, smoke a cheroot, debate a proposition, swim the Volga. She wears what looks sometimes to an uneducated male eye like trousers. She has been known to carry a pistol.

Almost all of the others, though their passports may be stamped "Enemy of the State," are mild and shy, easily thrown off balance by contact with the rich, the noble, the powerful. Maria is the same with everybody. Twice Mother invited her home with some of my new circle. The rest seemed a bit ill-at-ease with the layers of white lace on the tables, the silver utensils heavy as bath fittings, the china you could hold up to the sky and see the moon shine through. Maria spattered tea on the cloth, dropped jam on the floor and rarely ever fell silent. Mother watched, wide-eyed, like a child at the ballet.

"Isn't Maria Ivanovna a bit like Oly?" I asked later.

Mother paused. "I was just thinking she was exactly like you."

Last night, Maria said to me. "Sometimes I imagine I am some condemned mortal in Greek myth. Forced to take great boulders of falsity and hammer and blast and split them until I get to the nugget of indestructible truth at the center. Only I feel it is a privilege, not a punishment. Is that silly?"

She *is* like me.

JANUARY 15   SAMARA   1892

Maria is still called "the Jacobin." I have survived several nicknames, such as "Bakunin II"! But we are now both firmly enrolled followers of Marx. We have read together everything we can find about the revolutionary tradition, talked long, late and deep to those who have played their part in it. We have compared the advance of the cause of socialism in the West, especially in France and Germany. We have studied capitalism in Britain and America. We have no doubt about the main road ahead.

Let me tick off the impasses, side streets, long-cuts, deviations, we have rejected *en route*. Well, first, Bakunin's way. Not one that ever really attracted me, despite the joke *nom de guerre*. I did enjoy the way he enrolled himself in every uprising of his day—Prague, Dresden, Poland, Lyons,, etc. And who can resist his first words to Herzen, after he had escaped from Siberia, worked his passage via Japan and America, across the Pacific and the Atlantic, arriving off the Liverpool train and flinging himself on the daybed in London's Westbourne Grove—"Do they have oysters here?" But he had stupid prejudices, anti-Jew and so forth, regarding Marx and Marxism as an enemy as much as Tsar and tsarism. Part of the history of European anarchism, not Russian socialism.

Bakunin scorned liberal half-measures, hesitant compromises. For him, it was never enough to unseat the Tsar. Instead, his manifesto decreed the rejection of religion, repudiation of marriage and the two-parent family, equality for women. The end of inheritance of private property, to individual ownership of land or industry. A right to free education for everyone. Above all, the abolition of the state as we know it. Mass opposition to any government founded on class or armed force. Motto: "The passion for destruction is also a creative passion."

Herzen's route? Well, a good radical gelded by too much *gelt*. Who could think, feel, plan as a revolutionary on the income from one million gold rubles? Romantic, idealist, emotional, willing to believe in reform from above, a Slav nationalist beneath a European veneer, unable to imagine a capitalist Russia, putting his faith in a "socialism" of the traditional peasant commune. Also an enemy of Marx, who starved in Soho doing hack work while Herzen was a rich exile in Wimbledon whose satirical magazine *Kolokol* (*The Bell*) had correspondents in the highest reaches of the state machine. Copies of his latest issue, leaking details of recent imperial Cabinet meetings, would appear, as though by legerdemain, in the Emperor's anteroom. He was a socialist, and often backed direct action with public applause. But he retained a conviction that democracy was the supreme good, that unless socialism cherished political freedom it would degenerate into tyrannical communism.

Among his most influential living adherents is Pyotr Lavrov. He too wants democratic socialism, if necessary by revolution. However, it should be a takeover of government, not just for the people but by the people. The problem is the people are "not ready yet." They must be given even longer exposure to the "moral ideal." He regards as "an antiquated notion" the theory that a small, ideologically advanced minority can make the doughy multitude rise like yeast. Motto: "The end only justifies the means so long as *the means does not undermine that end*" (his italics).

Nechaev I already know by heart. Now I have committed to memory almost all of the rest who have sounded the trumpets that sing to battle against the dictatorship.

Peter Zaichnevsky. Only nineteen, while still in prison, he issued the most pitiless proclamation of total war against *Them*, even in 1863, "the year of the manifestos." "Soon the day will come when we shall unfurl the great banner of the future, the red banner, and with the battle cry 'Long Live the Social Democratic Republic,' march on the Winter Palace to exterminate everyone there." Suppose the hundred or so of the Imperial Family are defended by thousands of supporters and hangers-on? Then, confident we Russians are destined to be the first to establish socialism, Zaichnevsky will issue the order: "*Use the ax!* Kill them! Kill them in the public squares, in their homes, in the streets of the cities, in the villages, in the forests!" His motto: "Who is not with us, is against us!" He sees no objection to "seizing" power. A small, centralized organization must govern through a dictatorship, build a new order by any means at its disposal, and "*stop at nothing.*"

To my surprise—I had somehow got the impression all the revolutionaries had vanished before I was in long trousers—Maria Ivanovna tells me P.Z. is still alive somewhere in Siberia. When she met him in her teens, he was nearing forty but still, she says, "hot as hell to the touch." Also a born charmer of young women.

Peter Tkachev believed that the people were always ready for revolt everywhere because they are always oppressed everywhere. It is the revolutionary's right, and duty, to summon them to insurrection as soon as possible. Time is not on our side. There is only one way—insurrection. But that does not constitute revolution. It is only a prelude. The central task is the rooting out of all conservative, reactionary elements, destroying all institutions that prevent humanity living in liberty, equality and fraternity. This will be the work of a revolutionary minority alone.

This is the line of pioneers that appeals most to Maria Ivanovna, to many of her Samara friends and colleagues, some of whom, like her, have known Zaichnevsky, Bakunin, Tkachev, etc. I honor and respect them too. And I note the persistence of this tradition as evidence of the continuing, self-perpetuating evil of tsarist autocracy. Where in the West would such extreme concentration of hatred against the ruling class find a history of support among the educated middling sort?

But what is the history of these ideas? When we have finished analyzing how and why they developed, we will know which is correct for our place and time. Personal, subjective emotions, such as admiration for the courage of the terrorists or the nobility of those who serve the people, or even distaste for the duplicity and ruthlessness of some insurrectionists, are irrelevant. We are seeking the mechanics of economic change, the chemistry of revolutionary explosion, the physics of building a new society, the laws of political biology. How can the characters, the morals, the aesthetics of the engineers and scientists involved matter? Any more than they did with Galileo, Copernicus, Newton, Darwin, and now (I believe) Marx and Engels? *Eppur si muove!*

MARCH 12   SAMARA   1892

Have I fallen in love? Stupid phrase. For intelligent people, love
must be a matter of *choice*. Despite being immanent (as theologians
would say) with such powerful emotions, such vigorous stimuli, it
should remain under the control of the mind. The more rational
the decision to elect one person above others as a partner, a companion, a fellow-comrade, in flesh as well as in intellect, the more
favorable must be the prognosis for the future of their relationship.
Surely? Anything else would be submission to what is little more
than mysticism, a concession to the supernatural, an admission of
the power of the occult. So I have *decided* to love Maria Petrovna,
my Jacobin. And she me.

We shall behave in the honorable, admirable and human tradition of Chernyshevsky. Our love will be founded upon equality
above all else. If one wishes to terminate the relationship, then the
other will not resist, or refuse to accept. How can you love someone
who does not love you? That would be voluntary serfdom, an
autocrat/slave connection willingly perpetuated. Intolerable!

And yet, I have to accept that it happens. The majority still
love the Tsar and he does not give a shit for them. Many, perhaps
most, wives and children treat like little gods the husbands and
fathers who neglect and abuse them. Even among the most exploited class, the worker still has a proletariat (woman) for him to
exploit. (Engels.) The worker himself is deluded by his employer,
his monarch, his God. There is something dreadful about love
today at all levels—can it be a kind of mental illness induced by
the powerful in the weak?

Oh, to be somewhere (Peter preferably, or Paris?) where such
things can be soberly discussed and analyzed. *Marxism and the So-
Called Love Phenomenon* by V. I. Ulyanov? How Dostoievsky, Turgenev, Goncharov would laugh! Though not Chernyshevsky nor
Engels. Whether the study would be mainly psycho-physical or
socio-philosophical I do not know. I am sure it comes within the
concept of Marx known as "false consciousness" that Maria and I
have been trying to pin down.

However, in pursuit of that truth we both honor, it must be
allowed that "love" does have a distinct effect on those who have
"fallen" in it. It is like being a child again. The world sparkles

under a coat of clear varnish, and is seen through newly cleaned windows.

Consider how often I have roamed the Volga forests. Few animals know the woodlands of Kokushkino and Alakaevka as I do. I make that assessment quite seriously. A human observer looks at everything, large and small, vegetable, animal and mineral. The fox or the wolf or the bear only takes in what is important to its own life and survival. Whole days I have sat astride a tree trunk, high as an elephant's eye, book in hand, soaking in the world below me as its inhabitants creaked and snapped, opened and closed, jumped and crept. But I never saw the apparition that Maria Ivanovna, my Jacobin, and I encountered this morning early.

We had turned off a sunlit alley into a little half-dark close, a kind of natural cave, with the boughs curving at either side, rounded at the sky and at the ground. Across the center of the hollow sphere, suddenly illuminated, was a great star of silver webbing. Spun ropes, radiating from an off-center hub, seemed as thick as fingers yet delicate as silk. In the same split second, we recognized at its heart a Fabergé-style spider about the size of a large frog. As it danced sideways, twiddling and polishing various spotless movable parts, it could easily have been clockwork. I couldn't help feeling that, in a way, it was quite frightening, slightly repellent. Yet also a piece of technical design so ornate and showy as to be almost unbearable in its ingenuity.

On the way home, I put to Maria Ivanovna my theory that it may have been this kind of discovery that inspired mankind to develop jewelry, to cut and polish and set precious stones. She objected to "*man*kind" and wanted to know why men always assumed that all history had been made by them for them. I tried to make a joke about "*woman*kind" being more likely to want to cover themselves with diamonds and pearls. She said this was even more offensive. We went back angry with each other. But still very happy. How can that be? It is not allowed for in my theory of the rational love affair.

MAY 10   **SAMARA**   **1892**

The drought has cast a gigantic scab over the countryside for weeks now. More and more peasants are sprouting up in Samara. That is the correct word, I think, *sprouting*. For nobody sees them on the dusty roads. Nobody sees them leave their firewood villages, or the tinderbox huts scattered across the dried-out fields. Anyway, they would need passports, some sort of official permission or recognition, if they wanted to leave their "place of domicile" and settle in the city. Nevertheless, every morning, here are crowds of them, grown thicker overnight, streets of human mushrooms, pale, skinny, giving off a smell of drying leather and smoked flesh.

The famine, long dismissed as a seditious rumor, has at last been officially acknowledged. The government in Peter has certified last year's harvest the worst in a generation. But it classifies this year's mass starvation of country people as the unfortunate, inevitable result, a regrettable lapse of nature, an act of God.

We are at the center of the hardest-hit area—14 million inhabitants of the Volga region at risk. The government is encouraging town dwellers to set up charity committees.

All the bleeding heart liberals, the reformed populists, the parlor pinks, the peasant-worshipers, even opponents of the Tsar here in internal exile, are competing with each other to be the most caring; sixty-three-year-old Tolstoy has abandoned preaching Christian anarchism and set his family to organizing feeding points, soup kitchens, medical services. Poets are writing epics about the nobility of suffering, selling off their manuscripts for charity. Composers are churning out ethnic dirges by the dozen, donating their royalties.

Maria Ivanovna and I seem to be the only members of the intelligentsia who do not spend our lives running canteens. This has aroused much animosity among rival socialist groups. We are accused, as Marxists, of crude and infantile attitudes which are not Marxist at all. It is said that we believe in standing aside from all relief work on the grounds that "the worse it is, the better." That we welcome the famine because it "serves a progressive function." That we condemn any expression of pity for the dying as nothing but "sugary sentimentality typical of the emotional intellectual."

Of course, as ever in places such as this, no one will listen to the views we really do have, let alone offer us any way of disseminating them. Those admirers of Zaichnevsky who used to clap hands at Mother's tea parties when Maria quoted her former leader—"Any revolution that is afraid to go too far is not a revolution"—now warn us that we are becoming dangerously extreme. It is apparently not good form to advocate the overthrow of a government when it is off balance.

Maria points out that even populism's respectable philosopher, Pyotr Lavrov, has just argued, apropos this very famine: "The only 'good cause' we can possibly embrace is not the philanthropic but the revolutionary cause." All we get in answer is that it is all right for him, he isn't here.

Yet, *we* are here, Maria and I. And I find it fascinating to note that the truth Samara does not want to hear is exactly that truth which is being illustrated now in Samara. This is embodied in our slogan—"The struggle against famine is only possible in the context of the struggle against autocracy." Look around! Each group is acting according to its own political interest. As a Marxist would expect.

The government is basically concerned with its good name abroad, its security at home. Reaction to the famine: deny it; belittle it; now sensationalize it. Colossal, unprecedented calamity beyond blame, or cure, of mere humans.

The liberals emphasize famine too serious a failing of the monarchical system to be left to courtiers and bureaucrats. Liberals will show by practical, businesslike approach what dependable colleagues they could make in local, even national, government.

The populists—serving in canteens, rolling bandages, raising money. Another better (safer) way of "Going to the People"?

We Marxists have our own, partisan attitude—*eto vierno*, that's a fact. Not against feeding the hungry, one of the reasons we exist. Against *illusion* that a cobweb will staunch the wound of a beheaded man, you can put out a forest fire with a thimble of subsidy. The reason why the government is at last increasing its aid to the suffering millions is its fear of revolutionary socialist agitation. So. Even on the pragmatic level, the quickest way to put bread into mouths is to threaten autocracy rather than to collaborate with it.

Various things people ought to know about how the famine happened. Even with poor harvest and spring drought, *the government's own figures show,* still enough food already available to feed everyone.

The true cause of the famine? (1) profiteering and cornering of supplies; (2) inefficient storage in badly run, jerry-built warehouses; (3) antiquated wagons leaking all the way to the railheads, overloaded trucks breaking down every few hundred miles of track. Famines are the inevitable by-product of our society, a society built upon a peculiarly Russian amalgam of greed, sloth and callousness.

We have not been able to get any of this into the underground press, let alone the official papers. Yet anyone who can afford to buy any Western publications, from Germany, France or England, will see our government's hypocrisies spelled out in print. Example: during the first weeks of the famine, this country continued to export grain in the usual amounts. Then, after criticism (from Westerners) the trade was banned for the next three months. However, a blind eye was turned to its continued flow. Foreign financiers note that this is essential to guarantee the government's stability in the overseas money market. It provides an assurance to international capitalism that "we" remain capable of paying the huge interest on "our" debts.

So, while the rest of us along the Volga are being bullied into contributing our tens of rubles, the government is still withholding its billions. Our rulers remain unabashed at paying off their mortgages with the people's lives. So far only one-twentieth of the minimum sum estimated as necessary for effective relief (even according to the government's own experts) has been made available. And these are the same gentlemen with whom we socialists should show solidarity because, in a national emergency, all "petty differences" must be shelved?

Use the ax!

JULY 23   ALAKAEVKA   1892

At last, after almost six months, I have acquired the right to practice on my own as an attorney. When I was sitting the exams in Peter last year, I thought—or convinced myself I thought—that qualifying would be the key that opened up my whole future. Working as an assistant to Andrei Khardin has rather disillusioned me.

A.K. has a brilliant, adversarial mind. He is the best lawyer in the entire province, as few would dispute. I am tempted to add that his weakness is that he treats the whole business as a game, except that he is at his best in games, particularly chess. Even Chigorin, contestant for the world championship, has had to concede games to him, and admits that he rates a 4½. (Chigorin only gives the top mark of 5 to himself, and his next opponent.)

We started playing by post when I was in Kazan. Then he gave me the advantage of a rook. When we started again, in the back room at his chambers here, it was a pawn. After a few months, as litigants would knock respectfully on our outer door humbly requesting to know what was happening in their case, he would shout, "I'm consulting precedents." And we would carry on playing. By the time I left Samara as usual for this summer vacation at Alakaevka, we were starting level. I very rarely win, unless I can survive until the endgame when I become unbeatable. The point is, I am accepted as an equal.

Since I can't see the law as a game, I foresee that I am unlikely to be very successful. Most of my clients will be taken from Andrei's "charity list." Those who can just about afford the lowest fee and are ignorant, oppressed, desperate, and guilty. The judges will understand this as well as I do. Some may possibly sympathize with these victims of society. But the judges will be unable to reach any verdict but guilty, whatever I say. The more I see of law, the more I turn to politics for justice. As Marx might have said—lawyers have only made speeches about the world; the point, however, is to change it.

APRIL 1   SAMARA   1893

Almost two years ago, I had just met Maria Ivanovna. How little I knew about women. About men for that matter, about almost any other person on terms of social equality. I strove to cultivate a deadly eye for observing others, for examining, classifying, mounting them, like a lepidopterist. But I had been brought up apart from contemporaries and coevals: expelled from university, forbidden any other teaching establishment, deprived first of a brother, then a sister, who might have alternated as tutor and fellow pupil. I packed four years of instruction in law into one. I read nearly a century's literature, philosophy, history, politics in two country retreats, keeping working hours like a clerk, clocking in at my green study among the trees, my floating library in a moored punt.

No family could have protected, encouraged, indulged me more. But I had no experience of mixing with congenial, yet critical, outsiders. I was like a half-tamed bear, reared as a pet, which never knew when it was treading on strangers, scratching them with its paws, wounding them by a playful bite.

I was immediately taken with Maria, by her agile, acrobatic figure, by her pretty, monkey grin, her constant changes of expression like scudding clouds across the moon. She seemed someone acting herself on stage, yet always spontaneous. I had never come across anyone like that before. I did not understand that she was attracting me. The first thing I said to her was "How old are you?"

I truly wanted to know. The older these exiled revolutionaries

in Samara were, the more they could teach me. I had a vacancy
for an informant about ten years ahead of me. (She is nine.) I
could not imagine why there was such an edge to her voice. She
pointed two fingers, thumb raised, miming a dueling pistol. "Bang!"
she said. "Two years younger than *you* look." Everybody laughed.

I knew there had been Marxists (Social Democrats was the
usual title) in the Volga region. N. N. Fedoseev ran a flourishing
"study circle" in Kazan, with a network in other cities around, while
I was a student there. Perhaps it was fortunate I never got round
to joining. In the summer of '89, while I was rusticated to Kokushkino, he was picked up by the police. All the members, many
who were only friends of members, were tracked down, tried and
sentenced to long spells in Siberia. If I had been there I would
have been one of them, even though I was then more Narodnik
than Marxist.

Maria and I have no longer the faintest doubt that Marx has
provided the intellectual lever with which to move the world. For
long months after we decided this together, we were a lone pair,
not exactly cut (slightly grazed, say!) by the other radicals. Our
lowest moment was the famine. But since then more and more
have seen that violent slogans are not enough. Even bombs and
pistol shots, heroic though they may be, are not enough. We must
act to a plan, to a timetable, with mass support. Can you imagine,
many Narodniks had read *Capital* (published in Russian before it
appeared in English or German!) interpreting it as a warning of
what to *avoid*? A view apparently shared by the censor who summed
it up as "abstract speculation."

Now, at last, they are beginning to see that Russia cannot avoid
capitalism, an essential phase in every society's development. But
we will use the capitalists, their money, their newspapers, their
hirelings, to impose a bourgeois democracy on the Tsar. Capitalism
produces a proletariat, its own gravedigger. The Social Democrats,
using as tight, tough, and organized a party as ever the Narodniks
managed, will lead the workers in revolution to overthrow capitalism. The only difference between us and the West is that we
will telescope history and perhaps achieve our goal before the
advanced parties of Europe. Why not? I am now leader of the
Marxist section in Samara. There is a bigger one in Nizhny-Novgorod, almost a full-grown party in Peter. Go west, "Old Man!"

AUGUST 4   SAMARA   1893

After almost a year, a decision from the Provincial Supreme Court
in the Arefyev case. Now that Anna's internal exile is over, Mother
is moving with her, Marya and Dmitri to Moscow. At last, I am
free to quit Samara for Petersburg. Ever since I was authorized to
operate as an independent advocate, working out of the Khardin
chambers, in the winter of '92, I have lost one case after another,
thirteen in a row. I have appeared regularly in the defense of the
indefensible, according to the law of the land that is. Time and
again I have been tempted to rise to my feet and advise my client
to take an ax, or better, a flaming torch, and settle the matter in
his own favor. Still, I have done my best. Except on one occasion:
he was a wife-beater, tried to break her nose in court after he was
found guilty. I refused to make any statement in mitigation, and
he was flogged.

But in the Arefyev affair, I have been plaintiff, chief witness
and prosecuting attorney. It all started last August, even before I
was awarded my license. Brother-in-law Mark and I were on a visit
to his kulak brother, downriver from Samara, near the rail station
of Syzran. To get to his village, we had to cross the Volga at one
of its wider points. The monopoly in transporting passengers and
freight had long been owned by a puddle of candle grease known
as Arefyev. He squatted underneath a canopy on a small pier,
keeping travelers queuing up in the glare of the sun until there
were enough to warrant him starting up his little steamboat. Meanwhile, he sold them tepid drinks, dried pastries and anything else
he had kept in warm storage, at inflated prices. (Another monopoly.) I was damned if I was going to be delayed as well as fleeced.
I insisted on hiring a local boatman to ferry us across in his small
skiff.

Mark was nervous. He'd been through this before with his
brother "Ole Mustard" (*Gorcheeza*), a neighborhood bloodsucker
not easily bested. Arefyev would let the rebel go. Midway across
the river, out of sight of shore, the steamer would catch up, and
a crew of mercenary brigands would seize your boat and drag it
back to the pier. "The law's on his side," Mark said.

I knew better.

The steamer loomed up behind us out of the summer haze.

The grappling hooks hauled us up on board. I took out my note-book. I demanded, and was given, identity number, name, and address of all Arefyev's employees. When we returned to our orig-inal bank, I took his details too. Then I wrote out and handed round, as a form of citizen's summons, my indictments of them all. He *was* within his rights in insisting that his monopoly be re-spected. He was not, however, permitted, while enforcing his right, to obstruct the passage of legitimate subjects on their lawful travels. This sort of contradiction is what gives us lawyers our living.

Andrei did not consider I had much more than a 40 percent chance of winning, particularly since my opponent was notoriously obstinate. I was determined to show Arefyev what true dedication to a vendetta really meant. I was reinforced by the knowledge that every time he appeared in the dock, appealed to a higher court, traveled to Syzran, Kazan, Penza, Tambov, finally Nizhni-Nov-gorod, he was paying out a fortune. It cost me little. If I stayed in Samara, I would only be losing one more case for which I would probably never be paid anyway.

It was like, in chess, realizing early on that you are unlikely to win and you could settle for a quick draw, but instead fighting on until it is your opponent who asks for the draw. In the printed results, the difference may seem small. But, to the true gamesman, the first is surrender, the second a fight to a standstill.

So I waited, sweated, climbed on and off trains, rose and fell in stuffy courtrooms, determined that I should not give way first. To my delight, the official message now tells me that I have won outright. The brigand crew have been fined a thousand rubles a head. Arefyev has been sentenced to a month's imprisonment. Andrei adds a note—owing to overcrowding in the nearby prisons, he has been sent downriver, in a convict hulk, to *Simbirsk*!

Such are the petty, overheated triumphs of provincial Russia. My appointment with the big city is overdue.

SEPTEMBER 10   PETERSBURG   1893

On the way here, I stopped over in Nizhni-Novgorod to pick up some names of Social Democrats in Peter, even more important, the recommendations without which illegal activists will not meet a stranger. Then I made a detour to Moscow where the Family Ulyanov have now settled. Sister Marya in her last year at grammar school. Dmitri in his first at medical school. Anna's husband, Mark, has turned out to have more than a dose of the old Volga kulak in him (*Gorcheeza II?*). He is making a pile selling insurance. Mother has found a house, large, ugly but almost rent-free, through her mysterious connections (perhaps she *is* a Rothschild?). She looks after them all, with only a couple of servants.

Jolly reunion. No talk of politics, though they are all S.D. sympathizers. Little personal chat either. Anna asked after my "soul mate" Maria Ivanovna. I told her that she had given an all-night party for my departure (I made a speech explaining to everyone that there was little chance I would ever pass that way again) which Samara may never forget. She danced, sang, recited, threw fireworks, extracted my promise to make her a Revolutionary Judge when the Marxists took power. "We parted greater friends than ever," I said. How many soul mates can say that?

As I got on the train for Peter, Mother whispered in my ear, "Look at Olga's grave, my son, and tell me how it is."

Olga is buried in Volkovo Cemetery's new section. Here the grief is relatively fresh, not yet a formality or a habit. The banal writings, the stock images, have some gloss of real emotion. Though even here, nature seems already reasserting itself, protesting against this misuse of its acreage. A sapling sprouts from the heart of a plot, thrusting aside the glass globe with its fragile china ornaments. A probing root starts to displace a tombstone. Underground activities of unknown origin spread trenches, throw up parapets, as if the tremors of a minor earthquake. Nevertheless, I am able to write to Mother reporting that Olga's cross and wreath still lie there, unruffled, medals on the dress uniform of a star pupil.

But what a satirical place is the old-style cemetery, a veritable play by Gogol! Here, a cracked marble representation of a crow's nest, bent in the middle, leans nearer the green sea of the earth than ever did the mast of any but a foundering ship. There, a scroll of verse, bought by the yard, proclaims the immortal memory of a great one whose name has been long erased by moss. Golden letters on a toppled urn promise that the deceased will be missed forever by mourners who have not visited the spot in a generation. All around, symbols of a pathetic, infantile yearning for immortality: vacuous girlish angels with clipped wings and busted lyres; imposing, classic, dowager muses with one eye and a missing nose; antique warriors in battle pose despite lopped-off spears, swords, arms, legs, even heads. Presiding over each estate in the country of death (as in life) stands a manorial mausoleum, rising amid this junkyard of statuary in forlorn assertion of superior status.

I have to admit—cemeteries do energize me. They even cheer me. I look at these relics of the famous, the great, the rich, the powerful and I can assure myself—no one lasts forever. They will all go some day. Why not hurry their class into its grave, even if the burial is a trifle premature?

OCTOBER 12   PETERSBURG   1893

My letters of introduction, picked up in Nizhni-Novgorod, are to Stepan Ivanovich Radchenko, He formed a Social Democratic cell earlier last year. Though I have been calling on him since my arrival on September 10, only now is he prepared to introduce me to "the others." Apparently he got the impression that I was too committed to individual terrorism, perhaps assuming I must share Sasha's views.

The others number eight. Radchenko is their control. He is immensely tall—well, most of the time I am in intimate chat with his bottom waistcoat button. He is also incredibly thin, at least from the front. From the side, he resembles two hook-nosed profiles pasted together. He is the nearest thing on two legs, which could almost be one, to a walking playing card. He also has a birthmark, shaped like the ace of clubs, over his right eyebrow. I may be a novice in this business but I can hardly imagine that the addition of a black eyepatch, a wooden leg and a parrot would make him any more conspicuous.

OCTOBER 20   PETERSBURG   1893

Radchenko has finally inducted me into his underground Marxist circle. It is called "The Elders" (*Stariki*). One of the first things I must learn is how to survive when under surveillance by the political police. Though, as a newcomer, I am unlikely yet to be watched, I must now operate as though I were. My instructor over the last few days has been "Ivan."

He begins by explaining that the first interest shown in me will be from the outside. The Okhrana's "tail" will be a low-grade operative, possibly a petty criminal released to supply this service, paid around 50 rubles a month. (Not exactly a fortune, also not negligible: Mother's allowance to me will not be more than 25 rubles a month.) The "tail" has only one task: to follow you for as long as he is ordered, usually an eight-hour shift. He does (or should) not know anything about his subject, even your name, referring to you always by an agreed nickname—Baldy, Big Fellow, Blue Eyes, the Barmaid, the Coachman. The report is written in minute detail, covering every movement, however trivial.

At the end of the shift another "tail" takes over, though the first does (should) not know who his successor is. Sometimes, with important suspects, two "tails" work simultaneously, unknown to each other, and their logs are used as a double-check. This is the jigsaw principle.

A rather childish upsurge of resentment when "Ivan" mentions that the political police are more interested in the newest guise of Narodnik, Social Revolutionaries, than in our Social Democrats. The Revolution will not be made by bombing palaces and assassinating governors, police chiefs, even Tsars. "Ivan" points out that the political police are not working with an eye on the judgment of posterity. Their job is to please their bosses. Bosses are more worried about being blown up tomorrow than being expropriated in the twentieth century. A typical agent, even just a "tail," will carry with him the photographs of up to fifty or more well-known (to the police) terrorists. They also often carry a portrait of Karl Marx—a picture of him in someone's room will be a giveaway of anti-government feelings.

As well as having you followed (remember, says "Ivan," by a woman as well as a man) the O. can progress to tapping your telephone—apparently quite an easy procedure. They can open your mail—a hot razor will melt away most seals; most envelopes are penetrable at the corners or along the secondary flap—and copy your letters in a couple of hours. They may eavesdrop on your conversation in public places—the O. employs "ears" who do nothing but lounge around bars, cafés, railway stations, large shops and record what is being said. They do not note who speaks to whom but simply copy down the arias of speech that rise around them. He showed me an example—like dialogue in that Chekhov play I saw in Moscow a couple of years back.

The Okhrana have now developed their clairvoyance, their long-distance character reading of opponents they have never met, to a high art. They (could he be one of them?) develop an insight into character worthy of a Dostoievsky, says "Ivan." The whole point about a jigsaw puzzle is that it is capable of solution. Each piece has a place in the end. The Okhrana believes that life obeys the same rules. (To tell the truth, so do I!) Take the example of Marx and Voght. Marx became convinced that Karl Voght was a police spy, not a distinguished and admired Social Democrat, solely on the evidence of his *prose style*! He wasted months writing letters, memos, pamphlets denouncing Herr Voght. Even close comrades regarded Marx as unbalanced on this topic. Herr Voght went on being influential and respected until the Paris Commune opened up the archives of the fallen Emperor Louis Napoleon. There, heading the list of longtime French government agents, along with his salary, stood the name of Karl Voght. And Marx had fingered him just on the way he wrote! When we have our Petersburg Commune, we will open up the archives of the Okhrana. What unexpected names will we find?

"Ivan" says a revolutionary government should not hope for too much from secret police files. Suspects are listed under *noms-de-plume*. So are important agents. Only a few top "spiders" know the real identity of the spies and counter-spies who shuttle across this national (*inter*national) web. They will not hang around long enough to be asked.

Each "spider" has his own key suspects to whom he applies the *Diagram Method*. He sets up against the wall of his office a rectangle of semi-transparent paper on a wooden frame, after the fashion of a painter's canvas. In the center, like a visiting card, is the name and address of the person who may be a danger to the state. From this, lines radiate out to the periphery of the board, linking up with different colored circles, which themselves possess their own solar systems, and are boxed within variously shaded enclaves. Each color, shading, shape, direction, area has a meaning.

This can be geographical, political, social or economic. The diagram reveals, like a map, through its conventional signs, where the suspect goes, whom he meets, what he reads, how he spends his time. Far better than any dossier, it can put on show the skeleton of a life displaying all of it at once.

I was quite overcome by the brilliance of the device, and said so to "Ivan." He laughed: "That is only the first layer, my dear friend whose party-name I will not even try to recall. Remember, your alias often tells us more about you, because you chose it, than your real name."

There seems no end to the ingenuity of the enemy. I did not appreciate what power is opposed to us, every day, round the clock. No Oblomovs here! But I also appreciate that we radicals, subversives, revolutionaries, who seem so few and weak to most of Russian society, are taken very seriously by those who study them. *They* think we can overthrow the Tsar. Why should *we* doubt it?

"Ivan" went on to explain that once one diagram was fairly full, it would be lined up with another. The two would then be coupled together with a strong light behind them. Now I understood why the paper needs to be semi-transparent. The police examiner could see at a glance where the diagrams coincided or differed; what they had in common, or did not share at all. Up to half a dozen or so, even the total of the specialist's particular surveillance, could be thus superimposed, showing new patterns and connections with every different combination.

Once a month, or more frequently if one "hot" subject is being dissected, the analysts will swap around their diagrams, trying out fresh superimpositions. The jigsaw puzzle is three-dimensional! Moreover, any layout can be adapted to uncover the blueprint of any neighborhood group: a party cell, a trades branch, a discussion circle, a social salon. No one is impervious to Okhrana infiltration, or protected against their probings. "Ivan" tells me the political police recently discovered a hotbed of subversion, unknown to any of the anti-government movements, in the National Union of Midwives. And the wives, mistresses, creditors, gambling cronies, old schoolfellows, as well as wine merchants, jewelers, estate agents and bankers, to any minister, high official in the service or the army, or rich and unconventional aristocrat, are kept under observation as a matter of routine.

The diagrams are normally of the same size and scale. But sometimes, when a specific conspiracy is being monitored, one may be blown up to take in the detail of a certain part of town, or the ground plan and topography of some house and its estate. Or it may be reduced to accommodate all of European Russia with the visits of the conspirators plotted, from town to town, like a sketch of trade routes and caravan trails. The analysts, "Ivan" announces with a touch of pride, work by a mixture of intuition, memory and documentation.

"Ivan" is obviously pleased by my interest. He is delighted to give examples. Suppose a suspect receives a careful letter which mentions in passing a friend, "Blondie," a Bridge Street, a medical student. The Okhrana specialist would then run through his list of contacts for someone who had very fair hair, or skin. Or perhaps a name like "White" or "Gold." This figure would then be cross-referenced against all Russian towns which have a Bridge Street, and a medical school. This can be done by a system which uses only a box full of punch cards. These can be separated, divided and subdivided, by rods which connect their punch holes, until a single person or place is identified. Sometimes, it will be done within minutes.

Here is a new science, almost a kind of artificial intelligence, a machine that makes choices according to logic. I must study this. It can be used both ways—for us to sort out them. Why not?

OCTOBER 21   PETERSBURG   1893

At last Stepan Ivanovich has introduced me to three male members of the Stariks—under party aliases, of course. They then instantly told me their real names. I will only note the first names: Vassily, Pyotr, and Gleb. They are students at the Technological Institute. The four women are dedicated volunteers to the cause of elevating the proletariat. They do this, I gather, by teaching them to read and write in the "Adult Sunday Schools" which charitable folk have endowed and some employers support! But them I will meet later.

For the moment, the four set about instructing me in the techniques of underground work.

The basic message, R. said, was to apply common sense. "You will have heard from Ivan all the resources that the police can draw on. But, remember—the best aid the Okhrana have ever had is a careless revolutionary."

The advice then ran like this:

1) *Assume you are always being followed.* Never neglect the obvious precautions—never go directly to your destination.

2) *Do not assume you can always recognize a policeman.* Your tail

could be a woman, a couple, even a child. They can appear to be doing a variety of jobs—streetsweeper, postman, cabby, soldier, a worker in a boiler suit.

3) *Do not assume every person you encounter is a policeman.*

4) *Write down as little as possible.* Never take notes of anything that might compromise you or your comrades—it is better to forget a detail than to hand it across to the enemy.

5) *Assume your mail will be opened.* If essential interference should be noticed, sew letter to back of envelope, seal flap with unusual wax stamp.

6) *Assume your telephone is tapped. Assume your contact's telephone is also tapped.* Arrange regular calls between telephones in cafés, stations or other public places, preferably not otherwise used by you. Try to compose a message only the person you intend to understand will understand.

7) *Know your way. Choose your seat.* Learn by heart the map of your town, or city center. Study carefully any area where an exchange, a rendezvous, a demonstration is to be made. Get to know your way like a cabdriver. Make note of all places—shops, bars, stations, office blocks, even large houses that have more than one exit. Take a seat away from the light, or with the light behind you. Beware of windows. Try to be where you can observe without being observed.

8) *How to treat comrades.* Learn how to be silent. Learn how to forget. You should never know yourself more than you need to know, so never tell anyone else more than they need to know. Do not be offended by another's silence, or fear to offend by your own. What you know is your responsibility.

9) *How to deal with police.* When arrested, or detained, the golden rule is—say nothing. Never confess. Do not be tempted to lie—everything you say is valuable to the experts on the other side.

No. 10 was the Supreme Rule. Stephan Ivanovich asked me, as a test, whether I could guess what it was. All four stared. I knew instantly what I was going to say. I had not read all those fat, dusty volumes of old radical mags for nothing. This was my supreme rule: "Beware of *conspiracitis*. Do not adopt the pose of the man of mystery. Be natural and simple. Never treat your task as a game."

For a moment, I thought they were going to take this as an insult, but the pause was admiration! Then they applauded me, banged me on the back. I was a full member of The Elders.

DECEMBER 12   PETERSBURG   1893

My official pseudonym among the Elders (*Stariki*) is K. Tulin. More often I am known as *Starik*, the Old Man. Not because of the pun, I'm afraid, but because of the way I look. I'm not worried. There are enough things on this earth that need changing, *must* be changed. Pointless to waste energies over something about which so little can be done.

Still, catching sight of myself unawares reflected in a shop window, I can't help thinking—is that really how other people have to see me *all the time*? This morning I glimpsed a note Radchenko sent identifying me to another comrade.

"Did you have to write a short story?" I asked Stepan Ivanovich at tonight's cell meeting. "Wouldn't a couple of key words have done?"

He was so apologetic even his ace of clubs went pale. "My dear Tulin, of course, you're right. I got carried away. Do you realize what a visual paradox you represent? One angle, striking, unusual face and bearing. Another, quite ordinary, forgettable. Ideal ambiguous portrait of a revolutionary leader."

I let the matter drop. Still, I folded the piece away into my diary:

> Tulin's face is worn. His entire head bald, except for some thin hair at the temples. Scanty reddish beard. Eyes a bit squinty, peers slyly under knitted brows. Voice old and hoarse. Could be typical middle-aged tradesman from Northern Russia. Though only twenty-five [twenty-three, to be exact!] is already known among us as *Starik*.

JANUARY 10   PETERSBURG   1894

Here in the capital of tsarism, I had intended to become the epitome of the post-Nechaevian plotter, a revolutionary without human weaknesses or failings. Around me, I would clear a deadly desert blighted by the loss of the two people I loved beyond sense or thought, who were as much to me as my legs or arms—Sasha and Oly. From now on, nobody could grow close to my heart.

Mother I exempted from the ban, for reasons not entirely clear. Even in my godless cosmos, she remains like the Christians" Mary, the eternal maternal principle, the enveloping blanket that blots out all our insecurities. Nothing the world sees as a crime would alter her regard. As for her own person, it seems armored against all outside threats, as if she were some *grande patronne,* or possibly *protégée,* of a powerful secret society—the Freemasons, or the Elders of Zion, or the Tibetan Immortals of the Theosophists. Can it be a coincidence that her maiden name was Blank—a magic word in English?

After parting from Maria the Jacobin, I determined to avert my face from erotic love, from any deep attachment beyond the family. I did so.

And found myself looking into the eyes of Apollinaria Alexandrovna and Julius Osipovich. I had fallen again. Deeper perhaps with the man than the woman!

I have known the pair for nearly two months. To the outsider, I'm sure it would be difficult to imagine two more different people. Even to another Social Democrat comrade, privy to their shared dedication to our cause, the two would seem characters as disparate as any invented by a novelist to make an extreme contrast of types.

Comrade Apollinaria Alexandrovna Yakubova works fitfully by day at a smart, Liteiny Prospect bookshop, a job that allows her to duck in and out on illegal work without attracting attention. It also helps that the shop is owned by "Auntie" (Alexandra Kalmykova), wife of high government official, heiress in her own right, who backs all progressive causes. Evenings and weekends, Apollinaria teaches reading and writing to groups of workers, our so-called "Sunday Schools," a cover which allows a two-way flow of information essential to our struggle.

Her party name is "Goldilocks." Not a very safe alias, since the point of such *klichki* is to be as far from the real person as possible. If you searched among all the young beauties of Peter for a month, you would not find one who fitted the description more neatly. Apollinaria is the embodiment of that dimpled, pinch-waisted, marigold-haired doll we used to win as boys in the shooting galleries of traveling fairs along the Volga. Put another way, the Platonic ideal of that very earthy Aristotelian specimen—the perfect bedding partner.

Perfect . . . but for whom? Surely not "Goldilocks" and Father Bear, *Starik,* the "Old Man"? It seemed an unlikely combination, to everyone, including me. I told myself that what attracted me in women was the same as in men, the mind. If a body was part of the compact, as with my Jacobin, then that was a bonus. But here I found myself gravitating into orbit round Apollinaria before I heard her open her mouth. I did not keep my distance, but spun off helplessly like a planet into the sun. Or was I like a Jules Verne rocket, under control, landing on the moon? We two have since become very close. All male revolutionaries have long since forsaken the old philistine jealousies, the competitiveness of stallions or pashas. Nevertheless . . . our relationship, so swiftly cemented, is causing some thinly veiled hostility. Even Gleb (Krzhizhanovsky), himself passionately paired with the dark, dashing Zinaida K., emitted a flash of irritation. "Remember that Chekhov short story about the Liteiny Prospect Don Juan? His advice was—'Buy a pretty woman a book, give a plain one silk underwear.' I reckon that must be our *Starik*'s secret, don't you, lads?"

I could not believe that these sophisticated metropolitans, all of them Petersburg graduates, could be so conventional and obtuse. Five minutes talking to Apollinaria about things that really matter and I'd honestly forgotten it was her looks that had drawn me in. She is one of the most intelligent persons I have ever met. Indeed, now that we have begun to snatch half-days, weekend nights, together under the same ceiling, I find myself wishing she could be more of the old-fashioned feminine type.

Revolutionaries are wonderful comrades-in-arms. But talking to them in private hours, when arms have other associations, is like haranguing yourself in the mirror. You yearn, guiltily, for some other kind of company. You find yourself anticipating what is about to be said about everything, often down to the exact word, its inflection and stress. I was just about to remark this last night to my Goldilocks when she pointed it out to me.

JANUARY 15   PETERSBURG   1894

This morning Apollinaria tells me we are "in each other's pockets" so much she begins to wonder which is playing the man and which the woman. As if to prove the point, we then both begin to explain to each other just how very illogical and reactionary such a complaint against equality would be after centuries of women's oppression. It looks as if we will have to separate, because of overcompatibility! Ha!

Yuli Osipovich Tsederbaum, code-name Julius Martov, does not look my type at all. Around twenty-one, he has already taken on the humped, awkward shape I am certain he will retain all his life. Behold, your characteristic, horizontal political thinker (often, as with Martov, but not always, Jewish). He is feeble in build, slightly limping, a face that looks as if it had been dropped while still warm, a wispy beard leaving his chin almost as bald as his wispy, retreating hair has left his forehead. He smokes like a man desperate to win a wager, drinks more than enough absentmindedly, and hardly bothers to observe the world through pince-nez which are always clouded with dirt.

I avoided Martov my first days around the *Stariki* as much as I sought out opportunities to be around Apollinaria. Then I had to deliver some figures to him. He began talking, more or less to himself. I saw his eyes projected a gaze at once mild, penetrating, kindly and subtle. His intelligence was firm but gentle. He handled the most unruly ideas like a veteran lion tamer steering his beasts. Where he drew the line, he was uncompromising. But a hairbreadth away, he remained open to discussion, displaying his views always with scholarship and scruple.

I saw that this dusty dummy in the stained dressing gown, with buckled legs and glazed lenses, hustled around by friends and admirers like a grown-up doll, was the counterbalance and complement my own talents needed. Between them, Julius and Apollinaria may replace the Sasha and Olga who died before I could really appreciate them.

FEBRUARY 15   PETERSBURG   1894

Clandestine Marxist discussion meeting, disguised as Shrovetide celebration. I hear a young woman, about my age, expressing admiration for Chernyshevsky, particularly his *What Is to Be Done?* (*Chto Delat?*).

She feels he is one writer of popular fiction no socialist need be ashamed of enjoying. But she keeps an absolute admiration for Turgenev. Even if he was a soft liberal, a conciliator, afraid of the threatening growth of a rural proletariat, an insurgent peasantry.

"There are passages of his," she goes on to a slightly bored male companion, "I regard as almost *sacred*. Just the recital of them confirms me in my revolutionary faith."

I turn round to get a better look at this interesting oddity. She is tallish, extremely thin, with carroty curls brushed hard back. The sort of face that gets called *jolie-laide*. But that would be quite wrong for her. She could never seem pretty—that suggests, to me, the *soubrette* in the operetta, a favorite barmaid. Nor could she be ugly—that suggests an appearance that has gone wrong, fallen in the oven.

No, this Turgenevian has high cheekbones, a long jaw. Eyes, eyes recall a phrase that Oly used once, tongue-in-cheek, in our family mag—"buttonholes in an emperor's greatcoat." A chalk-white skin. Teeth that protrude in a balcony even her generous lips cannot cushion.

It is an unusual face. Why does it remind me of several faces I know well, so well I do not have to make an effort to identify them? They are engraved on the inside of my eyelids. She might have been Sasha's twin in a school group photograph, an Olga caught in a solemn pose, perhaps Mother when young. She feels like family.

I have already discovered with Maria, and now Apollinaria, that Chernyshevsky's "new women" really exist. But I had never met a potential Turgenev heroine. So I addressed her somewhat too formally perhaps. However, since my mouth was full of pancake, it hardly mattered. She listened to what I was intoning. Then produced the correct responses!

> "You, young woman, who are going to cross this threshold, do you know what awaits you?"
> "I know."
> "Cold, hunger, hostility, contempt, irony, shame, prison, disease, and death."
> "I know, I am ready to endure all this."
> "Even if all this were to come not only from your enemies, but also from your relatives and friends?"
> "Yes, even then."
> "Are you even ready to commit a crime?"
> "I am ready for that too."
> "Have you considered that you might be subject to a delusion, that you might have sacrificed your young life in vain?"
> "I have considered this too."
> "Enter, then."
> "Imbecile!" said someone.
> "Saint!" the echo answered.

We *had* been thinking of the same passage, from Turgenev's *Prose Poems*. "Saint" we said together.

I went to fetch two glasses of lemon tea, but when I came back she had gone. Apparently, her name is Nadezhda Konstantinovna Krupskaya.

MARCH 1   PETERSBURG   1894

Julius Martov is a Jew (Tsederbaum). But he understands that any ethnic, or whatever, group must subordinate itself to the greater struggle. He is usually hunched and sedentary, his eye on the tip of his cigarette. You might think him a permanent invalid. Three years younger than I am, he seems to have given up battling against the weakness of a puny physique. Yet his mind moves on greased ballbearings. Nobody I know matches him in a swiftness of pouncing on an unfamiliar, complex concept, holding it up to the light to reveal all its difficulties, then reordering it so that it becomes simple and direct. His thoughts always aspire to become deeds.

Today we discussed the crucial differences between propaganda and agitation, a key confusion that often muddies our tactics. While I was still searching for the explanation in their origins, Julius found it in their usage. He closed his eyes, pursed his fine mouth and explained:

"A propagandist, when he discusses unemployment, must explain the capitalist nature of the crisis, he must show the reason for its inevitability in modern society; he must describe the necessity of rebuilding society on a Socialist basis, et cetera. In a word, he must give many ideas concentrated all together, so many that all of them will not be understood by the average person. In their totality they will be understood by relatively few.

"The agitator, on the other hand, will pick out one more or less familiar and concrete aspect of the entire problem, let us say, the death of an unemployed worker as the result of starvation. His efforts will be concentrated on this fact, to impart to the masses a single idea—the idea of the senseless contradiction between the growth of wealth and the growth of poverty. He will strive to evoke among the masses discontent and revolt against this great injustice and will leave the full explanation of this contradiction to the propagandists."

MARCH 3   PETERSBURG   1894

It has taken me some time to ask Apollinaria if she knows a comrade called Nadezhda Konstantinovna Krupskaya. I felt shy.

She only pretended to consider.

"Krupskaya? Hmm. Strange-looking, girlish-boyish? Skin like watered-down milk? Carroty-hair scraped back in a plait? Soft-spoken, shy, modest. But tough as old boots underneath? That the one? We call her *Minorga* as a cover-name. 'The Lamprey.' Can you see why? No, men never can. Nadya's my closest friend at the 'Sunday Schools.' By day, she's a railway clerk. Do you want to hear the story of her life? Settle down then. And don't interrupt."

The story of Nadya's life turns out (as, I have noticed, do the stories of many women's lives) to be a perfect short story. The story of almost any man's life remains an unconvincing anecdote, starring the narrator, told over and over in slightly different terms. More boring if you believe it than if you don't. You've heard one, you've heard them all.

So, daughter of the old blood-aristocracy on both sides. Each parent an orphan. Father descendant of rebel Prince Andrey Kurbsky-Krubsky (?) who defied Ivan the Terrible. His regiment sent to suppress Polish rebellion of '63 when a young officer. Later military governor remote Polish province. A liberal, supporter independence of subject nations, hater of cruelty, pacifist. Sheltered his people from Russification, stopped occupying force humiliating the Jews. Built a hospital, a school, became adored by the inhabitants. Visiting general thought him too soft, too radical. Arrested on charge of disloyalty and lack of patriotism: witness his failure to attend church, dancing mazurka, speaking Polish. His case trekked through courts for ten years while he traveled country, supporting wife and daughter as factory inspector, insurance agent. Vindicated by Senate just before he died. His daughter was fourteen.

Nadya, child of the old nobility helped mother with lodgers, washed up, scrubbed floors, worked as pupil teacher, while still schoolgirl, taking night classes to get degree.

Apollinaria notes my interest with amusement. "Makes your life seem a bit sheltered. Eh, Ilyich?"

APRIL 4   PETERSBURG   1894

First attempt circulating leaflets around the Odner and Beier plant not great success.

Taken great care over typesetting, printing and, of course the writing of this protest. Subject: employers' habit of refusing to allow unskilled workers leave factory for midday meal. Actually, at some smaller plants lower-paid men are provided with food on spot for token deduction (twenty-five kopeks a day). Cabbage soup and *kasha*—always the same, what I have in my room. A bit monotonous but not uneatable. Still, the workers regard this as an abuse. So, by definition, it *must* be one. On that we are all agreed.

Decide hand out leaflet, one per person, just round corner from each factory gate. Out of sight of watchman, or resident copper on duty.

To my surprise, mounting irritation, one after another took the leaflet in hand, felt it with finger and thumb, then either carelessly threw it away or politely handed it back. About the tenth worker turned out to be one of my undercover contacts, Ivan Babushkin.

"Nikolai Petrovich!" he cried, my cover name. "Here, let me help you." He took a wad. Only to hand them back almost immediately.

"You have only put the message on one side."

"I'm glad someone noticed. That is deliberate. The message would not stretch. Thought the workers might like to use the free side for writing, making notes or calculations, little drawings. As you know, paper is expensive. You could call it a sort of present from us to them."

He began to laugh—a horrible sound like an ass braying. He laughed on the intake of breath.

"Dear clever, good, brave, old, Nikolai Petrovich. Permit me. To explain. God, it's so funny! I've never seen a worker end up using a leaflet, even after reading it, for any but one purpose. Can you not imagine? Our latrines are cold, wet, windy places. No employer has ever dreamt of providing sanitary material. We're just a lot of runaway landless peasants. Our hand is good enough for us. And that's all we had. Until the revolutionaries came along and began giving us leaflets. That's why everybody scrambles for them. Charge-hands, foremen, even some office workers. But these leaflets here are stiff and thick as an invitation to tea from the Tsar. Even the hairy-arsed peasant can't use that. You'll be lucky to give them away."

He was right. Information! We need more information!

MAY 9   PETERSBURG   1894

Martov's diagnosis emphasizes that agitation, rather than propaganda, must be our first priority. In the fight to earn enough to afford some scraps of food in his belly, a roof without too many holes over his head, the worker will learn to stand up for his own interests. No use us *telling* him he is exploited, cheated, degraded. He must undergo and survive confrontation on the shop floor, in the factory yard. This alone will raise his courage, give him self-confidence, teach him to trust his own strength. Once he discovers how the economic struggle is won or lost, he will begin to be ready for the political battle. He will then know, from experience, how essential it is to change the system to the advantage of the working class.

Almost all of our circles have agreed on this tactic. The problem now is, how do we identify the inflammatory issue, often apparently trivial to outsiders? How do we establish the auspicious moment, which easily passes unmarked by observers? By what criteria do we decide which method is best, in that place, at that time—strike, overtime ban, go-slow, round-robin petition, mass deputation?

In every factory, there are countless minor abuses. These are passionately discussed by the workers, at work or over a beer, with an attention to detail that might seem obsessive in a medieval monk. Our job as agitators is to take each seed of dispute seriously. To discern the correct moment to raise the protest against the key injustice. To see ahead what may be the complications involved in presenting a demand.

To feel in our bones the worker's conditions of life and work. To share his emotions. Whoever among us can do this will be not just their, but *our,* natural leader.

MAY 25   PETERSBURG   1894

My idea of issuing questionnaires about factory life, handed out to sympathetic workers, now collected and in the process of being analyzed, was an ingenious stratagem. I am in the process of becoming the city's expert on wages, piece rates, hours, shifts, lavatory positions, skills needed or not needed, drafts, roof leaks, bullying overseers, occupational diseases, sexual demands.

My sympathy goes out to these volunteers who bring me back this precious intelligence. But I must show little of this. If I weaken, so will they. I am working them harder than their bosses. One complains that his toolbox is so packed with the forms I have given him, he has no room for his bread and sausage. Only recently had the girls in the "Sunday Schools" taught him to write. It is not easy to practice such a fragile skill under cover of a bit of sacking, especially while pretending to look the other way.

Ivan Babushkin I have been pumping dry when he calls round at my room after a twelve-hour day. I may now have every bit of information anyone would ever consider worth collecting about his gigantic factory, the Odner and Beier metalworking plant. Today we had the last interview. Ivan wiped the sweat from his brow. "I'd rather do another couple of hours overtime than answer any more of your questions," he complained. But with a smile.

At last, we are getting the information we need. We need to be able to speak not only to them, but for them.

JUNE 19   PETERSBURG   1894

No one will ever publish volumes of my collected correspondence. Not of the pre-Revolution letters anyway. When I sit down to write, all personal tidbits, all humorous or colorful descriptions, any intimate account of what I think, feel, do, any gossip about old friends or relatives, have to be deleted from my head. Even that regular monthly dispatch, insisted on by Mother, stops being individual after "Darling Mummy."

A revolutionary has to assume everything he sends through the post may be read by others. The result: mostly it reads like the secondhand report of a sewing-circle, or the gardeners' club dance, in the *Samara Echo*.

A revolutionary, under a dictatorship like ours, must aspire only to be forgettable. Not for him, even courting his mate, the pleasure of dressing up. Marx used to wear, in one photograph at least, what looks like a monocle. Engels hunted in the correct pink, donned evening dress for Manchester dinners at the Cotton Exchange. Our own Plekhanov, "Father of Russian Marxism," is said to be a bit of a stuffed shirt in his villa by the Swiss lake.

But I have never thought about clothes. In Samara, when I was losing all those court cases, Maria Ivanovna used to see I conformed to some semblance of a professional man. As much as possible, that is, for someone with a chest like a lobster pot, the head of a stone cannonball, short arms and legs and no income. Admittedly, I came to Peter with Father's top hat and tailcoat, but only because Mother packed them specially. Nevertheless, if I wore the dreariest of provincial work clothes I should get stoned in the workers' slums here. Only this morning proletarian infants pelted mud balls at me. This despite concertina trousers, a horse blanket of an overcoat, and knee boots with holes in the toes.

Apollinaria—is it my imagination?—is getting a bit nigglesome about the Sunday best I wear for our one free evening together a week. It is a shiny, almost-fitting, office clerk's uniform, acquired for my supposed occupation as junior advocate in the law office. I point out that revolutionaries must be the only people who have to dirty their hands and faces *before* setting out to work.

NOVEMBER 5   PETERSBURG   1894

Apollinaria, like Maria Ivanovna in Samara, has what most men and women have been conditioned to call a "masculine mind." Even she says so sometimes. This evening we had a tremendous discussion (hardly an argument, or a debate, since mostly we were on the same side) about this. It hit us at the same time—what evidence is there, except the consensus of the stupid, that the male actually operates on reason, the female on emotion?

Examine the history of the world over the last 15,000 years. Man has been the ruling gender. Would you say it displays signs of being run by an intelligence devoted to order, logic, reason, common sense,, etc.? Look at the caesars and sultans, the prophets and judges, the messiahs and conquerors . . . look at Jehovah, the

Old Testament archetype of them all. Did you ever encounter such a vain, hysterical, selfish, jealous, greedy, changeable, murderous, touchy creature as the Lord God of Hosts? Does he embody the failings and vices we traditionally associate with women, or with men? Would you trust your children to a Father who sacrificed his only-begotten Son?

No woman should fear that she is deserting her sex by cultivating the "masculine" view, that is to say, the scientific approach. It may not be very common among women so far in history. It has been ever less common among men. Yet only such a rational view of the world's problems will save us from barbarism or decadence. Possibly the extinction of civilization through a new Armageddon. This approach must needs be shared by all of us, regardless of sex, if humanity is to survive.

True, we should not underrate the so-called "feminine" virtues—sympathy, tenderness, altruism, tolerance, forgiveness, care, concern. But, I fear, the time for them is *after* the Revolution. The qualities needed to destroy the old order are not those we will need to build the new Jerusalem. Now, history demands that the Revolution be made by people who are stern, pitiless, rigorous, dominating, determined to win whatever the cost. After our victory, such "masculine" warriors may have to be liquidated for the good of the commonwealth. Me among them. On the eve of battle, they are worth a thousand bleeding hearts.

DECEMBER 20   PETERSBURG   1894

Moving between Apollinaria and Julius, I switch from one extreme of myself to another. She is ever on her feet, striding, gesturing, arguing, building up a head of steam, compressing her springs, for action. No sooner has she expressed a thought than it must become a deed. Take our discussion the other day about men and women, masculine and feminine modes. She then urged that "equality of women" must be part of our S.D. program.

I explained that all these "questions" have to be put to one side, or better still used as fuel for our central drive toward revolution. This goes for the "Jewish Question"—Marx himself said that we cannot ask for freedoms for Jews that are still denied workers. It also goes for the "Woman Question"—she is enslaved, but only because the man is also enslaved. Socialism will solve both problems. What about the "National Question"? What about the

"Social Question"? she insisted. The test is, I reiterated, does it advance the struggle? The colonial peoples oppressed by imperialism include all classes. We must join with them in throwing out their occupying power. By doing so, they advance from feudalism to capitalism and its limited freedoms—one step on the way to socialism. The same goes for a developing nation that rules itself, like Russia. The first target is the autocracy. The question about such "questions" is: Which of those involved will fight on our side? I do not see the Jews or the women taking to the streets.

Apollinaria is all the more angry because she knows I am right. She has come to the same conclusion. A typical end to such an expression of views is an agreement to have our German lesson. We are teaching each other. She sits on my knee, my Goldilocks. She is a scented bolster, an hourglass cut from a satin mattress. Before our twelve irregular verbs are finished, other preoccupations have taken over. The "Woman Question" gets its answer, well, one answer. Even the most rational, logical, scientific, etc., etc., of us have moments when bubbling, hot passions pour in and turn off the lights in our heads like gypsy dancers at a student party.

DECEMBER 31   MOSCOW   1894

The end of five days of Christmas holidays with the family. Mother, Anna and Mark, Mitya and Marya, and me. I feared we would feel depleted, but the six of us made a merry crowd. You'd have thought there were at least a dozen dancing, singing and hallooing round this riverside mansion. I'd put aside my brain in the icebox as I entered, and there it remained. So nothing but mindless, emotional, *sensual* celebration. I think it helped being Moscow. No ghosts of Father as there would have been in Simbirsk, or of Oly and Sasha as there would have been in Peter. We talked of them, drank toasts to them with wet, smiling faces, but they remained invited guests.

SIBERIA

1 8 9 5 - 1 9 0 0

Our tsarist Russia is the only regime in the West where the authorities require that its subjects ask permission, and give reasons, why they would wish to cross their own frontiers. This is part of our Asiatic inheritance. I had given "health reasons" as the justification for a trip to Europe planned for mid-March. Actually, I am as fit as a circus strongman. Or I was, until I got my external passport stamped with an exit visa. Then I collapsed with acute pneumonia. Moral—try not to tell lies about your health, they so easily become true. The body is a touchy servant to the brain, always ready to betray the overconfident master in a moment of *hubris*.

Even now, I see the world outside through a shivery membrane, like a pane of ancient glass, rinsed with heavy rain. But my spirits rise, mercury in a thermometer, as I approach the magnetic West. Over there, Germany, the home of radical philosophy; France, the conservatory that grew political revolution; perhaps even England, the nation of shopkeepers who revolutionized economics. This is the trivet on which Marxism came to the boil. Also raising my temperature is the introduction I carry (in the lining of my hat) to George Plekhanov, the sprig of a nobleman who led the first workers' demo ever in Russian history when I was six years old. His "Emanicipation of Labour" group broke away from the direct-action terrorists of Populism, *Narodnaya Volya,* in order to support proletarian revolution.

I suspect that this expatriate cabal may now be out of touch with what is happening back home, on the streets and in the factories. To bring the message from the battlefield gives me anyway a walk-on role across the international scene.

Getting away from Russia is like crawling out of a cave. I can see that the police and the customs officers know who I am if not precisely what I am. For various reasons, mainly organizational, my passport is in my real name, Ulyanov. Well, *one* of my passports is. But the border officials don't much care who leaves carrying what. They are concerned far more with who returns with what, from where. I owe it to my contacts on either side to vanish once my foot touches foreign soil.

I think I will sleep until Berlin.

MAY 14   SALZBURG STATION   1895

Today would be May 2 in Russia, our vast folktale country twelve days behind in the calendar as in almost everything. But not forever!

Though this is only a two-hour stopover, I got off and took a quick loop around the city aiming for the GPO and the swift dispatch of a letter to Mother. Fortunately, having consulted Baedeker, I knew exactly where the express postboxes were. Unfortunately, I almost missed the collection, and my own train, owing to a clash with my conductor on a Salzburg tramcar.

He cannot understand a word of my German. So far as I can make out, he inclines to the theory that I must be Finnish or Turkish. Possibly Basque. I understand only every fifth word he says, he speaks so quickly. The sounds he makes with his elastic lips show little resemblance to the German that Oly and I taught each other, Apollinaria and I recited together.

I appeal to the populace, making an address in German to the travelers on the tram. They look equally baffled, increasingly annoyed. Can there be something wrong with my system? Learn all the likely nouns, learn all the irregular verbs, memorize a selection of idioms and everyday phrases, then master the grammar. Surely that has to be the rational way? It's the way I learned Latin.

Despite this ludicrous fiasco, I refuse to be discouraged. I shall continue distorting German, and any other language, with zeal until I break through into communication, both ways. Now for that sleep.

MAY 15   SWITZERLAND   1895

First stop, Geneva. Now I find my French is worse than my German—we have a choice at the station here. I discover the universal language. Everyone in the world (excepting only, of course, the English themselves) can be made to understand English spoken badly, and loudly.

I took a cab out to Plekhanov's villa on the lake, a country-gent retreat, rather like a scaled-down version of Grandpa Blank's old mansion overlooking the water at Kokushkino. Eventually, a starchy silhouette, like a Grand Duchess in an operetta, appeared at an upper-story window—the housekeeper.

"The Master is away for a few weeks in the mountains."

"Holiday?" I asked, for something to ask.

"The Master does not take 'holidays'!"

MAY 17   GENEVA   1895

Letter from Plekhanov by return post (Swiss efficiency!) invites me to call on him at Les Ormonts in the mountains. This leads to more linguistic problems since my cabby does not recognize the name. I point it out on the map.

"Oh, you mean *Ormoni*! I thought you were after some French place, *Les* Something-or-Other. *Ormoni*, that's Swiss."

"The Master!" My stomach starts a life of its own, skipping the ropes of nervous tension. Naive of me to forget that the superior sort of people never take holidays. They drift off to spend "a few weeks" in somebody else's house or in some second or third home of their own. My twinges get worse for the moment.

"The Master!" Still, that is how I think of him myself. The first Russian Marxist. Founder of Russia's first workers' party. Man of action then, giant of theory then and now. He is almost certainly feeling cut off from Russian roots. This is my chance. I must not be bilious and resent rejection before I have been rejected.

So far I have always overcome any obstacle in my way. By the same postal delivery as Plekhanov's letter came from Russia one from Martov hailing me as "first among equals." I feel like Shakespeare's Macbeth. Still, Plekhanov is one of the great men, friend and colleague of Engels, Kautsky, Bebel. He is Our Master because we are all his pupils.

When I got to Ormoni, P. could not have been more courteous in his manner, reserved yet welcoming. The cottage is almost as sizable as the villa by the lake. Through his presidential study two daughters flit like socialist princesses, off to pony riding, piano lessons, amateur dramatics, language classes, beseeching the Grand Pasha's attention in throaty French. Madam Rosaliva Markovna, Lady George, medical doctor, handsome, busy, sharp, accepts my introduction with the cry "Oh, *politics*!" as another wife might indulge hubby's hobby with "Oh, stamp-collecting!"

She leaves, giving me a warning, diagnostic look. Any trouble from me and I'll find I only have a week to live.

Plekhanov is polymathic. He quizzes me about Peter today, about its music and theater, its art and literature. He is interested in men's and women's fashions, in the best restaurants, in the jokes going round the clubs. I can only shrug and tell him that I did not even know there were men's fashions.

We move on to Marxism and German philosophy. He quotes Hegel from memory. He takes books from his shelves and reads aloud, translating at sight when they are in languages I might not know. He summons up parallels from anatomy, geology, chemistry, aesthetics, zoology. It becomes a very theatrical performance, accompanied by vivid gestures, eyes flashing, features rippling. You cannot help feeling he must intend to dramatize the contrast with his *bourgeois-gentilhomme* costume—frockcoat, button-boots, spats, cravat, wing collar, oiled beard, coiled *mustachios*.

I congratulated him on his luck in finding such a library in a mountain village retreat. He smiled: "I'm here every summer and I found I had to duplicate almost everything. Can't keep lumping your favorite books backward and forward, lake-mountain-lake, can you?"

I felt a spurt of bile, an adrenaline surge. For a second, I wanted to lure him into the thickets of controversy, drag him from his high horse and club him with reality. But I need him, the whole movement needs him. And he needs us, for without us he is going to vanish, the thinker who was buried under his own books.

There are several angles from which I could have attacked him. Over terrorism, for example. I had purged myself of its attractions by the time I reached Petersburg from the provinces, aged twenty-three. Plekhanov, at thirty-nine, still finds the sickly excitement hard to resist.

Year after year, working-class groups come on pilgrimage to him (as I am doing) and ask for help, and advice, in conveying the Marxist doctrine to the masses. Intellectually, he knows how to proceed. Practically, he cannot write for them, or talk to them, the way they think.

He above all has advocated what Martov and I understood only when we experienced it in action—revolutionaries must learn that the difference between a sect and a party is the same as that between propaganda and agitation. The first is narrowed down to conveying many ideas to few people while the other is broadened into spreading a few ideas among many people. What must never be forgotten, in his own words, is that "*history is made by the masses.*"

Who has the masses? Not him, but us! Nothing in my life so

far has promised me greater satisfaction than bringing the Russian workers under his influence. So I provoked him only on one point.

It was common ground between us that the key revolutionary force, even in newly capitalistic Russia, must be the proletariat. But it needs allies—who should they be? The backward peasants or the educated liberal middle class? I had no doubts. I hit the liberals with every argument I knew. I tried a Plekhanovian approach by citing literature, history, art, philosophy, home and abroad, but above all the streets and factories of Russia, now, now, *now*.

When I finished, I almost blushed, the approval so shone from his eyes.

"Style three, research four, but attack five, logic five, effect five! My dear Tulin, you may be the practical intellectual, the thinking agitator, the working revolutionary for whom we have all been waiting. Do visit Axelrod. He and Vera and I will back you all the way. You have my hand."

I left, with giggly waves from the girls, a gloomy prognosis implicit in Dr. Lady Plekhanov's scowl, and the great man himself leaning down from the top step to say through the cab window: "About the liberals, finally we agree. When they've served their purpose, we'll wipe them away like chalk off a blackboard. But for the moment, our tactic is to woo them, face to face. You, you show them your *arse!*"

As I was driven down the drive, I saw Plekhanov was laughing. Black eyebrows bobbing. Perfect teeth bared. Stiff cuffs raised with gold links tinkling.

MAY 21   **ZURICH**   **1895**

I found Axelrod at Affoltern, a working village near Zurich. Older than Plekhanov, coarser, kindlier, a Jewish farmer, he little resembled the Russian peasants I had known in Samara. His whole place had the look of an exhibit at an international fair—scrubbed, silky cows, flower-patterned meadows, well-washed air, white-laquered walls, soaped-down tables, platters of cheese, bricks of butter, milk by the gallon, hot soft loaves ripe as melons. He'd just got a letter from Plekhanov, enclosed with a pamphlet. Did I mind if he read it now? Meanwhile, eat, eat! Where was it written that revolutionaries should starve in the midst of plenty?

He finished. "Marvelous, marvelous! Who is this Tulin?" I

hadn't finished. I pointed a finger at a full mouth. He leaped up, embraced me, danced around.

"Show them the arse, eh? More likely kick them up the tush, I'd say. When you get back to Peter, start a Marxist party and a Marxist newspaper. We'll get you the money. Me, Georgy Valentinovich, "Aunty," Prince Obolensky, Morozov. Don't worry, that's the easy part. You want a party of staff officers, like Nechaev or Tkachev. We want a broad front of every rank. We can spar over that in the future. What matters is to get moving. More milk, dear fellow? Butter, cheese, cream? My cows have been waiting for this moment for years."

Success, then. Yet somehow no great desire to go home just yet. Switzerland is amazing, one great dairy. A sideshow staged by the capitalists to show how happy the people can be without socialism, so long as they eat well and breathe fresh air. An illusion, of course, but a pretty one. Just staring at the Alps can induce sentimental idealism in anybody. Almost anybody.

JUNE 30   PARIS   1895

If Switzerland sometimes seems one great cow-farm fenced round with mountains, Paris is a huge fairground or amusement park masquerading as a capital city. I've been here six weeks now and I still can't get over how, day and night, everything is so bright! Day and night everything (everything frivolous and entertaining) is open for business.

I can see why it is called the city of love. Love, at least first love, gives the world a gloss and a sheen as if you'd been issued with fresh eyeballs. Paris has the same sort of effect. Foreigners arriving here revert instantly to their adolescence, behave like students drunk for the first time.

Everybody talks to everybody, as during the last hours of a party. When they're not talking, they're reading, usually about themselves. This is a city proud of its revolutions, the last only twenty-five years ago. I've been taking classes in how to seize power for the people from those who were there when it happened with the Paris Commune. I even spent an evening with Marx's daughter and son-in-law, Laura and Paul Lafargue. I had planned to cross the Channel to see the ailing Engels, but he is too sick for visitors.

Another characteristic of Parisians, each one knows his worth. Our radical Russian exiles, egalitarians to the gallows' steps, complain continually about how servants here insist on being well-paid and will only eat the best food!

My French is definitely better than my German, but then I have been speaking it since the kindergarten. I refuse to feel guilty because I keep waking in the mornings thinking I am playing truant. Why should being a rebel not be enjoyable sometimes? I shouldn't have asked that. Once more, the body intervenes to discipline the wayward mind.

Within minutes of such thoughts, I suffer a bloated belly, as if my bowels had given sanctuary to some gorged boa constrictor. I can almost feel my intestines pressing against my heart and I fall into fits, jackknifed with midriff constrictions.

I feel calmer now, on the midnight sleeper to Geneva, headed for Swiss medical spa. I don't have much faith in doctors, but this one is not only a French comrade, but a professor of medicine and official consultant to the president. Added to which he promises no cure, money back. As I have almost no money, there would seem to be little alternative. Funny how restful no alternative can be.

JULY 28   SWITZERLAND   1895

Since the beginning of this month I've been lodged in what amounts to a penal colony for those convicted of the grave crime of falling ill of no known disease. Diagnosis is not important since there are only two treatments: (a) huge daily intake of pebbly spa water that tastes like boiled essence of stalactites, or (b) huge intake of palate-puckering dregs of soured milk known as "yogurt" especially manufactured (would you believe it?) at "Dr. (med) Axelrod's Therapeutic Laboratory Farm, near Zurich."

Worse is yet to come. My treatment was even-days (a), odd-days (b). And it worked. As soon as I was cured and the symptoms disappeared, it was decided that my ailment had been "abdominal catarrh." Permission has been asked for my case to be written up in learned journals.

For most of my time here, I have lain in bed mesmerized by the Alpine peaks outside the window. It is a sight unnerving rather than inspiring, I find. How tiny our figures, how brief our existence, like fleas dancing on the red-hot lid of a stove, must we seem by comparison with the size and the span of a great mountain.

Feel ill, you feel poor: feel poor, you feel ill. It seems one of life's syllogisms. Infirmaries, poorhouses, asylums, and prisons are interchangeable termini for much the same kind of people. Looking up the letter-index I keep at the back of this diary, I see that I have written four letters to Mother in twenty-five days. And I know I have asked for money in each one. Disgraceful.

Nevertheless, I had to write again, last weekend. This simple life is very expensive. The filthy water costs me more per pint than any champagne while those pernicious milk solids are spoon for spoon more expensive than caviar.

The hypochondriac who shares my room, a Finn and a bore, tells me Axelrod's potable poultice was originally Bulgarian, properly pronounced "yort," and widely used in the Balkans as a dressing for various venereal contagions such as herpes. I can believe that. The first person who *drank* it deserves either a medal or the firing squad.

By this evening's post I received 300 rubles from Mother and 400 marks from my German publisher. My recovery is complete. Tomorrow morning early, I take the train for Berlin.

SEPTEMBER 18   BERLIN   1895

Foreigners stand out in Berlin, perhaps because they are crowded together in fewer places than in Paris. You can't mistake them. Russians here turn scruffy, vague, eccentric half-castes, all tufted, uncombed hair and a whiff of dirty linen. French are identified as lightweight, gossipy, spendthrift pleasure-seekers, all macassar oil and pinched waists. Even the English, Nordic cousins to the locals, seem less impressive—overgrown, shiny-faced, loud-voiced ball-kickers and horse-racers, schoolboys uneasy in their middle-aged stiff collars and indestructible hats.

As for the Germans themselves, well, it is hard not to see in their faces that they are born schoolmasters, drill instructors, grand inquisitors, customs inspectors, hotel directors, highway builders, armaments manufacturers. To us Russians, Germany epitomizes the West. Though the French and English sneer, we see it as the future powerhouse of capitalism. We see the Germans as imminent rulers of Europe, tomorrow the world, the executive class of the new imperialist bourgeoisie. To them, war is the continuation of business by other means. They see themselves as the only real adults among nations, the only genuine scientists and industrialists this side of the Atlantic.

All the twentieth-century extremes will be theirs: the next popular tyrant, the next overthrow of the state, the ultimate anarchy, the ultimate anthill. I cannot help envy, even admire, them as instruments of evolution, power tools of change. No wonder Marx and Engels were German. German socialism, banned the year I was born, is now the most powerful mass movement in the world. I must try to inject some of that Hunnish steel into the banana backbones of our so often spineless comrades.

The Prussian Staatsbibliothek may not be Europe's greatest library (I long to sample London's famous British Museum bookstacks) but nowhere else, I bet, are books circulated so nimbly, at the double, marched to your desk with such soldierly precision. I often have felt in these six weeks that I have enlisted in their army. I study most of the day, sitting at attention. Dismissed, I circulate on sentry-go round the Tiergarten each afternoon. I parade for the fording of the river Spree each morning, equipped with regulation issue swimming costume. I muster for meals at 12 Flensburger Strasse, flat II (Frau Kurrieck), in Berlin-Moabit. I fancy I even chew by numbers.

My German makes my French seem fluent. I mainly avoid the tourist round, museums, churches, opera houses, theaters, public buildings, the shopping avenues. I have tried one play, Hauptmann's *The Weavers*. But despite locking myself in the evening before, at Frau Kurrieck's boardinghouse, and reading the text from cover to cover, I still hardly understood a word.

I find more amusement and interest in the street markets, the stand-up bars, the singers along the quayside, the café vaudeville, the boxing pavilions, the boating docks, the angling competitions. I enjoy following the crowd to an occasional German Social Democrat rally—e.g., Arthur Stadthagen thundering on about agrarian policy in an open-air stadium. Imagine being able to say such things to thousands in public! And sometimes even the police applauded!

My most awesome political contact has been William Liebknecht, once Marx's drinking companion in London, now a crony of Plekhanov. We talked in broken English.

Tomorrow my Grand Tour ends and I will be recrossing the frontier. My urgent recall message was routed through my family for security, a prearranged signal reading: "Abroad is nice but to be invited home is best—Mother." I am sure it means that the police are getting close. But for the life of me I can't remember whether it is here or there.

SEPTEMBER 19   ON THE FRONTIER   1895

Passengers entering Russia from the West may wait at the border station anything from an hour to half a day. It all depends on how long it takes to change trains. Here you abandon the low, sleek greyhound of a European locomotive on its neat, narrow gauge and mount behind the high, swaying stagecoach of a Slav locomotive with its wide, wandering track. Meanwhile, we are not allowed to remain on the platform but are dragooned into a chain of great barns, some way from the railway line, which make up the immigration and customs sheds. This is a structure of blank walls, recessed windows, flush doors, remote, shadowless lighting, resembling a turnpike in the suburbs of limbo.

Our authorities follow nothing so simple as a chronological or alphabetical scrutiny of passports. All get to be examined in the end but according to some perverse, threatening priority known only to gendarmes and frontier guards. Luggage is picked out and turned over, apparently at random though it is hard to be sure. Axelrod was once a regular courier through here. I follow his advice—never stand still, never be seen trying to hide behind others, keep "slowly eddying."

I amble in and out of the washrooms, hover near the samovar on the drinks/snacks counter, linger having a free read at the newspaper stall. It is my brand-new documents case which is conspicuous. Hard to describe it except in the terms used to advertise it in the society magazines. The warm, soft sheen of burgundy buffalo-hide . . . massy, brassy locks and hinges, hand-crafted with a jeweler's precision . . . silky linings, cobwebbed as a ballerina's underwear!

These accessories are specially designed, in this model, for the use of revolutionary smugglers by a certain comrade Nabokov, "Leather-goods supplier to H.I.H. Tsar Nicholas II, Emperor of All the Russias." Presumably our new Tsar does not order our supply of extra, double false bottoms which can enfold, without a glimpse of a bulge, many hundreds of pages of contraband propaganda, printed in Russian on a Zurich press. Still, I cannot help feeling that this gorgeous trinket leaves your average comrade-conspirator looking a bit shabby.

After the several hours' delay, I began experiencing a few

nervous stomach spasms. I started thinking I was going in and out of the lavatory rather too often. There was by now nothing else new for people to look at with a trace of genuine curiosity. Within minutes, I was selected out of several hundred other undistinguished passengers to have my single item of hand luggage opened.

Another Alexrod axiom for plotters is—try slowness and clumsiness, made accidental, for this often provokes the speedy, light-fingered searcher into giving up and moving on. As I kept fumbling with sausage fingers at buckles and catches, it seemed to have worked.

A superior official (cocked hat and a sword!) intervened. "Beautiful craftmanship. A Nabokov? I *thought* so." He turned to his junior. "Odds on, Sergeant, you can trust anyone with such taste." He flicked over my passport, saluted and waved me on to the new train, first bell now clanging. What a relief!

Yet my blue litmus paper was turning pink. Was it reacting to a heavy whiff of irony, barely hidden? The dressy officer must also have noticed my baggily cut suiting, several sizes too big, patterned to provide concealment for wads of illegal money and secret documents. Did he admire *that* taste?

I turned to have a look, but he had disappeared. I was left with a nagging unease which lingers on. As if a strange hand had rifled through my pockets in the dark.

SEPTEMBER 29   PETERSBURG   1895

After crossing the frontier, I changed trains in Warsaw and broke my journey to Peter at several places where support had been reported—notably Vilno, Moscow and Orekhovo-Zuevo. In each one, I passed on to newly active groups the message that Axelrod promised a subsidy, and Plekhanov contributions, for a Social Democrat organ, tentatively entitled *Rabochee Dyelo* (*Workers' Matters*). I then sounded out my own project for a serious, disciplined, undercover party instead of the loose chain of left-liberal supporters and sympathizers we have now. Martov and I put forward the name: "League of Struggle for the Emancipation of the Working Class." Much enthusiasm for both suggestions.

Back now in Peter, I increasingly have the impression that eyes are on me night and day. (The recall from "Mother" had been a false alarm from our man in the Okhrana, warning of an imminent roundup). It could be a trick of my mind. If the authorities are going to snatch us, it must be soon, before the paper's first issue.

It is stupid to allow myself to become jumpy over such as my landlady. But she is not just the low-grade government informer so many of them are, she is the worst kind of nagger and nosy parker. And she looks like a drowning snail, eyes on stalks, quivering, three-cornered mouth, long mournfully corded neck.

Nor are nerves helped by my unseen neighbor in the next room. He plays his balalaika without ceasing during all his waking hours—admittedly, not all that many. But such as they are, they coincide with my sleeping hours. The plucking fingers, the squeak and thrum of the strings, the boring, repetitive tenor rhythms, seem to play inside my head.

NOVEMBER 29   PETERSBURG   1895

Back from abroad, the poverty, the degradation, the oppression suffered by Russian working people seem almost impossible to credit. You cannot understand why they do not take their hammers and their sickles and simply slaughter the rest of us who live on exploiting them. The hundred and fifty million of them only need to spit and we would drown.

Appearances are deceptive. You cannot judge the way of life of a class by the way they behave on the street, in the cafés, in the parks. Especially the working people of Berlin and Paris and Zurich where everybody, rich and poor, lives so much outdoors. But I would pledge my right hand, there are few even among the lower middle class here, who eat so well, dress so interestingly, have available such refined amusements, simply enjoy being alive, even if they possess nothing but their own skills, as the French, German or Swiss wage earners, at least in the three major cities.

There is an old night watchman here who comes round to my office in the early evening once a week. He is almost an alcoholic, practically a cripple through industrial accidents, at sixty looks over eighty, and is convinced (almost certainly correctly) that he has not long to live. He is a socialist and wants me to read him extracts (his demands are modest) from famous foreign authors about whom he has only just heard—Zola, for example. Today I picked out some bits from Engels's *Condition of the British Working Class* which I had just acquired, in English, translating as I went along. At the end of what seemed a particularly shocking description of work, food and lodging of the Manchester proletariat, old Stepan Fomich shook his head. "They are far ahead of us, those English. That's not Paradise, but I wish I thought the workers in my factory would be able to live like that some day soon."

I thought he was joking and I laughed. He was hurt. I explained that Engels was writing about England in 1848, less than halfway through the nineteenth century while we were almost into the twentieth. Surely, there had been some progress? He shook his head again.

"You find it, Mr. Tulin, and show it to me. Just do that and I'll die happy."

Stepan may be exactly right, I fear. The Russian worker has suffered all the drawbacks of capitalism without any of the advantages. He is still under feudal restraints while his bosses operate without any rules; a galley slave manacled to his oar on a ship ruled by cutthroat buccaneers.

In England, France and Germany, they are campaigning for an eight-hour day and may win it before long. Here, it is considered laughable to campaign for a ten-and-a-half-hour day, besides being against the law. The worker is legally at the mercy of his employer in a way that is not much different from industrial serfdom. He can be forced to sleep and eat in monstrous barracks within the factory gates, without a key to get in or out except on Saturday afternoon and Sunday. He is charged for everything: food, drink, straw bed on the floor, working clothes. He can be fined for rudeness, slowness, breakages, illness. He can be beaten. He can be poisoned by decaying food, contaminated drink. He is encouraged to gamble, booze, fornicate, borrow, brawl—anything that keeps him in debt to his employer who pays him once a fortnight, often once a month. He is starved of fresh air, outdoor exercise, dry and warm lodgings, decent clothes against the weather. tsarism plus capitalism creates a vastly profitable system of slavery. You need never give a kopek to those you kick out when they cease to earn, a privilege that would be the envy of the southern American plantation owner or the landlord of ancient Rome.

How guilty I feel on days like today when I find I am getting low on cash. No one could be less extravagant or self-indulgent. But my pretend-work as a lawyer only earns me a pretend-salary. Despite the simplest habits, I see from my account book that I have spent 54 rubles 30 kopeks this month so far. True, some of the outlay is not repeatable, for a while anyway (galoshes, peak cap, a book). But even deducting that lot (16 rubles) I am still expending far too much—38 rubles in less than thirty days. There is something wrong about my approach—imagine 1 ruble 36 kopeks on tramfares!

Apollinaria tells me that many shopgirls earn only 64 kopeks more than that—a month! And stand on their feet from nine A.M. to nine P.M., forbidden to sit down even without a customer in sight, sleep under the counter at night often with the owner or his sons, and perhaps half the male staff if they're at all attractive. Plain girls don't get hired and even the pretty ones are fired when their looks go. She says a salesgirl over the age of thirty is almost unknown. Many places of business, where women are in the majority, turn out to be little less than brothels.

Tsarism and capitalism, the big Tsars and the little Tsars, they will pay for all this if I have to go the way of Sasha.

DECEMBER 3   PETERSBURG   1895

The League of Struggle was officially founded yesterday. Martov and I are joint chairmen. Not before time. A proletarian storm is about to break. The air is heavy, sulfurous, ready for the spark. You can smell rebellion. It must not anymore be random and aimless. We exist now to guide the lightning, channel the flood.

Last week Julius and I were sneaked into the Petrovsky steel foundry to see the conditions of the men. The giant caldrons of silver-white, bubbling broth, the rolling loops and hoops of metal like outsize noodles, too blinding hot almost to watch, let alone approach, burned into our memory. Today J. reminded me of the "slave-hands," those prehensile claws, fearlessly pouring and clipping away in the heat of hell, controlled through gears and pulleys at a safe distance by their operators.

"The workers are *our* 'slave-hands.' Every member of the League, behind smoked glasses, inside protective helmets, must manipulate his tens and hundreds. We cannot afford to risk ourselves among the furnaces. We must remain in the control box. And that is *Rabochee Dyelo*. Nothing must stop its publication. Agreed?"

Agreed! But there are still five days to go before it rolls off the underground presses that once printed the words of *Narodnaya Volya*. Already, I fear police spies are thick around me as mosquitoes on a summer dusk, just waiting the fall of darkness, the lighting of the oil lamps, to arrow down in their swarms.

We must move carefully, but decisively, in the daylight that remains. This means all contact between us will become indirect. Apollinaria and her friend Nadya, dressed as country girls, have been selling off the last of autumn's fruits (apples, nuts, sugared berries) around the factory gates. Little profit to us, since we usually have to pay more for them than we dare charge. The point is— every purchase is wrapped in one of our leaflets.

DECEMBER 7   PETERSBURG   1895

Tomorrow, our paper will be everywhere in the workers' districts. The expected strikes, sit-ins, demos and petitions to the Tsar have not occurred. It is almost as if they are waiting for us. I have moved to a new room. Nadya told me a girlfriend of hers worked in the Address Bureau where the Internal Affairs Ministry registers everyone's arrival and departure whether they notify the authorities or not. She reported the visit of a top detective who was overheard saying that the revolutionary subversive Ulyanov was back from abroad and could be picked up at a moment's notice.

"Goldilocks" almost seems to be avoiding me altogether, though I have other things to think about than lovers" tiffs. "Lamprey" ignores me in public (as instructed) but always includes an affectionate, friendly note with whatever material she leaves for me to collect. She is brave, dedicated, trustworthy, efficient though perhaps not overintelligent or enterprising. She is also good-looking in an individual way, a way not physically appealing to me.

JANUARY 25   PETERSBURG   1897

As I was saying . . . Well, I hope that there will not be many such enforced gaps in this diary. For the last thirteen months I have been Prisoner No. 222 in the House of Preliminary Detention on Shpalernaya Street.

I was captured on December 8, 1895, only hours after delivering copy for *Workers' Matters*. A dawn swoop at the printers, and homes of leading League members, rounded up forty-six of us and ensured that the paper never appeared. Twenty-nine are still inside, uncharged, untried, interrogated once a month. Only the women seemed to escape on the initial roundup.

However much you prepare yourself—I had rehearsed the sequence in my head a dozen times—arrest still comes as a shock. Hostile, strangers' hands gripping your body. Steel cuffs clamped on wrists wrenched behind your back. You sense a punitive violence bottled up inside these antagonists. Though professionals, they too have had to nerve themselves for this physical contact. It is easy for them to be overready for resistance, anticipate counterviolence perhaps with guns or bombs. Often the kickings and beatings which follow are a release of surplus energy, stockpiled in readiness for a fight which never came. My four, I have to record, were steely but polite, like male nurses restraining a notorious madman in a rare fit of docility.

I determined then to become, and still am (officially), a model prisoner. So I do double the daily number of Swedish exercises I have done since I was a schoolboy. I reject the lifeless soups, the mushy, teeth-rotting meat sludge. I follow a one-meal-a-day diet Mother had devised by a Swiss nutritionist for those obliged to work indoors at sedentary jobs: oats, nuts, dried fruit, herbs, washed down with skim milk and orange juice. *Muesli*, it's called.

Fellow prisoners, comrades among them, label me a Nordic crank for paying for this to be sent in, for trying to build my body, like a circus strongman, in a damp box, eight by eight feet. Yet few of them climb into the icy coffin of a bed each night with hands and feet hot as pease pudding. They were the ones with sniffles, coughs, fevers, drowned lungs, which laid low, carried off, so many inmates *and* warders last winter. They are the ones who smash furniture, burn mattresses, in childish rages, smother themselves in fits of suicidal gloom. I can honestly say, have said, summing up this year and a bit—I have been too busy to feel like a convict. The word *prison* is worse than the thing itself. The same may be true of other night-terrors we revolutionaries nurse in secret— single confinement, exile, torture, poverty, betrayal, humiliation, pain, failure, oblivion.

The one activity which proved impossible is the one I am carrying out now—diary-keeping. Today all restrictions on writing, and talking, to outsiders are relaxed because the decision about our disposal is to be made soon. Earlier, there was no one there to whom I could trust my innermost thoughts. If I had been discovered, my diary would have given the authorities various holds over me, and my jailers would have turned deeply hostile and vindictive. These underlings care, understand, little about indictments of the system, of the state, even of the Tsar. What they cannot bear is the tiniest personal criticism of themselves.

We "politicals" are usually permitted to write books, so long as the early chapters suggest they are academic and speculative. Long-windedness is a help too. Some older members churn out this sort of thing naturally. But among the young there is much sport thinking up the most arid of titles to bluff the prison officials. *A Characterization of Divergent Approaches Towards a Thesis on the Monist Conception's Limitations as a Form of Hegelian Dialectic* was one I believe was even published and turned out to be a beginner's guide to Marxism and Religion.

Summoned before the deputy-governor, monitor of our scribblers' overflow, I asked him how much he had read of that particular work. "Nodded off halfway through the title," he scowled, casting a tired eye over a dense patch of my MS, provisionally entitled *The Process of the Formation of a Home Market for Large-Scale Industry*. In other words, the development of Russian capitalism. This too is provisionally authorized because it is understood to be *anti*-capitalist! The ruling ideology behind tsarism is that of a hereditary feudal-mercantile élite who still feel that the only "natural" source of wealth is land. If surplus cash is to be invested in such things as factories, railways, shipyards, etc., it should come from state corporations or foreign financiers. The censor is far more antagonistic to native private owners of the means of production than Marx! Indeed, Marx's *Kapital* appeared in a legal Russian translation before it was published in French, German or English. It was regarded as an awful warning of what could happen to a happy despotism if the industrial revolution were allowed to pollute it.

Writing books means reading books. Peter's libraries are stretched to their limits by the demands of our imprisoned men-of-letters. A dozen deputy-governors could not scrutinize more than a page or so of any volume in this two-way traffic. So we have been able to turn out a few unauthorized publications as well, mainly pamphlets, transmitted by dots under words in already printed volumes, or invisible sentences inscribed in lemon juice or milk between lines. The first takes forever and is highly unreliable. The second quicker but messy. Your "ink" has to be secreted about the cell in "wells" fashioned from moistened bread pellets. Only last week I had to ingurgitate six inkwells in one handful and almost choked to death.

"It's that turkey-feed you live on," advised my warder. "Not natural. Here try this." And he stood over me while I forced down his prescribed rod of Italian-style purple sausage. I have every reason to believe it is made from minced donkey offal.

JANUARY 27   PETERSBURG   1897

At last, my sentence on summary conviction. Three years internal exile in Siberia. No allowance for fourteen months, without charge or trial, served here in Peter. My crime is to be classified by the state as an enemy of the state. After the first week, no introduction of the smallest scintilla of evidence. Whenever I am questioned about the League, about my associates, about my trip abroad (it seems I was followed every foot of the way) I reply only: "Name, Ulyanov Vladimir Ilyich. Rank, Hereditary Nobleman. Profession, advocate. Address, Cell no. 133 House of Preliminary Detention, Petersburg."

Who was the first person I saw through the snow this morning as I came out of the prison gates? Mamouchka, imperial in furs, crowned with a halo of white hair. By her side, holding her elbow, glittering in his new uniform, old Roman, the Kokushkino coachman.

Inside the *tarantass,* she promises me all her strings are being pulled. Her Volodya will not be sent too far north. He will travel in independent comfort. It will cost a first-class fare, but the alternative is chains at state expense. Can she do this?

She smiles. Has she not already fixed my first wish? Five days in Peter, on my parole "as a gentleman," to "wind up my affairs," i.e., get in touch with the new generation of the League. Once we crossed the Neva, I gave her another big hug and slipped out of the door furthest from the pavement where the traffic was thickest by the Mikhailovsky Riding School.

FEBRUARY 2   PETERSBURG   1897

I have found no one I know from our old network. Martov, Starkov, Krzhizhanovsky and all the other founding members of the League were lifted along with me. They remain under guard, awaiting the train to exile.

After the first month of detention, in a moment of depression, I sent a message to Nadya asking her to stand with Apollinaria at a spot on Shpalernaya Street where I could glimpse Goldilocks from an insecurely shuttered window. She replied that "our friend

Yakubova is away on a long holiday." She is still away. Nadya herself is in the women's section of Peter & Paul. Of all I met when I arrived here from Samara, only Radchenko remains at liberty. (Strange?) From a safe house on Liteiny, almost opposite, I have several times seen his ace of clubs going in and out of Aunty's bookshop.

Last night, an oldster from among the Elders, *starik* of the *stariki*, I felt, at twenty-seven, as if I had just emerged from a lifetime's entombment alongside Nechaev! At their request, I had turned up to address about fifty of the present members of the League. None of them knew what I looked like. So I just stood up on a chair in the middle of floor and said: "Can I give you young comrades the view of an Old Decembrist?"

Now, the Decembrists were, of course, those radical junior officers, energized by the French Revolution, who gathered their troops outside the Winter Palace to overthrow the Tsar. In 1825.

It was a joke.

Nobody laughed.

We had started out in 1893, half a dozen intellectuals, trying to *force* sullen and suspicious industrial workers of Peter to understand that they could improve their conditions. Within two years, we had forged a web of study circles, penetrated every factory and workshop, given our supporters clear, winnable objectives. We had founded the League of Struggle for the Emancipation of the Working Class, the general staff of the vanguard of the proletariat.

Without us, last year's giant strikes, the present rising wave of unrest, would not have happened. And yet, today's activists could stand around one of the League's founders, a militant who planned the people's battles even from prison, who was on his way to Siberia, and regard him as an already-vanishing anachronism.

I went over into the attack, reading phrases from their leaflets and throwing them on the floor.

"There is a name for your brand of politics. But it is not Marxism. It is 'Economism.' You have conceded in advance the defeat of our revolution. You think the strength of the workers best used winning a few kopeks on their pay, a few minutes off the day. Instead of unions, you are content with friendly societies, charitable clubs, cultural classes. You will comfort strikers' wives and bring toys for the children. Prick the consciences of the middle class with plays about the horrors of being poor. But you will not fight for political power, for overturning capitalism, for the triumph of socialism.

"You might as well be subsidized by the church and the court. Why not ask for legal recognition? Put your names on brass plates outside this door. No one is coming to arrest *you*."

Well, I had their attention. It was time to punch home a positive message while they were still off-balance. I told them about the one-legged sailor who had been in the next cell to me. Illiterate, he'd never read any of our propaganda, let alone heard of Marx. But he was a born rebel, locked up because he could not resist getting drunk and attacking the police.

Every few months, he'd offer to show us all a magic trick. We politicals knew what it was but there were always enough common criminals who had never seen it, and warders who had but had forgotten. Anyway, life behind bars gets dull for everybody, even those writing books.

Pegleg would ask for a bowl of black-eyed beans. Squatting in the corridor, he would set out some beans, one by one. In the middle, the Tsar. Then a thin ring of Nobles. The Church, the Landowners, the rich Peasants in larger circles. But left in the bowl, still the majority of the beans, the Workers and Poor Peasants.

"Keep watching!" he'd say. "Got your eye on the Tsar, have you? And the Court? Now the magic!"

And he'd put all the beans back in the bowl.

"For a thousand rubles, which is the Tsar and which is the Worker? Where have all the rich gone?"

The warders were indignant. "How can we tell? You've scrambled the beans."

Pegleg would crow with delight and point to us imprisoned revolutionaries.

"That's their problem in life. *How to scramble the beans?*"

I got down and walked to the door.

"Now that's your problem."

On Liteiny, I took a cab back to prison. My five days of "settling affairs" were over.

MARCH 2   OB   1897

River Ob more like lake or vast duck pond. Five miles wide, sometimes only inches deep. Still, too large an obstacle for the Trans-Siberian express. You have to leave one train at a station on the west bank, cross by whatever means happen to be available, and get aboard another train, with a new ticket, at the station on the east bank. Everyone involved, staff and passengers alike, regard this as a normal way to run a railway. No point in inveighing against these Asiatic complications. Only another 400 miles to go. And I must say I enjoyed riding a horse, all alone across this mirrored plain, where for over an hour there was nothing else alive to be seen—no trees, no grass, no hills, no birds or beasts. It was like being Noah, exploring a washed-clean world as the waters ebbed.

Just over two weeks ago, February 14, I was allowed out of my ark at last, the House of Preliminary Detention, cell 133. My destination was given me as Krasnoyarsk, sometimes called "the Siberian Italy"—that was Mother's doing, though not until I get there will I know my exact place of exile. I was also allowed to stop off in Moscow—Mother's work again—where I nearly ruined her good relations with the Okhrana by overstaying my leave by two days. It was difficult to think straight, what with headaches, stomachaches, insomnia, hair loss, asthma, boils. I was expecting plagues of locusts and showers of blood. Was it the indecision and uncertainty? I *was* in two minds whether to escape now. If not, there will hardly be another chance in the stony, frozen heart of the steppe for the next three years. Or could it have been too much family, perverse as that seems?

Mother, Marya, Anna and husband Mark traveled with me as far as Tula (about 140 miles) and all of them had to be persuaded, individually and collectively, from staying aboard until my destination. What courage, what solidarity! Yet I must confess only here, it was after they had waved me off that I began to feel my nerves relax and my spirits rise.

Monotony has its pleasures. Since then, bare, bleak nothingness, as if we were in an endless tunnel. And I have never felt so well for years!

MARCH 18   KRASNOYARSK   1897

Here now for fourteen days. I arrived with the spring and in this weather I could recommend it as an excellent spot for a holiday. Well, for anyone whose idea of a good time is plenty of books, congenial company, interesting walks, creamy fresh air, bright cool sunshine.

Every day I visit the famous library of the self-made millionaire Yudin—100,000 volumes! To me that is like it might be to another being given the key to the champagne cellar or the *corps de ballet*'s dressing room. The pursuit of knowledge is, I'm confident, also a sensual pleasure, one that never stales, and for which you need never grow too old. Once you have captured a piece of truth, alive and wriggling, there is no excitement (or very few) like laying it out, cooked and filleted, your very own catch and dish, before your friends. And Krasnoyarsk is full of rebel intellectuals, some passing through, others long residents, who are socially, if not economically, the dominant élite.

So much so that the province's governor-general, on tour from Irkutsk, observed to me quite seriously a few days ago: "This must be heaven for you communist-anarchists. I suppose all Russia would be towns like this if Plekhanov were the Red Tsar?"

It turns out he was at Kazan University in Father's day and remembers Grandpa's house-parties at Kokushkino where all the young graduates were in love with "the beautiful Blank sisters." I took the opportunity to press for a posting, due to my "weak state of health," somewhere to the south, around Minusinsk perhaps, which I'd heard had a beneficial climate, and also (though I didn't say so) a low cost of living.

Doesn't sound *very* Italian to me, unless the top of an Alp qualifies.

APRIL 4   KRASNOYARSK   1897

Still here, still enjoying myself, mainly discussions and debates, and a little writing. No longer use Yudin's library, though he actually called on me yesterday to repeat his invitation. Truth is— all truth is not equally valuable. Very few of these 100,000 volumes deal with economics. You would think statistics was a dirty word. And there is nothing at all about the working-class movement, now or in history, here or in Europe. I would rather go to the public reading room for the newspapers and magazines, even if they are twelve days late from Moscow.

Today's great excitement was the arrival of the rest of the Petersburg *Stariki*, Martov, Gleb Krzhizhanovsky with the dazzling Zinaida, now his wife, and the rest. They have come third-class, practically cattle-truck, under armed guard, manacled at all stops. The arrival was meant to be secret, but nothing is secret in K., and I was there on the platform when the battered old wagons steamed in. It was also forbidden for them to speak to residents and they

were quickly marched off to a dormitory in the next-door warehouse. However, in the usual authoritarian confusion, I managed
to have a word with almost everyone and promised I'd get through
to them within the next two days. How, I don't yet know.

APRIL 6 KRASNOYARSK 1897

Did it! As usual by the simplest method. I just dressed myself up
as near to Yudin as I could afford—fur hat and coat, silk waistcoat
and gold chain, polished high boots, bronzed beaming face, and
a supply of small notes. I breezed past the guards, tipping them
openly, and claiming to be a Siberian baggage agent—i.e., someone
who makes a fat living, importing, exporting, buying, selling, bribing, taking, whatever anybody supplies or needs. I must have looked
the part.

Anyway, I was soon in the warehouse dishing out champagne
and caviar in token proportions (to show it was a celebration)
backed with plenty of milk, cheese, sausage and bread (for the real
hungers and thirsts). Julius, Gleb and I embraced in a *troika*, like
lovers. These are indeed the salt of the salt of the earth. As for
Zinaida, she kissed me for so long I thought I should suffocate.

"That's for little sister Sofia," she said, wiping her hand across
her mouth. "Now for me."

"No, no," I said, beckoning the others as if to a party game,
and whispering, "No more playing doctors." She blushed, and the
rest of the evening was politics.

I felt a pang, but I knew this was the right thing. A couple of
years ago, January '95 in Peter, I had looked after little Sofia
Nevzorov when she was ill with an ulcer. Zinaida had been touched,
and when I went down with pneumonia in March, the two of them
slept in my room, never left my side, until I recovered. Even Mother
and Anna were made to wait outside when they hurried to my
sickbed. As often in such a relationship, we grew very intimate, in
an innocent though extremely exciting way.

What was a possibility in the capital city could not be encouraged in a provincial town of exiles. It would lead to strains and
scandals we could not afford. I will make sure I am sent somewhere
on my own. And if I am to have a woman companion it must be
someone I can trust to be quiet, ordinary, hardworking, undis-
tracting. I have an idea.

APRIL 17   KRASNOYARSK   1897

Yesterday, I got three letters from Mother, darling Mamouchka.
I must have written five or six on my journey here, without reply.
How slow every system works in Russia, coiling and uncoiling,
deformed and venomous like a wounded snake! Rumors about my
future place of exile, as usual, vary from the utopian ("the Italy
of Siberia") to the hairraising ("the arsehole of the Arctic").

What seems an improvement to the local yokels can appear
just the reiteration of his fears to the citified newcomer. For instance, in the town's central café, they are all celebrating the promised extension of the "express" train service in the spring. This
means that it will take only eight days from Krasnoyarsk to Paris.
It also means six days from Moscow to Krasnoyarsk. At my final
place of exile, now confirmed as Shushenskoye, I will be able to
count on a twice-a-week mail service where one can almost guarantee a reply, by return post, within some thirty to thirty-five days
instead of the present twenty-two to twenty-three from here. I
suspect this is about five times slower than the average under the
emperors in ancient Rome, or under the Incas in Peru before the
Spanish arrived, when the carrier was only a man on foot, running
from post to post (hence the name).

Mother writes that our little Mitya, currently a medical student
in Moscow, is consumed with an urge to go south and serve as
volunteer orderly in a government campaign against "the plague."
My first thought is—can he be doing *so* badly in his studies? Perhaps that is unfair. But my experience of undergraduates is that
their desire to give selfless devotion to the community increases
proportionately with their fears of failing their examinations. How
lucky I was to be kicked out of Kazan U., made to work on my
own, undisturbed by congenial comrades, in my green study under
the trees or in my floating library on the lake. I must remember
that brother Dmitri is now a grown man, very soon to be twenty-
three. True, his education has been distorted by his relationship
to an enemy of the state, that is *me*. But my education was similarly
interrupted by *my* relationship to an attempted regicide, Sasha.
And, despite all the logs and pits lodged in my way, I achieved a
first-class degree, with top marks in eight examinations, while still
twenty-one. On the other hand, Medicine claims a longer period

yet spent rote-learning lists that could be looked up in a textbook within seconds, even than Law.

The truth is, I fear, Mitya has grown into a kind of amiable dolt. Of course, it is always difficult to take seriously your younger brother. What I mainly recall from childhood in Simbirsk is the way he was always *not* on my side. The six of us children paired off, mainly by age, but also by temperament—Sasha and Anyuta, me and Olga, Mitya and Manyasha. There remained also another division. Mother, Anyuta, Sasha and Mitya were long heads— Father, me, Olga and Manyasha round heads. It's as if nature had already chosen us in the womb according to which team we would be on.

When our parents were out, nurse in bed, Alexander and Anna away at university in Peter, the four youngest would be left alone in the house. I would turn out the light and play ogre-games, especially where I was *brykaska*, a strange, hairy monster, like a sheepskin turned inside out, which roared and scratched young humans, carrying them off to its lair on the sofa. The ogre almost always won, nobly freeing those who struggled most heroically (usually Olga and Manyasha) while keeping imprisoned and tormented, under the sofa, those who capitulated in cowardly fashion (usually Mitya).

Even ten years ago, at thirteen, when we left for Kokushkino, Mitya was still more easily frightened than either of the two younger girls. I could tell the tale of "The Little Goat" and be sure he would beg and plead for me to stop. Let me see, yes, 1887 must have been the last time I enjoyed the awful sickly, exciting thrill of hearing someone beg for mercy—the dreadful tyranny of childhood that tyrants never outgrow. "No, no, no!" he used to pant as I came to the bit—"and then the Big Bad Wolf ate him up." He would bury his white face in the pillows, hands over ears, shutting out the even worse final words—"so there was nothing left for Granny *except the little hoofs and horns.*"

I have written home suggesting that if Mitya has such a passion for training and dispensing he could take a chemist's job in an emigrant center in Eastern Siberia. I'm told there is one—they always have vacancies!—in "my" village of Shushenskoye. He would be very welcome as a free companion in exile. We could shoot together, his favorite sport, Mother says. If anything can turn me into a hunter, it will be Siberia.

It was only on the way to the post office at the railway station that it occured to me what a Siberian I have become already in only three weeks that I am inviting other people to exile themselves! I'll have the entire family out here in three years. Still I am determined to keep Mitya away from "the plague" for Mother's sake—we don't want another casualty so soon.

APRIL 30   ON BOARD THE STEAMER   1897

Up early, posted off request to governor for standard allowance. Eight rubles a month, pleading no other income. Just as well. Returned find four gendarmes stamping their feet, consulting the squad watch, and worrying I might have absconded. Already under their control, Gleb and Zinaida, Starkov and his "close companion," Olga Rosenberg. We are being shipped out of Krasnoyarsk together, downriver to our next places of isolation. Other four bound for Tesinskoye; I, alone, for Shushenskoye. We share quarters and boat until the country center of Minusinsk.

Two couples retire to bed early. One police officer stays on duty in the stern. I lie awake, between dozes (!), in deck chair, parceled by coach rug, and gaze at the whirling stars as we steer our winding path.

MAY 9   SHUSHENSKOYE   1897

The people here call it Shu-shu. By the time I am released, it will be 1900, last year of the nineteenth century (not, as the idiots in the cheap press are already proclaiming, the first year of the twentieth). By then, I must be ready to join the leadership of a new party. We stand for liberty, equality, fraternity—though in what proportions, events must dictate. For work, study, growth, this will have to do.

Our steamer trip took a week on the Yenesei, landing me yesterday at the Minusinsk ferry. I waved good-bye to the others and continued here by cart, bumping against two snoring gendarmes at every rut, for twenty-four hours. Arrived in the dark, handed over to village constable, billeted on peasant proprietor Ziranyov. Became proud renter of his only other room, i/c wooden bed (single); ditto table and four chairs; large, medium, small metal bowls; mug, knife, fork, two spoons; heavy counterpane; log-basket, stove; china chamber pot. All signed for, to constable. Compared cell 133, *de luxe*! Especially door without lock.

This morning, Shu-shu not so attractive as under moonlight. Example—manure. No, give it right name, *shit* human/animal. Not gathered into midden, or public dung-heap, but deposited during the hours of darkness in steaming heaps all round the perimeter. You can hardly enter/leave Shu-shu except through the barrier of sulfureted hydrogen. Water supply from the Shushensk, flowing length of village, does not look too healthy.

All in all, kind of oasis in reverse. No garden greenery, few bushes, nearest tree two miles off in forest. Further two miles to nearest tributary of Yenesei for summer swimming, winter skating. Humanity also shrinks away. We are 360 miles from any railway. Letters from Moscow take two weeks, from Peter another couple of days. Tried to buy, then borrow, perhaps steal, a newspaper, any newspaper. *No one* in this entire community of about 1,200 souls subscribes to a newspaper! If I order one it will take a month after publication day to arrive!

This afternoon, buying some beets from a passing peddler, I was given a strange coin in my change instead of a 50-kopek piece. It didn't much resemble one, but Ziryanov assured me—"That's our half-ruble all right, always has been."

Under my magnifying glass, I established it is Scythian, certainly six hundred years old, perhaps a thousand! Incredible! Roll on the Middle Ages!

MAY 12   SHUSHENSKOYE   1897

Have set up my icons, my "traveling shrine"—photographs of Marx, Engels, Chernyshevsky, Pisarev, Herzen, Zola. Apollon (Ziryanov) has lined my room, all four walls, floor to ceiling, with shelves. He's done good job, but cannot understand what will go on them. I tell him books. He looks skeptical—am I here for life sentence, then? Even then, who could read so many in thirty, forty years? I tell him books discovered to be world's best insulation. We both laugh loud and long, slap each other on back, down some vodka.

Nevertheless, he believes me.

List of books needed, not difficult. Bigger problem, who will buy/send them? And how? Bulk of trouble/expense will rest on Mother, Anna, for Dmitri, Marya too poor, too disorganized be

much help. Post will cost fortune, but then, hard luck. That's what
money is for. Perhaps, someone could bring them. Someone who
could stay for some months. But who? Well, not family, already
rejected their offer. Some comrade? My loins pump out jet of heat
at thought of Apollinaria. Her face starts to melt into that of Zinaida. No future that way. Everyone on my list has lover/close
relative, whatever. What about Nadya Krupskaya? There is her
mother, of course. According to my files, she *hates* traveling. I
would have contacted N. in Peter when I was released, but I thought
she was still in Peter/Paul fortress. I have a note; acc. Zinaida, she
was freed in February too when the authorities panicked over the
Marya Vetrova affair. (A revolutionary student, raped in her cell,
burned herself to death.) Nadya could be exiled to Siberia! NB.
worth considering.

First, get newspaper/magazine list straight. To begin with,
Russian and German will suffice, so *Russkoye Bogatstvo, Vestnik Fin-
ansov, Novoye Slovo, Obozreniye, Niva,* and *Archiv fur soziale Gesetz-
gebung und Statistik, Soziale Praxis, Die Neue Zeit, Frankfurter Zeitung.*

As for agrarian relations, my book on future of Russian capitalism, my *Kapital* so to speak, all around me I have more evidence
at first hand that any research could ever desire.

Slight fug of depression burns off. I can be *useful* here, perhaps "happy." Plenty of books, magazines, lots of correspondence,
plenty to read or write, in a small, warm room. Not what I call
punishment for *my* enemies. But then my enemies will not be like
me, will they?

JUNE 15   **SHUSHENSKOYE**   **1897**

Death of my aunt, Mother's last sister. It turns out that our family
has inherited Kokushkino, a possession long forgotten as a source
of income, remembered (by me, anyway) only as a land of dreams.
Perhaps I am right since Mitya writes that the estate has been
allowed to fall into ruin since we left and is heavily encumbered
with debts. As a lawyer, I warn against the danger of acknowledging ownership without a full audit. A Siberian prisoner, I have
no civil rights. So Mitya as official male head of family will have
to go back there and sort out the details. "Sign nothing, except
receipts for cash" is my advice.

JUNE 30   SHUSHENSKOYE   1897

In Siberia, you only notice the days that are different because something happens, something from outside. Otherwise, the summer seals you under its lid like an ant beneath a microscope. Nobody ever warns you about the *summer*.

If you are a free man—and oddly enough, I am almost the only free man, despite being a state prisoner, because I am free *not* to work—there are always pressing reasons for doing nothing. Only in the first hours after dawn can you count on being cool and exempt from mosquitoes. Throughout the heat of the day, I float below the rapids on the Little Yenesei with just the tip of my nose above the swirling surface. Ears blocked, eyes closed, neither hot nor cold, your whole body at the temperature of your saliva, it is easy to slide into Nirvana, forgetting even your name. In the evening, you are stuck indoors, a dropped sack, too exhausted to do more than talk like a village idiot.

Today was shattered by two bolts of news from another world. First, my allowance of 8 rubles a month has finally been agreed and will be paid me, with arrears, by the constable! The second is also about money. Mark writes to say Kokushkino has been sold —not a very advantageous price, he thinks—and Mother has been awarded the proceeds. From this, she is awarding me my share, 150 rubles a month. Doesn't sound bad to me. Now I will be able to send for those little luxuries that are necessities here but I feared the family could not afford. Meat is terrible, but also only 2 kopeks a pound. With 158 rubles a month, I may be not only the freest, but the richest, inhabitant of Shu-shu.

SEPTEMBER 12   SHUSHENSKOYE   1897

In Siberia, everybody tells lies about the weather. Agreed, it's awful now. But you should have been here last month, last year, stay on for next month, next year. I have been here long enough to see through this self-deception. At the moment, the weather is . . . beastly. Cold, gusty showers, old mattress skies, damp, chilly nights. Excellent weather for writers, anyway. Autumn is said to be spectacular. I only hope it is not too distracting. At the moment, I am getting words on paper at least.

What else? The only way Wednesday differs from Tuesday or Thursday is whether you read this paper or that, walk through the village north-south or south-north, take the path to the right or left, write this kind of piece or that.

If there should come a lovely day (not raining, that is) it will mean I can hire a horse and cart and make the long, long day trip to Minusinsk to buy a new lamp, some flea powder, a couple of sacks of flour. My heart beats at the thought like a bird in a trap. I do not know whether I will be able to stand the excitement.

NOVEMBER 5   SHUSHENSKOYE   1897

Monotony, the worst. No fusser over *cuisine,* even I notice deadening sameness about meals. An old ewe slaughtered start of month, served as chops in first week, roasted in second, stew in third, hash in fourth, or so it seems. Anyway, whenever I ask what it is, it is mutton.

Now, when meat can be frozen in the icehouse, hunting makes sense for variety and I have some companions in the chase. Not Ziryanov, though, since I taught him chess, he helps pass an evening. (I only wish he would win once or twice.) He taught me the guitar in return. (Perhaps he wishes I would extend my repertoire.)

No, my fellow guns are a couple of exiles I did not meet until a few weeks ago. The peasants did not think to tell me there were any others like me. Not that I would quite describe Oscar and Ivan as like me. Bless them! Like Pegleg in Peter, they are natural rebels, almost totally without ideology, or education come to that, but spontaneous haters of injustice.

Ivan Prominsky calls himself a Social Democrat and was exiled here in 1895 for the crime of joining a cell in Poland. This is all he has ever done to threaten the state, and he remains unable to explain quite what his group had stood for. A sweet, mild character, accompanied by his wife and six children, he is best at singing revolutionary songs. He is not even much good at his trade, making hats. I have become very fond of him, and describe his life often to Mother in my weekly letter. His wife has become deluged with children's toys and clothes, bearing a close resemblance to those once used by little Ulyanovs, from unknown donors.

Oscar Engberg is a Finn, younger than me, who arrived just after I did. A fitter in Peter's Putilov works, he led a strike in '86 which makes me feel about him the way the bourgeois would feel about a hero of Balaclava. I have started his education in Marxism. Uphill work, but it makes me hone and polish my own ideas.

Oscar and Ivan have a much harder time than I have. But they really enjoy shooting wild creatures (I insist none is killed that cannot be eaten). And to see them tracking back, singing and whistling, carrying between them duck, snipe, squirrels, sometimes goat or even deer, is to feel a sense of relief that humanity can so easily be happy at so little cost to the rest of the inhabitants of this planet.

NOVEMBER 7   SHUSHENSKOYE   1897

Mitya has been arrested. While the rest of us thought he was just neglecting his studies, or possibly messing up the liquidation of the old Blank homestead, he was actually dipping a toe into the mildest underground stream of revolutionary politics. The name "Ulyanov" will not be much of a help when the Okhrana look up the files on his elder sister and two brothers. On the other hand, his activities must seem like peccadilloes compared to plotting assassination of the Tsar and overthrow of the state.

I have telegraphed Mother with the names of a couple of radical lawyers, and Mitya with a brisk, encouraging slogan signed "Brykaska." At least, it's better than the plague! I'm able to take a fairly light view since I have discovered Mitya's connection was with "Workers' Benefit League," a semi-legal, tame craftmen's friendly society actually run from behind the scenes by the police. The device was invented by the authorities as a safety valve for proletarian discontent where they could keep their hand on the tap.

There are several ironic splash-backs. For instance—in order to keep the member loyal, the WBL has to win an occasional dispute with employers. So some bosses, the smaller ones anyway, experience the unaccustomed knock on the door at three A.M. and burly thugs in big boots handing them increased wage agreements they have no alternative but to sign. Great care has been taken to keep out any genuine Social Democrats, the vast majority of whom regard these "unions" with suspicion and contempt. To make sure they cannot be turned into genuine anti-capitalist movements, it has been made almost impossible for anyone, not a fellow worker in employment, to join. As a student, Mitya must have broken some law by becoming a member, having been bound to make several false declarations of occupation, address, identity perhaps, on the way. Professionally, I should estimate punishment as expulsion and short non-Siberian exile.

FEBRUARY 10   SHUSHENSKOYE   1898

After I promised Mother I would be in "no danger," Dmitri chose for me last December an early New Year's present, a wonderful English shotgun. The better shot I became, the bigger my bag, the less reward it gave me. But I have at least, like Mother's father in Kokushkino, to pretend now and then to hunt. Especially when Oscar Engberg and Prominsky keep calling on me and begging me to join them. On my own, I make a point of only firing off at the odd clump of bushes. I like the sound of the noise, crisp and ringing on the ear, clearing away a lining of cobwebs; also the smell of the cordite, sweet and acrid at once, a dangerous incense. I savor the schoolboyish thrill of seeing a hole the size of an elephant's head punched in the solid façade of the forest. But I never encounter any living forest thing I can destroy.

Today was a bit different. There was a lot of rustling, crashing and crunching ahead of me whichever direction I took. When I turned away, it moved round to keep in front. Was I being ambushed by bears, by gendarmes, by neighbors? I was just about to give whoever a couple of barrels over their heads when across my path, high-stepping like an Arab steed, tail sailing high, wicked tongue lolling through side teeth, there progressed a fox.

All the scenery seemed to wait for the sound of a shot. I didn't fire. Bursting through the undergrowth came E. and P. "Didn't you see him? Why didn't you bag him?"

I found it difficult to phrase my answer. They were crowding my private world. Yet why should the truth be embarrassing? "Because he was beautiful," I said.

They then looked embarrassed. Started punching each other, and swinging around their geese and hares, laughing noisily.

They had spent all morning driving this one piece of game in my direction. They thought I must be getting desperate at never hitting anything. Have asked Mark for three revolvers.

FEBRUARY 24   SHUSHENSKOYE   1898

Holiday mood all morning. Prodigious correspondence this month from all over Europe, all over this country. Without secretary, or even literate assistant, not yet counted all. But must be several hundred separate pieces of mail. And this is after exceptionally heavy deliveries twice a week for all of this year. Have the authorities been piling up some for censorship, or security checking? If so, they have given up. Certain 99 percent unscrutinized. What am *not* getting through the post are the books, clothes, stationery, etc. I have been requisitioning, some of it probably best brought by hand.

I must have a helper, a keeper of accounts, questions and replies, orders and deliveries. Also a companion closer to me than Oscar can manage to be. When first here I could not face my wall map of European Russia and the West. Paris, Berlin, Zurich, Moscow, Peter, even Samara and Kazan—the black dots were so tempting in dusty, dreary Shu-shu. Now I can look at them without a tremor. During the two visits last year by Gleb and Zinaida, Vladimir and Olga, with their friends from Tesinskoye, I felt like a Grand Duke entertaining old school chums. We had sports competitions, wrestling, boxing, pistol shooting, swimming races the first time, skating the next—I tried not to win all those, leaving over the "free expression" for others. I organized picnics, barbecues, outings, evenings of song and dance. Only that moment when their carts, or sledges, melted into the forest did I feel a wrench, like a child parting from its mother. By bedtime, I was readjusted to my solitary regime.

But now I look at my list of urgent requirements, they will need a couple of trunks! Works by Marx I've only read about—*Poverty of Philosophy, Critique of Hegelian Philosophy of Right*. Other philosophers—almost anything by Helvetius and Holbach and Kant. Verbatim (v. important) unedited reports of parliamentary debates, Britain, France, Germany—"how" as well as "what" is argued. English, German, French dictionaries. Socks in any number, ready-made winter suit, my old straw hat if still in existence, pair of kid gloves. Never wore these for elegance, Peter or Paris, but essential against mosquitoes. I wear net over my head but hands unprotected. Squared paper for graphs. Macintosh cape—how could I not have brought one? Zinaida says I look "square and bronzed," that is—"typical Siberian." I must adapt to climate and work with the right clothes, the right intellectual tools. *And I must have a partner!*

Anna says Nadya Krupskaya is in exile in Ufa. I will write tonight and invite her to ask permission to live here instead.

MARCH 28 SHUSHENSKOYE 1898

Mail subsided a little, still two sacks a week. Yesterday's most important letters: (1) from governor in Irkutsk authorizing the transfer of N. K. Krupskaya so long as I swear affidavit she is my fiancée, and we are married on her arrival; (2) from Nadya reporting she has petitioned governor serve sentence in Shushenskoye as my literary amanuensis assuring him keeping separate accommodation, with her mother as chaperone. Clearly His Excellency will think one of us is lying. We could both have our sentences doubled.

Rode in Minusinsk on horseback with two urgent telegrams. No public service, but after some argument bureaucrat gave way when he saw one message was to governor. I promised governor affidavit on way and I was as keen as he was to see the marriage. I asked Nadya if she would agree to marry me since there was no other way she would be allowed to transfer.

Slept in Gleb and Zinaida's comfortable, roomy house. All rest of day at government telegraph station. Just about give up, ride back alone on horseback under the stars (the way Father must often have done) when the machine started to click. The most enthusiastic reply was from the governor: "Congratulations on whirlwind courtship." Nadya's message was—"If wife it must be then wife it will be stop Mother and I plan arrive seventeen May repeat seventeen."

MAY 12 SHUSHENSKOYE 1898

Mitya has been in prison now for six months. What I had forgotten in estimating the sentence was the time tsarist bureaucracy, and general Slav inefficiency, are likely to keep anyone behind bars before bringing them to trial. After all, I was locked up in Peter from December '95 to February '97, never tried in any court, simply banished by government decree.

I am a bit worried by Mother's description of his physical condition. A twenty-four-year-old ought not to be putting on a layer of yellow fat. I have written to him ordering the strictest observation of a healthy, natural scientific diet, plenty of nuts and fruit, which *by law*, as a person on remand, he has a right to have sent in from outside. I have also instructed him to keep up a regime of exercises. *These are essential!* I can tell him from experience that the routine I carried out each day before going to bed gave me great benefit and pleasure. It loosened my joints, whipped up the circulation, so that afterward, even on the coldest days, when icicles hung on the pipes of my cell, I slept like a babe.

I can recommend an easy sequence, even if fairly ludicrous —fifty stiff-backed, low bows from the waist, fingertips touching the floor, no bending of the knees. It is exactly what I used to make myself do. And I was not in the least put out when the warder, peering through the Judas hole, would wonder aloud in amazement that this inmate was so pious he would make fifty prostrations daily and yet had never once asked to visit the prison church.

Doctors, and would-be doctors, like Mitya, learn how to talk about keeping fit, but rarely listen to their own advice. Doctors! Vodka-breath roaring like a blowtorch, smoke-fuming nostrils, wormy-red eyeballs, pot belly like a monkey in a sack, curtains drawn against the light, they sit there like portraits of the perpetual patient rather than the venerable healer.

MAY 16   SHUSHENSKOYE   1898

Returned home at dusk with basket of every kind of fungus, also knotted handkerchief of the delicious Siberian pinenuts. Treats for the newcomers' arrival tomorrow. Lights were on in my room and various neighbors stood around peering in the windows. I asked the nearest what was going on. Like all peasants, he gave me the least important information first and held back on what he well knew I most wanted to know.

"Your anarchist friend Oscar is drunk in your house throwing your books around."

I went in like a police raid, dropping my basket, with fists doubled. If he'd been there, I'd have broken his head on the stove. He wasn't. And the place looked quite tidy and inviting. In the center stood a tall, slim woman around thirty, with parchment-white skin, longbow eyes, and a *retroussée* chin. Her sweet smile radiated calm. Next to her was a kind of caricature, or smudged copy, with a tight smile which radiated disapproval. She was looking at me through lorgnettes. It was Nadya and her mother.

By the time I explained why I was apparently geared up to murder my guests, Apollon had brought in some homemade beer, Oscar had picked up my mushrooms and nuts and begun frying them in butter, Ivan's wife sent across one of the children with a fruit cake, and we were all in the best of moods.

Around two in the morning, a second bed was acquired and the two women retired in my room. I slept on the hay in Apollon's loft. I think I may take to marriage after all. If it must be, then it will be.

MAY 17   SHUSHENSKOYE   1898

While my future mother-in-law inspected the village, Nadya and I went through the trunks she had brought. Such riches! Looking forward to feast of reading.

Have to complain, however, about other missing items. Where are the no. 6 pencils, the seal for wax, the small scissors, the pen-wiper, the replacement chess set requested in my letter to Mother of April 17? I had explained how vital these things were. The scissors for cutting out extracts from newspapers—at the moment I use sheep shears! The pen-wiper—at the moment I wipe the pen on my lapel! (Interesting patterns, actually, but how could any mother resist that plea?) Oh, and of course, I specifically underlined *as much money as possible*.

Nadya assures me *her* Mother had made a list of everything advised by mine on a special trip to Moscow. If any were missing, the letter must not have arrived. As for the money . . . She had assumed that was always welcome. And she unbuttoned her tunic a little, extracted a fat roll of warm notes: 855 rubles.

They smelled faintly of lemons.

MAY 30   SHUSHENSKOYE   1898

The most important event in the history of the socialist movement
in Russia was the First Congress of the Russian Social-Democratic
Labour Party held in Minsk on March 1. I agree with every proposition in their Manifesto. This is the end of our adolescence. We
are grown-ups. Now and forever, I am a Social Democrat. How I
wish I could have been there!

No, that is an empty cliché. For every one of the nine present
was arrested within days (except for our old conundrum, Radchenko, whose strawberry-marked head has once again escaped).
This has turned the triumph into failure. The government is dragging in everyone suspected of sympathy. The safest place to be is
in Siberia! As so often, organizational defeat leads to ideological
vacillation. I have lots to write on the subject.

Unfortunately, in my personal circles, here and at home in
Moscow, minds are preoccupied with a much more significant
question—when will I get married?

Anna has written twice in a fortnight asking it. The governor's
aide is also concerned. Elizaveta Vassilyevna demands each
morning—"So when is the day?"

A tragi-comic situation, a Chekhov short story. Police superintendent in Minusinsk insists N. must return to Ufa unless married *immediately*. Only legal Russian marriage in church, but Shu-shu
priest cannot perform ceremony without documentary evidence I
have permission to be here. Police superintendent in Minusinsk
cannot provide this as he has no documentary evidence I even
exist. An everyday mixup in Siberia. And I have been here more
than a year!

JULY 10   SHUSHENSKOYE   1898

Our wedding night. I am making brief diary entry. Nadya sits
watching me in the bedroom of our new half-house. She is wearing
only a silk embroidered nightdress, once her mother's wedding
gown—a curious custom, with overtones of incest, which might
possibly deflect a less rational bridegroom. It is very warm.

No point in detailing all the nerve-rackingly farcical obstacles which have delayed this moment for nearly two months—arresting gendarmes defied; threats against Nadya from Minusinsk; support for me from Irkutsk; interference, making everything even more confused, from Petersburg. And all in slow speed because of the long pauses between each message and its reply across these empty spaces where even the soil seems stunned by the sun.

Elizaveta Vassilyevna, who is deeply religious, insisted on all the usual superstitious, barbaric customs—not seeing each other on wedding day, entering opposite ends of the church, the crown and the oil, etc., etc. We have left her supervising the celebrations. Several hundred self-invited guests. I must be more popular than I thought. Or perhaps there are not many free celebrations.

Nadya is now in our very narrow *letto matrimoniale* staring at the ceiling. I feel more desire than I imagined. These last weeks have shown her to be sweet-tempered, generous, courageous, well-read, dedicated, like a Turgenev heroine, to the cause whatever the consequences, and through the cause to me. For me personally, I see the Woman Question is solved. I can now put all my attention where it is needed, into the struggle. But there is nothing to say we both should not thoroughly enjoy Nadya's Answer to my Question.

NB. Tomorrow morning we are starting joint translation of Sidney and Beatrice Webb's *Theory and Practice of Trade Unionism.* Must remember send off for English work on idioms, dictionary not enough. Afternoons plan pushing ahead with "Markets" book while N. makes fair copies of my pages.

OCTOBER 20   SHUSHENSKOYE   1898

It is four months now since Mitya was released from prison, condemned to a month's exile in Tula, then left to live under police surveillance in Podolsk (not too bad, Moscow Province after all) for an indefinite period. As expected, he has been expelled from Moscow U., only to find that all sorts of difficulties are being put in his way about completing his course at Yuriev U., at least for another year. But for Mother, it might begin to look as if he is unlikely to graduate as doctor of medicine before sometime in the next century, perhaps not until 1902.

I had hoped that Mother would come to visit us here—the trains have much improved in speed and comfort, especially first-class, and we are running a pleasant, quite bearable household in Shushenskoye. But she does not feel she can leave Mitya alone in Podolsk. That's her excuse to me. However, I am sure she remains within raiding distance of Moscow and Peter so that she can execute more of her famous "*dodges*"—an English schoolgirl term, like "*crush*." It was a dodge that allowed me to travel out here under my own steam, and probably another that got me assigned to a village the right side of the Arctic Circle. Now her first aim is to prevent Mitya being called up for military service, or if he is, not in the ranks but in a specialized place in the medical corps. The second is to get him back to university without losing this coming year.

I'm sure she'll succeed. And I'm glad, even if the price I pay is not seeing her for another couple of years.

NOVEMBER 5   SHUSHENSKOYE   1898

The danger of winter here is sinking into a gluttonous stupor. Cold makes you hungry. Eating makes you sleepy. You feed on yourself, a snake biting its tail. You enter a kind of hibernation, one by one closing down the senses, locking doors behind you, until you exist in a tiny, darkened chamber, deep within a castle of solid fat. When Nadya arrived with her mother, the old lady gave me a long stare and snapped: "You're obese!" A friend might have said "putting on weight," an enemy "getting fat." But Elizaveta Vassilyevna was once a schoolteacher.

Last year, Siberia was too much of a surprise—no, that's not strong enough—too much of a shock for me to summon up real defenses. Its winter casts a *spell*. Nadya is under it now for the first time. To think I believed Simbirsk or Samara had shown me the extremes possible in our Slav weather. Here, 1,500 miles to the east, Siberia out-Russias Russia. A new-old world. A separate planet.

I have taken Nadya by the hand to conduct her through its mysteries. (Elizaveta Vassilyevna does not ever leave the circle round the stove, so far as I can make out: a tall, pink sausage toasted on one side.) I show my wife how a white landscape, blank as paper, daubed with an occasional splodge of green, can gradually develop sketchy objects and creatures. If you stare long enough you see, first, the division between a pale earth, paler sky. Then outlines of a tree, the shape of a hut with a veranda. If you stay quiet, the view becomes a moving picture. That snowy mound turns into a hare that pole-vaults along an invisible pathway, strong back legs thumping the hidden ground, as though they belonged to a much larger animal, maybe a kangaroo. A spiky pattern of silvered icicles resolves into the head of a wild goat. A parti-colored blob shakes itself, growing brown all over, and walks out of the frame, a bear in a fur coat giving an unconvincing imitation of a man. A wolf howls, not really a threatening noise, more a cry of despair. A call for help? Your quarry is somewhere behind the white curtain, determined not to be seen by humans.

N. is overcome—"It's like living in an enchanted kingdom." As she speaks, at 40 degrees below zero, her words freeze. The water vapor in her breath turns to ice crystal, falls tinkling to the ground. No one believes it who has not experienced it. Siberians call this "the whisper of the stars." And laugh.

JANUARY 15   SHUSHENSKOYE   1899

Ever since marriage have been working, day and night, on both Webbs' and my own book. Each month sent off Nadya's beautifully transcribed exercise books of next chapter to Mother who acts as agent with publisher. Anna proofreads the galleys. So the routine has gone. Sometimes I felt I would never stop, that it was a work without end. But at last, after three years, the final full stop on the final page.

Now sister Anna is in Peter representing me through the pre-publication disputes. I didn't see how there could be any. But I suspect publishers invent them in order to justify their existence. Days have been spent over the title, surely simple enough decision?

I wanted *The Process of the Formation of a Home Market in Russia* from the beginning. They want *The Development of Capitalism in Russia* because it "sounds better" and will "sell more copies." They only shrug and smile when she objects that that is misleading. Their argument, as befitting the tricksters they all are, is: "When the buyer gets it home, it will be too late to complain it's not what he thought. With Ulyanov's title, nobody will bother to get it home." Already, the creation of my mind has become a commodity, a commercial property, that exists only to be bought and sold for a profit.

Anna hung on. Tried for *On the Question of the Development etc.* Eventually, feeble compromise—*The Development of Capitalism in*

Russia subtitled *The Process of the Formation of a Home Market for Large-Scale Industry*. By Vladimir Ilyin.

After I had stamped around the house, emptied a dozen or so bullets from my pocket Browning revolver into the archery target at the bottom of Nadya's cabbage patch, I became cooler. After all, the subject really *is* the development of capitalism in Russia. There is no point in revealing the secret of the universe if nobody ever reads your revelation.

MARCH 30   SHUSHENSKOYE   1899

Development was only published on the first of this month. Now publishers telegraph me direct reporting that entire edition of 2,400 copies has sold out. Perhaps they do know something.

Anna has already written telling me my concept of "de-peasantizing" is being discussed everywhere. The process is so obvious, going on before our eyes. Capitalism, as ever, leads to opposition, confrontation, splitting. In country as in town, competition concentrates production in hands of minority, dividing the small producers, the peasants, into rural proletariat and rural capitalist, hired laborers and rich kulaks. It is happening all over. But if I had not been in Shu-shu I might not have seen the process so clearly. The old-style peasant, in his solid, unsplittable mass, is no more. So . . . "de-peasantizing."

I must get out of here! I am yearning to gallop to the sound of battle!

AUGUST 5   SHUSHENSKOYE   1899

Mitya writes from vacation in Podolsk that he is studying like mad at Yuriev, his instructors think very highly of him, and next year he should become M.D. with honors, possibly a few prizes. He is also, by his own account, a great hunter. Should he bring Mother out here for a visit?

I estimate I have only five or six months left to serve. With all the work Nadya and I are up to our ears in, the truth is I'd rather he stuck to his studies. He has sent me a gun ahead and I suspect I have has as much pleasure from it as I would have from him. I trust he is more careful in his prescriptions than he has been in his cartridge sizes. He also sent a box of 2¾ inches. They fit, but the recoil is really painful. Those in the box from the village store—2½ inches and like it!—also fit but give a sweet, steady pop. M.'s advice is to favor the left barrel. I have noticed little difference, though perhaps I have been testing it over too great a distance, sixty paces.

I don't like to turn down darling Mamouchka so I have given her advice she will find off-putting. I've asked her to bring a few yards of smooth black tulle for use as mosquito netting, essential outdoors even more than indoors. This is no lie. But I know also that she detests flying insects. Me too, if not quite so passionately. I had hoped, when I was shipped off to these frozen wastes, that at least I would be safe from the torture of winged bloodsuckers. But, according to my encyclopedia, they are bigger, hungrier, more determined here than anywhere in the tropics.

IV

EXILE

1900-1917

There were times when I thought I saw Dante and Virgil ahead of me. Journeying back into the living world from Siberia has some resemblance to emerging from a frozen Inferno (already I've begun to forget the summers!) into a real, moving, breathing world of flesh-and-blood.

The three of us rode into Minusinsk—the sight of mother-in-law in the saddle, lorgnette in hand, would be enough to unseat the Four Horsemen of the Apocalypse. "God kept me warm," she said when I congratulated her.

After an overnight stay at Gleb's, he and Zinaida soon to follow us, we left in a sledge like a giant's cradle with Starkov and wife (formerly Olga Rosenberg) for Achinsk; 180 miles, day and night, jammed tight, no heat, little food, faces bare to sleety rain, is something of an ordeal. But amazing the difference it makes going in the right direction! The train from Achinsk felt, smelled, tasted of paradise. We all, except Nadya, became younger, fitter, more optimistic, as we moved in more or less 400-mile sections toward Peter—Novosibirsk; Omsk; Ekaterinburg; Vyatka. Here we took a branch line to Ufa where Nadya and her mother must serve out the remaining year of her sentence.

Nadya and I discussed whether we should stay here together but decided there was too much work ahead of me before I left for Europe. I would like to be in Peter or Moscow but my instructions are unequivocal—the quiet, orderly, safe-town of Pskov, another 700 miles to the west.

The past five months have found me crisscrossing the northern half of European Russia like one of the new commercial travelers. My closest companion, physically and politically, has been Julius (Martov)—together, we have the formula to create a fighting, disciplined party. Together, we nearly ruined the whole scheme! Having made one illegal trip to Peter in early May, we felt confident enough to make another in late May. With what seems now incredible stupidity, we broke our journey at Tsarskoe Selo and got a local train to avoid the secret policemen at all the Peter termini. Minutes after we arrived in the capital, we were captured, carried off with elbows pinned to our sides.

The Okhrana colonel almost died laughing. "You've spent three years each in Siberia for plotting against the state. And you don't remember that the Emperor lives at Tsarskoe Selo and we have an agent behind every blade of grass?"

It took us ten days to argue ourselves out of prison again.

JULY 15   PSKOV   1900

In Siberia, I still felt a free man. Officially a non-person, deprived of rights to property, to a profession, to travel beyond five miles of the village without an escort, I was in fact no more restricted than Crusoe on his island.

I went hunting in the forest, skating or canoeing on the Yenesei, whenever the mood took me, without consulting a soul. I made trips to meet other exiles, in Minusinsk or Tesinskoe, on the most transparent excuses. I practiced law illegally, with more clients and more success than when I was a registered practitioner in Samara—I even got our local policeman the back pay he'd been claiming for twenty years! My open correspondence, to and fro across Russia, was immense—heavier than the Governor's, so a comrade in the Irkutsk administration assured me. My secret communication with Marxists abroad, hidden in the spines of books, etc., would have been enough to keep one civil servant busy, full time. I read all the books I needed. I wrote as I pleased, give or take a little Aesopian language to avoid a charge of subversion.

After eight months, Nadya, my woman Friday, arrived. Then I was really able to forge full speed ahead. Indeed, with twice the head of steam.

When I saw her first, she seemed out of the past, one of the "repentant" noble girls who idolized the dark peasant people, ready to endure martyrdom at the hands of friend as well as enemy, so long as they purged their hereditary guilts. In other words, the old-fashioned Turgenev heroine. By the side of rouged Apollinaria, so fast, so aggressive, so thoroughly modern, so citified, Nadya glimmered like a black-and-white ghost.

In Shu-shu, she had reinforced my virtues and strengths, while also complementing them. I had taken a great risk, especially when marriage (and a mother-in-law) was part of the gamble. I could

have been chaining myself to a hindrance or a harridan—Queen
Log or Queen Stork. But I had calculated the odds accurately.
Also, to be honest, I was lucky. Nadya is bold but wary, candid but
tactful, thorough but imaginative. She will never be an initiator.
She will remain a secretary, an amanuensis, a *good left-hand,* an
archivist, of *the highest caliber.* She has proved herself my other half.
Well, to carry on being honest, let's say my other *third.* I cannot
now imagine waging the struggle without her.

Of course, it's true, I am leaving Russia tomorrow without her.

Anna, for one, finds this rather inhuman, or so I gather from
Mother. In her view, I ought to have stayed on with N. in Ufa
until her own exile was over. But that would have been the same
as extending my own sentence for another sixteen months.

Nadya understood. As anyone who knows her would expect.
Mother showed me one of her letters when I made an unauthorized deviation to Podolsk, en route to my official place of surveillance, Pskov. "It is a great pity, dear Mamouchka, that we two have
to part just when the 'real' work is beginning. But it did not even
enter Volodya's head to remain in Ufa when there was a possibility
of getting nearer to Peter." *Exactly!*

Not that I felt much of a free man in Pskov. Like Samara it's
a town where known dissidents can be insulated from radical workers or students. The Okhrana even found me a job, clerk in the
provincial statistics office. My colleagues were caricatures from
Gogol, so unhandy with figures they would spend whole mornings
arguing what day of the week the first of last month had been.
When I told them there was a handy formula to establish this for
any date since Christ, they didn't believe me. When I proved it,
they nicknamed me "Mr. Memory" and urged me to go to the
Court at Peter and entertain the Tsar! I had little alternative but
work (I dug up some very useful statistics). I talked politics only
with such well-protected parlor-pinks as Prince Obolensky, a generous supporter of anti-government movements, and very helpful
in the matter of my passport.

Fortunately, before Pskov, I had managed to smuggle myself
into both Moscow and Peter—what a delight there to meet Vera
Ivanovna Zasulich, also an illegal visitor to the capital. Here is a
comrade clear as crystal; the intimate of Plekhanov! a correspondent with Marx! the avenging hand of the people who in the
seventies, when I was only eight, shot down General Trepov, the
governor of Petersburg, was triumphally acquitted and escaped
into the cheering crowd! We talked of all this but mainly of the
new all-Russian newspaper, now called *Iskra (The Spark),* which we

intend will spread the call to revolt like a flame along a fuse. Various subterfuges got me to Riga; to Samara, Nizhni-Novgorod, and Ufa, where I have spent two weeks with Nadya. Then finally, even in stuffy, conservative Pskov, I was able to call a meeting of *Iskra* backers, including some from the old Peter gang of the "Elders." Martov, of course, but also Radchenko, birthmarked leader of my first Marxist circle, who bears a charmed life (suspicious characteristic among conspirators). Still, I made sure nothing was said that could prove useful to authorities wooed into tolerance by my giving Prince O. as guarantor, and by the official chairmanship of a "Legal Marxist"—what a contradiction in terms (might as well be a bearded lady, or an atheist priest) under a dictatorship where all parties, all unions, all opposition are forbidden, by law.

Our bearded lady in Pskov was Peter Struve, brilliant polemicist, author of the manifesto proclaimed at the founding Congress of the Russian Social-Democratic Labour Party in 1898 while I was in Siberia. Alas, using his talent for propaganda he had argued himself ever rightward. Into "reformism"—society can be changed by peaceful persuasion! Into "revisionism"—Marxism must be updated for the twentieth century! Into "economism"—first better wages, hours, conditions, later abolish the ruling class! "Legal Marxists" are no more than a polite debating society.

So why give "the Twin" (Struve's original Party name) the time of day? The cunning little Pied Piper has a magical way with rich, middle-aged, liberal ladies such as "Aunty" (Alexandra Mikhailovna Kalmykova). Who knows what he gives them in return? Julius has made some highly inventive guesses. The point is—the Twin regards *me* as his best link with the illegal Marxists. (And he was exceptionally generous in supplying me with books and magazine subscriptions in prison and Siberia.) I regard *him* as my best link with the milch-cows who will finance my papers because he advises them to do so. As his commission, I may even print some of his articles. Topped and tailed with rebuttals and refutations by Plekhanov, Axelrod, Martov, the formidable Tulin, and others. That goes without saying!

JULY 16 Russian Style—
JULY 28 For the Rest of the World   1900
ON THE FRONTIER

The last thing I wrote was "That goes without saying." I wish this damned train would. I have been stuck here on the Russo-German border for more than half a day. Nothing to do but reread my diary. I don't know why, but that breeds a certain melancholy. Ah! A grunt, and a jerk. Good omen. We are off!

What did Marx say was the locomotive of history? War, surely. No such luck. Too much to hope for, after thirty years of deathly peace. No reason to be downcast. Between us, Julius and I have been to all the most promising places for our plan. Smolensk, Samara, Kazan, Nizhni-Novgorod, Minsk. Some business and pleasure for me—Podolsk, just outside Moscow, where Mother lives with Mitya; Ufa for my two weeks with Nadya. Everywhere we have arranged communication codes, smuggling routes, networks of distributors and reporters, for the new Marxist paper.

The Tsar is behind, Europe ahead again. When I make this return journey I intend it to be to start a revolution, or better even *extend* it. Now I remember the thought that I did not want to think. If I die at the same age as Father, more than half my life has already gone. Hurry, hurry, hurry!

AUGUST 10   GENEVA   1900

The last week here has been a toboggan ride around the Alps. So many ups and downs, dizzying corners, almost head-on collisions with immovable roadblocks, I began to think—Bless Inertia!

When I arrived in Zurich, I found Potresov almost gibbering with frustration. Alexander Nikolaevich was a member of the *Stariki*, the "Elders," in Peter along with Martov and me. We three had corresponded long and often across Siberia about a new all-country party and a new all-country paper. We agreed these could not be controlled and run from within Russia. As a way of gathering as many as possible likely sympathizers (and subsidizers) under one heading, we had helped found the Union of Social Democrats Abroad.

Potresov is fine, if a little too conscious of not being common clay. Father is a cavalry colonel, he inherited pots of money from his aristocratic heiress mother. He is not slow to dip into his pocket and forms a useful tie to Struve, son of the governor of Astrakhan (deceased). His wife, Nina, some kind of minor princess, is related to Nadya. Among the Union's members are many "economists" and "revisionists," as is to be expected in a broad-front organization. However, when the "Veterans," Plekhanov, Axelrod and Vera Zasulich, marched in on the Union's first meeting, they denounced almost everyone as betrayers of Marx and marched out again. Plekhanov has now launched a rival League of *Revolutionary* Social Democrats Abroad. A curse on these awful, nit-cracking, internecine, émigré quarrels!

Next scene: Plekhanov's "mansion" by the lake. Her Ladyship, the girls, their *beaux* taking coffee in the early-morning sun under trees that grow out of the water. Nothing moves. Except me, along the drive. Pate dabbled with sweat under the bowler; dark suit now a light dust-brown; boots heavy as horseshoes. I should have ignored the expense and arrived in a hired cabriolet.

When I was finally admitted into the presence of *le maître*, I sensed I was on the real slippery slope. It was frockcoat time, that is, just after breakfast. He received me like a monarch in exile giving audience to a delegate from the plebs. He was suspicious, distrustful, haughty—a perfect Bourbon, not just confident of his own judgment, but *rechthaberisch* to the *ne plus ultra*. I tried to be unassertive, evade all the "sore" points. But the constant restraint on expressing myself naturally and straightforwardly, having to use "diplomacy," made me awkward, ill at ease. Once or twice, a homicidal urge zigzagged, like the toothache, through my brain. I could feel my little Browning in my palm, see the spurts of flame from the barrel, hear the bullets splintering his protective frockcoat, as he fell apart like a toppled statue. However, I remained attentively still, left hand at my lapel, right in my trouser pocket, intoning the mildest responses.

Plekhanov was the one racked by destructive anger. When I wondered how we could advance without a united movement, often agreeing to disagree, and a single paper, open to all opinions within our ranks, he began to shout like a German drill-sergeant. He would not have any disagreements at all with orthodox Marxism. These so-called "allies" were police spies, swindlers, scoundrels. His excitement verged on the indecent. He aimed a shaking finger between my eyes: "I would not hesitate to shoot such traitors myself!"

The most effective way to deal with an intellectual beside himself in such fashion is often to give him something to read. So I produced the manifesto I had composed for the first issue of *The Spark (Iskra)*, and intended to submit to its full editorial board, whoever they should be. I laid it on his desk. The bait worked. He stopped trembling, wiped his moustache and sat down. After a speedy riffle through, he gave a lipless smile. "No objections to the content. But it is not, as the French say, 'written.' This is not a literary work. It is totally without style. It does not look like anything. Leave it with me. I will get Vera or someone to elevate the tone."

He rose to his feet. My audience was over.

Then came two days Potresov and I spent discussing the best way of keeping Plekhanov on our side. If only Martov, still in Russia, could be with us—"the Triple Alliance" we used to call it. In Peter, we might have passed as "the Elders." Here we are whippersnappers in the presence of the old stagers, Plekhanov, Zasulich, Axelrod.

How little we had understood the Father of Russian Marxism was apparent when the five of us got together for an editorial conference in the upper room of a *bistrot* at Cordier, just outside Geneva. The first thing Plekhanov did was to hand me back my manifesto, insultingly unaltered. Presumably some tones could never be elevated. This was more than tension between generations.

Then, with an air of humility that would not have fooled a stuffed cod, he said: "Gentlemen, lady, comrades. I fear I am here in false face. It would be much better if I remained a contributor, just an ordinary contributor. Otherwise, there will be continual friction. Evidently, my views, tested and tempered over a lifetime in the movement, differ from some here. I understand our new friends, respect their youthful opinions, but I cannot share their approach. So, let *them* take over the paper! Let *them* edit! I shall simply be one of many who write on their pages."

Potresov and I were dumbfounded. It was the last move we expected. All I could do was object and insist (genuinely) that an *Iskra* without George Plekhanov was unthinkable, impossible. He *must* be on the editorial board.

This was clearly the move he had expected, and he was ready to deal with it.

"Too kind, too kind. But how can such a board function? It will, I assume, consist of me, Vera and Paul, plus young Potresov here, the boy Tsederbaum, I mean Martov, and you, Vladimir Ilyich—Ulyanov, is it, or Tulin now? Six members, are there not?

Split three and three, as now, for and against allowing Struve and the like to be contributors, ordinary contributors, of course, how would we ever come to a decision?"

Vera had been primed. Guileless, truthful, tender-hearted, she would commit any crime for an Olympian nod from Plekhanov. "Why, simple!" she cried. "Let George have *two* votes!"

And so unanimously (me casting Martov's proxy) Plekhanov was given what amounted to perpetual control of our paper—the paper for which I had risked being sent back for life to Siberia as I pegged out the distribution routes, appointed agents and correspondents, borrowed and begged money. *My* paper!

Within minutes, Plekhanov was demonstrating how an Editor-in-Chief operates. He dished out the various departments among us. He ordered articles from one after another in a tone that allowed no objection. Potresov and I sat there, I'm almost ashamed to confess even here, as if we had been sandbagged, "coshed," mechanically agreeing to everything, unable to understand as yet how we had been ambushed. Only as we left, the first to go, did Alexander Nikolaevich and I catch each other's eyes. We had been fooled by a virtuoso.

What I can only call my "infatuation" with Plekhanov disappeared as if by magic. Never, never in my life had I regarded any other man with such sincere respect, indeed veneration. Never had I stood before any man so humbly, and never before had I been so brutally "kicked." That's what it is, we have been booted up the arse. Or is it in the balls? When a man with whom you desire to cooperate, cheek by jowl, plays chess with your emotions, deals with comrades like a confidence trickster, then there can be no doubt that he is a bad man, a kind of criminal, inspired by pretty motives of personal vanity and conceit. In a soldier of the Revolution, sincerity is all. I see now Plekhanov thinks only of the marshal's baton in his knapsack—and now it is in his hand.

Instead of taking our hired gig back into the city, Alexander and I walked and talked together in the moonlight by the sequined water. The later it got, the more furious we became. Our hero had been destroyed—all right! From misery, we moved to gloating. We trampled him underfoot, the last of the dethroned gods. We drew up an indictment with an ever-growing list of charges. We would not go on like this. We do not want, we will not, we physically *cannot* work with someone under these conditions. Goodbye, *Iskra,* your spark is extinguished!

We will throw up everything, go back into Russia. We will start all over again, right from the very beginning, concentrate on nothing but a new, illegal, Marxist newspaper. We refuse to be pawns in the hands of that manipulator. He does not know how to maintain comradely relations.

But finally, we had to admit it—we do not dare undertake the editorship *ourselves*. It would appear positively repulsive to announce a rival publication, for then it would seem that we were the *Streber,* the careerists. That we too were inspired by motives of vanity. Our feelings that night (only last night!) are difficult to analyze, so mixed, muddy, heavy, confusing were they.

As dawn flickered on the mountaintops, we were purged. We had to agree that all this had happened only because we had both been seduced by George Plekhanov. Had we not been so starry-eyed, had we observed him dispassionately, with a more Marxist rigor, had we studied him objectively, our conduct would have been different. We should not have suffered such a blow on the head.

We took coffee at the only village hotel, as the cook warmed up the ovens, and we shook hands in agreement that we had been given the most bitter lesson of our lives, a painfully bitter, painfully brutal fable with a moral.

The moral is—always keep a stone in your sling. Or—*si vis pacem, para bellum.*

"Even between you and me and Julius?" asked Potresov.

"Yes," I said. "Between each one of us, and the entire world."

We promise not to talk of this incident to any but the closest, most trusted friends. Outwardly, it must be as though nothing has happened. But a cord has been broken. Instead of the splendid, noble, personal warmth that once surrounded our relations with the Veterans, there should be a dry, correct, business-like coolness.

So it proved tonight. As if to underline the wisdom of our new strategy, we two won our way against the other three on every important issue.

OCTOBER 10   MUNICH   1900

I have become Herr Meyer, lodger at Kaiserstrasse 53, a workingman's beer hall where the landlord passes for some kind of a Social Democrat. Mine's a windowless room, walled with tall cupboards I no longer open. I did the first night and was flogged by a series of falling brooms and mops. In other words, this is a cleaners' closet. Here I can relax undisturbed, with my folding

bed, my tin mug and a brass tray that serves as a table, except
when the cleaners stumble in at eight in the morning to set up the
bar for the day or at three the next morning to clear up the bar
after the night.

What does it matter? I am only here between midnight and
six A.M. So I only get woken once. Our proletarian comrades consider this a cozy billet for a single man. But then they are Germans
and by nature impervious to rowdy singing or the smell of stale
beer and pickled gherkins.

What counts is that I am in Germany and I have brought *Iskra*
with me, to edit in Munich, print in Leipzig. Plekhanov and Axelrod argued strongly that it should remain in Switzerland where
no doubt they would have edited the paper to their policy and
pleasure. Potresov and I urged that secrecy was essential for an
illicit publication. Among the émigrés of Zurich or Geneva the
identities of our contributors, the addresses of our undercover
distributors, could soon be known. Vera leaned (mostly) to our
side, and the two other "old-timers" gave way without much trouble.

Do they really understand, fully comprehend, what can be
done with a newspaper? What I plan will be unprecedented in the
history of journalism. Not George, not Paul, not Vera, not Alexander, not even Julius, appreciates the multipurpose potential of
Iskra. I do. History has given me the right to commandeer the
driving cab. The rest can travel behind. First-class, of course.

DECEMBER 24   LEIPZIG   1900

Their Christmas Eve, the continuation of capitalism by other (i.e.,
religious) means. Back home, it will be twelve days before Mother,
Anyuta and Mark, Manyasha, Mitya, gather at home for their
Russian family reunion. In the river house at Podolsk, on the
fringes of Moscow, as everywhere among Slavs, Christmas will be
an austere, traditional coming-together, costing little more among
the rich than among the poor. With the Huns, all is getting and
spending, buying, buying, buying. It is difficult not to suspect the
whole thing is a Western device to move the unsold stock of the
shopkeepers.

No matter. Tonight is my best cause for celebration since I
can remember. At midnight, Alexander, Vera and I put to bed
our newborn baby, the first, eight-page issue of *Iskra*. As in *The
Arabian Nights*, it magically multiplied itself into 8,000 copies.

In Munich, Alexander, Velika (as Vera Zasulich prefers to be called) and I have been the executive editors—commissioning, reading, revising, discussing, rereading, subediting, laying out, marking up, proofreading, pasting in, as well as writing our own stuff. I have done most, no one would deny. Potresov is such an amateur, Velika is so slow. I have also had to make all the financial and practical arrangements *and* I have written three sizable stories—"The War in China," "Urgent Tasks of Our Movement," "The Split in the Union of Russian Social Democrats Abroad."

For security reasons—and also because we are already spending eighteen hours a day together—we rarely meet outside our basement publishing office. We never forget we are illegal immigrants, with false identities and passports. But I expected to be at the printers in Leipzig only for ten days, V. and A. here for just the weekend. Surely we could afford a few hours on the town at festival time when the beer halls and saloons never close?

Velika, looking like the severe, ever-middle-aged head girl of some convent school dressed up in granny's dress and a gray wig, found herself a jug of tea in places that had never put anything on the table, even a vase of flowers, that was not 50 percent alcohol. Alexander, a bloated choirboy with yellow hair and blue eyes, wheedled champagne from barmen who had never seen a glass of rhubarb wine. I, the youngest, treated everywhere as the oldest, sampled small helpings of the new bottled beer, a technological advance born of Germany's imperialist penetration into tropical Africa. Despite this variety of intakes, we all became equally high-flown.

I ventured a toast in one low tavern to our circulation of 100,000 that had us sobbing with senseless laughter. We were thinking of the subterfuge, suggested by Velika, of inflating our production in rumors leaked to the bourgeois press, letters designed to be intercepted between legal Marxists and radical aristos. Velika kept hiccupping and chuckling at the future agony of the secret police: "You see, they'll get a third of the papers anyway, somehow or other. Let's say, three thousand. But because they believe we've printed one hundred thousand, they'll think they've only seized three percent instead of thirty-three percent. They'll feel such dreadful failures, I'm becoming quite sorry for them!"

FEBRUARY 21   MUNICH   1901

Second edition of *Iskra*! What's more, put to bed here in Munich, saving that dreary journey to Leipzig. Not that German printers are much different, or better, one town than another. "Social Democrat" firms could be the worst. Their workers and bosses fight all the time, thus doing a poor job, then unite across the class barrier to rob the customer. Especially if he is a foreigner, and operating outside the law.

I changed printers, somewhat to our advantage, and can now be confident we are not cheated more than 10 percent of the time. Even Plekhanov and Axelrod, here for the second edition, expressed admiration for my business ability. It stems from two qualities, one inborn, one acquired. First, I am a prodigy at mental arithmetic—while pretending to puzzle over Russo-German translation, I have already calculated their prices, their profit, their sticking figure. Second, I drive a hard bargain. When Mother tried to persuade me to be an agricultural businessman in Alakaevka, I refused. The only way then I could have made a profit was to side with the kulak against the poor peasant—that would have been obscene. But now I see nothing wrong with always getting the best of a load of bourgeoisified Boche when it is for the sake of *Iskra*.

Paul and George left their precious Switzerland to join our negotiations with Struve. Before he got his extra, dominating vote, George was always ranting against the "wet" liberals (his adjective) and refusing to allow them space in any paper which had him as a contributor. Now he imagines he is editor-in-chief, *Iskra* has got to be a success, even if it means taking articles (and money) from such spongy creatures.

Before the editorial meeting with "the Twin" (how glad I am there is only one of him), George gave us the impression S. was coming over to us. Instead, within minutes, Struve made clear he thought we were in decline and he was tomorrow's man. He was buying his way into the only opposition paper circulating inside Russia, and made much of his guarantee of 4,000 rubles a year from "Aunty," 2,000 from Prince Obolensky, and more to come from "influential friends." I see him in a totally new light—he is a careerist parliamentarian. He wants a Western-style, capitalist "democracy" only so that he can intrigue his way to the top job.

He is a "politician" in the true sense of the word—a huckster, a confidence trickster.

There was no reason why he should not win a seat on the board, given George's famous casting vote. Then we would be only three against four *forever*. So I put in my bid—8,000 rubles a year from Russia's great radical poet and playwright Maxim Gorky, 4,000 from our own well-padded colleague Potresov, and more to come from "anonymous workers."

I made the choice look as stark as possible. *Either* X + rubles and an editorial board one quarter liberal minus three Marxist writers (Martov is due here in March, and while we would obey the majority vote, we were under no obligation to remain), *or* 2X + rubles, a Marxist board of six working members, and a commitment to a forum for Struve & Co. without ceding any control over content.

As I sensed, the Twin needed our two sets of Triplets more than we needed him. He gave way. *Iskra* now has all the financing it requires, and more. As we left I said as much to Plekhanov, adding: "If you need any cash to support yourself in Geneva, please feel free to ask for a sub without embarrassment."

His face was swept with as many bars of color as the Northern Lights—purple fury, pink embarrassment, green greed, yellow apprehension, blue shock. Childish of me to find revenge so sweet.

MARCH 4   VIENNA   1901

Vienna, huge, beautiful, effervescent city, a sort of spring-cleaned Paris, Berlin after two bottles of champagne. I have come here, via Prague, to arrange Nadya's journey to join us in Munich— passport from the Russian consul, letters sent by devious routes to provide her with the address of our current "safe house." To be on the move, to see new places, to regain the beady concentration of the child setting eyes on fresh worlds, the effect is much underrated in analyzing character. Geography explains much of biography.

Not that Munich is dull, now that the pace of publishing has slackened. (Next *Iskra* late April/early May.) I have been much alone to the theater, usually for opera, especially enjoying *Die Tochter des Kardinals* and *La Juive*. Music is a kind of rational intoxication, but so slow! I resent being hypnotized by such repetition. My fault, I fear—I am obsessed by information. I become irritable at waiting for the end of the decorative variation. What takes ten minutes to tell in an opera takes five minutes in a play, takes three minutes in a lecture, takes one minute in a book. Life is not long enough for the performing arts.

Nevertheless, not all information is in words. Sometimes the content has been absorbed almost entirely by the style. Take the Munich carnival last month—a parody of the first days of a medieval revolution? The streets seized and held against any modern traffic—trams, cabs, trucks, police, shoppers, office workers, dustmen, deliverymen—an enforced holiday for all. Converging on the seats of power, the people come, masked and costumed, carrying fearsome joke weapons, ear-blasting drums and trumpets, banners and streamers, some on foot, many on horseback, more and more in wheeled floats. Nobody can refuse them, a kiss, a coin, a dance, a cheer. It is exciting, innocent, powerful and sinister, at once the past and the future, a remembrance and a rehearsal.

APRIL 16   MUNICH   1901

I have never seen Nadya so furious before, and with me. It is not true that anger makes women beautiful. How could it? Flushed cheeks, magnetized hair, enlarged pupils, reddened lips, restless body, heaving breasts, an afterglow of hot flesh, sweat, froth. It sounds more like . . . and I'm sure it is—a kind of sexual arousal, or an imitation of it. No wonder husband-and-wife rows often quickly sidle across to bed. One silences the other with a kiss.

Not in this instance.

"Where were you?" she shouted. "I came all the way on the train from Ufa to Moscow to Prague. I telegraphed you when I was arriving. *But you weren't there!* I waited and waited.

"Your last cover-name was Modracek at a place in the workers' district. I piled everything into a cab. The cabby had a silk top hat. We could hardly understand each other. Then we got stuck in a narrow alley in front of a great tower of a tenement block. Mattresses were hanging over all the balconies. Washing was stretched across like flags.

" 'Modracek! Modracek!' I kept calling. People pointed me on and up. At the fourth floor, a blond woman said 'I'm the wife of Modracek. What do you want?'

" 'My husband is Modracek,' I said. 'I want him.'

" 'Not this Modracek,' said the blonde. 'It better not be this Modracek.'

"A dark, bristly workman appeared.

" 'It better not be this Modracek,' he said.

"We stared at each other, all suspicious in turn. Then the man hit his brow with the heel of his hand.

" 'Frau Rittmeyer!' he cried. 'Herr Rittmeyer has sent letters and newspapers through me to Ufa. For you? Of course. He lives in Munich.' "

By now, Nadya was laughing, as were all of us sitting on up-turned beer barrels around the yard—Martov, sister Anna, Potresov, Velika and me.

"So, I took my bags back to the cab and went to Prague station. I came all the way by train from Prague to Munich. *Why weren't you there?* This time I left my luggage with a porter. I took another cab to the address that Modracek had given me. This time it was a lowdown saloon, full of men with faces like boiled pigs. The most boiled one was behind the counter.

" 'I am looking for my husband, Herr Rittmeyer,' I said.

" 'I am Herr Rittmeyer,' he said. 'Who is your husband?'

" 'Your husband better not be Herr Rittmeyer,' said a blond woman polishing a table. 'There is scarcely enough of Rittmeyer for me.'

"We stared at each other. The boiled pigs stared at us. Then the blond wife slapped her thigh.

" 'Not Herr *Ritt*meyer,' she said. 'Herr Doctor Redactor *Meyer* of the secret newspaper. Our lodger. He has been expecting a wife from Siberia. In the yard with his sister and the others from the secret newspaper. Go through. Give him a surprise.'

"Why weren't you there?"

They all embraced. I explained. I had been three times today to the station. I had sent my Munich address inside a letter inside a book taken by a friend across the border. I thought this would be quicker than using Modracek, my usual turnpike. Clearly, the friend had forgotten.

"I wonder how many copies of *Iskra* go lost that way?" Nadya asked. "It shows how much you need a full-time, professional correspondence secretary."

"Right, right, you're absolutely right," I cried. "Did you know just five minutes ago the four of us elected *you* to the job?"

MAY 18   MUNICH   1901

Out of the broom cupboard into the suburban flat. Nadya's mother, Elizavita, has arrived. For the last fortnight, Nadya and I have been separated. She sleeping on Velika's sofa (not too bad) and sharing her food (appalling). She complains: "I have not even been able to make tea because the sugar is always mixed in with tobacco."

We have become a Bulgarian couple Dr. (Jur.) Jordan Jourdanoff and wife, plus their aunt, Frau Maritza. We are to be found at 14 Siegfriedstrasse, Schwabing. Can't say the increase in home comforts means all that much to me—I like the feel of a compact burrow. But, as in Siberia, the pair's arrival is going to at least treble the amount of work I can do and the control I shall have, through Nadya's correspondence, over the internal network.

JUNE 17   MUNICH   1901

Not many Russians here, but that is enough. I am working a twelve-hour day and feel fine. Somehow my body compensates, improving my health as I load it with more and more tasks. When I become seedy, with headaches and stomach gripings, is when I fear I am wasting time. First six months of the twentieth century and still no revolution in Europe or Asia.

Fortunately, I am not popular with such students, émigrés and remittance men as I do stumble across in the cafés when I drop in for my rare nightcap. Arguments are inevitable. Not the precise, exact, rational dialectic of serious theoreticians and philosophers who instantly catch each other's references and toss back each other's propositions like a team of jugglers. The way Plekhanov and I used to debate, Axelrod and I still do. Instead, they display the Slav disease of the running mouth. Like Velika, they speak first and interpret afterward, forever wandering off the point into deserts of idealist moralizing, or thickets of romantic ethics. They think that because they feel something strongly it must be true. Even Martov, my favorite marathon monologuist, has become a café-lizard, basking all night under the gas mantles, a distraction to be avoided.

I have had to develop my counterdefenses. In the café, I take out Father's old turnip watch when I feel any speaker has had time enough to finish his case and announce: "Two more minutes, then drink up and shut up."

At the press, I work in a nest of scaffolding, open on three sides, high over the machines. Uninvited visitors are permitted only a distant view of Dr. Jourdanoff on his perch. Nadya blocks the bottom of the iron stairway, like a gatekeeper at the zoo: "*Starik* is busy. If you wish to contact the Old Boy, write your name on this side of this card, reason for visit on the other."

In our Schwabing suburb, a little town with its own shops, cafés, entertainments, etc., we are safe from most time-wasters. They are too lazy to make the trip. Access to our first-floor three rooms is anyway restricted by mother-in-law Elizavita, who sits in the hallway, Russian style, like a *dvornik* or *concierge,* blocking everyone's path. She has learned from a lifetime's experience with tsarist bureaucracy. All she says, not looking up from her knitting, is "Come back tomorrow."

JULY 21   MUNICH   1901

"L'audace, l'audace, toujours l'audace, eh?"

The speaker, accosting me in a Munich park, was a stranger. But Potresov, whose arm was linked with his, behaved as if we two must be good friends already, chuckling and muttering and nodding first to one, then the other.

"Alexander Israel Helphand," said the unknown, with a faint click of the heels, meanwhile enfolding me with his free arm. I observed his bulldog face, ugly but alive with intelligence, the dusky tips of his fingers, his expensive but well-worn suit bending at the knees, the guttural undertone to his French, the Ukrainian lilt to his name, the book in one pocket, the notebook in the other.

"Dr. Jordan Jourdanoff," I said.

Damn, slipup. That was yesterday. Still, Potresov had not given me our "speak carefully" sign. This must be a comrade.

"Sorry," I said hastily. "I mean Professor Meyer."

"No matter," Helphand's teeth flashed. "I have more than one name myself."

I had now added up the clues. Printer's ink . . . craftsman publisher? Heel click *and* embrace, two accents . . . Russian, from

Minsk, long resident in Germany? Pockets . . . scholar, journalist? Clothes . . . sedentary job, intermittent prosperity, adventurer, financier?

"I know. One must be 'Parvus.' These *klichki* can be very confusing."

We sat on the grass. Parvus is all these characters and more. Most important, in my view, the brightest, boldest Marxist writer/thinker in Europe today. I'd forgotten he lived in Munich. After all, one of the reasons why Potresov, an old friend, urged us to move *Iskra* here.

His laugh was cold, frosted over with self-congratulation. Here was someone (like me?) who saw himself as a rare professional among a mess of amateurs.

"Herr Doctor, dear comrade Tulin, Professor Meyer, former Baron Ulyanov! I have followed your career closely. All the others—your Triple Alliance, those veteran triplets from yesteryear, the oldsters and the Elders, the Great Russian chauvinists, the cosmopolitan exiles in Switzerland—*they* may not understand what you are doing. But *I* do. I envy you. I applaud you.

"To them, *Iskra* is just another underground sheet, like Herzen's *Kolokol*. A daring venture. But not much different from the others that have been tried and usually failed.

"But to you, *Iskra* is far, far more than a means of getting round the censor. Right? I see it as an audacious concept, spectacular, poetic even. No, epic! Your *Iskra* does not exist to educate its readers but to forge a party in your own image.

"I have to be right. Like me, you have realized that our Russian intellectuals are basically chatterboxes. Long on talk, short on action. Know everything, do nothing. Even George.

"Without you, Plekhanov would be an Alpine thinker with no followers outside the libraries. He respects your energy, your dedication, your practical *nous*. He imagines you'll do the work while he remains the boss. I know. I've been asked to jump through that hoop myself.

"I thought so! That's why you, only one of six editors, have elected yourself publisher, that is, commander-in-chief. That's why you have hand-picked every correspondent, an officer in your élite brigade, taking orders only from you, direct from you. That's why you also operate your distribution machine like a spy network, manned by agents nobody else knows, collecting and circulating information useful to you.

"I have long wanted to thank you for that generous but searching review you gave a book of mine a couple of years back. From Siberia. You were 'Tulin,' I think?" He paused at last.

"Ah, yes—*World Economy and the Agricultural Crisis*. You demonstrated from a close study of all the economic pointers that the long industrial predominance of England is now at last at an end. The twentieth-century capitalist rulers, according to your thesis, will be Germany over Europe, and America around the rest of the globe. And even earlier, in '95, did not you forecast some unexpected role for Japan? What *was* it?"

"You mean that Asian number of my review, *Aus der Politik*? I publish and print it here in Munich myself. It's the only way people like us can be sure what we write reaches the page as we wrote it, eh? In an article in that issue, I envisaged a twentieth-century world divided between Germany, America and Japan. And I saw these three more likely to form an international cartel of imperialist bandits than attack each other as competitors. This might not be so bad for socialism as some comrades think. Precisely, I prophesied in the next decade a war between Japan and Russia, a Japanese victory—and a Russian revolution! Four years to go!"

This is what I call conversation. My test is—has anyone said anything worth putting in my notebook? Parvus has reminded me of several lines of thought I had been neglecting. But what I really want to know is why he greeted me with that quotation from Danton.

"Your *Iskra* is a collective circulator of facts, opinions, ideas. But also a collective agitator, even more valuable, a collective organizer. Eh, eh, eh?"

His chuckle was like a sausage machine grinding dry bones. "This is how you are recruiting the next generation of ideological leaders, battle-hardened by conspiracy, trained to respond to your voice in print. Each cell activates the next cell, multiplying in every direction until armies are on the march, fortresses and cities under siege, autocracy attacked head on. This officer caste will be given a sense of mission by your words. And what supports, binds, electrifies this web? An eight-page folder of onion-skin sheets printed a thousand miles away, in another country, once a month. How many of these never reach their destination? *Iskra!* You are going to make it a fighting program. Some day the newspapermen of the world will honor you for showing how recorders of trivia can become makers of history. Talk about the power of the press!"

I kept my jaw from falling agape. He had read my mind. Not what I am thinking now, but what I have been thinking since I took the train into Siberia. Was everyone else so obtuse? Certainly, he was very sharp, knowing, smug, *dangerous*. The best defense here was candor.

I clasped his hand. "*Iskra* is an enormous pair of bellows. It will blow every spark of class struggle, popular anger, general fear, private despair into a nationwide conflagration. I invite you to join us in heaping coals on the blaze."

The smile was colder, yet more pleased with itself. Glassy eyes, clouded as the bottom of milk bottles, pale, but impenetrable. Said the pursed lips of Parvus, the "Little One," "I am already there, thank you. I am half-owner of the press that prints you. I am Gorky's European publisher. I am the, shall we say, conduit through which you get eight thousand rubles a year. Believe me, money will be the least of your worries."

OCTOBER 19   MUNICH   1901

"Our people," as Mother always calls the family, have certainly been suffering back home. I've been so busy with *Iskra* I hardly remembered I had any relatives. On September 1 Manyasha was arrested along with Anyuta's husband, Mark—both suspected, though without any strong evidence, of distributing and information-gathering for that illegal paper! There is little doubt that the public prosecutor is making a head on attack on the family Ulyanov. Sister and brother-in-law have been remanded, as Mitya and I were, for an initial six months "on suspicion" in Moscow. Manyasha's health is fragile (acute neurasthenia) but her brother, Mitya, now a doctor, is refused permission to visit because he has served a prison sentence. This is monstrous! Against the spirit, if not letter, of the regulations governing prisoners' rights. As to being held without interrogation or charge, that is definitely a breach of the law.

I have laid down for Mother all the relevant statutes and urged her, health permitting, to take the train to the Ministry of Internal Affairs in Peter. Here, if she finds the right people (I gave her some hints) the sophisticated officials of the capital will usually be happy to put down, and censure, the provincial red tape spinners of Moscow.

Divide and—if not exactly *rule,* then at least—*survive!*

DECEMBER 17   MUNICH   1901

Parvus and I meet almost every week. Talk, talk, talk. Like fledglings in a nest, our beaks never close. Which is the parent? Does it matter? I now understand enough about myself to realize this is another of my "infatuations," my "pashes," Nadya calls them. I accept there has been a train of these and probably will be more. Sex itself is unimportant, sex and *gender*. Sasha; Maria, my Jacobin; Apollinaria; Martov; Plekhanov; Parvus; Nadya, I suppose. I move on, if I have to, with a certain amount of understandable pain, like tearing off a bandage. Not, if not necessary. It seems I usually take more than I give, but then that is how we all grow.

I hope Alexander Israel will last. We share enough in common to enjoy some marvelous flashes of silence occasionally. Enough at variance to regularly explore how we came to the same conclusions by separate paths. His immediate understanding of my *Iskra* strategy stemmed from observation of himself as much as of me. He too had nursed a dream of a paper that acted as a party backbone though on a more grandiose scale—a socialist daily issued simultaneously in half a dozen European capitals and languages. He had also set up, and seen fall down, a socialist publishing house in Germany which aimed to stamp the Marxist message on every page—novels, guides, histories, biographies, textbooks, reference works, no matter what.

All now left is a half-share in our printers, and that somewhat esoteric theoretical monthly, *Aus der Weltpolitik*. Yet his confidence never flags, sometimes to my regret. "I am as determined to sacrifice myself to the revolution as you, Volodya. Unlike you, I will not rest until I am a multimillionaire as well. I will give up my ill-gotten gains when the proletariat takes power, of course. But amassing wealth will be my pragmatic test of Marxism. If old Karl was right about capitalism, he should be able to guide me into getting my hands on *das Kapital*. I'm not joking."

I can only hope that, for his own good, he never makes it. Money is as much a poison to some constitutions as drink is to others.

Chez Parvus—somehow the ironic Latin surname suits him better than anything else—I meet Rosa Luxemburg. I try to keep my memory active, my powers of observation sharp, by noticing

how my contacts dress, speak, live. In our illegal world, small details
may save your life and carry heavy significance. A poor man suddenly spending money! A solitary woman with half a dozen mugs
in her cupboard. I had not registered how well Parvus cossets
himself until Rosa went round his rooms pricing all his possessions.
He followed laughing, almost naturally, and claiming each one as
a bargain from the Munich flea markets.

"I'm just a poor Bohemian!"

As he spoke, I observed for the first time how sumptuously
dressed he is becoming. The familiar well-cut suit no longer looks
as if it had put in a twelve-hour day at a desk.

As usual, he apologizes for having no tea or coffee. As usual,
he stumbles upon a forgotten bottle of champagne.

Rosa is a delight. For a moment I thought she was a cripple,
which she is. Some childhood accident (I should imagine) has given
her torso a twist, left her with a long body and short legs, and a
limp. Yet the impression vanishes even as you record it. She would
need only a five-minute start on the prima ballerina of Peter to
seduce the most handsome dandy in Europe. You see only that
glowing face, an alabaster lamp lit by an incandescent spirit. You
hear only that musical voice, modulating through Polish-Russian,
Russian-German, Swiss-French. With Rosa, an afternoon's discussion of state and revolution, war and peace, capitalism and socialism, is as enjoyable and entertaining as a matinée at the theater.
(Much more so in my case.)

FEBRUARY 14   MUNICH   1902

Final call on Parvus which also turns out to be an opportunity to
say *au revoir* to Rosa. The police are coming too close here in
Munich—the Kaiser's flatfoots and the Tsar's spies are as near
cousins as their masters. The "Switzers," Plekhanov and Axelrod,
want the paper to move to Zurich. But the Triple Alliance, plus
once more good old Velika, may carry the day for London. I long
for the British Museum Library and Karl Marx's seat.

I had hoped to discuss my latest work, *What Is to Be Done?*
(*Chto Delat?*), bits of which I have been floating in *Iskra* and *Varya*
(*Dawn*), our theoretical quarterly. I was particularly pleased with
my new Archimedean slogan—"Give us an organized troop of
professional revolutionaries and we will turn Russia upside down."
Publication date now mid-March. Unfortunately, I politely men-

tioned a piece by Parvus in *Dawn* under the pseudonym of *Molotov*. And this diverted the conversation into the advantages and drawbacks of *klichki*.

"*Molotov!*" jeered Rosa. " 'The Hammer'! You're the third I've come across in the last year with that one. There'll be a *Stalin*, 'Man of Steel,' soon. *Starik* is not bad, 'the Old 'Un.' And I have a new friend, in Berlin, who's known as *Radek*, Polish slang for 'Thief'! I've heard you've got a new one."

"It should be *Volgin*," Parvus said. "I like that. 'The Man from the Volga.' "

I explained that Plekhanov (born in Tambov) has booked that one, didn't use it often, but refused to let it go. I said I'd decided for *What Is to Be Done?*, and perhaps all future works, on *Lenin*.

"Ah, yes. *Lenin*, better than *Volgin*. 'The Man from the Lena.' A Siberian river I believe. Full of gold too, they say."

"No, no," cried Rosa. "It's from Ilyich, isn't it? Your family pet name. I remember you also used to be *Ilyin* once. *Ilyin, Lenin!* Yes, no false heroics there. From now on, you're Lenin to me."

I shall miss these two comrades more than any I have met in exile. Each has taught me a lesson, not a political one (though all lessons are political) but a human, personal one.

Before Parvus, I had distanced myself from the sensual man, the careerist, the lover of power and possessions, the drinker and womanizer. Faint traces of idealism, childish superstitions perhaps, persuaded me that only a comrade who was purged of all vanities, luxuries, self-indulgence and individual ambition could be of service to the cause. Now I see, what I already realized without admitting it, that greed and genius, egoism and courage, determination and frivolity, can co-exist. Perhaps more often do so than not. Revolutions are not made by angels.

Before Rosa, indeed for as long as I can recall, growing up with a mother like mine, with sisters such as Anna and Olga, I had simply never doubted that any community based on truth and justice must recognize the equality of the sexes. But again, a certain ingrained philistinism and male survivalism led me to imagine that women had no desire to rule, to lead, to win. I put this down, without examining my thought processes too closely, to their innate generosity, a biological drive to succor and support instead of destroy and defeat, perhaps even a self-preserving instinct to avoid a role which usually coarsens and corrupts.

Now I see that this is just another form of pseudo-religious balderdash. Rosa was born a month before me in 1870—a woman, a Jew, a Pole, a member of three oppressed groups. She has been always ahead of me on the same road. She understood the same messages of life, but framed them earlier, sometimes better. While she was showing me the other day a letter she wrote when fourteen (about what, I forget), my eye jumped to a sentence that seemed outlined in scarlet: *My ideal is a social system that allows one to love everybody with a clear conscience.* So accurate, so obvious even—yet I could never have composed that then. Perhaps, not even now!

Even now, I feel . . . "yes, but." The prophetic schoolgirl went on: "Striving after it, defending it, I may perhaps even learn to hate." Yes, and no buts!

After a brilliant degree, a first-class doctorate at Zurich, in two foreign languages, she went on to found the first Marxist party in Poland at the age of twenty-three. Five years later, she arrived in Berlin, taking the city by storm and was appointed the editor of a great Social-Democratic newspaper. She is a key figure in three socialist parties. And she lies on Parvus's sofa, pouring down champagne, batting ideas back and forth with (though I don't say it myself) two of the brightest new stars in the firmament of European revolution, with all the confidence of a Bernhardt or a Duse. Only this performer writes her own text.

MARCH 15   MUNICH   1902

Seventeen issues of *Iskra* since No. 1 in December 1900! *Four* in the first six weeks of this year! It is even getting reprinted *inside* Russia. No. 10 on the secret press in Kishinev. No. 12, literally underground, on the secret press "Nina," in Baku, down an old mine shaft.

I have written at least two pieces in each edition. Not to say shouldering almost all of the editorial and administrative work. Yet if I stopped, I should fall down in a faint. I know my own constitution very well now. As Mother has always insisted, I am strongest when throwing myself into some deep end, mentally or physically. I do go for a swim in the new working people's baths almost every day. I make certain of giving myself, morning and night, a cold rubdown from a watering can over a sawed-off barrel in the yard. I do my Swedish exercises.

Tomorrow, *Iskra* No. 18 will emerge from the rollers of our Munich printers. (Interestingly, these now turn out to be *wholly* owned by that "poor Bohemian," Parvus.) I have to see the pages through myself because I am the only one who really cares about getting everything right. Where I should really like to be tonight, of course, is at Verlag J.W.H. Dietz in Stuttgart. Here my most important work so far, *What Is to Be Done?*, will be published. The title sounds best in Russian, *Chto Delat?*—like a punch on the shoulder, a push in the back, a clenched fist. In French or English, even in German, it sounds nearer a feeble bleat, I'm afraid: *"Oh dear, whatever shall we do?"* So far, it *is* only in Russian. And with its chocolate-brown cover, crisp question, single-name author, "Lenin," I hope it will attract the worker unused to reading, let alone buying, books. I have insisted it be the size to fit into an ordinary coat pocket. When it is read, I trust they will instantly realize the whole point is to knock off the question mark. *This Is What Must Be Done!* is the real title.

I cannot wait to find out what the workers think of my diagnosis of Russia's fatal infection, my prescription made up to give immunity to a new generation. Tsarism is a plague, capitalism is its most virulent form. Socialism is the only cure, Marxism is its most potent form.

I can foresee what the intelligentsia as a group will say, if only from the reactions of the brightest and best, Parvus and Rosa. In principle, they passionately support my theses. Needless to say, they never flirt with reformism, revisionism, economism. Where they believe Marxism can be adapted, it is always toward greater conformity with reality. "Nothing is more revolutionary than a clear view of the world as it actually is"—one of Rosa's favorite observations.

Nobody could mistake either of them for a mushy-brained Saturday-night socialist, the one-evening-a-week rebel, continually postponing that letter denouncing the governor, that searing indictment of Tsar so far offered only to the bathroom mirror. My two friends' central purpose in living is the abolition of tyranny, the inauguration of a new age. And yet . . . both draw back from full endorsement of the Nechaevian, the Tkachevian, full-time agent, enrolled in a centralized, disciplined militant élite, who concentrates on practical, organizational routine twenty-four hours a day.

Parvus's pale, milky eyes polish up like diamonds only when he talks of his other hobby—planning how to make a fortune. "After all, if you were the Tsar, which would you fear most—a Marxist millionaire or a Marxist pauper—eh? Everyone wants money, just as they want good looks or good health. My view is that prosperity is too good to be left to the rich. What we will bring to the masses tomorrow, I am helping myself to a bit of today. *Do dna!* Bottoms up!"

Rosa's diversion from my formula is different. It is not so much that she yearns for a private life, for love, for a home other than a furnished room, for the joys of personal relations. She does. But it is a life with Leo Jogiches, her lover since they met as students in '90, fellow founder of the Polish Social-Democratic Party. She waved one of his letters under my nose the other day, crying: "Six sheets covered with stuff about debates within the Party. Not a word about ordinary life. Not a word about me. I feel quite faint."

Yet, even though they are often apart, it is socialism, revolution and the future which cements them. He is the thinker, the spawner of ideas. She brings them to birth, gives them wings, teaches them to fly. Together, they are unsurpassed.

Her weakness (in my view) is part of the weakness of the whole PSDP, perhaps of the Polish character as it has developed in the constant ebb and flow of occupation, uprising, suppression, uprising, occupation over the centuries. Polish Social Democrats all act on their own initiative as individuals. No one will take an order from anyone else. There is hardly any policy; what there is tends to be made up as they go along. Rose encourages this slackness. She refuses to talk about money, to consider qualifications for membership, to even hear about the day-to-day work of a party. I'm told her CenCom have even passed an official decree licensing her to read and write and make speeches without bothering her head about the nuts and bolts! The "Red prima donna," the press call her—in other words, a sort of female Plekhanov!

This makes it easy for her to scorn my suggestions in *What Is to Be Done?* as being full of "the sterile spirit of the night watchman." And she wins widespread applause for such aphorisms as—"Freedom is always freedom for the one who thinks differently."

That may be true: in Utopia. In another century, after socialism has changed the world and its people. But Marxism tells us no statement is always true absolutely, regardless of context, or history. I answer her: "But until there is enough freedom to go round for everyone, it will have to be rationed."

That is why I have written *Chto Delat?* and why it is so necessary. Rosa's claims sound fine and will find their echo among the romantics, the phrase-makers, the sentimentalists, the soft-hearted —Martov, Gorky, Axelrod, Vera Zasulich, Potresov. My blueprint will be recognized as nearer to the real world by the pragmatists, the street-people, the scientific examiners of the actual evidence before us—Rosa's own Leo, Parvus, Plekhanov, Chernyshevsky, Marx, Engels.

APRIL 14   LONDON   1902

"Mr. Alexejeff, 14 Frederick Street, Gray's Inn Road, London WC 1 (mark inside: for Lenin)." We have been sending this address, in secure form, to selected correspondents, including Anna and Mother. How strange it looks and sounds as we spell it out to each other with English accents.

London retains a special place in the gazetteer of Russian revolutionaries—the safest place in the world for the political refugee. Berlin is the capital of the country with the largest, most powerful Social-Democratic Party. They won almost half the votes in the last general election based on universal suffrage. Paris is the capital of the country with the longest tradition of revolution. Not a single party now existing but has been involved at some time in armed uprising, advocated seizure of power, or been discovered plotting to stage a mass insurrection. I visited both cities in '95 and soaked up the experiences of our German and French comrades.

But London ranks in a different table, almost seems from another planet. This is the capital city of the country which not only invented capitalism but also discovered the first principles of how its invention worked. Without such British political economists as Adam Smith and Ricardo and Mill, Marxism might still be waiting to be evolved. Not only has London played host to Bakunin and Herzen in the past, Kropotkin and Tchakovsky today, it is renowned above all as the home, for forty years, of that otherwise stateless, proscribed emigrant, Karl Marx. German and French authorities, for all their protestations, collaborate with the Russian secret police. Maybe it is because the London authorities feel so superior to all these crude and cruel European autocrats, regarding even the Tsar of all the Russias simply as an Asian warlord, that they refuse to believe any foreign conspirators, with unpronounceable names, can ever do any harm. They will never hand over any legal resident, whatever his nationality, who does not wish to leave.

Nikolai Alexeyev, a misspelled russky name around town, has found us a furnished room in his boarding-house—14 Frederick

Street. It has been a two-night journey from Munich, via Cologne, Lièege and Brussels to the North Sea port we thought was called "Har-wick" but natives pronounce "Harridge."

I had insisted we visit the Cathedral in Cologne—what a monument to the grandiose idiocy of our past, a medieval folly typical of those benighted times when the Western world was a huge asylum run by the inmates! Martov once told me some famous rabbi had advised Jews to attend all processions where the kings and heroes of the Gentiles were to be seen. Why? So that, however magnificent and resplendent these seemed, the devout Jew could be sure they were yet as nothing to the coming Messiah! So it is with cathedrals. If serfs could build these to honor something that does not exist, what will the free citizens of tomorrow erect to celebrate *socialism*?

Liverpool Street Station—in a fog. All the world has heard of these. Somehow I never imagined they could be so different from the lemon-yellow mists of Neva as winter leapfrogs into summer, the first warm sun driving out the hidden frosts long-congealed in Peter's dark corners. Or from the water-crawling, woolly clouds on the Volga as summer ends, and the long-baked banks feel the first chills. But then the London fog is unique—it is man-made. It is the incense of the industrial revolution.

I admire America's "Mark Twain." What a wonderful remark he made when People's Will blew up that Grand Duke the other day. "If Russia has the sort of government that can only be changed by dynamite then I say—Thank God, for dynamite!" But he was wrong when he claimed that, though everybody complained about the weather, nobody did anything about it. England's capitalists have learned how to change the weather, for the worse, without even thinking. They have built the world's largest city, crammed it with citizens whose only protection against the endemic damp is the coal fire. Result—*fog*!

It is impossible to believe you are not walled off, six feet around in every direction, by gray-brown blankets, retreating in front of you, trailing behind you. Your common sense tells you that you are now little worse off than anyone with short sight, nowhere near as handicapped as the blind. If you walk at a reasonable steady pace, stay close to the walls, and have studied the map, then you will have no problem. But irrational fears crowd in. You have a powerful intuition that at the end of this pavement is a canal, an unmarked trench, a precipitous flight of steps, perhaps a precipice itself. You may be in the middle of their Trafalgar Circus, or some other great *piazza*, yet you suffer from fear of enclosed spaces, claustrophobia.

Fortunately, I like enclosed places, backing into them like a hermit crab into a chance shell. I had studied my Baedeker maps and was confident I could have found my way to Gray's Inn Road, or anyway to King's Cross station, terminus of the Great Northern Railway Co. But Nikolai had brought a cab, and I had to leave it to the horse. I wonder if the English revolutionaries—there must be *some*!—have thought of staging an uprising in the "pea-souper'? The poor, the foot-soldiers of the industrial army, always know their city better than the bourgeoisie, their mounted superiors who move around at speed, cut off from the detail of the street. In the silence of the fog, London's strong points could be seized before the ruling class heard the click of a pistol.

JULY 24   BRITTANY   1902

Almost a month here. When I arrived, my nerves were in shreds. I really had begun to wonder if I should ever work again.

Ever since the beginning of my exile in Europe, I have been nagged by certainty that so many decisions must be quickly made about our RSDLP if we are to become a movement, not a monument. And I have been increasingly surrounded by comrades, old at heart whatever their age, who waste their lives walking in their sleep. They rouse occasionally when they bump into somebody or something, exchange a few snippets of socialist dogma, then glaze over again. When you can get their attention, they excuse their lack of involvement by pointing out that Marx himself had declared the proletarian revolution the task of the proletariat alone.

It has been almost a one-man struggle against the Economists. Now the stream of social life is running against them. They are a declining tendency. But one thing they used to be able to deliver—visible, tangible results for the workers. A few kopeks on the pay here, a few minutes off the day there, a little help for widows and orphans, better conditions for some. At least, bread-and-butter (sorry, bread-and-dripping) issues that everyone could understand were aired. Now and then, the bosses listened.

The new deviation is to another side of the path. The newly formed Social Revolutionaries are the old Populists, the People's Will group, in a fresh mask. Once again, they interpret "the peo-

ple" as peasants and petit bourgeois rather than workers. They
have added dilute socialism to a formula which includes some
rather dubious ingredients—patriotism, mysticism, an appetite for
violence, distrust of the West, of Jews, of modern industrial progress. But the results they deliver can also be seen and heard—
Terror! Gunned-down secret police chiefs, blown-up ministers of
state, continual attempts on the life of the Emperor himself. It has
its attractions!

Against this, we propose a tight, tough underground machine
which will have a finger in every pie, ready for the moment when
our hand closes on the lever of power and overturns an empire.
Until then, our members get no public admiration, no applause
from massed crowds, no excitement from the noble crime, the
honorable murder. Few ordinary citizens have ever heard of us as
real individuals—until I settled on Lenin, I went through 150
cover-names and may need more. What we are seeking to do in
our own way seems to a majority of the nation totally impossible.
This is our greatest strength. It can also be a cruel burden.

But here I am in Loguivy, and here I am on paper, still refusing to open my mind and let the sea breezes blow through. In
my defense, I have to plead that this is the longest I have thought
about politics since the end of June. Mother is here! As soon as I
set eyes on her, I could feel the spring inside me unwind. I see
now that sixty-seven is no great age. She has grown yellower, like
an ivory figurine. Her features are more ingrained. This only adds
to the beauty and the dignity, suggesting immortality rather than
antiquity. Like a goddess, she exerts her magnetic influence through
hills and walls, over great tracts of this strange land none of us
had ever heard of. Fishermen knock at the door with whirring
lobsters, new-caught and weeping sea-tears. Warm, brown eggs,
appliquéd with a feather or two, are pressed on us in the streets.
Each morning, no matter how early I rise, there on the doorstep
is the bundle of loaves, hard-shelled outside, almost molten within.
It is easier to drink wine than water since there are always nine or
ten bottles in the middle of the table while the bucket goes reluctantly to the well.

Mother speaks a kind of Court French even we (sister Anna,
Nadya, mother-in-law and me) barely understand. The Bretons
catch only the key word but are delighted with that, repeating it
round the room or the village like a sacred "mandala." They have
their own language—I suspect a kind of Old English. After all,
only a narrow channel separates them from the British Isles, and
the name *Brittany* must have some significance.

They even look a bit British to me—amiable, knobbly faces, more or less interchangeable, and despite their openness, to foreigners anyway, inscrutable. There is something Oriental in this Celtic strain, an elaborate politeness so delicately veneered as to be near-transparent, which permits them to tell you the most enormous lies, not for their own advantage but to cheer you up and prevent you learning the worst.

Socially, of course, they are still in the age of feudalism. Everything centers on the *seigneur,* even if he is never there. The Church is also into everything: dances, festivals, processions twice a week in fancy dress behind the crucifix. Politically, complete reactionaries, not yet adjusted to their own bourgeois revolution. Yet withal, people of kindness, warmth and vivacity, despite freezing winds and morning fogs even in July—that bit very British.

Mother has had a marvelous time looking after all of us. What a woman! I suppose it must be the most ridiculous emotion in the world, not only to love your mother but to be in love with her as well? I defy almost anyone to resist. How else could she have twisted so many officials round her little finger to benefit her children? What a curious fate for a revolutionary, whose personal life must be swept almost as bare as a desert anchorite's, to have a mother who is a *femme fatale!* We are all under her spell—including mother-in-law Elizavita. What a pity I can't swap the two of them. I must remember it is not E.'s fault I am with her every day and with Mother only after gaps of years. This must be the longest Mother and I have spent together since . . . Well, ever, I suppose. In Volga days, there was always something else I must do.

Well, there isn't now. No one else I have ever met is so able to relax that overtight spring of mine. The holiday is almost at an end. I must stop myself scrutinizing my metaphors. A mechanism, say a watch, with a relaxed spring is "run-down"—ditto, a human. If I want to keep time, to overtake the future, I must be wound up *tight.*

AUGUST 10   LONDON   1902

Turned back to my entry for the day we arrived—what arrogance! I walk at a steady pace, stay close to the wall, have learned the street maps by heart. My nose is pressed into my Baedecker as a curé's into his missal. There is no fog. And I still get lost!

London defies the cartographer. Always another passage, alley, close, cut, mews, extra to those in the book. A straight main road with a small branch turning off on the page becomes a fork with two identically sized arms. One wrong turning in this maze and it takes an hour to retrace your steps. London has no center. Rather, half a dozen centers. An immensity hard to visualize until you see it.

Then there's the language. Little resemblance here to what we were taught at Simbirsk grammar school, relearned with the family, coaching each other at Kokushkino and Alakaevka, studied again in Europe. I go every Sunday to Hyde Park, not because the speeches tell me something new but because they are usually the same. I stand in the front. I watch the lip movements.

I am determined to get it right. I have found myself a pupil/teacher from an advertisement in *The Athenaeum*. His name is Raymond. He looks like a headwaiter in a Nevsky Prospekt restaurant, stately, plump, silver-haired. He converses only in English, I only in Russian. He is office manager for a publishing house, G. Bell & Son. He is even a socialist (English-style)—that is, socialist by permission of the capitalists. He used to discuss this topic at seminars in suburban parish halls. His boss heard of it and presented an ultimatum: shut up or step down! He stirred up no class antagonisms in the office. He did not even mention politics there. It was enough that he had been rumored to be advocating such doctrines, in his own time. From now on, he was free to be a secret socialist, a rebel behind closed doors. He tells me this, and I can see he thinks I will regard him as a hero and a martyr. This is typical.

English politics drives every Continental socialist to despair. That is why very few of us even bother to take an interest. As Marx observed, this country has not only a bourgeois bourgeoisie, but also a bourgeois aristocracy and a bourgeois proletariat. We have settled into two rooms on the first floor of 30 Holford Square, Finsbury, ten minutes from King's Cross. It is pretty much of a hole, dreadfully overcrowded since Nadya's mother has joined us. One room is where Nadya and I sleep. The other serves as kitchen, dining room, study and Elizaveta Vassilyevna's bedroom. The only heating is from the open fire for which coal must be dragged upstairs in a wooden crate. Slops from washing up, cooking and various et ceteras have to be taken down in jugs or bowls and emptied into the ground-floor drain.

Nevertheless, our landlady behaves as if our accommodation were the equivalent of gentlemen's bachelor apartments in Mayfair. She is disturbed to find we have no curtains on our windows—the only neighbors who can overlook us are far away, through the trees, on the other side of the square. She is upset because Nadya does not wear a wedding ring. We brush past her mouthings on the stairs, pretending not to understand, though the words "curtains" and "ring" are becoming as familiar to us as *"dorogoi drug,"* "dear friend."

The women seem happy enough to adopt a *tryn-trava* attitude—who cares? But I have been studying English law and I begin to wonder whether this strange people may not have laws that could actually punish us for not wearing a ring, perhaps even for failing to put up curtains. This is not as ridiculous as it sounds if you know anything about the English legal system.

This morning, the law solved the problem. We had a caller, none other than Apollinaria Takhtareva, my one-time intimate, Nadya's dearest friend, in Peter, formerly Yakubova. Though I knew she had been living in London for some years, I also knew she had moved over to the opportunist, economist wing of the Social Democrats. So I avoided both her and her husband, Takhtarev, former editor of rightist-leaning *Workers' Thought (Rabochaya Mysl).*

When we told her about the curtains and the ring, she laughed that dark, treacly laugh I once knew so well. "My husband will settle Mrs. Yeo with a word," she promised. I didn't see what another newspaperman could do to help, but when he appeared I discovered he was now a professor of law. He rapped on our landlady's door and when no more than her nose was spearing out, he intoned: "Slander, madam, *slander!*"

It was the word all right. And, I sensed, a word she had heard before in not too pleasant circumstances. He informed her that Dr. and Mrs. Richter (our cover-name) were indeed married, ring or not, and any suggestions to the contrary would be met with an instant summons.

Mrs. Yeo folded on the spot. She had never doubted the legality of the union between the lady and gentleman. And she would be only too happy herself to supply the traditional lace curtains at no extra expense, plus pole, hammer and nails. All she asked was that we not do the work on a Sunday.

For once, we are on the winning side of the law.

OCTOBER 16   LONDON   1902

Knock, knock, knock, tap-tap-tap, knock, knock, knock! SOS, SOS, SOS! It felt as if it were inside my head. We get up early, at this time of year before dawn, though at this time of year in London neither dawn nor dusk properly exist. All you get is a slight lightening or darkening of the daily murk with perhaps a glimpse of an orange stain at noon. Triple rap, three times, heavy, soft, heavy. The Party signal.

Nadya is already padding her way down. I hear her careful whisper. Then the counting out of five coins. We have only shillings—must be for a cab. Yes, I can hear it jangle and creak away. Now a male voice, improperly muffled, squeaky with excitement, Russian, Black Sea Russian, probably Jewish, under thirty—probably not much more than twenty-one. Has the Pen arrived?

Nadya brings him right up to my bedside (she never has much sense of occasion), a lanky, long-haired, rather starved-looking youngster, pipe-cleaner arms and legs but the barrel chest of an opera singer, bird of prey's hooked nose, and a mouth that could tear and rend. The whole figure still swirling with London fog. "The Pen (*Pero*) is here!" she proclaims.

The Pen! (Ha!) I shouldn't laugh. After all, I suggested that Party *nom-de-guerre* myself. It doesn't do any harm to butter new young recruits (he's twenty-three). Especially one who volunteers to escape from Siberia, cross Europe with false papers, turn up in London in the early hours—all to write for a newspaper. And it seemed an appropriate title for someone who writes with such flashy, impressive, studentish use of color and drama, highlights and shadows, positive *chiaroscuro* (as he might put it). It's not any style I could use, or really much enjoy. But I can see it may be a phase (a bit like Marx's youthful puns and jokes on the *Neue Rhenischer Zeitung*). He is a natural polemicist, an orator on the page. Perhaps on the platform as well. Anyway, I need all the fresh talent I can get out of Russia to strengthen my hold on *Iskra*. "I'm in love with it!" he cried, hovering around my camp bed like a buzzard, then sitting down on my hand under the quilt and practically paralyzing it.

His real name is Lev Davidovich Bronstein. He comes from a highly improbable family (given the institutionalized racialism of tsardom) of Jewish cowboys in Kherson province. He is traveling under the alias of Trotsky, an identity he took at the last moment, writing it into his forged passport on impulse with his own hand. This is, of course, a very common name in Russia, not quite like Smith and Jones here, but Robinson perhaps. It was only when it was too late to reinscribe it that he realized it was also the name of his head warder in Odessa's model prison. That Trotsky was a tyrant of towering build, powerful intelligence, and immense presence.

"What do you think that means? *Psychologically*, so to speak?" he asked. I remarked that I did not so speak. Indeed, I had to say that I could not understand the formulation of the question. He looked rather disappointed.

He is a master of words, a born tale-spinner. The simplest, most familiar proposition begins to take on the properties of a short story. I warmed to his partner, Alexandra Lvovna Sokolovskaya, the lone Marxist woman in their illegal student discussion group in Odessa. He was then a Populist, a romantic conspirator, aching for direct action, the smell of sweating dynamite, the tremor of illegality. He mocked her political philosophy, saying he could not understand how any passionate, hot-blooded person could preach such narrow, dogmatic, arid, pseudo-scientific stuff. He even raised his glass at the group's New Year party to invoke a curse on those—i.e., the Social Democrats—who want to introduce hardness, dryness, toughness into all human activities. She answered the toast by demanding how it was possible for a vigorous young fellow with a highly developed brain to fill his head with a soft mush of vague, wet idealism.

Alexandra was ten years his senior—I thought of my "Jacobin" in Samara. As the parallel launched itself onto the rapids of his talk, I took one of those instant leaps of memory. It was like turning over a whole wedge of pages in a book. Indeed, it was hardly *memory* for I was there, as if transported, actually, physically, backward in time. He is spouting on, in another room in another house, while the Jacobin and I walk those tunnels of interlaced blossom, the dew (or was it rain?) spotting through on us like sprinkles of perfume, the air cool and creamy, even (can this be true?) various animals, hares, field mice, sables, bluebirds, cavorting ahead of us. It is an illustration to a folktale. Even though, hand in hand, we are talking of the dictatorship of the proletariat, the permanent revolution, the withering away of the state, and other such lovers' trifles. I had thought no one ever learned the real facts of life (i.e., Marxism) in such idyllic surroundings, pupil and teacher emparadised in one another's eyes. But I realize, of course, now a *starik* of thirty-two, that it must be part of the experience of each generation. If they're lucky.

"What became of Alexandra Lvovna?" I interrupted.

There was a pause. Trotsky—I shall call him that, since Bronstein brings up unfortunate associations, and I cannot go around addressing someone as "The Pen"—seemed taken aback.

Nadya said: "Lev Davidovich was just telling us about how he read his first Marxist work in prison. Plekhanov's *The Monist Conception of History,* and he was so struck by the realization that 'Ideas do not fall from the sky' he started to research a study of Freemasonry."

"Well, we got married, so that she could be with me in Siberia, you know," he explained. "It was quite a wrench to come here, leaving her behind in exile. Her and the two little girls. But I felt *The Spark* needed me. I asked her—'Ought I to go?' "

There was another pause. Only the second since he had come through the door. Then Nadya spoke.

"What did *she* say?"

"She said: 'You must.' "

Poor Alexandra Lvovna—she had wanted a philosophy hard, and dry, and tough. And that's what she got from her romantic with a head full of mushy idealism!

"A good place to end the chapter," I said. "Nadya will take you to meet Julius and Vera. They'll put you in that five-room den George calls 'the menagerie.' "

"George?"

"Plekhanov," said Nadya.

I'm afraid it's a thousand to one Alexandra will never see "The Pen" again this side of the revolution. The name he gave himself sounds even more appropriate—"Antid Oto."

He took it, at random, from an Italian-Russian dictionary. Or so he says.

JANUARY 15   **LONDON**   **1903**

Back from lecture engagement in Paris. Called in on the menagerie for an hour or two as on most days after a morning in the B.M. Library. Trotsky handed me the latest edition of *Iskra,* edited and printed in my absence. I thought he seemed unusually taciturn.

It was all much as we had agreed at our last editorial meeting.

Except for the "dead spot"—center spread, left-hand page, bottom section. (According to reactions I had tested of a sample of readers, this was the space most likely to be skipped.) Here Martov and Zasulich had inserted an editorial positively commending an act of individual terrorism against Val, the governor of Vilno, who had just flogged several hundred demonstrators in the main square. This was a clear breach by them of our paper's agreed policy. I was determined it should not pass without a reprimand.

I told Vera that I understood why she, the would-be assassin of another flogger, General Trepov, should feel strongly about the atrocity. However, I pointed out, *feelings* are not a good guide to party policy. We are not teachers of private morality. I had just launched a campaign against the Socialist Revolutionaries, calling them "Liberals with bombs." Any support for such SR-style reactions to public events would be seen as a softening of our attitude.

Julius, though he had backed Vera, saw the point immediately and agreed it was an unfortunate deviation. Vera, whose brain obeys only her blood pressure, does not understand how what her emotions tell her can be wrong. I felt she needed my disapproval reinforced with a little pain. So I pointed out that if she had not allowed herself to act on impulse in the *Affaire Trepov*—had, for example, bothered to examine her pistol and practice firing a few shots—the general would have been executed, not grazed. He would not still be governor of Petersburg today, still on hand to kill and torture workers. Vera winced, and muttered that she had not advocated terrorism as a system. "I just thought a bomb or two might teach them not to flog people, that's all."

She wandered off into a corner of the flat, walled by packing cases, still unpacked, stacks of books, almost ceiling high. She lives, dresses, looks, like the poorest of students. In moments of stress, where others might turn to alcohol, she will indulge in one of her two luxuries: tobacco or mustard. Which would it be? Within minutes, she returned, her face split by a schoolgirl grin. She was carrying a plate on which an old heel of bread, a hank of ham, were buried under a glowing yellow mound.

Trotsky pretended righteous disapproval. "Watch out, comrades, Vera Ivanovna is off on a binge."

Our tension dissolved in laughter.

Later this evening, Trotsky called round to explain that he had tried to discourage the piece but had no authority to interfere. He also cheered me (since I had felt Plekhanov and I were moving apart) by revealing that George had written to Julius and Vera rebuking them and taking the same line as I had. He described

Vera epitomizing the two of us. "George is a greyhound. He will shake you and shake you but in the end he always lets you go. Vladimir Ilyich is a bulldog. He has a deadly grip."

A deadly grip? I liked that.

"You like that," said Trotsky. "So should I. She has her faults. But she senses the approaching tread of the Revolution more directly, more personally, than almost any of us. That is the deadly grip she respects and fears." Lev Davidovich has *his* faults. But he is correcting them. I need him on the editorial board of *Iskra* now.

MAY 12   **LONDON**   **1903**

Iskra has worked well from London. We found typesetters with a Russian alphabet in the East End; printers who run off the British Socialist paper *Justice* every week on Clerkenwell Green and agreed to "squeeze up" with us. But now the call comes, in tones difficult to resist, to move back onto the Continent—all Brits, whatever class, insist this offshore island is not part of Europe!

I tried to obstruct the move. But gradually, I saw that it was not just Plekhanov and Axelrod, then Zasulich and Potresov, finally Martov and Trotsky who urged that the best way to organize our Congress must be from a spot in the landmass center—i.e., they say, Geneva. I too need a better fulcrum than London to tip the delegates my way. So we leave within days. I have exacted one concession—the Congress will be in Brussels. Neutral ground, let us say. At least not on the home turf of the previous generation.

My game plan for the Congress depends on two positions being won. First: control of the Party abroad must rest with the Party organ, *Iskra*. The old board of six no longer represents reality. Never once in the last three years has it met with all members present! We have published forty-five issues. Every single one has been made up and put to bed by either Martov or me, usually both. No one else! Go through the contents index, and see who is writing it too—39 articles by Julius, 32 by me, 24 by George, 8 by Potresov, only 6 by Vera and a miserable 4 by Axelrod. Who can object to a new three-person executive board, Martov, Plekhanov and me, possibly Trotsky? Second: the control of the Party inside Russia must rest with the CenCom. This should include the editorial board of the Party organ plus an open conspiracy of professional revolutionaries with as many workers, as few intellectuals, as possible. If I can seed the ground for this, I don't care where I live.

MAY 13   GENEVA   1903

Painful feelings, as if of nostalgia and deprivation, exile within exile, as we leave London for Geneva. *Iskra* summoned back by Plekhanov and his trusty Axelrod, Vera, Julius and Potresov feebly concurring. If only I'd been able to get Trotsky on the editorial board!

My mistake was to mount too strong a case. "The Pen" has written in every issue since he arrived last October. A brilliant all-rounder, energetic, tireless, *eloquent*. Also would simplify our voting, board of seven instead of six. I should have known. None of these reasons weigh with George. Quite the opposite. He has never forgiven Trotsky for modestly contributing anonymous pieces since many readers assigned them to Plekhanov. He distrusts all talent —especially young, and Jewish, and spectacular talent, and especially recommended by me. One Martov is enough. Far from wanting to "simplify" voting, he is delighted to have the second casting vote. How can I be so naïve?

George twitched every string. Vera was the key—Trotsky and Martov are like her adopted sons. She was happy in London. Like many confused, myopic travelers, she was expert at finding her way around even such a vast, confusing metropolis. Trotsky, now, always turned the wrong way, given a choice, even outside their commune's front door. Being Trotsky, he had a name for it— "topographical cretinism."

One thing every comrade knows (or soon learns) about Vera is that she has no interest, except the most basic, in food. Once some wives of English socialists, paying a visit, asked her what her system was for cooking meat. She replied: "Why, I put it in the oven. Then it depends how hungry I become. If after half an hour, then I take it out after half an hour. If after six hours, I take it out after six hours. It seems to me always cooked right." The wives shuddered.

Crafty Plekhanov writes commiserating with her over the English cuisine—"an oxymoron" he calls it. Claims to be saving her from everything fried, and chips with everything. Oxtails and heads of skate, sprout soup, steak and kidney pudding with dumplings.

I'm sorry to say she was flattered, though I doubt she has ever seen an oxtail or a kidney. I look forward to her introducing Julius and Leon to the culinary delights of Geneva. Like nearly every Jew I have ever known, assimilated or orthodox, I prophesy they will retreat from each dish, raising the right fingers to the left breast, shaking the head, and intoning—"I like it but it doesn't like me."

Anyway, here we are, Nadya and I, in quite a spacious flat. It runs horizontally as with most European accommodation. Only the English construct all housing vertically. It must be to do with their special class system where no one can bear to be on the same level with anyone else. The paper had to arrange this for me because I am suffering an attack of what we called along the Volga "holy fire" but more resembles the pains of hell burning the nerve endings in a great blanket. One of our comrade doctors in London, treating me free, diagnosed "shingles" and prescribed iodine. I now feel ten times the pain, and beg to be allowed to leave my bed and kill him. I think I shall have tattooed on my chest: "Positively No Treatment by Leftwing Medical Personnel."

Possibly I am not quite myself. If so, *it is the fault of that bloody red torturer* . . .

JULY 17   BRUSSELS   1903

Our first Congress of the Russian Social-Democratic Labour Party. (We have to call it the Second because of that gathering of eight people in Minsk in '98.)

How can anyone with a free, questing intelligence find politics boring? The outstanding event of this opening day was Plekhanov's splendid, emotional welcome address, more for its manner perhaps than matter, since there will be plenty of time later to get down to details. Seedy émigrés, used to living frugally in slummy, Bohemian quarters of foreign cities, or gray revolutionaries back home, used to slinking around their own cities like thieves or assassins: we were all invigorated by the sight of Europe's most distinguished Marxist, a Russian, an intellectual with a martial air, reminiscent of "General" Engels in his prime. There is something about his stance, his accent, the way he wears his clothes, the way his clothes armor and enhance him, that suggests a Grand Duke of the intellect, the paterfamilias of the blood royal of socialism. Never mind—his dedication to our agenda is uncompromising.

Hard to imagine the hand of a gendarme, the butt of a police carbine, the bailiff's handcuffs, reaching to him—surely it would wither, and drop off, in midair?

Soon we will start to debate the Party program, going through it clause by clause, concept by concept, phrase by phrase. It may even come to word by word. Over this last year, I have hammered out the proposals with exiles newly released from Siberia; with agitators from Petersburg, Moscow, Kiev, Minsk arriving with the police just behind them; with Parvus and Trotsky; with Martov, Zasulich, Potresov, Axelrod, Plekhanov—that is, each Iskraist separately. In the course of these working spells, I burned off the dross, scoured out the irrelevances, purified, concentrated, hardened the message. The others could come and go, but I was always there. Some deviated, weakened, diluted, leaned this way and that. But, in the end, I not only nailed my flag to our mast, I nailed my *Iskra* supporters to the flag.

Even George seemed about to melt and dissolve for a time. He wanted to adopt the phrase "the power of the proletariat." I insisted on *"dictatorship."* That was what we are aiming for. That is what we must say. He swung back into line.

How right we were! In today's sessions after the keynote address, an attack was mounted by reformists who want to revise Marxism. Make it "more appropriate for this age and our country," demonstrate its consistency with liberalism, democracy, trade-union legality, bourgeois parliamentarianism.

But "the dictatorship of the proletariat" is supported by almost all the delegates, except a handful of "economists" from *Workers' Cause.*

JULY 18   BRUSSELS   1903

The site of the Second Congress is a former flour warehouse in Brussels just behind the Belgian party's GHQ, La Maison du Peuple. This in turn is behind the Coq d'Or where the *peuple* from the Maison have been getting drunk for twenty years, making long speeches at each other, and singing "L'Internationale" with the comrade-waiters at what our London neighbors used to call "chucking-out time." Around 4 A.M. our socialist *patron* (who once ran a soldiers' drinking-den in the Congo) enters, shouts the traditional cry, "Time to call in the dogs and piss on the fire," then falls down.

I try to go past on the far side of the street. But delegates spot me and drag me in so that they can complain about some flour that is seeping out of old sacks. Now they mention it I see that I too have acquired a few snowball prints. So what, I explain, you're not going to be presented to King Leopold. I am more interested, as an exercise in scientific detection, to note how the number of marks coincides quite accurately with the personality of the complainer.

For example, Julius (Martov), who bumps into everything and everybody, a pet universally adored and embraced, is so embossed with white he might have just staggered in from a Siberian blizzard. George Valentinovich (Plekhanov), who keeps his distance, an autocrat universally admired and feared, touching only fingertips, has preserved his famous frockcoat from any contagion except the tiniest spray of light powder like dandruff.

I had thought everything was going so well. I have longed for this Congress. I have driven Nadya night and day, like a pack mule, prodding her with my cane when she seemed about to slide exhausted from the table, transcribing letters to all our *Iskra* agents, our literature distributors, our agitators, across the whole of the Russian continent. Everything, in such undercover work, needs to be done twice. First, I must compose a cover letter, interesting enough to convince the police one must expect to open it that it is genuine, not too dull yet not too well-written. Second, I have to construct the real message, usually about political tactics, probably somewhat abstract and technical. This has to be copied in invisible ink between the lines by Nadya, not only treasurer but (literally) general secretary to the *Iskra* group of the Russian Social-Democratic Labour Party. As we get some three hundred letters a month, the task we perform is no sinecure. I must absolutely, for my sanity, spend half of each day in the library. When I am not writing polemic, I answer these letters, and initiate more.

No wonder my hand grows cramped. My back aches. Few people who do brain work also do such manual work. Nadya does not even have the doubtful reward of using her mind. Her job, all done by hand, is a kind of infernal needlework. No wonder her head grows heavy. Her eyes become blurred. And there hangs about her the mingled smells of heated paper, chemicals and lemon juice—what Plekhanov, in a typical cruel jest, called "*le parfum de Nadya.*"

The first three sessions have made all that worthwhile. I have been elected (a) deputy chairman of the Congress, (b) member of the Presidium, (c) chairman of the credentials committee. These are key power points. And our forces are in good array. Total of 51 votes confirmed by the credentials committee. Of these, 31, a clear majority, support the *Iskra* position and our team, Martov, Axelrod, Plekhanov, Vera Z., Potresov and me.

The rival paper, *Rabochee Dyelo* (*Workers' Cause*) is controlled by economists but carries only 3 votes. The Jewish Bund has 5. And the unaligned center, the loungers, or "The Swamp" as George has christened them, claims 6. If we stick together, this will be *our* Congress.

The last thing I want is some awful farcical element, so common to all Russian enterprises, to rob our deliberations of their authority. Clearly the flour business must be cleared up. Interesting to see that most of the delegates, of whatever group, search out me when they want some practical action. Imagine George or Julius trying to find a hall to rent. I am seen as an organizer and administrator as well as a theoretician, journalist and lecturer.

JULY 19   BRUSSELS   1903

The spirit of low comedy has struck once more. One gain from hanging around the Coq d'Or into the early hours is that sooner or later, usually later, everyone in Brussels labor circles drops in. So I made contact with Jules Ansèle, left-wing chairman of the City Co-operative Society, who offered me a tumbledown stable the Co-op owned.

The Congress moved in there this morning—hardly ideal. No seats, no windows, just a hole to let in some light and a few boxes to elevate the Presidium. But it will do.

I left them all there and went back to my lodgings to make notes for a speech. When I turned up for the afternoon session, I found about forty delegates scattered across the wasteland near the stable. They looked very pink, a bit puffy and irritated with everybody—the Co-op, each other and me.

"We've been attacked by Ansèle's army," said somebody. I looked around, thinking of yesterday's threats from right-wing hooligans.

"You can't see them out here," said Trotsky. "But you'll feel them all right inside. I think they are the secret commando of Belgian Social Democracy, intended to be launched on the capitalists in the last great battle. We just got in the way."

People were beginning to laugh now. "What is the next plague

Jehovah will visit on us?" asked Axelrod. "Ask the Jewish Bund," shouted Martov, sinking down onto a stone and scratching himself. The Second Congress of the Russian Social-Democratic Labour Party was in retreat from an epidemic of fleas.

JULY 20   BRUSSELS   1903

Fourth day of the Congress, sessions six and seven. Are we really in business at last? The kitchen staff at the Coq d'Or are enterprisingly sponging down and brushing up the magpied costumes of the delegates. The *patron*, seen by us for the first time in daylight, proves to have a practical mind hidden behind all those purple, speckled, country-sausage jowls. This morning, seen for the first time by *anybody* before noon, he presented me with the address and the keys of a small, clean, discreet trade-union hall near the lake shore. Here, he guarantees, we will be free from fleas, flour, tourists and street-gangs. All we have to do is agree, each of us, to eat a meal a day at the Coq d'Or.

JULY 21   BRUSSELS   1903

The *patron* forgot one perennial pest. The police. Having ignored us for the first part of the week, this morning they are harassing us on every possible excuse. False passports. Illegal visas. Failure to undergo health checks. Breaches of the building regulations. Carrying concealed firearms. Publishing and uttering seditious materials. Inclusion on wanted lists of international criminals. Emile Vandervelde, leader of the Belgian SDLP, has sent a message, through several intermediaries, warning that the Ministry of Home Security is about to issue a general warrant seizing us all as undesirable immigrants. We have until tomorrow to leave.

So, it must be London. The great maw will swallow us without even picking its teeth. Telegram to Alexeyev, asking for accommodation and some places to meet. It will be almost like coming home.

AUGUST 14   LONDON   1903

Back here in London a week now. Everyone, the *Iskra* group anyway, arrived fizzing with high spirits. We were escaping not just
from Brussels, from an atmosphere of puerile feverishness, flour,
fleas and *flics,* which had become just too . . . On the front deck
of the Ostend-Dover ferry, floating on fog like an airship through
clouds, we searched for the word. "Un-English?" suggested Trotsky. In London, one can *guarantee* being ignored.

Nadya and I are once more on the patch we know best, a
square bounded by King's Cross and Gray's Inn. That first night,
too exhausted to sleep, we all packed ourselves into Alexeyev's two
rooms, herrings in a jar. How wonderful not to have to move, held
up, feet just touching floor, by the bellies and bosoms of your
comrades. Talking of bosoms, Apollinaria acted as resident mascot,
"the thinking man's barmaid" in Martov's phrase. She stood, flashing her skirts, on a pub table handing round gin and that local
delicacy, "sausage roll." We were in such good humor, some of us
ate one.

After four days settling into lodgings, the Second Congress
of the Russian Social-Democratic Labour Party reconvened for its
fourteenth session, in the hall of the English Club, Charlotte Street,
Bloomsbury. Everything has gone well. Majority support, only occasional backslidings in our bloc, for the program I had hammered
out in advance. Crucial interventions from Plekhanov, backing
from Trotsky and Martov. We have declared ourselves a fully
Marxist party, dictatorship of the proletariat the aim we scorn to
conceal. One useful addition from the floor—the election of judges.
The "economists" largely isolated, though occasionally mounting
well-organized, original attacks on our "What Is to Be Done?" line.
For example, Akimov, the eventual sole dissident, argued:

> Lenin's program sets the concept of "party" and "proletariat" in
> opposition to each other. The first is pictured an active, produc-
> tive, virile entity—the masculine principle. The second is seen as
> a passive, docile, mindless mass, a medium to be operated upon
> by the Party.
>   And so the name of the Party is used throughout as the
> subject of any sentence about our program or our policy—the

nominative case. The name of the Proletariat is used throughout as the object of the sentence—the accusative case. Such patterns are not accidental.

Just the stuff intellectuals love, word games, bright ideas! But try interesting working men at the factory gate with politics as grammar! I interrupted to ask whether masculine personal objects should not in fact take the genitive? A dubious proposition. But enough to distract him. Finally, he abstained.

His best hit was when he asked how the Party would be able to reconcile any "dictatorship" with a demand for a democratic republic. Here Plekhanov was invaluable. The success of the Revolution was our highest law, he thundered. No government, even elected by universal suffrage, had a better mandate. Freedom of speech must take second place. No democratic principle existed in the abstract. He sat down to cheers.

Martov and Trotsky followed, apparently reinforcing his point, but to my mind diluting and weakening that iron absolute. Martov reassured the nervous that Plekhanov, *of course,* really meant to emphasize that "it is impossible to imagine so tragic a situation as that the proletariat, to consolidate its victory, would have to trample on such inalienable rights as total freedom of speech." Plekhanov lifted his coattails, bowed, and trilled an ironic *"Merci!"*

Trotsky also seemed unable to comprehend how ruthlessly our proletarian dictatorship must face harsh realities, particularly the reactionary ideas still staining the minds of the people, the fears and prejudices that could be played upon by capitalists as they struggled for survival. He too wooed the indignant by promising that the working classes would never take power until the mass of them agreed in wanting to do so. There was no possibility of *coups* by little bands of conspirators representing only themselves. "It will be *true* democracy, the immense majority ruling in the interests of the immense majority."

He still has not understood Marxism. More important, he has not understood Russia. We are a *tiny* minority. The Russian proletariat is a small minority. How long can we wait until we have a Party and a Proletariat the size they have grown in Germany? And how soon will Germany start to create socialism, with its party rotten with reformism, opportunism, careerism? The best it will do, the way it is going, is to give us Capitalism with a Human Face. Still, as long as Martov and Trotsky vote the correct line on essentials, I can forgive their deviations on trivia.

AUGUST 15   LONDON   1903

Twenty-second and twenty-third sessions—discussion on paragraph one of the Party Rules, "Definition of Membership." Who could have foreseen that this could lead possibly to the bitterest defeat of my political life?

Long before the Congress opened, I had been lying awake at nights calculating the ways the delegates might divide. Whenever one of the counters on the board seemed under the hot glare of my eye to be about to melt, to slide toward the "softs" and the "wets," I would leap from bed and get out his file. I would read, through and through, the details until I knew him by heart. Then next day I would plan how to stiffen him, make him respond to our pressures without knowing he was doing so. I would pick his companions, choose his tasks, surround him with "hards," with my Men of Confidence. If he still seemed to be moving toward the opposition, I would try to disallow him as delegate to any key party body.

Callous, inhuman, manipulative this may be, but to me it is the only way to win at three-dimensional chess where the pieces struggle and twist in your hand. Our stakes are as high as they can be—the future of the Russian Revolution which may control the future of humanity. Each time, mandates came to a total of fifty-one, and out of forty-three delegates, thirty-three were *Iskrists*.

Ever since July 30, session one, I have dozed at nights, sitting up with my arms round Nadya, dreading a time when my arithmetic might start to go wrong. As it has done today.

My proposal has always been that a Party member is someone "who recognizes the Party's program and supports it by material means." I put this and there was no disagreement. I then added: *"and by personal participation in one of the Party organizations."* Martov seconded my main definition but he wanted to substitute for my addition: *"and by regular personal association under the direction of one of the Party organizations."* How is it possible that by the end of the day both he and I are barely on speaking terms, and the largest group in the party, the *Iskrists*, split from top to bottom over these few words?

Many delegates are also puzzled. Some cannot see any difference at all. Others argue it is simply a difference in temperament.

A duel between Martov (whose second is now revealed as Trotsky) and me (Plekhanov holding my coat, carrying my pistols). It's true there is a contrast of personalities—"Robespierre versus Hamlet," according to those who, like children, see life as toy theater with cardboard cutout heroes. But underneath, as the debate progresses, it is becoming clear that there may be deeper divisions, on almost every conceivable aspect of socialist politics, than any of us had guessed.

The "Martovites" yearn for a broad, flexible, popular party, including on its fringes both anarchists and liberals. They think we are in England or in Germany. They dream of a day when they will be able to point at any and every opponent of the autocracy—bomb-throwing student, disappointed officer, suiciding priest, satirical cabaret performer—and say "This one too is working *under the direction of the Party!*"

I have never spoken so often in any group, so passionately, so conscious that defeat will be a disaster from which our movement may not easily recover. Surely Martov could see that for a party confined to secret, exclusive cells, summoning meetings that are illegal and private, it is extremely difficult, let's face it, *impossible,* to distinguish those who only talk from those who do the work. In no other country in the world is the jumbling of these categories so common. Nowhere does it lead to such confusion, such harm, so many losses.

My voice cracked. I could feel my face purpling. I tried to make my argument as direct, simple, immediate as I could: "It would be better if ten who do work should not call themselves Party members (real workers don't hunt after titles) than that one who only talks should obtain the right and opportunity to become a Party member. We must not forget that every member is responsible for the Party and that the Party is responsible for every one of its members."

I looked around the hall, trying to catch and hold each pair of eyes in turn. I wanted to deliver both halves of that message like two blasts from a shotgun. One: Have you put the Party first every day since you joined? Two: How many others do you know who are fit to embody the Party? We must construct a definition that would keep out the opportunists and careerists.

Martov was on his feet almost as much as I was. But it was Trotsky who carried the lance most fiercely against my supporters, speaking with a wealth of wit and irony that disarmed his most dedicated opponents. (All except me, and of course Plekhanov.) He laughed until his snaky pince-nez almost slid off his beak at my idea of Party rules. "I had not realized a special spell of words would act as a statutory *exorcism* of these intruders! I am totally unable to follow this *mystical* interpretation. Are we protecting ourselves from vampires, zombies or the walking dead?

"*We* are Marxists. We know that opportunism is produced by many more complex causes than the wording of rules. We must look instead to the relative development of bourgeois democracy and proletarian consciousness."

Plekhanov restricted himself to seated interjections, but such is his influence that each one rolled back the Martovian ranks for a while. When someone observed that my interpretation would drive away intellectuals who were above all individualists, he said: "So much the better. Such people are usually without any real ideology or political commitment. For this reason, if for no other, opponents of dilettantism should vote for Lenin's draft." When someone else objected that it was impractical to expect inexperienced, backward elements now joining the movement against tsarism to devote themselves as selflessly as the advanced veterans, he snapped back immediately: "If we are to have strict discipline *à la Lenin,* then it is only logical that it must be accepted by every one in the Party, leaders and rank and file."

We wrangled on into the evening. A lot of mud was being stirred. Some was being thrown. In the end we should be the cleaner for it. But then there was the vote, catching me slightly off-balance. The hall fell silent when the figures were announced. Did the Martovites know what they had done? My version of the rules was defeated by twenty-eight votes to twenty-three. The *Iskra* group had divided nineteen to me, fourteen to Martov. Those deviators, plus the five from the Jewish Bund, the two economists from *Raboche Dyelo,* and a couple of centrist floaters from the Swamp, had given the Martov-Trotsky-Axelrod camp their majority.

It was hateful enough that my Party, that Spartan band of brothers (and sisters), should now be encouraged to grow fat and lazy. How could such a diffuse, amorphous soup of unstable dissidents, loosely described as a party, whose members need not even be members if they didn't feel like it, expect to work like yeast in the soft, doughy pulp of the masses?

But a much more disturbing thought struck me—was this to be a permanent majority for the rest of the Congress? Would Martov, that vague, wispy dreamer, be able to have his way on every issue from now on?

AUGUST 16   LONDON   1903

Today I bumped, head on, into one of the "Swamp"—we both, abstracted and thinking of other things, tried to exit through the same door at the end of the morning session. Since he was among the nonvoters hanging around the sides of the hall, cigarette smoke rising from them like steam from a samovar, a late arrival from Russia who had missed the Brussels opening, I had not taken much interest in him. But all opinions are useful, even if only to allow you to decide "this one is not useful." I asked him how he was enjoying our Congress.

He stood there, squinting in that English sunshine which even when hot, as all this month, looks somehow thin and miserly, like workhouse gruel.

"I find it utterly oppressive, the atmosphere. I cannot abide this bitter fencing, this plotting one against the other, these harsh polemics. Such attitudes are deeply lacking in comradeship."

"That's what makes our Congress such a marvelous experience," I replied. "Opportunity for free and open struggle. Opinions have been expressed. Tendencies have been revealed. Groups defined. Hands have been raised. A decision has been taken. A stage has been passed. Forward! That's the stuff for me! That's life! That's not like the endless, wearing word-chopping of our intellectuals which comes to an end, not because the question has been settled, but simply because they are all too tired to talk anymore . . ."

The comrade, staring at me in perplexity, finally shrugged his shoulders. We were talking different languages.

AUGUST 18   LONDON   1903

Over the last two days (sessions twenty-four to -six) the renegade *Iskrists* and their allies have commanded what Martov somewhat apologetically calls a "fortuitous majority." They have won every vote. The issues have been minor and I have not bothered much to defend my corner. Instead, I have used the opportunity, every single time I have been called, to restate our case on Rule One of the Membership Statutes, trying out new angles, coining fresh slogans. Even Apollinaria, who is now an "economist" like her husband, laughed loudly and clapped when I insisted, slumping back in my seat, almost *sotto voce*: "We want a Party where all the members are invited by name, and all know each other—no gate-crashers!"

But that is over. There will be nothing "fortuitous" about *our* majority, I promised myself. So, like a stage magician, I have been openly diverting attention to one hand while the other has been moving, according to plan, out of sight. It is our game! "Mate in two moves," said Trotsky, flashing by in his cape, as the twenty-eighth session broke up and we emerged blinking into the pale, delicate light of a London evening in summer.

It was session twenty-seven that snapped my trap. I could not believe the Martovites could not recognize my strategy, especially since I made what was essentially the same move *twice*!

First piece to be taken was the Jewish Bund. Now Julius (Tsederbaum) and Leon (Bronstein) are both Jews, at least in the eyes of a largely anti-Semitic world. In their own, since both are rationalists, internationalists, socialists, Jewishness is an irrelevance. Nevertheless, nobody creates himself entire, to be honest, perhaps only 10 percent. We are all still part of everything we have been, retaining geological traces of our autobiography, the biographies of parents and ancestors, the history of our region, our class, our race, our nation. So without any philistine, vulgar prejudice, I can register my opinion as sociological/anthropological observer that it is basically because Bronstein senior, that conservative, conformist, Black Sea grain baron, is Jewish that he continues financing the mother of his son's children even though he regards his son's activities as criminal and deluded. *My* father would not have done the same. My *mother* does, it's true. But then all mothers are Jewish mothers. Similarly, no Marxist Ulyanov, descendant of Kalmuk serfs in Astrakhan, German expatriate technicians along the Volga, could hope to travel Russia meeting with relatives who aided him without question in his illegal tasks. (I hope it will never be held against me, by which I mean damage our cause, that I can almost count the few drops of Slav blood in my veins.) Yet Martov-Tsederbaum, while I was in Europe arranging that *Iskra* should actually be printed, was carpetbagging Western Russia, dodging the police, and finding, in the most unlikely corners, Jewish cousins of cousins willing to act as distributors/contributors for the boy Julius's paper.

Sudden thought—is that how he was able to gather as many as fourteen defectors from the *Iskrist* group, delegates I thought I had bound with hoops of steel?

The Bund obviously thought they had friends, if not relatives, making up the majority of the majority. Within the loose-linked, broad-fronted RSDLP *à la* Martov, it seemed only reasonable that the Bund should be allowed, nay encouraged, to decide its own policy, edit its own paper, authorize its own officers, operate as a separate entity for most purposes, while being able to regard, and describe, itself as part of the Russian Social-Democratic Labour Party. I could not have asked for a better example of the extremes of wayward vacillation to which our Party might be exposed under its new Rule One.

Anxious to forestall any charges of partiality or feebleness, and to demonstrate their continued loyalty to the idea of a united fighting force, the Martovites supported my motion to deny the Bund this separatist privilege. They raised their hands in support of my insistence that we were above all internationalists, and we no more wanted independent competing nations inside the Party than we did outside in the world. When the votes were counted, it was obvious that the former *Iskra* group had reunited. The Bund's claim had been denied by forty-one votes to five with five abstentions. The Bund had on its side, standing up to be counted, only its own delegates.

What would they do? I looked away. There was a lot of stamping and throat-clearing. Then shouts—"Good riddance!" "Don't listen to them!" "We're better on our own!"—and then cheers. They had walked out.

With the loss of those five, Martov's majority was gone. We were equal, twenty-three a side. I pressed on to the next division. *Rabochee Delo* wanted to be recognized as one of our official mouthpieces abroad, despite preaching a doctrine condemned by the Congress. Overwhelmingly, it was decided to reaffirm that *Iskra* was our sole representative outside Russia. The "economist" group walked out.

With the loss of those three, Martov was now in a minority of twenty to my twenty-three, even if the floaters stuck with him. He was getting a practical lesson in the superiority of my recipe for a party. My twenty-three remained organized, disciplined, drilled to win. His lot, like the party he had advocated, grew unruly, lazy, ill-informed about policy or tactics. From now on, we were the ones who would win. I could not retract the early decisions, carried though they had been by delegates no longer members. I could make sure all later decisions buttressed the image of a pure, fit, aggressive movement, purged of all lard and dross.

AUGUST 23   LONDON   1903

The last day. Sessions thirty-six and -seven. Ever since the self-liquidation of the Bund and *Rabochee Delo* factions, ours has been the dominant role. We, the "hards" and "drys," have preserved our position as delegates of the Majority (*Bolshinstvo*). The others, the "softs" and the "wets," the compromisers, the conciliators, have stayed as representatives of the Minority (*Menshinstvo*). This has given me the names I have been searching for. Despising the cult of personality, I could not bear "Martovites" and "Leninists." I needed something strong, memorable, instantly recognizable, and precise. This is it—*Bolsheviki* for us, *Mensheviki* for them.

The Bolsheviks are not a party within the Party. We *are* the RSDLP, virtually identical and coterminous with it. We award ourselves the jobs only because we are the ones who do the work.

Only four out of twenty-four items on the Congress agenda have been discussed. Only two of these are important, but they are crucial.

The Party is to be controlled by a Supreme Council, with Plekhanov as chairman. That Council will have four other members, two appointed by the Central Committee and two by the Central Organ. The three-member CenCom is all mine, with Gleb (Krzhizhanovsky), my old neighbor from Siberia, as the major figure. It does not really matter to me which of them is on the Council.

The CenOrg was a more awkward problem. Arguments over it occupied the entire time of nine sessions! I had been careful not to leak my scheme beyond my Men of Confidence. So most delegates assumed the old *Iskra* editorial board of six would be re-elected, with perhaps the addition of a new young talent or two. Trotsky and Rosa Luxemburg had been mentioned, and I had, in earlier times, highly praised both. But rather than expand the board, I insisted that it should contract. I pointed out for the umpteenth time that it had never once met with all six present. Never was a major theoretical issue raised by anyone but me or Plekhanov. I read out the miserable contributions of such as Axelrod—four articles in forty-five issues over three years! He, Vera, Potresov, and Martov had declared themselves entrenched opponents of *Iskra* policy. Did it make sense that they should keep control of that paper?

My proposition was simple—a working *troika*. One Bolshevik, me. One Menshevik, Martov. And, with the controlling vote, the Father of Russian Marxism, Plekhanov. Uproar!

Day after day of shout and counter-shout, not much of it on a very high level. Trotsky, who would have been happy enough to be coopted by the board, argued that we had no moral or political right to change its membership just because we happened to command most of the delegates for the moment. I read out to him the rules the Congress had just reaffirmed, unanimously, giving itself power to elect all Party officials. If Congress could not appoint the editorial board of the CenOrg, who could?

He it was who also started the long-running hare that membership of the board was "too delicate a question" for open debate. Late last night Vera made one of her typical interpolations—as ever, she simply rose, ignored the speaker on his feet, sought no permission from the chair, but revealed what was flickering, like carp across a tank, through her mind. "How will those editors who are not reelected feel about the Congress not wanting to see them on the board anymore?" Martov, tears in his voice, added his words to hers. "I myself will never accept an invitation I am told I cannot refuse. I am not a serf. I do refuse!"

The delegates were tired, depressed, confused. This was no occasion for personal appeals, for individual oratory. I decided I must put the issue as plainly as possible, hosing down the emotion, exposing the reality underneath. I wasted little time on Martov. He was unknowingly the victim of an unattractive minor ailment, "aristocratic anarchism." The point about the serf was that he was *always* at the base of the pyramid, *always* receiving orders, never giving any. In our Party, we proclaimed equality of discipline. Comrade Martov was one of our leaders. He must learn to fulfill the duties the Party imposes upon him just as would any member of the rank and file. "You simply cannot remain here and refuse," I explained. As for Trotsky and Vera, I pointed out:

> Such arguments put the whole question on the plane of *pity and injured feelings*. They are an admission of bankruptcy as regards real arguments of principle, real points of policy. This is a middle-class, not a Party approach. If we adopt this standpoint, we shall have to practice it at every election within the Party. We shall have to start asking each other, "But will Popov not be offended if Petrov is preferred over him on the CenCom?" We shall have to start asking, "Which is the more sensitive, Ivanov or Fillipov?"
>
> Where would this end? Why are we gathered here? Is it to

create a party? Or is it to indulge in mutual back scratching, the passing round of compliments, a bath in schoolgirl sentimentality?

Comrades, we are engaged in *electing officials*. There is no question of lack of confidence in those not elected. Our only consideration should be, and must be, the work to be done and the candidate's suitability for the particular job for which he is being elected.

We are a young party. But already we are showing signs of developing a snug, little, old band of insiders who cannot imagine the continuity of their magic circle being interrupted. These comrades are so accustomed to the bell-jar seclusion of their intimate salon that they almost faint away when an outsider speaks up in a free and open arena inhabited by the rest of us.

There was silence. But it was the silence of agreement, at least of acquiescence. We have won, despite the loss of Rule One. We are the *Bolsheviki*.

JANUARY 10   GENEVA   1904

In the days just after our Second Congress, I thought I had won the almost perfect victory. I had suffered defeat on Rule One. But otherwise my views had triumphed. I had my way on the editorial board of *Iskra,* on the CenCom and the Council of the Party. In effect, I had become leader of the Russian Social-Democratic Labour Party.

In the weeks after that, I decided it would be more accurate to say I was leader of the dominant section, the Bolsheviks, and that my first task must be to rally the dissident minority, the Mensheviks, behind me. I could not believe that a complete split was either possible, or desirable, over what I myself called "trifling" disagreements. Of course, the issues had to be brought into the open, but that would be enough.

The two wings—almost every party, parliamentary or revolutionary, has *two* wings at least—were divided. But not on program or even tactics, only on organizational methods. It was a matter of shading, perhaps even of vocabulary. Did it not seem childish, and absurd, that these might hinder harmonious joint action? Certainly, many Party workers in the factories of Russia wrote disturbing letters complaining that majority and minority were now treating each other as enemies . . . that committees were chosen according to whether they were Bolos or Meks and not the best comrades for the position . . . that it was becoming harder to wage both an internal and an external struggle.

I was so concerned that I wrote to Alexander Potresov, for circulation round the firm of Martov & Co., explaining that I could not see any principle that should leave us parting as opponents for life. Well, here it is, the key passage. Not a total grovel, but nearer to an apology than any of them have come.

> I go over all the events and impressions of the Congress. I realize that I often behaved and acted in a state of frightful irritation, in a "frenzy" some say. I am quite willing to admit this fault of mine to anyone, though I think it less of a fault than a natural product of the atmosphere, the reactions, the interjections, the intoxication of the struggle, etc. But examining now, quite without frenzy, the results attained, the outcome achieved, by that frenzied struggle, I can detect nothing, absolutely nothing, in these results that is injurious to the Party, and absolutely nothing that is an affront or insult to the "Minority."

I threw my bread upon the waters, and the result was rather like being sick into the wind.

Martov refused to join the *Iskra* board with Plekhanov and me. Plekhanov, who had backed me throughout the Congress, suddenly announced: "I cannot bear to fire on my comrades. Rather than have a split, it is better to put a bullet in one's brain." However, instead of doing so and leaving me sole editor, he defied the Congress decision and invited not only Martov, but Vera Zasulich, Axelrod and Potresov, back on the board.

I immediately telegraphed my resignation from *Iskra* and set about agitating for the all-Bolshevik six-man CenCom inside Russia to call a new Congress. By five to one, they denounced my agitation! They endorsed the authority of the now all-Menshevik *Iskra* board! They condemned the split into Majority and Minority! I immediately telegraphed my resignation from the Party Council.

The CenCom wrote a personal letter to Nadya: "We all implore the Old Man to give up his quarrel and begin work. We are waiting for leaflets, pamphlets, all kinds of advice and guidance— the best way of soothing one's nerves and answering slanderous accusations." Do they think I am a machine? I cannot work in this poisoned climate.

Barely five months after my decisive battle, I am retreating on all fronts while my army deserts. The other side have all the marshals—i.e., not just the Veterans, but the best new names, as well as Martov and Trotsky. They are supported by the international movement, by Rosa Luxemburg, Parvus, Kautsky and Bebel. Even my few big guns misfire. I have written to the editorial board with an Open Letter entitled: "Why I Resigned from *Iskra*." They have refused to publish it. I have written to the German Party organ, *Neue Zeit*, defending myself against an attack by Rosa and explaining "Why I Resigned from the RSDLP Council." They have refused to publish it.

I am still defended by the real proletarians inside Russia who are working in secret to stir up a wave of angry demands for another Congress. I am looking everywhere—and I mean *everywhere!*—for backing for another paper. The Mensheviks are nearly all intellectuals. I begin to think I was right originally and have been wavering since in a shameful way. We need a split between real and pretend revolutionaries, men of deeds and men of words. What *is* an intellectual exactly? I must get all my definitions as neat, and clean, and ready for use as—what?—my bicycle. I remember Martov looking at it, rather apprehensively, and saying, "It's like a surgical instrument." I'll show them how to carry out an operation under fire.

MARCH 12   GENEVA   1904

"In order to hold back the Revolution, we need *a nice little, victorious war!*"

Only hours after Count Viacheslav von Plehve, our minister of the interior, made that tyrant's jest to General Alexei Kuropatkin, our minister for war, it was being circulated among Petersburg society. That was toward the end of January. Two or three days later, it had reached us in Geneva on the international gossip circuit. So several thousand people must have recalled it when von Plehve's provocatively aggressive anti-Japanese policy led to the Japanese surprise attack on the Russian fleet at Port Arthur.

That was on January 8, two days before the hoped-for nice little victorious war was officially declared. Two dreadnoughts, *Retvizan* and *Tsarevich*, and the cruiser *Pallada*, were crippled at anchor. On January 9, the Japanese Navy severely damaged four more battleships. On January 10, war *was* declared, and the Japanese went on to sink *Yenesei*, *Koreyets* and *Varyag*.

Von Plehve, virtual prime minister, is said to be the only member of the Cabinet who favored a war. Even he, the fat, pale slug with eyebrows like a misplaced cavalryman's mustachios, wholesale slaughterer of unruly peasants, organizer of pogroms against the Jews, may have been momentarily aghast at the catastrophe he had unleashed. Two days ago came the worst disaster, the sinking of the unsinkable *Petropavlovsk* which went down with all hands, including the veteran hero of the Turkish War, Admiral Makarov. Would you think this would drive any politician from public life? That even the Tsar might lose confidence in such a tragic blunderer?

Every politician knows those times when the government makes every mistake imaginable, is visited by every calamity, seems to have lost all control and yet is buoyed up, and cheered on, by the people who ought to be stoning them. It is a phenomenon difficult to endure, especially by those dedicated to a rational, scientific approach to social life.

So it is today. Despite the incredible losses, all undeniably due to inefficiency and carelessness, the Tsar has never been so popular. Students march in their tens of thousands on the Winter Palace to sing hymns of praise to him and his advisers. Civilians gather indoors and out to cheer speeches of loyalty and admiration. Soldiers are mobbed by patriotic crowds and smothered with gifts. Millionaires announce donations of lorry-loads of rubles for "our boys." And this is duplicated, multiplicated, all over the nation. None of my correspondents can remember such an orgy of national unity behind our beloved Monarch and for our sacred Fatherland.

Von Plehve's nasty, big, disastrous war holds back the Revolution, anyway. No wonder I feel empty, tired, gloomy. I do not want to hear any more about the war—the war between Russia and Japan; or the war between the people and the autocracy; or the war between Bolshevik and Menshevik. I seem to be on the losing side in every one. What I need is to get out of town, away from people, and let my nerves slacken in peace and quiet.

APRIL 3   GENEVA   1904

Halfway through writing a review of the '03 Congress. I am calling
it *One Step Forward, Two Steps Back.* As I write, I have to think. As
I think, I rewrite what I am about to write. Explaining the split to
others, I cease myself to waver. I begin to see why it had to be.
The Party has divided—correctly, fortunately—into two wings. To
the left, the wing of the proletarians; to the right, the wing of the
petty-bourgeois intellectuals.

An extract from a diary kept by Leo Tolstoy has never left
my head since I first read it. He was walking along a path between
two fields. In one, he could see a man squatting, crouched over.
The man was looking down, absorbed, shouting now and then,
gesturing strangely. He seemed a madman. Tolstoy walked across
the grass toward him, unable to imagine what he could be doing.
It was not until he came close that Tolstoy understood. The man
was performing an essential, sensible piece of work—he was sharpening a knife on a stone.

Tolstoy drew no moral. To me, it is an image that fits so much
we do in this world. All the feuds, squabbles, bouts of abuse, lengthy
dissections of words, at the '03 Congress look to the outsider, even
to some insiders, like the posturings of madmen. It is only close
up that it is possible to appreciate what we were doing there. It
was the performance of an essential sensible piece of work—the
sharpening of a Party on its opposition.

MAY 10   GENEVA   1904

Rewarding topic for study by socio-psychologist, preferably trained
in Marxism: How far are individual revolutionists affected in their
political approaches by their inherited temperament and personality?

Very much, one would say, considering Martov—a born "soft,"
or "wet," as these temporizers and compromisers, slaves to idealist
abstractions such as "democracy" and "liberty," believers in objective truths and eternal standards, are becoming called. He and his
kind are like the chicken that will not move once its beak had been
pressed to the chalk mark on the cobbles. Example: I took the title

Bolsheviks, the majority, or dominating, faction, in '03 from a single voting victory on a single issue. And I dubbed our opponents, the Martovites, *Mensheviks,* the minority, the subordinate faction. Even during that Congress, and frequently since, we have been out-numbered, becalmed and marooned on the unpopular side. But we have stuck to our claim to be the real Bolsheviks, while Martov and Co. meekly agreed to be categorized as the Meks, the number twos, forever!

Very little, one would say, considering Trotsky—a born "hard" or "tough." Deep down I sense a diamond-sharp, steel-strong rev-olutionist, as attracted as I am to the words, and the concepts, "irreconcilable" and "relentless." Yet he tends, three out of four times, to side with our ideological, temperamental, enemies in the movement, the Martovites, Axelrod, Vera Zasulich, now increas-ingly Plekhanov. Even armored, head to toe, by my philosophy, I still feel the bruises as Trotsky's blade strikes sparks at every loos-ening joint. But I can admire the dexterity even as I wince.

Example: *Our Political Tasks.* In his new pamphlet, Lev Dav-idovich portrays me as a bargain-basement Robespierre, a bour-geois radical autocrat in a socialist bonnet. My enemies, he cries, I consign to the guillotine. My supporters I bind in shackles. I claim that necessity has decreed I alone am free. I seed local or-ganizations across Russia, and pretend they are already in fruit. Each one parrots a Leninist parody of Descartes—"I am confirmed by Lenin, therefore I am." My policy of centralism is really "ego-centralism." And he foresees the logical result of my policies when "The organization of the Party takes the place of the Party itself; the Central Committee takes the place of the organization; and finally the dictator takes the place of the Central Committee. . . ." This is what I like, the joust on the open plain, the duel in the sun. Fighting the Martovites is too much like being besieged in a fog by a horde of old women, digging away out of sight, until they undermine you so much you sink into the swamp.

So I order an immediate counter-barrage against Trotsky and his roaming lancers. Such Cavaliers, gents on horseback, mounted matadors, are condemned by history to fall before us new Round-heads, in helmets like bullets, firing over open sights at point-blank range. While I welcome his head-on charge, his own allies snipe and mutter. They think this is no way for him to behave, comrade against comrade. After all, Lenin is "on our side" against the au-tocrats. I light the fuse of our heaviest artillery piece, the Friedrich Engels. Let them take cover when *this* drops on their heads! The "General" sounding off in a very similar situation:

Have these gentlemen ever seen a revolution? A revolution is certainly the most authoritarian thing there is. It is an act whereby one part of the population imposes its will upon the other part by means of rifles, bayonets and artillery, all of which are highly authoritarian means. And the victorious party must maintain its rule by means of the terror which its arms inspire in the reactionaries.

JUNE 25   GENEVA   1904

Strange, interesting, *mysterious* day in the country. I see that a personal life could be a full-time profession were there not so much more worthy, more important, jobs to be done in the world outside. Actually, my political career for the last few months has lain so scattered in such ruins I might as well explore the dangers and excitements of personal relations. A pity I have no male friend with whom I can talk. To consult women about women (I know that much at least) can be to leap out of the frying pan onto the breakfast plate. It is not that I have any particular problem. It is just that I can't quite make out what is happening. And above all things I hate that.

Maria Moisseyevna Essen has been staying with us in our two-up, one-down cottage outside Geneva at Sercheron. It is the sort of place that city-dwellers rent impulsively one hot, stuffy day for a summer by the sea or the lake, then hate after ten days of nothing to do and no one to visit. On the bleak side, but we like it. We create our own neighbors by importing them from the town. Two/three bedrooms, half/workroom, and large tiled kitchen, strewn cushions, perpetually set table, and steaming samovar.

Maria's party-name is *Tver*—"wild creature." Such names are supposed to be noncommittal, though the fashion is growing to make them flattering to the user—"Fearless," "Indomitable," "Invincible," like battleships; or "Giant," "Man of Metal," "The Sword," like characters in children's adventure tales. Tver is more-or-less a neutral, objective description. She is one of those Jewish heroines nothing can dash or downcast. I suppose she must be thirty-two, since she was a friend of Oly's at Peter U., and a longtime friend of all the family. Anyway Anna says so. Though only Anna would think it seemed plausible on the face of her.

On the face of her, Tver is a black-and-white mosaic. Black hair parted in the middle, black eyes, black lips; white cheeks and brow, white fingers, white feet. She might be a plaster cherub pelted with balls of soot, or an imp of darkness rolled in flour. Who can tell? She never stops long enough in one place or one pose.

Originally, I had been hesitant about using her on missions where she might get hurt. It seemed like employing a butterfly to do the work of a carrier pigeon. But she is a born survivor. Sent to Siberia around the turn of the century, she decamped in '02 and traced *Iskra* to Munich where its editor, this "Lenin," turns out to be *me*. I sent her back to Peter to peddle the paper. In May '03 she was arrested again. She escaped again a few weeks ago. Even I had to agree she needs a holiday. Especially as there is now no *Iskra,* except for the Mek rag that has retained its name. I've no doubt, though, she will be back over the border soon. Witness this morning. I woke to my iron cot rocking and a voice crooning: "Ilyich, Ilyich, a farewell spree! One of your outings! One of those famous outings I dreamed about in my cell. And not a word of politics."

We set off, a quartet, by boat to Montreux. We lost mother-in-law, Elizaveta Vasilyevna, among the shopping arcades. Then we went on to the Castle of Chillon, where in the sixteenth century Swiss rebel Prior Bonivard, legend has it, was chained to a pillar below the level of the lake for four years. All three of us have been behind bars, so we had some fellow feeling. Tver kept trying to remember the opening of Byron's sonnet, written on the spot in 1816. Coming out of the darkness our pupils dilated like cats' eyes, the sunlight was a lightning flash that never ended.

Our little friend became excited. "Look at this turbulent, *exultant* scenery, Ilyich, Nadya!" she cried. "How can you bear to just look at it? I want to be *in* it! I want to *be* the scenery!"

Her voice was all exclamation marks, "screamers" we call them in the newspaper business. I squinted around. The spreading countryside didn't look very arousing to me. More like a patchwork quilt in a very, very chilly bedroom. Still, she deserved to be indulged.

"All right, wild one. The old man will race you to the top of that mountain. Both of you."

Nadya waved a declining hand and said she'd wait for us at the hotel.

My arms and legs are so used to my daily exercises, my regular, long, fast swims, my short, fierce bursts of weight-lifting, that they operate free of conscious control. I steamed along the road, then cut off into the snow, seeking the most direct route to the top.

Maria kept level, though wasting energy leaping and cavorting, talking away to me, about what I still do not know. When locked into physical work, my mind separates from my body and rides free on its own kite strings. What the body does, I barely notice.

So it was a while later that my ears began warning me that there was a worrying noise nearby. I looked round. We were nearly at the top. Breath was sucking in and out of Maria's lungs with a gurgle like a bath emptying. She was still keeping up with my piston knees, but on all fours, the snow melting in her hands. I surged ahead and reached the summit. This was the view of the world in miniature that Satan, Hebrew for "the Enemy," that is, Rome, conjured up to tempt Jesus, the Jewish revolutionary.

I was back to politics, and sat down to think.

Maria was muttering something about holding in her palm all the zones and climates of the planet—ice and snow, juicy Alpine meadow, the valley edged with the hot vegetation of the south-lands.

She sat in front of me, wrapping me round with limbs that were slippery with sweat under layers of wool, kissing me with a cool, sweet mouth.

"What are you thinking now? Now. This very minute."

"I was just thinking how wonderful the Party would be if the Mensheviks didn't keep messing things up."

She let out a deep howl and gripped me tighter.

"Have you no soul? If you must think about the class struggle, can it not be a thought for Bonivard, the chains and the pillar, the lake rising? *Eternal Spirit of the chainless Mind! Brightest in dungeons, Liberty! thou art: For there thy habitation is the heart—The heart which love of thee alone can blind . . .*"

The Byron was in English. I didn't understand it entirely— whose heart was it being bound or freed? Swiss history is one of my specialties. I brought Tver up to date with the latest scholarship.

"Did you know Bonivard was never chained? Nor kept beneath the level of the water? Four years is hardly an eternity—think of Blanqui! After his release, he lived on into his seventies. He was married four times. He had his last wife, a beautiful, passionate, young, wild beast, drowned because of her adultery."

She pressed closer and I could not retreat. Anyway, my body had still not returned to my control.

It was dark when we followed our own trail back down the mountain. As we reached the lights of the hotel, I said: "About the Mensheviks . . ."

JULY 1   GENEVA   1904

Maria, our wild beast, left today for Kiev. I have briefed her to sound out the demand among militant workers in Greater Russia, not just around Peter and Moscow, for a real, fighting, illegal paper as an alternative to that puling, apologetic sheet, the Menshevik *Iskra*. She will bring back a true picture, quite unvarnished. We are, to use a technical term from Popov's invention, the "wireless," *on the same wavelength*.

The three of us have been on several more outings, rucksack on back, through deserted landscapes that made Nadya shudder and complain: "You two go where there isn't even a living cat. I like some company about." So Tver and I leave her on a rug by the tree line with her dictionaries and notebooks, translating away. We climb into nothingness where there is only you and the sky, with an occasional surprise cloud of snowflakes the size of a bathtub sliding by like a liver spot on your eyeball. Looking down, however high we go, Nadya never becomes so tiny that she ceases to be Nadya, such is the magnifying lens of the air. There is something about mountains that brings out the worst in humanity—here individualism becomes a mania. Mountain-lovers become seduced by the desire to imitate supermen, to serve living gods, to advance divinely chosen dictators. No place for a decent socialist!

We talk little on these ascents, some of which are quite difficult, and not always very safe. We move together, like acrobats, like dancers. It is all a matter of balance and leverage as in an Oriental martial art where a tiny pressure produces a powerful force, a second's finger rest can support the entire body weight. But we have never come together again as we did on the afternoon of the expedition to the Castle of Chillon.

Sometimes, as we stand there, panting and grinning, her black eyes nail me. "About the Mensheviks . . ." she will say, taking my hand and squeezing it. "No politics!" I reply, squeezing her hand and returning it.

I will miss her, though I think I have had enough of climbing for a while. Nadya and I intend to spend the next week or two tramping the side roads, as much on the level, or up and down slight inclines, as Switzerland can provide.

SEPTEMBER 19   GENEVA   1904

Back again in Geneva since last weekend, this time in the center of the city, also the heart of the émigré district, a two-room flat at Rue Carouge 91. Almost next door to Lepeshinsky's, the famous "CommCaff" where all the socialist factions eat, though not always meet, in separate clusters along its long tables.

Nadya and I have been away on holiday since early July. To our surprise, it was almost ten weeks. It could have been equally ten days or ten months. We wandered, without plan or timetable or map, like vagrants or refugees through a sort of lost world. I remember one day coming on a roadside sign saying "Frutigern" and wondering where it was in Switzerland. (I knew it must be Switzerland because it had a post office.) I sent off a postcard of cowbells to Mother, "Greetings from the Tramps."

We have eaten mainly bread and cheese and eggs. We drank whatever was poured from the nearest jug—warm, sweet milk; stony-cold well water; cloudy, strong beer smelling of hops; white wine, clear and dry and sharp with faint acid aftertaste. For the first few nights, we had not the energy to face an evening meal. We staggered into the hospitable farmhouse or the somewhat more stuffy small hotel, like competitors in a marathon walking race, tore off a few clothes and fell unconscious on the bunks.

Gradually, we found our form and could qualify as professional gypsy-travelers. When it suited, we slept rough, picked our food from the hedges, washed ourselves and our clothes in the frothy mountain streams. Then came a period when we skipped washing for a few days every few days. Nothing seemed to get much dirtier if you ignored it.

It was interesting about faces. Visitors who stick to a regime in the lakeside villas or the mountain village guesthouses brown all over like roast chicken. We became weathered like old clapboard in a pattern of overlapping patches, ranging from burgundy to mahogany, as if camouflaged. Quite attractive aesthetically, perhaps, but not encouraging trust among the natives. At some farmhouses, the dogs kept us at a distance, while small hotels did their best to discourage us from wanting a room. We hit on an admirable compromise I would commend to anyone. It was a piece of advice from an SDP comrade we met on the way. "Go to the hotel, but ask for a servant's room. It's less than half the price, the food's better, and it's all much jollier belowstairs."

This gave Nadya more satisfaction than almost anything else on our meanderings. "Talk about bourgeois democracy and there being no class antagonism in Switzerland. But it is more than any of these ladies and gentlemen could stomach, sharing a table with waitresses, coachmen and kitchen-hands." In the early mornings, I was out with the bootblacks in the courtyard, larking around, gossiping about the guests, and hearing sometimes hair-raising anecdotes about a routine exploitation of ordinary folk that is still taken for granted.

In the middle of all this rusticity, ever and anon a Bolshevik thought struck me. I would turn my boots toward the post office and give wing to a flock of telegrams instructing, questioning, advising, summoning, what comradely colleagues I still retain— almost down to the dimensions of the Apostles. At the end of August, I even descended on the Lac de Bré for what we christened, for publicity purposes, the "Conference of the Twenty-Two"—a gathering of hard Bolsheviks who petitioned the CenCom, now solid with "conciliators," for a Third Congress. Actually, only nineteen turned up. Though these included some exceptionally talented and original figures, who will be more than a match for Martov and Trotsky when we launch our new paper. Still, I made a point of flushing out another three, just to keep the record straight, before we adjourned.

My own physical appearance did no harm. It gave them all something to joke about. Dr. A. A. Bogdanov, medical man, economist, novelist, sociologist, philosopher, one of our promising new recruits, pretended to identify me as Jack o' the Woods, or the Green Man, that pagan vegetation deity, who has co-existed with Jesus for 2,000 years. He can be found peeping out among the tendrils on the papal throne, between the legs of saints and prophets in Christian cathedrals! Not to be outdone, another recent adherent, A. V. Lunacharsky, philosopher, dramatist, journalist, compared my impact to that of the Old Man of the Mountain (I had not realized there had actually been such a person). He unnerved the whole Middle East by keeping out of sight but hiring out his assassins to remove his clients' enemies. This was a true *holiday* conference, not to be taken too pompously.

Nevertheless, it is coming to fruit. Before I went on my *wandervogel* trip, I had been bemoaning our central weakness—money. Big money. Without it, we were condemned to a sterile, dusty, vegetable existence. Now, we have pipelines that are starting to stiffen and swell with cash flowing in. All our pseudonyms are coughing up. "The Bucket"—Aunty Kalmykova (2,000 rubles). "The Letter"—Maxim Gorky (3,000 rubles). The one nobody knows beyond his/her cover name—"The Great California Gold Mine" (3,000 rubles). The mad millionaire Savva Morozov (2,000 rubles). They have grown fed up with me writing—"First and foremost comes an organ, and again an organ, and money for an organ." The "Twenty-Two" are impressed.

This is another source I ought perhaps not to note, even here. Even the solidest anti-war Bolsheviks—and the Japs are smashing us back, a crushing blow every month—have a streak in them of the jingo. I assured Konni Zilliacus, the Finnish left nationalist leader, that our part of the Party unconditionally backed the independence of small nations, specifically Finland. In return, he has passed on one of his most generous backers, someone whose treasury has already financed many kinds of socialist and revolutionary—Colonel Motojiro Akashi of the Mikado's secret intelligence service! (Possibly 20,000 rubles.)

Morally, I see no problem—our enemy's enemy becomes our ally. But as a matter of practical politics, there are difficulties. The more I investigated, the less important they become. Precedent is all in such transactions. I was following in the footsteps of a Finnish socialist, Zilliacus, legally a Russian citizen; also Joseph Pilsudski, a Polish socialist, whose brother was hanged with my Sasha, also legally Russian; the Socialist Revolutionaries of Russia; various Ukrainian and Georgian groups, more nationalist than socialist, but still today *Russians*. The colonel has approached Plekhanov and Vera, who didn't accept but *didn't refuse*. What can I lose?

Now we have the cash for *Vperyod* (*Forward*), our own organ. It will appear in January next year. At last, we will be able to arouse the people against the war. Like Pilsudski, like Zilliacus, like all progressive subjects of the Tsar, we will demonstrate that the defeat of Russian tyranny is *our* victory. Nineteen five may be the year of our revolution.

DECEMBER 20   GENEVA   1904

What *is* an intellectual? Odd question from me since I am one, since I am surrounded by them, since I think they are essential to the Party. Yet without a precise understanding of their nature, their function, their strengths and weaknesses, we will never solve the disputes raging among us about how the Party must operate. My method has always been to argue through the answer to such questions, simply, directly, concretely. So . . .

The intellectual is not a capitalist. True, his standard of living, his taste, is middle-class. He is conscious that he must maintain this if he is not to slide into pauperism. He is compelled to sell the product of his labor, often his labor-power by the hour. And so he himself is often enough exploited, and even personally humiliated, by the capitalist or his agents. Hence he does not stand in any direct opposition to the proletariat or to the bourgeoisie. He holds himself at a right-angle to both. But his status in society, his style of life, the conditions in which he works, are still not proletarian. This gives rise to a certain antagonism toward ordinary people in his sentiments and ideas.

As an individual on his own, the proletarian is nothing. It would be sentimentality to imagine otherwise. He does not have the education, the leisure, the incentive to make his personal dent on the fortress walls of society. His whole strength, his chance of progress, all his hopes and expectations, are derived from solidarity, when he forms part of a big, efficient, powerful organization. This is the main thing for him. By comparison, the individual counts for very little. The proletarian fights quite naturally as part of an anonymous mass, without prospect of personal advantage or personal celebrity. He has been conditioned to do his duty in any post to which he has been assigned. There is nothing alien to him in acting the same as the others. This is his protection as well as his power and it stems from a voluntary work discipline which pervades all his feelings and colors all his observations.

The situation of the intellectual is quite different. He does not fight by means of physical presence, by weight of numbers, but by argument. His weapons are his personal knowledge, his personal talents, his personal convictions.

The proletarian does not expect to rise in society, to be given better jobs with better pay. At most, he wishes for a mild, evolutionary betterment. The worst would be a revolution in his circumstances and the loss of his work. The intellectual can attain almost any position at all, but only through his personal qualities. Witness my father, son of a serf, who died a hereditary nobleman.

The successful intellectual feels no gratitude, no loyalty, to any group, sect or class. It seems to him there is only one prime condition for worldly advancement and that is the freest play of his own individuality. It is only with difficulty that he submits to being a part subordinate to the whole, and then only from necessity, not from inclination. He fully recognizes the need for obedience to some rules but only for the masses. Not for the élite, for the elect minds. It goes without saying that he is among these last. Nietzsche's philosophy, with its cult of the superman, for whom the fulfillment of his own personality is everything and any subordination of that individuality to some great social aim is vulgar and despicable, is the real philosophy of all intellectuals. Unless this can be cut out of them, it renders them unfit to take part in the class struggle of the working people.

Today, in our Party, Martov, and now Trotsky, and now Plekhanov, behave like intellectuals of the most self-corrupted kind. They have not cut out the fatal growth. They are feeding it until it blossoms.

JANUARY 6   GENEVA   1905

Strange tale in a French paper that usually carries accurate, unsensational reportage from Petersburg. Two days ago, during a twenty-five-gun royal salute from the Peter and Paul fortress, not all of them fired the usual blanks. Two live shells sailed across the Neva and landed on the embankment in front of the Winter Palace. They did not explode—just like many of the duds fired at the Japanese. But could the unidentified artillerymen who loaded them have known that? Or wished that? Was it the sort of accident that could happen to any Tsar? Was it a bungled attempt at assassination?

According to the French correspondent's dispatch—Russian papers not being allowed to print such details—the Tsar has decided to take no chances. He and his wife and children have put some fifteen miles between them and more such mishaps by moving out to a slightly larger palace at Tsarskoe Selo.

So it seems that Father Gapon's famous pilgrimage next Sunday, leading some 200,000 tame, timorous, respectable paupers, will find no one at home—certainly no exalted, semi-divine Romanov—to accept their humble petition and listen to their bleating prayers. My agent, Gusev, has been assuring me for months that Gapon is a paid agent of the secret police. His government-financed union, the Society for Mutual Aid for Working Men in the Mechanical Industries, has apparently been solely designed to siphon off the people's frustration. Its members are permitted to respectfully request half a ruble on the week's pay, half an hour off the day only so long as they have police officers present at all their meetings. Every plea must be linked with expressions of deep respect and endless loyalty to the Tsar.

I have urged our people to explore the possibility that a few infiltrated Bolsheviks might be able to politicize their demands, stiffen their language, and radicalize those sincere working men who are rising in the leadership. I don't have much hope, especially since I hear that the Mensheviks are ahead of us here, but it's worth a chance.

The first number of *Vperyod* is out today. Now we ourselves can say these things.

JANUARY 9   GENEVA   1905

Gusev, our would-be Bolshevik Clausewitz from Geneva, nose always in some military history ("I've been thinking about what Caesar would have done," he said to me once in the early days of our war with Japan), has been three months in Peter. Return to Russia, shop floor contact with the workers, daily experience of dictatorship, have toughened, sharpened, altogether improved him.

He writes to congratulate me on the reincarnation of our old *Iskra* on January 6 under the title of *Vperyod*. He has just received the first issue. And he complains, rightly, that this single copy is hardly much of a weapon in the struggle against tsarism. Still I am glad he approves of my piece, on page one of number one in volume one, which he is arranging to circulate as a leaflet. Particularly this nub:

> A military collapse is now inevitable, and together with it there will come inevitably a tenfold increase in unrest, discontent and rebellion. *For the moment*, we must prepare with all energy. *At that moment*, one of those outbreaks that are recurring, now here, now there, with growing frequency, will develop into a tremendously popular movement. *At that moment*, the proletariat will rise to take its place at the head of the insurrection to win freedom for the entire people and to secure for the working classes the possibility of waging an open and broad struggle for socialism, a struggle enriched by the whole experience of Europe.

He likes that bit, I realize, partly because it is about his favorite subject—fighting. And I sense that he also considers some of the rest is wishful thinking, the triumph of hope over experience. As he is our man on the spot—and I have repeatedly stressed to all my correspondents that I want facts, not theories—perhaps he ought to know best. Noted and logged also his report that the workers as a body still distrust Social Democrats of all shades. Amazingly, thousands prefer to pin their favors on the damned police-unions originated by Okhrana chief Colonel Zubatov, and fronted by such as Father Gapon, the former prison chaplain. It is true that, here in Geneva, I am far from the factory bench and the tenement hovel, the coal face of the movement. Nevertheless, I am able to put together my map of the terrain, pinpoint the forces involved, estimate the chances of success, by using information available to me from all over Europe and Asia. I do not have to rely as Gusev does for every item of news that I have not checked at first hand, on a corrupt, biased and, above all, censored press. Zubatovism must be made to operate *for* us, not instead of us.

He goes on to rebuke me for my failure to use the Japanese war, and our government's litany of defeat after defeat, as ammunition to destroy the Russian masses' faith in their rulers. He has combed through every speech, letter, pamphlet, and newspaper editorial by me in 1904. He can only find three acknowledgments that there is a war on. I have thanked him for this. I do not hesitate to berate the backslider or the slacker. Bolshevik democracy requires I open myself to being scolded. Even if my critic is wrong, it shows that he is *thinking* about what we are doing.

What he writes is true. I *have* ignored the war, as have Trotsky and Martov. Partly because of the amazing strength of what I dubbed last February "the Far Eastern Effect." Many people now find it convenient to forget that even Tolstoy turned into a jingo! When such storms of irrational emotion grip a country, it is best for those of us immunized against the infection to bend rather than break. But I was never in any doubt that this poisonous froth would melt away, leaving behind a deposit of shame, guilt, anger and a desire for revenge against those at home who misled us. Most of my energies during '04 have been devoted, as indeed they have been since 1900, to building a revolutionary party. When the opportunity arrives—and here in beastly abroad, accursed afar, I can already glimpse it raising its fist to hammer on the door—we must be ready to take the offensive. Our machine must be the first to advance oiled and ready. And it must be *our* machine.

I wish Gusev and the other comrades on the Peter Bolshevik Committee had been here around me just before Christmas when

the news came of the fall of Port Arthur. I spoke within minutes
of being shown the headlines in the foreign press. Russia's military
might, long the bulwark of European reaction, the mercenaries of
international capitalism, had been broken and scattered across the
Manchurian plains, sunk deep among the Pacific seaweed. Yes,
Europe's bourgeoisie had reason to be afraid! Yes, the world's
proletariat had reason to rejoice! We were celebrating the catastrophe that had struck our vilest enemy. A blow not only for Russia's freedom but also a signal for the upsurge of workers everywhere.
Progressive, advanced young Asia had inflicted a fatal wound on
retarded, autocratic, old West. I gave a toast—the capitulation of
Port Arthur, prologue to the capitulation of Tsar Nicholas!

I must reprint it as an article in *Vperyod* No. 2. And make sure
Peter gets plenty of copies.

JANUARY 23   **GENEVA**   **1905**

Despite my confident prediction in the first number of *Vperyod* that
"every step brings us nearer to a great new war, the people's war
against absolution, the war of the proletariat for freedom"—nothing of this kind was much in my thoughts as Nadya and I walked
into town this morning.

I was actually resenting the fact that Swiss bakers have such
a powerful union they refuse to work Sunday nights. For this
means that there is never any fresh bread for breakfast or even
lunch on Mondays. A typical strand in the curtain of trivial ob-
sessions which shrouds all exiles. Others are—prejudices against
the host-nation's food, boredom with your intimates, malevolence
against your allies, homicidal hatred of possible rivals, overfami-
liarity with the same walk, the same desk, the same seat by the
window, the same wait for the postman, the same late arrival of
hometown newspapers. So the news I met in the street struck me
like a lightning bolt. And that is a simile more accurate than it
sounds. What I heard left me as it did the others not so much
excited and invigorated as shocked and almost apathetic.

Coming in the opposite direction, on their way to our flat,
were the Lunacharskys. Anatoly Vassilievich is one of those clever
fellows who give "brilliant" a bad name. With every degree his
brain gets more precise, his character becomes softer. For every
bright idea, he has a stupid emotion. He impresses you as a marvelous orator so long as you do not need to report a single worth-

while thing he has said. He looks as if he must be a born leader, except to those who know he is incapable of organizing the seating plan for a dinner for four. He does not know that everyone likes his wife very much and, if it were not for her, almost nobody would speak to him. Anyway, there they were today, more colorful than ever, their faces blushing and blenching with successive feelings. Anne could not speak. She just waved her muff in a helpless way. Anatoly had half a dozen papers under his arms. He kept pointing to small items in the late-news stop-press boxes. "It's the Revolution, I think. . . . They've shot them all down. . . . The people are crying out 'There Is No Tsar.' They're calling it 'Bloody Sunday.' "

All they knew (all we know, still, in the early hours of Tuesday) was that the army fired into Gapon's unarmed procession; that the official figure for those killed then was one hundred; that the street fighting that has followed the throwing up of barricades may result in two or three thousand more casualties. There is little point in talking since all that would do would be to shuffle rumors and arouse false hopes. So we found ourselves drawn back again toward "Karouzhka" (the Bolshevik corner of the city where our Rue Carouge meets the river Arne) like iron filings tugged by a magnet. Here are the editorial offices of *Vperyod,* not much bigger than a *kvass* stall on the Nevsky, the late-night post bureau, the apartments of several of the leading comrades, including ours, and, most frequented spot of all, Lepeshinsky's brasserie, the "CommCaff," next door at No. 93. Here, as the day wore on into night, almost everyone we knew appeared. Since no one had anything to say, and Russians can never remain silent, we began to sing—folk songs, laments, popular ditties of our youth, an occasional satirical ballad, finally, of all things, the "sacred" revolutionary Funeral March— "You Have Fallen in the Struggle."

We filled the six long trestle tables, sitting on benches: for Lepeshinsky's is arranged more like a soup kitchen, or the canteen of a regiment, than a conventional European restaurant. And when we came to the lines

> Tyranny will fall,
> And the people will rise up—
> Great, mighty and free!

we all stood in obedience to some atavistic instinct, such as that which makes birds wheel in unison, and clinked with our neighbors whatever was in our hand. This was by no means always alcohol.

The émigré community contains many eccentrics and individualists—not just vegetarians and nondrinkers, but devotees of every kind of diet and health regime. So vodka glasses rang against bowls of fermented mare's milk, China tea and Turkish coffee were twinned aloft. Mad Mikhail from Beyond the Arctic Circle, at eighty-nine our oldest member, quaffed that mysterious rusty beverage rumored to be his own urine.

To any outsider, we must have looked very odd—nearly 250 exiled revolutionaries cast into deep mourning by the possibility of revolution at home. Probably suspended animation best described my own feelings. Just so might the Pope greet the first report that someone called Jesus had just climbed down a golden ladder from the sky. Of us all, Julius (Martov), who lives an upside-down bat-like life working all through every night, had been there longest because he had heard the news first. He sat quite still, chain-smoking—N. says she counted thirty-five cigarettes in three hours. Trotsky came through the door, back on the milk train from a lecture in Berne, clearly expecting an almost empty room (Lepeshinsky never closes). He looked at us and then at the fresh, clean newspaper in his hand (ours were all worn to tatters).

"The Gapon Demo was called off, then?" he said, scanning the stop-press. "Is that it?"

There was uproar! Was it all an hysterical invention, a journalistic lie, a trick of the Okhrana? Trotsky could find no mention of any clash between people and army in Russia. But in half a minute, I established that the Pen had made an untypical slip. What he had picked up at the station was *Sunday*'s paper. We were now all in such a state that nobody cared what anybody was doing. Everybody drifted off to bed (except for Martov) still unsure exactly what had happened in Petersburg on "Bloody Sunday."

JANUARY 31   GENEVA   1905

We have now assembled the Russian and the foreign papers, checking them against the reports from Gusev and our other agents. "Bloody Sunday" is the most significant event of this century. Zubatovism has been blown to pieces with its own explosive—the proletariat! The way lies open for a train of revolutions across Russia!

The key text for any study must be the remark publicly attributed to General Trepov in 1901—"Policemen are obliged to be interested in the same things as revolutionaries." He should know. Commander of the Peter gendarmes, he still carries the scar from Vera Zasulich's bullet. By the turn of the century, opponents of the Tsar's rule were to be found metastasizing across society. There had been three murderous famines in five years, yet the rent of land to smallholders had doubled. The grain barons continued to export at high profit while bread in the cities was too expensive for whole neighborhoods. There were risings in the countryside put down by punitive expeditions who machine gunned villages and flogged the survivors just as if they were hill tribes in British India or black mutineers in the Belgian Congo. The Tsar was colonializing his own subjects.

The peasant need for protection and revenge evokes a nostalgia for Narodnik terrorism among some intellectuals, hence the Socialist Revolutionary party. The shortage of capital among the rising entrepreneurs reveals a middle-class need for a liberal opposition. Wherever industry expands, Trans-Siberian railway lines are laid, armaments factories set up, the investment comes from France. The huge profits return to international financiers on the Bourse. Russia is classed as an underdeveloped continent ripe for looting, another Africa or Canada. The founding of the Constitutional-Democrat party, the Kadets, by a professor of history does not quite rank with the Liberation of the Serfs or the assassination of Alexander II. Only the war, as ever in Russia, finally precipitates change. But the Japanese War, like the Crimean War and the Turkish War, shakes the foundations. Former radicals, such as Peter Struve, begin 1904 telling us "War is the supreme test of our nation." Now, as 1905 dawns, they discover "War is economic nonsense." Neat proof of the analysis I made before either the SRs or Kadets existed—liberals and terrorists are two heads on the same body. "In their single heart, neither has any faith in the masses."

The Okhrana, however, knows better. Around 1900 General Trepov's equivalent in Moscow, Colonel Zubatov, hit on the device of keeping control of the only real revolutionary force, the proletariat, by secretly providing its organizations with leaders from the government service. These trades associations became immensely popular, powerful, militant—why wouldn't they? They were awash with state funds, even paying out strike benefit. Since they had to be seen to win their struggles against the employers, at least occasionally, the authorities gave them a helping hand. Capitalists began to complain to Zubatov that their foremen and managers, loyal employees and nonstrikers, were threatened by burly toughs, often with revolvers down their belts, who took no

notice of the police. Who were they—Japanese agents, SDP assassins, SR terrorists, liberal mercenaries? Zubatov could not reply.
Unlike almost all big-city workers and bosses, he knew the toughs
were his own plainclothes detectives in the service of "Police Socialism." History steam rollers on, regardless of individuals. Zubatov lost his job, was sent into exile in '03. Von Plehve was blown
up by an SR bomb, made by one of my rising stars of Bolshevism,
Leonid Krassin. It is only halfway into 1904, the year of von Plehve's
nice, little, victorious war.

In the capital, Father Gapon's government-financed union of
metalworkers is one of the great successes of Zubatovism. When
12,000 of his members from the huge Putilov works went on a
four-day strike on January 3, because four of them had been sacked,
most people assumed they would win some concessions.

Instead, the owners dismissed them all and refused to take
them back. If management were not allowed to manage, they argued, free enterprise would be crushed between the workers and
the state. By the second week, the strikers' families were turning
knobbly and gray with hunger. In the third week, the owners began
hiring non-Association labor shipped in from the impoverished
countryside. Father Gapon's reputation was in danger.

The Putilovites appealed to their idol. A puritanical lecher,
blasphemous believer, government rebel, he proved able to convince himself in whatever role he chose. On January 21, he wrote
an oddly preachy, rhetorical, wonderfully insolent letter to the
Tsar on behalf of his members. He and they would be marching
on the Winter Palace the next day. "But do not fear anything. I,
the representative of the working men, and my comrades, guarantee the inviolability of Thy person."

But the Tsar had decamped, warned off by those two live
shells on his breakfast balcony. The Tsar's ministers had seen the
letter, knew its demands, and ordered Gapon's arrest as well as
the banning of his procession. They were too late. The 200,000
carried icons into the city, pictures of the Tsar, slogans of love and
admiration. They also had with them a petition that covered five
closely printed pages. Workers' committees, infiltrated by anarchists and Social Democrats, mainly Meks, had written in many political demands. These appeared occasionally on modest banners
carried by the procession—"Ten Hour Day," "Free Health Care,"
"Constituent Assembly," "No Censorship," "Land for the Peasants," "A Living Wage."

Petersburg has been designed by its rulers, beginning with
Peter the Great, as a city easy to police and patrol, hard to invade.

Processions along those wide, spacious boulevards become magnified, easily frightening both marchers and marched against.

On January 22, all the strands of history came together in the square in front of the Winter Palace. So did all the strands of the massive demonstration pouring in through five entrances. As usual under tsarism, a combination of small weaknesses touched off the monstrous crime—mainly stupidity, stubbornness and inefficiency.

The front ranks of the mild, the meek, the poor, the naïve, the trusting, their wives and children beside them, were ordered to stop. Some couldn't hear. Some did not take the command seriously. Most were simply pushed on by those behind. The soldiers panicked inside while remaining standing to attention. Then somebody, somewhere along the line, gave an order to fire. It might have applied to only a few feet of the frontage. But somehow it was what the nervous troops were waiting, hoping, for. They sank on one knee and began shooting, reloading, shooting, rapid-fire, as if faced by waves of attacking cavalry. Their victims slipped and staggered, fell on the ice, clambered on top of each other. They could no more stop than the atoms in a bowl of water being poured down a sink. They were slaughtered on parade, red blood on white, by men in uniform who rattled on like machines, until the rifles grew too hot, and the ammunition low. No chance of fewer than 300 dead, 1,500 cut down, wounded, mutilated.

Within hours, barricades were up in the workers' quarters. Police and soldiers were ambushed. Jews and gentlemen and priests were lynched from lampposts. More than a hundred industrial towns across Russia were hit by walkouts and riots. A dozen railway lines were barred to traffic. A general strike was called for. Everywhere a bony finger was pointing toward Revolution.

FEBRUARY 10   GENEVA   1905

Gusev reports that Father Gapon has eluded his former colleagues, the police, and has probably left the country. Before ducking out of sight, he issued two proclamations. One was addressed to the Tsar informing him that he was an unworthy monarch, an abomination under heaven, whose crimes would never be forgiven. The other was an open letter to all the socialist groups in Russia urging them to dethrone the monstrous Emperor. He—or somebody—has a poetical turn of phrase in Russian, a combination of Isaiah and Nechaev. I find it impossible to get one phrase out of my mind unless I shout it aloud. He pleads with us to eliminate the hateful dynasty and the society around it by use of *bombi i dinamit, terror edinichniy i massoviy*—"by bombs and dynamite, terror single-handed and by the multitude."

His destination is most likely Geneva, Gusev notes. Why else, he asks, had the priest written on his mirror in candle grease "Gone to Lenin"?

APRIL 10   GENEVA   1905

The Mensheviks are holding a party conference here which the leadership in exile—notably Plekhanov and Axelrod—are using as a platform for their advice on how to run the Revolution at home. I see now that the split I enforced between Bolsheviks and Mensheviks, and have kept as wide open as I can ever since, marks a real basic division on so many key issues. Take the Kadets, epitome of the liberal bourgeoisie.

When a liberal is abused, he says: Thank God they didn't beat me. When he is beaten, he thanks God they didn't kill him. When he is killed, he will thank God that his immortal soul has been delivered from its mortal clay.

The liberal cannot be counted upon in any battle we wage against the autocracy. Why? Because being inherently middle-class, he fears to lose in the struggle the property which binds him to the existing order. He fears that any really revolutionary action of the workers will not stop at parliamentary democracy but push on to socialism. He is worried by any threat of a complete break with officialdom, with the bureaucracy, whose interests are bound by a thousand ties with the interests of the propertied class. His campaign for liberty will always be notoriously inconsistent and half-hearted. He is, and cannot help but be, a *counter*-revolutionary agent.

What, then, must we think of the Mensheviks down the road who call themselves part of the socialist movement and yet say things like: "The workers' parties are divided and can do little. Only the organized power of the liberal bourgeoisie can confront tsarism" (Axelrod)? Or like this: "Our task is give the liberals courage but on no account must we frighten them by making proletarian demands" (Plekhanov)?

MAY 10   LONDON   1905

For the last fifteen days, in the back rooms of pubs and cafés, we have been holding the Third Congress of the RSDLP here. The Mensheviks, having just staged their own in Geneva, declare ours irregular and unofficial, packed as it is with Bolsheviks. I rather missed the Meks. This is the first time (possibly not the last) that I have been booed, jeered, hissed and hounded by my own comrades.

One of our main tasks is to prepare ourselves for the Revolution now mounting like a great wave at home. Trotsky went to Petersburg, via Kiev, in February but was immediately chased out by the police into Finland. I shall follow as soon as it appears likely that there is any possibility of operating in Peter without always being on the run. Meanwhile, our network there needs a complete shake-up if it is ever to present a threat to anything but itself. At the moment I doubt whether it could seize an ice-cream kiosk by force. What is the point of Gusev being built like a blacksmith if he can't hammer them into shape?

I was pleased with the London performance under pressure of my new Men of Confidence. The villainous-looking Krassin is one the nation's most distinguished engineers with a technical genius which he uses to provide us with all kinds of ingenious armaments. He successfully moved the resolution on the training of crack commando units, mobile and deadly, for use in the coming armed insurrection. The flamboyant, faintly ludicrous Lunacharsky carried Congress with him on the method of power-sharing that should be permitted if we enter a provisional government—a solid, but flexible, bloc of proletarians and small peasants in a "democratic-revolutionary" alliance.

We had a report on the membership. It stands at 12,000—60 percent are workers—with twelve cells in Peter factories. Then Bogdanov and I walked innocently into a minefield with our proposition that it should be compulsory for each local committee to have a majority of proletarians.

I explained how we had neglected the opportunities presented to us by police-socialism. It had served a useful function in politically educating the passive worker. His class consciousness developed. He began to see how he and his employer were opposed, with no interests in common. The Zubatovites' clumsy imitation of our tactics made our tactics more impressive when workers were able to make the comparison. Just because they were so backward, these workers issued demands socialist comrades would not dare to risk. Their expectations rose as the police agents promised them whatever they asked—in one case, the handing over of the factories from the employers to the employees! These semi-legal workers' protection clubs could be deregistered but not so easily dismantled. As they grew into a self-conscious movement, they only ignored the Social Democrats for one reason—they saw themselves as proletarians but apprehended us as intellectuals.

"So, comrades, a mandatory proportion of eight workers to two others?" When I finished that sentence, I thought the entire room was snapping open bars of chocolate. They were copies of *What Is to Be Done?* Passages were cited. I was accused of blatant switching of sides. What happened to my small, disciplined party of professional revolutionaries? This was just naked vote-canvassing, empire-building. It wouldn't work. It dilutes and pollutes the well of pure doctrine. All this above a continuo of hostile muttering. I was out-voted, then reprimanded. If Martov or Trotsky or Rosa could have seen me in that debate, they would have looked in vain for the Napoleonic dictator.

I had run foul of the *komitetchiki*, the broad-bummed committeemen, veterans of illegality inside Russia, who did not want to have to justify their ideas and plans in open discussion before a vote. I demanded to know whether they thought none of the workers were their equals, fit also to be *komitetchiki*. I accused them of lack of confidence in the Revolution—even a partial success would let us go legal. Without workers, it would be harder to influence workers.

Despite all their obstructionism, these organization men rallied to me. But only on this, the final day. These were the first Bolsheviks. They had emerged at the previous Congress dedicated to following me in creating a party of a new type. They had worked hard to perfect the machine. But as the British philosopher Herbert Spencer remarked, the conservatism of any body is in direct proportion to its nearness to perfection. (He is buried just opposite Marx in Highgate Cemetery—I will give him a salute when I pay my usual visit on my last night here.) The *komitetchiki* had used *What Is to Be Done?* as their blueprint. Fine! But now we are in a different climate, we must build a different edifice. We had entered a state of war—not Russia versus Japan, but socialists versus the system. The logic is like iron. I can say that because it is not my logic, it is the logic of reality.

So we rounded off by adopting my Rule One, on which we had been defeated in '03 by the Martovites. The CenCom has five members—a couple of the old hands, plus Bogdanov, Krassin and me. Soon we launch a new daily central organ, *Proletary* (*The Proletarian*), with me as alternating editor, Mondays, Wednesdays and Fridays. All in all, including boos and catcalls, a wonderful fortnight. I am back, even more firmly, perhaps, as unquestioned leader of the Bolsheviks.

MAY 27   GENEVA   1905

Just put to bed the first issue of *Proletary*. I took a copy still wet from the press, and folded it in an envelope for posting to the International Socialist Bureau in Brussels. *This,* I wrote above the masthead on the front page, is the organ of the Russian Social-Democratic Labour Party, ratified by our Third Congress. It has replaced *Iskra*.

I was about to leave for the all-night post office across the Rue Carouge when I saw a small, dark, handsome man with wild hair and glittering eyes watching the two assistant editors doubling as folders and packers. He came across and stood in my way; *"Chto delat?"* he said. "What is to be done?"

I had seen enough pictures of him. There was one in this issue—Father George Gapon.

"I want another Bloody Sunday," he said. "But this time we shoot them down. For this, I need Lenin."

I posted my letter and we sat up all night at Lepeshinsky's. Gusev has been writing to warn me this "shady character" is on his way. He begs me not to be deceived since Gapon knew all along what Zubatovism was and yet he collaborated, until the soldiers shot his movement dead at his feet. I have replied that, just as societies can be revolutionized, despite a reactionary past, so can people. For the last eight hours I have tried to justify that view. I told the little father that he had better read Marx if he didn't want to end up in a ditch with a hole in his head. I gave him a book list—still no substitute for Plekhanov, on theory anyway. I have enrolled him in a pistol club and booked riding lessons.

No other socialist in Geneva will speak to him, he complains.

Well, a priest *and* a police-spy, I say, he shouldn't be too surprised. I am talking to him because I believe he knows more about the workers of Peter than anyone alive. That knowledge I must have. We agree to meet regularly.

SEPTEMBER 3   GENEVA   1905

What are they doing in Petersburg, apart from nothing? Gusev sits on a bigger bum than all the committeemen put together. Hardly a single letter from a genuine worker for the paper throughout the summer! No reactions to my articles explaining how Bolshevik policy toward the bourgeoisie, now about to be graciously granted some token power by the Tsar in a plutocrat's parliament, differs from that of the Meks. They cannot see further than a liberal victory where Kadets gain control of the Duma, expand capitalism, and permit socialists to fight legally for workers' rights and better conditions. This is assuming that progress from feudalism through capitalism to socialism is an unalterable law like frog spawn to tadpole to frog. But societies develop unevenly, like people. We Bolsheviks do not believe the Kadets will have the guts to complete their own bourgeois revolution without us. Why should we hold back? Let us push on to a democratic dictatorship of workers and peasants who can drive capitalism ahead into socialism at American tempi. Let that at least be the Social Democrats' aim.

Even more infuriating—this really horrifies me!—is the failure of our members there to arm themselves. Plenty of metaphors about bombs, but none of them made. Fighting squads must be recruited *instantly*. Let them arm themselves with anything and everything—rifles, shotguns, revolvers, explosives, knives, knuckledusters, clubs, rags soaked in paraffin for arson, rope ladders, battering rams, shovels and wheelbarrows, even prams, for building barricades . . . *I* shouldn't need to tell *them*. Let Gusev fulfill his dreams and open up a military academy for street fighters.

Gapon has proved a dynamo of activity here. Already he has arranged one ship from England, the *John Grafton,* to smuggle us thousands of guns and ammunition. True, the Russian Navy latched on to the project and ran the *Grafton* aground off Norway. All is not lost. Corruption, one of tsarism's rottenest vices, is also among the most useful. Litvinov bribed the naval captain, rescued half the cargo, and promises an arsenal in Moscow before December. There's a lot more to revolution than resolutions and manifestos.

OCTOBER 5   GENEVA   1905

We have been looking for a strike that will be 100 percent, highly visible and articulate, to touch off the fuse to the powder keg. (By the way, where are *our* powder kegs?) Workers, and others, are only waiting for a sign to leave their jobs and demonstrate. This morning, I woke with the ideal opening group in mind.

Nowhere are Bolshevik activists so concentrated as among the printers of Moscow. I sent an immediate-action order, in code and through various "cutouts," inviting them to down tools and march through the streets. My real inspiration was the choice of their official grievance. Here my experience as editor-publisher came in handy. Printers have often complained to me that they are paid piecework for casting and setting letters but nothing at all for punctuation marks. I remember one saying—"We could double our wages on your exclamation 'screamers' alone, *Starik*." So this will become their demand—"the Semi-Colon Strike"! I can see it in headlines all over Russia, possibly Europe, everywhere—except Moscow, of course.

Tonight I learn from Peter that not only have printers there followed the lead from Moscow, but almost nobody else is working! No papers, naturally. But no lawyers in court, no doctors in hospitals, no tellers in banks. No baking, no telegrams or telephones. Even the *corps de ballet* have withdrawn their labor! The entire adult population of the capital city is idle, or marching behind red banners. Every other place wants to join the chain.

It looks as if I may have jogged the trigger on the starting pistol for the biggest general strike in history. This will transform the national situation and call for new tactics. All strikes give the workers and their allies a feel of how power is operated. But a *general* strike, as any Marxist remembering the dialectic would expect, by a change of quantity enforces a change of quality. While it lasts, the strikers have to run society, otherwise they will starve. Willy-nilly, they become a provisional government.

OCTOBER 15   GENEVA   1905

Our euphoria here among the Bolsheviks is subsiding. The Mensheviks have never been pleased at this "typically Leninist" interference with "the spontaneity of the revolutionary process." We take the line, it works, it works. Actually, I see a few more pushes are needed. The problem is—another new twist—we also have a *bourgeois* general strike, not against capitalism but against relics of monarchical feudalism. Proof of this? It is supported by the Kadets. You need more? It is backed not only by intellectuals but by industrialists, employers, financiers. Many bosses are supporting their own striking workers, on half, sometimes full, pay. It is a kind of capitalist Zubatovism. The bourgeoisie are determined to let mass action proceed only within safe limits.

The masses are expected to back the capitalists in developing their new economic means of production against the outdated, restrictive bureaucracy of half-medieval tsardom. Reform is in the air but no smell of proletarian domination of the state. Kadets are hinting at a republic, no doubt with some millionaire prince like Lvov, as president; abolition of all restrictions on trade, or sale of land; disestablishment of the Church—France and Germany in 1848 all over again. Then, workers defeated kings and generals so the middle class could take over and use generals to put down workers. What is essential is something nearer the Paris Commune of 1871. Could this be the Soviet that set itself up a couple of days ago? *Soviet* is, of course, simply the Russian, as *Commune* is the French, for "Council" or "Committee." What matters is *who* the Soviet represents. Since the organization in Peter consists of shop floor delegates elected one for every five hundred workers, it can be plausibly defined as the first proletarian parliament. Versions are springing up across Russia. And if the representatives of ExComs from many Soviets can be gathered in the capital, this will be the nearest to a workers' democratic convention that Russia, or indeed any other nation so far, has seen. All I ask is, keep them out of the hands of the Mensheviks! Otherwise, in fifty days they'll be back under the control of the Kadets.

OCTOBER 23   GENEVA   1905

The Petersburg Soviet has been operating for ten days. I can't help counting, I realize, because I am unconsciously comparing it with its only known predecessor, the Paris Commune. Already it has extended the perimeters of a people's democracy beyond any rival. I am particularly impressed by the way all members of the Soviet are recallable by their constituents at a day's notice. Whatever their power inside, they are responsible both to those who elected them and to those who lay down the policy they follow.

In Europe, their "labor" parties started with a leadership outside parliament, but gradually succumbed to the glamour and fame of the legislative soapbox. The leader of the Opposition, earmarked as possible future prime minister, became automatically leader of the party. Control moved to a charmed inner circle, out of sight of the workers, linking old school chums, trade union buddies, in-laws, partners in secret pacts, personal or political. Socialism withered on the bough. Became simply a word, invoked in election manifestos, a traditional relic like "The Red Flag" at the end of the annual congress. A Soviet in permanent session would sweep away all that. Already, it directly represents just over 50 percent of the half-million workers of Petersburg.

No one socialist group leads the delegates, though the Mensheviks probably have the larger slice over us and the SRs. The Soviet publishes its own paper, *Izvestia* (*News*), at the moment the only one in Western Russia, except one run off by the Army High Command. The paralyzed limbs of the nation are slowly being warmed back to life under treatment by Soviet ExCom. In Bolshevik factories, militants fill in time making their own guns. For the moment, people have the veto over any moves by the tsarist government.

And who has become president of the SovExCom? Someone called Yanovsky, wears dark glasses, said to be near-blind, usually accompanied by a (to me) odd pair—Krassin and Parvus.

NOVEMBER 1   GENEVA   1905

"Yanovsky," as everybody, including the Tsar, very quickly realized, is Trotsky. Under any name, he is a celebrity, the young
revolutionary who turns up everywhere and makes a success of
everything. I cannot restrain my admiration—surely he is a Bolshevik without knowing it? Take his attitude to Professor Milyukov
and his liberals. He advises the leader of the Kadets of what will
happen to him:

> If the revolution does not ebb away, the bureaucracy will cling to
> you as a bulwark on a flood-wall; and if you really try to become
> its bulwark, the victorious revolution will pick you and throw you
> back into the sea. If on the other hand, the revolution is defeated,
> then tsardom will have no use for liberals. You boast that you will
> not be deflected by voices from the right, or voices from the left.
> Remember, the revolution has not yet said its last word. With
> powerful broad thrusts, it lowers the edge of the knife over the
> head of absolutism. Let the wiseacres of liberalism beware of
> putting their hands under the glittering steel blade. Let them
> beware . . .

When the Tsar issued his cautious October manifesto offering
vague concessions, the liberals rejoiced. Students danced in the
streets. But Trotsky/Yanovsky, not long arrived, still in disguise,
stood on the balcony, manifesto in hand, denounced it as a half-
victory no use to anyone, the laying of a trap, tore the manifesto
into pieces that fluttered over the crowds toward the Winter Palace.

As he becomes more and more well-known, he becomes more
beautifully dressed. He rides a white horse! And yet he is never
idle. He and Parvus have taken over *Russkaya Gazeta,* a rather staid
little weekly. Within days, it is selling 100,000. Latest figures, half
a million, making it the first popular socialist daily in the history
of Russia. Not content with that, he has adopted *Nachalo* (*Beginning*), a Menshevik organ, and turned it into his own theoretical
mouthpiece, also a daily!

Nevertheless, I have to record that all is not well with Soviet
and Revolution. Our Bolsheviks have been disgracefully slack and
wrongheaded. It begins to be clear that the Soviet has only some
negative power. Without an executive arm, it can take no positive

action. Even the threat of a new general strike no longer overawes the bourgeoisie or the autocracy. Once the Tsar indicated he was open to compromise, the liberals lost their zeal to press him harder. When the workers of the big cities stayed out for their own causes—an eight-hour day, no workshop fines or deductions, the right to join unions—the employers locked them out. Milyukov denounced any proletarian economic actions as "crimes against our liberal revolution." The Tsar was persuaded by Count Witte to encourage change, announcing an amnesty, a constitution, and Russia's first Duma or parliament.

Martov and Plekhanov, who gave a farewell dinner here in Geneva last night on the eve of their departure for "Soviet Petersburg," have canceled their tickets this morning. They do not care to be associated with defeat. This decides me. I must go there as soon as Father Gapon's enterprise with Litvinov gets under way. Meanwhile, watching what happens to theory in the furnace of praxis, I can get straight some revolutionary insights the events of '05 have given me.

NOVEMBER 8   HELSINKI   1905

After a week in Stockholm, I am now in Helsinki. Calls keep coming from Party leaders in Peter, and Moscow, urging my presence inside Russia. Can the revolutionary drive be weakening? The proletariat is clearly becoming isolated from its middle-class allies. We Bolsheviks in particular face barrages of violent hostility from the Kadets who denounce us as "criminal anarchists." We are no longer partnered, or even backed, in any anti-government enterprises by the Meks, the SRs or others among the increasingly despondent bands of rebels.

Gusev, on the telephone, still insists our Party members retain their stern determination to fight on, to launch new waves of strikes, to build toward an armed insurrection.

What is keeping Lenin?

My cover story is not very convincing—I am waiting for a valid Russian passport! A whisper is spreading that I am afraid to risk my neck over the border. There is no way to answer such a lie. To hear such things about yourself in silence is one of the wounds we all suffer in clandestine politics. Indeed, extra salt is often rubbed in when it becomes clear that it is better for the cause that a slander should be believed than the truth should be known.

I am operating here behind half a dozen layers of security and deliberate misinformation. I have to be seen to be doing nothing but kick my heels outside the consular office when I am out half the night negotiating, bribing, threatening and being threatened. I am here to salvage as much as I can from the wreck of the *John Grafton,* and some other fiascoes at sea, and smuggle it across to our combat groups.

Since winning the war in September, the Japanese have understandably lost interest in subsidizing native opponents of the Tsar. I miss their efficiency. Between them, the Finnish nationalist Zilliacus, an American radical millionairess, Mrs. Hall, our man Litvinov, anybody's man Father Gapon, and a few professional criminals, have managed to mislay around 5,000 rifles, and half a million rounds of ammunition. These I intended as basic arms for our fighting workers. And if our amateurs are to be pitted against fully equipped veterans, I must do better than this—a few machine guns and mortars at least.

By this evening it is apparent I have done all I can do. I have to rely on the promises of associates of associates that a shipment will arrive in time for our Moscow project, the major battle of the Revolution, I hope. Clean-shaven, slightly-limping, and short-sighted behind medical dark specs—this year's fashion among returning conspirators—I am catching the sleeper to the Finland station.

NOVEMBER 9 PETERSBURG 1905

In Peter for the first time in five years, I have to start stripping, cleaning and repairing another weapon, Gorky's newspaper *Novaya Zhizn* (*New Life*) which I intend to make the Party organ. It has been on the streets now for ten days and, I'm told, trails shamefully behind the papers published by Parvus and Trotsky.

"What a talking to!" exclaimed little sister Manyasha, tearful and thrilled, after my speech to the staff this morning. "Keep on listening," I said, and I summoned the CenCom of the Peter Party to tell them that every member, without exception, from crossing sweeper to matinée idol, must become a circulation rep. Each must be personally responsible for moving ten copies. I installed Bonch-Bruevich as managing editor and publisher, then left to meet for the first time the paper's owner, at his flat.

Gorky is the only living author about whom I feel that instinctive shyness I fancy is the tribute in any field that we pay to absolute genius. Despite that, I could not help feeling he is a bit of a booby. He is not deaf (or so his mistress, the dazzling Maria Fyodorovna, assured me). Why then does he stare anxiously at your mouth as though lip-reading? Why does he repeat what you say as if the sentences were in a foreign language? Why does he ask one person to tell him what another person standing there has just said? Is he a very slow listener? A little backward in some freakish fashion? Or is it a long-familiar mannerism he no longer notices? His friends ignore these requests for repetition and simply carry on, leaving him floundering behind but apparently quite well enough informed about the conversation. Gorky also has another habit. When it is his turn to speak, he will tend to describe his thoughts as they arise, commenting on people in the third person after the fashion of a novelist sketching in a character. This could be really devastating to the thin-skinned. Fortunately, I do not come into that category and I began to laugh because it seemed genuinely funny. The moment we were introduced, he observed: "I had not imagined Lenin that way. There's something missing. He's too plain. Nothing of the leader about him. His 'r's are guttural. Something about the eyes . . ." My laughter brought him to a halt. He shook himself. "I am a writer and it is my job to take note of details. I'm afraid it's become a habit, sometimes an annoying one."

"Notes are for notebooks, Alexei Maximovich. Or keep them in your head. You know, you need never forget anything if you file it away properly. For example, 1881. You were thirteen. You were a dishwasher on a Volga steamer, Kazan to Astrakhan. You and another boy sat in the stern, watching the convict barge on tow."

He went into a sort of trance, peering down at his hands. "A floating coffin. You said that or I said that? Vladimir Ilyich. I thought you were Ulyanov. Then in Samara, I remember hearing about a young lawyer, Ilyin Ulyanov, a Marxist. I thought that might be you. But Ilyin became Lenin. *N* Lenin. So I forgot you again."

He woke up, started laughing, embraced me. "Parvus was always talking about you. He was my agent until '02. I had given him some of my Western copyrights—a quarter of the money for me, a quarter for him, and half for the Party. A year later, I asked for my share. He smiled and said it was all gone. He'd taken a beautiful girl to Italy and spent the lot. I forgave him. But I thought

this 'Lenin' might not be pleased. Probably you never knew he'd
taken your half. At a party the other day, somebody pointed the
same girl out to me. She *was* beautiful. She came over and told
me, 'You are dear to me.' I said—'Not so dear as you have been
to me.' "

I see what they mean when they say he is irresistible. I too
have been very dear to *him* and I am going to have to ask for more
to pay for those guns. Perhaps I'd better tell him it is for newsprint.

DECEMBER 17   ON THE FINNISH TRAIN   1905

Theory and practice are inseparable. I would have given anything
for a chance to talk over with Trotsky how Marxism matches reality
in our first Russian revolution. But he and Parvus were arrested
this morning along with about half the members of the Soviet. It
had lasted fifty days.

He had been putting a brave face on the hemorrhaging of
power from what I regard now, despite its collapse, as the future
form of workers' democracy. I see in the last issue of *Nachalo* before
they closed it down, he says much the same—"an embryo of a
revolutionary government." Perhaps he should have gone ahead
during the last hours, calling, as he had intended, for an armed
rising. Instead, he was persuaded by Parvus to urge a typically
Parvusian attack on the authorities—all opponents of tsarism should
start a run on the banks by withdrawing their savings in gold. I
suppose the sort of workers Parvus knows, mainly pretty girls, do
have bank savings, but imagine what a horse laugh that would get
from Marx or Engels!

By all accounts, Trotsky's arrest was wonderful, Victor-Hugo
style theater. He made the officer put up a proposal, duly seconded, to the chairman of CenExCom (himself) for permission to
make an announcement. Then, after the announcement, instructed him to wait till the end of the session before intruding
again. Trotsky then supervised the destruction of documents, the
breaking of locks on the revolvers, before inviting in the platoon
as he proclaimed—"I declare this meeting of the Central Executive
Committee closed."

Gusev called round at midday to bring us this news about
Trotsky and then insisted we get in his droshky and be driven to
the Finland station. He says a roundup is starting of all leftish
democrats and there is a very convenient First All-Russian Bol-

shevik Conference taking place at Tammerfors for the next three days. As we were trotting along, I put my hand in my overcoat pocket. Deep at the bottom, I found a summons, dated the day I arrived in Peter, to the Conference. My name is down to propose reunification with the Mensheviks.

DECEMBER 23   TAMMERFORS, FINLAND   1905

I remain confident our revolution is still ticking over. Whatever happens, certain lessons can be drawn. One is—the transformation of monarchical tyranny into bourgeois republic, Nicholas II into Edward VII, will not happen as naturally and peacefully as chrysalis into butterfly. No authority ever surrenders except to force. The Tsar is still there, thanks to the cowardice of the liberals, the credulity of the Mensheviks, the slowness of the Bolsheviks.

The cardinal error in politics is to assume you can stand still. Once you have stopped, you are already going backward. What we need is *permanent* revolution—a neglected insight of Marx now being rediscovered by Trotsky and Parvus as well as me. We agree that the struggle must be continuous, pushing on through bourgeois dominance to proletarian dictatorship, not lingering over capitalism but hurrying on to socialism. The Mensheviks, and their liberal allies, find this prospect frightening, and have shown themselves willing to settle for less than even a parliamentary, free-enterprise republic. Indeed, many of them think *that* a rather radical extreme.

Faced with this, how can I move a resolution of unity based on equal power to Mensheviks and Bolsheviks? Because the workers have marched and struck and fought together, regardless of the split. Solidarity grows from the bottom up. When we next go into action, if we are a united party, the Meks in the leadership will have to side with us. Whatever doubts the leaders harbor in the heads, the feet of the masses will be going our way. My proposal was carried unanimously.

I was just writing this in my hotel room when dreadful news arrived. The Moscow insurrection has triggered itself too early! This was to have been the first operation of the broad left, supported by many liberals, that was planned with military precision. But without modern weapons, without a plan of campaign, without leadership and a chain of command, our most ambitious attack on the autocracy is doomed to fail.

DECEMBER 26   MOSCOW   1905

I have to take moral responsibility for the brave, bloody, horrible events here over the last three days. There is no use pretending that it will not get worse, or that there is anything those of us in Moscow, yet outside the great, smoking ring of death and destruction, can do. The largely working-class east of the city, "Red Presnya," is now encircled by an army of crack troops. Hour by hour they are driving back the inhabitants over a thousand barricades by a ritual sequence of heavy artillery bombardment, machine gun attack, bayonet charges, then a final, dreadful culling of what is left moving with swords and clubs.

Our military expert, Gusev, is certain this is not an operation that could proceed with such mechanical efficiency unless long-planned and held in readiness for just such an opportunity to teach the masses a lesson in terror. With him, in his ex-German Army surplus motorcycle and sidecar, I have toured the five-mile radius of the urban battlefield. There is no way in for us. No way out for anybody.

What went wrong? I have been advocating armed uprisings since "Bloody Sunday." But I wanted them prepared for, with the same—no, with *much more*—attention to every detail than our Army had shown against the Japs. I had read every work on the subject of guerrilla warfare in the cities—not a vast library. I had abstracted from Marx the principal rules of "insurrection as an art." They are too painful to list against this background of shot and shell. They begin: (1) Never play with an insurrection, but when beginning it realize firmly that you must *go all the way* on through. (2) Once the insurrection has begun, you must act with the greatest determination, and by all means, without fail, take the offensive. "The defensive is the death of every armed uprising," to the conclusion, citing Danton as the great master of the art—"*de l'audace, de l'audace, encore de l'audace.*" The irony burns deep. All that our fighters have in there to defend themselves is *de l'audace.*

JANUARY 1   MOSCOW   1906

There were periods during last year, which, taken at the flood, might have led on to victory. In the summer, the mutiny on *Potemkin*: it sailed off into the Black Sea through the lines of the entire Southern Navy, the other sailors not yet ready to join in, their officers not yet daring to give the order to fire. Instantly, I dispatched one of our best agitators, Vasilyev-Yuzhin, and waited for the frigate that he should have sent to collect me from Romania. Too late—oh, for my floating socialist city! In the autumn, the crushed mutiny at Kronstadt. Then Lieutenant Shmidt, again on the Black Sea. His sailors seized the cruiser *Ochakov* while he signaled the Tsar—"I assume command of the Southern Fleet. Shmidt." Such comic bravado paid off. He was joined by eleven other ships and only defeated in a full-scale naval battle off Sevastopol. There were revolts in other ports and garrisons. Patriotic rebellions in Poland, the Baltic States, the Caucasus. If there was not an opportunity for armed insurrection in Russia in 1905, when and where could there be?

The propaganda value of the freeing of proletarian Moscow would have been immense. I went along with an idea that was there and would not rest. Bolsheviks, Meks, SRs and anarchists were united in favor of the operation at ground level. They were backed by the Moscow Soviet, by municipal councils, by Zubatovian organizations, by many intellectuals, artists, professionals, middle-class rebels. During minor incidents, when the Muscovites barricaded a few streets, flew the red flag, hung out banners, showed only passive resistance, the Cossacks refused to beat them. The police skulked away and denied there *were* any incidents. Battalions of soldiers would not clear away crowds with rifle butts, let alone bullets. They joined them. There was one strike which cut off Moscow from Petersburg and the Tsar's own guards regiments, and another which paralyzed the telegraph and telephone. The Battle of Moscow could have been won before anyone outside had heard a word. The signal should have been the smuggled weapons now crossing the Finnish frontier. Gusev and Krassin had been at work on a timetable for taking the key points of the city. The entire democratic left of Moscow was confident its exercise would go like clockwork in the first week of 1906. Once they were in position, like the Paris Commune—we could have loosed the red cock across Russia.

Plekhanov has sent a message to the besieged workers telling them that they were wrong to strike, let alone bear arms. *"Merci,"* as he would say. I believe, we did not start *early enough,* wide enough, ruthless enough. When the uprising ends, the reaction will sicken the world with its beatings, rapes, tortures, shootings of all who showed the slightest sympathy for real change when the lid was lifted for a moment. We failed here because we had not yet a plan of campaign, no list of objectives, nothing to fight with except a few sporting rifles, old revolvers, and handmade "cold" weapons, enough for at most 500 warriors. Because the strikes stopped at the wrong moment—the telegraph sent the orders, the trains brought in the loyal troops, the crack Semyonovs.

As I write, the advance of the gallant 100,000 is quickening. The artillery is firing at point-blank range, blasting paths through solid blocks of houses like runaway locomotives. By dawn, there will be nowhere to hide. The year that began with the Tsar's loyal troops killing 1,000 men, women and children, innocent and unarmed, in the modern capital of Russia will now end with the Tsar's loyal troops killing another 1,000 who are guilty of dissent, and will shoot back if they can. Under Nicholas's empire of evil, that may be progress. In the holy capital of old Russia, a quarter of the city will lie flattened by tonight.

APRIL 25   PETERSBURG   1906

Yesterday, I watched from Gorky's flat on the first floor the ceremonial flimflam attending the state opening of our first parliament, the Duma, at the Tauride Palace.

The streets down below were decorated with stars, and bells, and crowns, and crosses, and eagles, as if for a coronation. The ornaments were only tinsel, of course, but the silvering and gilding on them, melted down, would keep a street-boy on his usual diet for a week. After Tsar and Tsarina, Grand Dukes and Duchesses, court officials and royal ministers, had clattered by in their fairground coaches, the hussars planted along the route relaxed. Spectators fell in behind the procession. And the barefooted ones swarmed up the pylons to harvest the decorations. Within seconds, the glittering tunnel through which the royals and their hangers-on had processed was stripped bare.

"Must put that in my diary," said Gorky, who had come in behind me.

"Karpov," I said, jokingly, adjusting my disguise monocle.

"Gorky," he said. "A pleasure to make your acquaintance."

The Emperor was on a day trip to Peter—he has not spent a night here since Bloody Sunday. Now he's clearly determined to show that behind this façade of sham-democracy what is being celebrated is the continuation of his dictatorship.

The Duma, however, responded by hurling what must have sounded out there, back at Tsarskoe Selo, like a barrage of bombs. This was their Loyal Address to the Throne. With hardly a dissenter, they requested that there should be an amnesty for all political prisoners; the confiscation of large estates with due compensation; universal direct elections; abrogation of the emergency laws; abolition of capital punishment; reform of the civil service. Quite radical—for a bunch of liberals.

But if Members of the Duma thought that the fact that they had been elected (after a fashion), and that they were presenting a joint program, would give the least one of these requests a chance of being granted, then they were soon disillusioned. Today, the Tsar issued what he calls his Fundamental Law. This is summed up in the following: "The Emperor of All the Russias has supreme autocratic power. It is ordained by GOD HIMSELF that his authority should be submitted to, not only out of fear but out of a genuine sense of duty."

So, you must not only respect the knout, you must love it, *sincerely*. Nothing much seems to have changed since I was trying to puzzle out what Sasha meant by tsarism, twenty years ago on the banks of the Volga.

The Russian people are reminded that only the Tsar can declare war, alter the dogma or structure of the Church, dismiss the Duma. Ministers are appointed by the Tsar alone, responsible to him alone, removable by him alone. Even the unanimous vote of the entire Duma cannot order them into action or prevent them taking some action. Just in case there are any doubts, the Tsar has established a State Council, or Upper House, half of its members appointed by himself, without whose approval no Duma resolution is valid. I should think that about wraps it all up.

However, just in case some sympathy for the frustrated liberals should well up among the workers and the left intelligentsia, I felt it was appropriate to make a little propaganda. Though we boycotted the Duma *elections* this does not mean we cannot use the results. One or two Social Democrats did slip in. I instructed one to use his official standing and approach the Ministry of the Interior to find me some figures. Despite its appalling inefficiency, inertia, corruption and boneheadedness, the tsarist state remains probably the best documented in the world.

MAY 1   PETERSBURG   1906

Though the Tsar's idea of responsible democracy does not stretch to tolerating the presence of Lenin, hence Karpov, for the moment we are able to publish a semi-legal daily, *Volna* (*The Wave*), edited by Karpov. In today's issue I had an "exclusive"—statistics from the government's own archives, never before published, never intended to be published, showing the bloody price that we, the real revolutionaries, have paid to allow the liberals to mouth their reformist slogans. Our people, the militant workers, the rebellious peasants, the Party intellectuals, have, as ever, been the ones who had to fight to win a bourgeois Duma. Between January 9, '05, Bloody Sunday, and April 26, '06, the opening of the Duma, the toll is higher, according to the official account, than I think any of us ever imagined.

The forces of law and order have slaughtered 14,000 of the country's citizens, many of them women and children, in revenge raids on rebellious villages; executed, after field courts-martial, another 1,000; left more than 20,000 wounded and maimed to crawl away (no public hospital is permitted to treat them); arrested, and still detain, more than 70,000. After these wholesale murders, we should beg our rights as favors?

Just the badly stated facts will make an impact that no passionate editorial could equal, even if it were published, which it wouldn't be.

MAY 24   PETERSBURG   1906

"Comrade Karpov" treated himself to a little outing today in only light disguise—monocle, beard grayed by a dressing of white flour and goose-grease, tendency, when he remembered, to limp with a malacca silver-topped cane. Not bad. I do not recognize myself in the shop windows. Indeed, I glared in disapproval at what I took to be some kind of confidence trickster. Well, there are plenty of those about and these days nobody looks at one twice, least of all the police.

I had decided to pay a visit to the new Duma in the Tauride Palace, a place I had somehow imagined as being full of other sober-suited fakes graying elegantly at the temples. Perhaps I ought to get out more often.

The Tauride was completed in the year of the French Revolution, as the Bastille was being stormed. It was a present to Potemkin from his wife and sovereign, Catherine "the Great," a reward for his generalship in subduing the Crimea (or Tauride) and it looks like it. No normal human could expect to make a home here.

As I arrived, its marble floor was thick with delegates and visitors. They appeared to have little in common, except the universal cigarette. Puff, puff, puff, they went, smoking away as in a competition, each trying to see how many crumpled cardboard holders and layers of ash he could combine into a low palisade around his feet, before the session resumed. There were some, Kadets, I bet, anyone would have sworn were English, faces like rolled pink roast beef, sweating a little gravy, sewn into works of art from Savile Row on which every stitch was like a painter's brushstroke; some could only be Poles, and probably princes at that, trouserless in rainbow tights, with pageboy tabards and high boots, walking court-cards. Proletarians, faces pale and blunt from long mole years in dark, bleak factories where only machines were made comfortable, collarless in suits like armor. Intellectuals, equally pale but preternaturally sharp-featured, forever peeping through the windows of their pince-nez, lank hair like the knotted strands of the knout, clothes that could only have gained those ingrained creases from several lifetimes of being slept in. All kinds of priest, from the hedge-pope of the backwoods village with a black muzzle that ought to have a ring through it to the dainty city *curé des dames*, all lace and polished fingernails, and the purple bishop, as heavy with gold lockets and jeweled crucifixes as a fashionable shrine.

The debate was on the land policy of the government.

First there was a Socialist Revolutionary (I could see that, though, of course, he did not identify himself as such) from Irkutsk, a provincial lawyer I would guess, much as I had been in Samara, sober, plain, sincere, forgettable in looks. But what he said caused a few twinges of unease.

And so, gentleman, when the peasants sent me here, they instructed me to champion their needs, to demand land and freedom for them, to demand that all state, crown, private and monastery lands be compulsorily alienated without compensation. . . . I want you to know that a hungry man cannot keep quiet when he sees that, in spite of his suffering, the government is on the side of the landed gentry. He cannot help demanding land, even if it is against the law. Want compels him to demand it.

But best of all was a real peasant, tall and skinny, a froth of hair like a sapling gone to seed. His people wanted land, not just because they would starve without it, but because it was *their right* to have it. And he spoke directly to those landlord members in a fashion few of them had ever experienced.

Nowadays we talk of nothing but land where I come from. And of course we were told, there as here—it is sacred! It is inviolable! [He spoke the word as if it were a magic spell.] In my opinion, it cannot be inviolable. If the people wish it, *nothing can be inviolable!* [A voice from the packed, majority benches of the Right: "Oh-ho!"] Yes, oh-ho! Gentlemen of the nobility, do you think we do not know when you used us as stakes in your card games, when you bartered us for . . . dogs? We do. We were all your sacred, *inviolable* property. You stole the land from us. The peasants who sent me here said I was to say this: *The land is ours.* We have come here not to buy it, but to take it.

I could hardly restrain myself from shouting "Oh-ho, yes!" from the public gallery. It has confirmed what I learned from '05. The peasants must be given *all the land*. No support for liberal renting or leasing; Menshevik nationalization. I have in my head the punch line for a piece in *Volna*. A big photograph of a really appalling-looking old *mujhik,* and underneath, in italics: *"The most ignorant, unenlightened, politically virgin, unorganized peasant has proved to be incomparably more Left than any of the Kadets."*

OCTOBER 19　　　PETERSBURG　　　1906

Trotsky has been in prison for more than a year, on trial now for a month. The charge: "preparing an armed insurrection." I would give a year and a month of my own life just to be inside the court, just to see Trotsky in the box, defying the massed power of tsarism.

Today it seems security precautions have been doubled and redoubled for the final speech for the defense. Troops have been filing all day into the yard, lining the colonnades of the court building. Now they are spilling over into the streets around; stacking rifles, lighting fires, putting up tents, mounting patrols. An entire quarter of the city is an armed camp. Not even the Archangel Gabriel could swoop down to perch on the brass rail round our twenty-six-year-old Young Eagle. I am obliged to sit in a café fully a mile away, waiting for shorthand notes to be delivered to me in what we newspapermen call "long takes."

I have taught myself shorthand. Now I am learning the rest of the journalism business. I had thought all my life I was a press publicist, and quite a successful one. But with our (temporarily) legal Bolshevik dailies, we are reaching mass audiences, not groups of committed sectarians. Style is as important as content. Display is part of meaning. Our working-class readers hunger for details —ages, heights, weights, color of eyes; prices down to the last kopek; number of shots fired, bombs exploded, amount of explosive; slogans and headlines more-or-less interchangeable, concise, memorable, arousing; an inch of anecdote is worth a column of analysis. Half the art of revolution is psychology. Newspaper selling is almost all psychology.

As I read Trotsky's speech, seeing it as it will be in print through the eyes of the masses, I realize again that he is without equal as an orator. Everything he says is vivid, sincere, loaded at once with emotion and with intelligence. He so stirs our blood that, like children, we feel moments of certainty that he must be acquitted. What judge's heart so stony, mind so prejudiced, that it could resist? Yet his logic also pierces painfully. I have to face the fact—as the leader who ordered the failed December rising in Moscow—that to advance the Revolution we must often start fights we cannot win. When Party leaders promise that victory is certain, imminent, inevitable, we keep our fingers crossed. We add under our breaths—in the end . . . following many setbacks . . . maybe after our time . . . We must face the paradox that the final triumph will depend on a whole series of failures. It is a hard lesson to digest. Am I sure I want to risk denting the morale of our militants by printing it? They certainly will not read it in any other papers.

Here is what Trotsky said in his summing-up of the true strength of a rebellious populace:

> Important as weapons are, the main power does not lie in weapons, Messrs. Judges. No, not in weapons. *Not the capacity of the*

masses to kill but their great readiness to die—that is what, Messrs. Judges, in the last analysis guarantees the victory of the people's uprising.

When the soldiers march into the street to quell the crowds and come face to face with the crowds and become convinced that these crowds, this people, will not leave the pavements until they gain what they must have, that they are ready to pile corpses upon corpses . . .

When the soldiers see and are convinced that the people have come to struggle seriously, to the very end . . .

Then the hearts of the soldiers, as has happened in every revolution, must inevitably waver. They cannot fail to become distrustful of the stability of the regime they are serving and cannot fail to believe in the victory of the people.

"Readiness to die"? Yes, a fairly obvious form of passive resistance. More preached than practiced even among the religious. But has it ever before been recommended, as a martial strategy, by a leader of a militant ideology? Have the rank and file ever before been told as they went into battle, that the more of them that fall, the better their chance of success? The longer their casualty lists, the quicker their enemy will sue for peace? The state forces will usually be better armed, better organized, than ours. Are we prepared to accept that the best way we can block the advance of their war machines is to barricade the road with our bodies, choke their cogs on our flesh?

Engels, toward the end of his life, aired a few doubts about the capacity of a civilian population in revolt to withstand the counterattack of the modern militarized state with its increasingly sophisticated weapons. Many more have been developed since his death—aerial bombs, armored motorcars, poison gas, mobile machine guns. He did tend, at least for advanced Western nations, to put some trust in legal political parties, with possible majorities in parliament, networks of clubs, newspapers, savings banks, sporting teams, bands of well-drilled auxiliaries, trade unions training their most advanced members in techniques of management. The ordered march of an educated democracy. Germany seems almost there, and Britain on the road. Yet, at the same time, he never underrated the steadily concentrating power of capitalism, the internationalization of monopolies. Big business has no country either. The exploiters of the world are already united.

Of course, I must remember that while Lev Davidovich is defying his prosecutors, inspiring his followers, he is also simultaneously arguing for the lives of the other fifty-two accused members of the Soviet. When he explains to his judges that a mass uprising is not man-made but an historical event, that it can be foreseen, but not manufactured, that revolutionaries of our scientific and philosophical kind do not prepare insurrection, but prepare *for* it—when he says this, he is only repeating what is in all textbooks of Marxism. The revolutionary leader must bring clarity into the minds of the people. He must explain *why* the conflict is inevitable. He should demonstrate that freedom is only ever preserved, and change engineered, by *force*. That, in a headline, *"There Is No Other Road."*

Where I differ is that I do call, day after day, for an armed rebellion. And I do actively prepare for it. I cannot, deep inside me, accept the image of our workers piling up, like cattle in an abattoir, at the feet of gun-shooting automatons. I cannot rely on our executioners at last sickening of their work. I will not wait for "hearts to waver." It may well be that government forces *will* stop when they confront masses who prefer to die rather than retreat. In my view, they will stop a damned sight quicker, and their hearts waver sooner, if each dying worker, man, woman or child, takes one of the enemy with them. Let the soldiers sicken at the sight of their own corpses piling up.

Stop press: Trotsky and Parvus found guilty, sentenced for life to the far north of Siberia.

DECEMBER 29   KUOKKALA   1906

Since the end of August, Nadya and I have been staying with the Leiteisens at their country house, Vasa, a sort of wooden pagoda enclosing a maze of creaky corridors lined with every size of sitting and bedroom. It is stuck on the edge of this blob of forest like a tiny jewel on a vast ring, almost invisible until you face it head on. Yet we are within easy walk, or quick trot, of Kuokkala and the twice-daily post, the newspapers, the trains to Helsinki or Peter, foods so fresh and new-made you would think old Adam had just named each one.

I write "staying with," but Gregory Leiteisen has made himself our host in a truly Arabic fashion.

Everything that is his is ours. He is one of the middle-roaders, heart with Meks, head with the Bolos, and he and I have survived several severe disagreements, when our personal relationships stretched but never snapped. As a young man, I was infatuated with Plekhanov. The situation was reversed for Gregory. Plekhanov nominated him as his favorite disciple.

I found my situation embarrassing, but understandable. Poor Gregory's was embarrassing, but weird. Two years ago, in Paris, he showed me one of several letters from our Lost Leader. Amid a lot of curses at Lenin, a swipe at Trotsky ("His new pamphlet is as rotten as himself"), Plekhanov begs Leiteisen to abandon the Mensheviks and follow only him. His life has been "a tragedy," Plekhanov complains, though he is not yet fifty. After twenty years" service to the cause, he goes on, he has no comrade who believes in him. He swears he is not asking for submission to his authority as the leader. He seeks only "comradely trust." With almost anyone else, I would instantly extend the hand of solidarity. But, as I pointed out to Gregory then, George supplies much of the evidence that makes so many of us doubt and distrust him in that same letter.

Nobody who solicits loyalty to himself rather than to a program or a policy, whose correspondence reeks of a bad novel, deserves to be a member, let alone a leader, of a serious movement. Gregory seemed a bit crushed, though also released, by my judgment, one I should have thought that any Marxist would have proffered. Anyway, it seems to have bounced him away from Menshevism. He now describes himself (rather boringly) as a "Party-Bolshevik" not a "Leninist-Bolshevik" which suggests to me that he may always have been an inveterate personalizer. Still, as old Gorcheeza used to say in Samara, "Never poke your finger up the hole of the golden goose!" Gregory's hospitality is out of the *Arabian Nights*. His doors are never locked. Every night a large serving of milk, cheese and bread is left out with a few blankets for any late arrival. And many a morning, we all come straggling down to find welcome new faces at breakfast. It is like one endless name-day party.

My favorite gadfly, Rosa Luxemburg, was one of our earliest drop-in visitors. Since then I have had the pleasure of walking and talking under the birch trees with many of the exceptional rebels of our age—Krassin, the most criminal-looking engineer I ever met, always half-shaven, with bristles that would make a boar wince, who pressed on me a chemical solution for removing numerals on banknotes; Elena Stasova, a perpetual inky-mopped schoolgirl, seemingly sucked in by accident to witness one after another of the autocracy's armed attacks on the people this century, from the ritual beating of the students outside Peter's Kazan Cathedral in '01 which inspired Gorky's stirring hymn, "Song of the Stormy

Petrel," to the '05 massacre of "Bloody Sunday," that first rehearsal
for the grand Revolution to come; Bonch-Bruevich, the most con-
servative-looking conspirator I know, Petersburg publisher, who
once turned back a threatening horde of Black Hundred thugs
near the Winter Palace by demanding, "How dare you approach
the presence of your sovereign with dirty fingernails and un-
brushed teeth?"; "Kamo" Ter-Petrosian, the cross-eyed Georgian
strong man, Bolshevik Robin Hood, stealing from the rich to give
to the Party, who is so far the only comrade to beat this Old Man
in Indian arm-wrestling; and now the latest, dear little sister Manyasha, the perpetual student, who has just arrived to join us in the
New Year celebrations.

She always has a soothing effect, much needed, damn it, just
now. Insomnia, headaches, stomach gripes, fits of fever, despite
the most wholesome, balanced diet imaginable and a program of
physical fitness worthy of a prizefighter training for the championship. Of course, the body is only suffering the blows inflicted
on the mind. My ailment is the failure of the Revolution, the
triumph of Reaction. We are entering the years of the ebb tide,
the drought, and the famine, in our movement. My task—I see it
in the eyes of caller after caller—is to preserve the seeds, guard
the roots, mulch and water the plant, so that it sprouts all the
stronger when our spring comes round again. (I have been doing
a lot of gardening here—hence the metaphors, though I'd better
not push the analogy as far as slugs and leaf curl, pruning and
pesticides.)

JUNE 1   LONDON   1907

Ever since the suppression of the Moscow Rising in December '05,
I have remained either in Peter, or, what amounts to the same
thing, just across the border in Finland. What was I waiting for?

The truth is I could not accept that our first revolution was
over. The great rehearsal had been held. We players, authors and
producers had learned from our mistakes. Now we must forget
what we do not need to remember—one of the secrets of life! All
eyes are on the first night of the actual show. The metaphor fits
quite well. Even to our main concern, until we are on stage again,
being money, money, money.

The last two years have featured the triumph of reaction in
our enemies, the failure of conviction in our allies, even in some

of our own. Socialism and revolution are declared outdated, nine-teenth-century illusions. The workers are now (it is said) baby-bourgeois, no longer resembling the proletariat of Marx and Engels. Plekhanov preaches that the lesson of Marxism is that Marxism too must be discarded in its turn.

Still, this Fifth Congress, in London, suggests that we are not as *passé* as the capitalist press proclaims—303 delegates repre-senting 150,000 members. The Party as a whole is still tipped toward the revolutionary side—106 Bolsheviks to 97 Mensheviks.

On every occasion, I hammer home the need for cash. What Marxist needs to be reminded of the economic basis for political action? I tell the Mensheviks that the coincidence of the bankruptcy of our treasury, and the bankruptcy of their ideas, is *not* a coin-cidence. In return, I am attacked from all sides for my use of small, armed bands (one good legacy of '05) to rob government institu-tions. I call these "expropriations," legitimate exploitation of the exploiters. Some Meks want me to promise not to act against pri-vate property because it alienates our new, radical, middle-class supporters! I arrange to dodge commitment though I am chal-lenged during nearly every speech. Finally, I silence my hecklers in a closed session on finance. I point out that this Congress alone has cost 60,000 rubles and *we cannot pay it!* All our old sources have dried up in the years of despair. Old Savva Morozov, who must have given us millions, shot himself after the failure of '05. His will leaving all the insurance to us is being held up by opposition from the High Court, and the failure of our joint Menshevik/ Bolshevik leadership to agree on how it should be shared. Much the same with the fortune left by Savva's nephew, Schmidt, who was tortured to death by the police after '05. If we did not get the cash today, many delegates would be stranded here forever. At the last moment, I produce the rich émigré, Joseph Fels, a soap manufacturer, who has agreed to pay all our debts against a note of hand, repayable *after the Revolution!*

Two people I have spent some time with here. Gorky and I traveled here together from Finland and have become such inti-mates we can agree to disagree—a rare thing with me. Only one oddity, he keeps on insisting that we have never met before! The other is Koba, as he prefers to be called, official cover-name "Iva-novich," occasionally "Stalin." He and Kamo (that immensely strong, mad, cross-eyed super-Bolshevik) have pulled some marvelous "Exes," and promise another that will hit the headlines round the world in June. Both Koba and Kamo (whom I knew mainly by notoriety) are Georgians. Koba-Stalin takes my fancy very much.

There is something odd but impressive about him, as if he is always going in and out of focus. Some say he is a hooligan, a savage, a bandit to the core. Others that he is the Marxist, self-made, proletarian gladiator we are always trying to find. Both pictures are accurate, on and off. Perhaps he is both?

JUNE 24   KUOKKALA   1907

Settle down to today's papers which arrive, around supper time, from Helsinki in one direction, Peter in the other. Almost all headline one of the century's most daring and spectacular crimes. The State Treasury in Tiflis, Georgia, has been attacked by heavily armed gunmen who shot their way in, and out, escaping with more than a third of a million rubles.

I hope they are not in notes of too large a denomination.

DECEMBER 30   STOCKHOLM   1907

At the end of June, Nadya and I left Vasa, where we were beginning to feel a little exposed. We moved out to a marvelous lonely beach cabin beyond the lighthouse at Styrs Udde. Strange, for most of any year I can work in a boot cupboard and never notice. Then comes the desire to escape into a landscape without humans. In Geneva, there were always the mountains. At Styrs Udde, we have the sands and the pines. We swim, cycle, do acrobatics on the beach. By the end of the summer, Nadya said I had put on so much weight it would not be decent to show myself in public. I have also been working hard proofreading and editing the first volume of my "Works." I never thought I would be collected in one volume *before* the Revolution. I've also been attending lots of conferences, here in almost-free Finland, and there in almost-SDP Germany.

But this autumn, the shadow fell again. Russian detectives have been conducting a drive for wanted subversives on this side of the border. My name heads the list. So two days ago, tubby, bald Professor Müller, some kind of German geologist, or possible diamond smuggler, hired two amenable Finns to guide him across ice into Sweden. These fellows were not entirely sober and halfway over the three miles of crunching, bouncy surface, they turned back. The professor went on, hearing it crack and tip and slide as he started to run for his life. Fortunately, I had experienced a lot of ice-leaping in my youth on the Volga. I had only one thought —"What a silly way to die!"

Nadya joins me here in Stockholm tomorrow. Then we travel by train, via Berlin, back to the accursed Geneva. How long will this second emigration last?

JANUARY 6   BERLIN   1908

Two nights ago, a wonderful meal with Rosa Luxemburg. Perfect combination of wine, food, talk, laughter. We seemed to float in an armored bubble of optimism. Life as it should be, will be, some-day, for everyone. Only a tiny part of me prowls the base of the brain asking—where is the catch?

I am not much of an expert on dining out. Like Nadya and Rosa, I chose oysters as my first course. But when they went on to other fish dishes, I stayed with oysters. Ideal food for a revo-lutionary agitator, though getting increasingly expensive—they are concentrated nutrient, with a potent and unmistakable taste, and go down in a gulp. The oyster-eater gets three more chances to speak than the patient dissector presiding over the autopsy of a salmon! With Rosa, this is important though I love to hear her talk. With her, political ideology is a form of *haute couture*. You give her your bolts of material, silk or cotton it doesn't matter, and she cuts, stitches, shapes until it reappears as some dazzling cos-tume you hardly dare touch!

We got to bed around midnight, then discovered there *was* a catch. At two in the morning, we were both up, green and wob-bling, victims of food poison. I asked the night-porter, in passable German, for an emergency doctor. He arrived within half an hour but turned out to be a prune-faced, puritanical Yankee with gold pince-nez. Communication was not easy. So far as I could make out, the main medical advice he wished to convey was "only a durned fool eats oysters outside his home." I complained about this choice to the night-porter who hung around showing close interest in all our symptoms.

"But your passports, sir!"

Passports? Then I remembered. I was traveling as a Finnish *chef* and Nadya as an American hotel proprietor!—what whimsical fellow forges these documents in our Bolshevik travel bureau? Nobody speaks Finnish, so the hotel servant plumped for a compatriot of my "friend."

Presumably it was the oysters, as I was by far the sickest of this odd duo. Our doctor suspected some irregularity but wasn't too puritanical to gloss it over for an unreasonable fee. I stumped up the outrageous blackmail. We hung on for another couple of days recovering, and then left this evening for Geneva, where a room has been rented for us at Rue des Deux Ponts 17.

APRIL 11   CAPRI   1908

All Russians are chauvinists. There are about fifty of us on Gorky's Isle of Capri, one of the most beautiful places in the world. If you took the items you most admired from everywhere you had ever been, combined them into a sort of *collage,* marinated them in wine and garlic, then set this floating paradise adrift on a sea so blue and transparent it made you feel faint, then you might convey the impression Capri makes on each new visitor, Russians included.

But by the second day, the Russian has stayed up most of the night in the most crowded, smoky and noisy backroom bar he can find. Here, sweating in self-propagating heat, pouring down the nearest liquid he can find to neat alcohol, he and the other Russians, who have naturally also gathered there, sing Russian songs, attempt Russian dances, tell Russian stories, and finally weep for home.

So many Russians here (enough that I have ceased to count) have said to me the same thing without apparently having any idea all the others are saying it. Standing on the terrace, looking down toward the beach, at that most incomparable moment of the day, just before breakfast, they are impelled to make a comparison. And they announce, in more or less the same words: "Isn't this wonderful? *Can you believe it is not in Russia?*"

Gorky has *insisted* I am his guest for everything. I refused (once), was overruled, and do not intend to mention it ever again. To a frozen Northerner, even one who has savored France, Italy comes as literally an eye-opener. To think I saw the world in black-and-white, like an etching, and only now find there is an alternative of color, like a painting. As well as Capri, we have been to Vesuvius, an extinct volcano (like Plekhanov) but still hot under foot and given to faint growling; to Pompeii, the first place I have ever been to where I actually felt the weight of a living past, so much so that the relaxed, explicit, open eroticism of the street of the brothels quite shook me for a while; Naples, dirty and beautiful, full of charming criminals, like an experiment in open prisons.

About half the Russians here are remittance men, Oblomovs who've discovered they can live happily in the sun, dozing by day, boozing by night, on a few rubles their bailiffs send them as absentee landlords. The other half are pupils at the Party school run by Bogdanov and Lunacharsky in Gorky's villa. It wasn't until my last day, today, since I was on holiday, that I took a look at what it is teaching. I am horrified. For me, Marxism is like a solid block of steel. You cannot take any piece away or add any new bits. For these two, it might be a jigsaw puzzle.

Though posing as ultra-leftists, defenders of the purity of Bolshevism, extreme *Otzovisty* who want to recall our best agitators from all public posts, they are in fact dressing up Marxism with buttons and bows, anything to make it "fashionable" and "faddish." Bogdanov particularly has started introducing mysticism, the occult, rational religion, even that obscenity, God. Their models are no longer Engels or Plekhanov or Rosa Luxemburg, but bourgeois philosophers I confess I've hardly heard of, Mach and Avenarius. I see no need for these tortured amalgams of physics and psychology in order to avoid materialism. The world is *not* just sense impressions. It would exist were man to vanish, to have never been created. I gave them all a few wasps up the arse on the polemical level. But clearly I must get to the British Museum and read up on these fellows and their "Empiriocriticism," "Fideism" and "Positivism." Were we a strong, unified, growing party, we could just about tolerate such theoretical whimsies. But in these years of depression and reaction, I will not have us shipwrecked by a job lot of God-botherers. Perhaps I can start my own school? Where would I find a setting to compare with Capri?

Last day at sea with the anchovy fishers. The anchovies are hauled up in great nets but there is also angling for another fish. I never got its name but you say *"Trin-trin!"* and strum the line. *Trin-trin! Trin-trin!*—it's soothing.

APRIL 12   CAPRI   1908

There is in Russia a smell of cruelty which hovers over the land. It comes wafting back occasionally as we exiles talk. I realize that I have been lucky not to encounter most real horrors, face to face.

Gorky's friend, Professor Zacharov, the bacteriologist, has stopped off here in Capri en route to America where the Yankee capitalists are eager to finance researches that tsarist ministers and businessmen find incomprehensible. He tells us a chilling tale in the Mediterranean sunshine. It was an incident that happened in Odessa when he was head of the Experimental Institute and obliged, through etiquette, to dine once a week with the city governor, General Bulgakov.

One evening over dinner he happened to mention that he was rather short of the monkeys that he needed for his experiments. The general was immediately concerned and knitted his brows trying to think how he could help.

"I say, what about using Jews? Wouldn't they be what you want? I think I've got a few Jews stacked away around here somewhere. They are all spies, so I'm going to have to hang them anyway. Nothing much to be learned from that experiment, eh? You would be very welcome to them if they were any possible help in your work." And he told his orderly to hurry off and discover how many Jewish spies were due to be executed, without waiting for Zacharov's answer.

Zacharov tried to explain just why human beings would not fit in with his series of experiments. But the general was baffled. Pursing his lips and opening his eyes very wide, he said: "Come on, Prof. You can't tell me monkeys are as clever as men, especially Jews. I mean if you injected a man with poison or whatever, why, he would be able to tell you exactly what he felt. Monkeys can't."

Fortunately for the professor, the orderly came back to announce, with many apologies, that there was not after all a single Jew among those the general had decided were spies. There were only Romanians and gypsies.

"What a shame!" said the general. "I suppose gypsies wouldn't be any good either? What bad luck!"

JUNE 3   PARIS   1909

Called round on Manyasha in her little flat this morning only to find her quite ill. My diagnosis, after ticking off textbook list of symptoms, is inflammation of the outgrowth of the blind intestine—that is, appendicitis. I've read so many medical books to treat myself and Nadya and various comrades who cannot afford professional advice, and I have almost total recall, so I reckon I know as much book-learning about medicine as your average country doctor.

It complicates things a bit when it is your little sister. Her broad, low-browed face, papery and damp to the touch, her abdomen so painful she shrank when I made to peel back the duvet. She is not what you call pretty. Indeed, among us round heads only Olga attracted all eyes, a real dazzler, dramatic and provocative. The rest appeal (if at all) through personality. No one could mistake the diligence, dedication and practical competence little sister beams out. If you were knocked down in a street accident, this is who you would want to see looking down on you as you opened your eyes. Our long heads are all *very* good-looking, except for Anyuta who nevertheless preserves a certain sour, challenging elegance.

The good sign, so Dr. Lenin believes, is that the patient has no temperature and insists she feels better walking about. So I put her in a chair and go round the corner for Dr. Dubouchez.

After his examination, the doctor agrees it is appendicitis. Not an acute attack at the moment. Manyasha is not in danger. But he recommends an early operation which he inclines to believe should prove a quick cure. I trust him, having seen him perform an operation on the wife of a comrade just two weeks ago. The hospital is excellent. And that woman was up and about, and working again, within eight days. Still, why have a doctor in the family and skimp on a second opinion? I have sent an "accelerated letter," a French invention which works in this country, though God knows what will happen across the Russian border, to Mitya. After condensing all the data, I ask him whether he too recommends an operation.

Five minutes after the letter has whistled down its tube, I realize how pointless it is and I give permission to Dr. Dubouchez to remove Manyasha's appendix.

The operation was this morning. Surgeon and patient are very pleased with themselves late this evening. Manyasha beams at him—her scar is *beautiful*! He beams at her—no more than a teaspoon of blood, a *classic*! He wishes he could have had a whole phalanx of students watching.

JUNE 5   PARIS   1909

Woken by heavy knocking around dawn. "Accelerated letter" from Moscow. Perhaps Mitya ought to have attended a few more surgical demonstrations such as Dr. Dubouchez imagined staging. His message read: "On no account operate since every indication this could be fatal. Put Manyasha on next train here where will arrange stay here in rest home with correct food exercise which essential banish intestinal catarrh. Dimitri Ulyanov medical doctor."

DECEMBER 10   PARIS   1909

Paris is, in many ways, a rotten hole. The Bibliothèque Nationale is a farce, very French. That is, it looks marvelous.

An impressive building where even junior staff dress up like Cabinet ministers and love to show visitors, especially foreigners, around. The only drawback is, it doesn't work. Or so slowly and so inefficiently that using it is like being landed in a mild nightmare—the one where your feet are stuck in molasses and nobody understands what you are saying. The result is I have to rise *very* early in the mornings (much harder for some reason in town than in country) and be at my desk by eight A.M. to have any chance of getting my next book brought me the *the same day*. Sometimes I could take an ax to chop down all the queuing readers, the lackadaisical assistants, the pompous section heads between me and what I have ordered. I have to stare at my notes and think myself into calm. As I relax, I imagine the blood pressure dropping, point by point, like a thermometer plunged into ice water.

We urgently need some new faces here—rather new *minds*. (People's externals rarely affect me except as clues to what is within.) I keep on hearing wonderful things about "Inessa," one of our

Bolshevik activists in Brussels, who sounds like a Chernyshevsky heroine warmed into life. In Stockholm's Russian colony, a disciple of Chernyshevky's *What's to Be Done?* read my pamphlet *WTBD?* and became converted to Bolshevism. Even the least vain of authors finds that testimonial hard to resist! I have asked Nadya to invite her to Paris for a visit.

JANUARY 5   PARIS   1910

I have discovered a new pleasure/pastime that is just demanding enough to keep me awake, yet scarcely more strenuous than lolling in a hammock—meanwhile it allows the mind to badger away digging up fresh thoughts, connecting new tunnels. I suppose it is the sort of relaxation others get from fishing without ever catching any fish. What I do is watch airplanes landing and taking off in the "drome" at Juvisy, not far out of Paris. I sit on a little painter's stool, wrapped in my fur coat, and track them through my field-glasses, rising, circling and falling in the rhythm of summer flies at a picnic. I am content just to follow them through the routine. That gradually increasing speed and roar as they hurtle across the grass like powerful but clumsy automobiles that will inevitably crash into the far fence. Then, two-thirds through, the tail perks up, sparrow-fashion, the beak dips and the noisy, land-bound, horse-less cart leaves one element and launches into another. Now it becomes more nimble, sprightly, even quieter. Finally it settles into a staid, correct promenade, a provincial burgher taking his Sunday stroll, at about 3,000 feet (so they tell me), in a rough square. Someday I must scrape together the price of a trip. I might be quite good as an aviator—it's got affinities to tobogganing, skating, bicycling and other sports I seem designed for.

Today's visit to Juvisy was rather different. This was a full-scale air display and I sat in the temporary grandstand while sky-borne vehicles of various kinds, owned by private firms, showed how they can pick up loads on hooks without landing, execute complete loops, shoot low overhead upside down. It was rather *too* exciting. Rather as if a fisherman should find his catch leaping onto his lap all day. There was little time for political musing.

What will they do in the future with these inventions about which most people have hardly heard? They must have a use in warfare (and that means civil war and revolution too). For 2,500 years, Alexander to Napoleon, infantry moved at the pace of a foot soldier—four miles an hour. Only occasional short bursts were possible at the pace of galloping cavalry.

The next war between great nations will undoubtedly be more mobile. Troops transported at high velocity, possibly forty/fifty miles per hour—technically possible—in long, armored, maybe gun-carrying, trains. The war after that will be decided in the air. Not by these little, individual, buzzing wasps but by great air-filled balloons carrying gondolas packed with sharpshooters, heavy artillery for use after landing, large explosive "eggs" for dropping on enemy lines. The airplanes we see now will be scouts and sneak raiders. The first army able to deliver super-dynamite by the ton from the air will win. (Though Krassin tells me current research is in the other direction. He himself is experimenting with a revolutionary weapon intended for our revolutionary street squads —a grenade the size of a walnut that can flatten a city block.)

Halfway home, I turned a corner on the frosty road, clapped on my brakes and skidded sideways under the bonnet of a Hispano-Suiza. For what seemed a minute I was sliding, as in a dream with time slowed down, bringing my right eye closer and closer to a large dilated headlamp. Then I was sitting on the pavement surrounded by the good citizens of Paris, unanimously on my side as the driver had charged on with a great retch of gears. I said I thought I was blind. But the crowd was more interested in bringing the *aristo* to justice. His name is Vicomte de Profiterole.

Late this evening, I was contemplating my vanished right eye in the mirror when the door bell rang. A socialist advocate, from the local *Maison du Peuple,* shook my hand, promised to represent me as Zola had Dreyfus, guaranteed me enormous damages, a sensational airing of this monstrous injustice. By the way, he hoped, as a fellow comrade, I would not mind but one should never let grass grow beneath one's feet. He had entered my case before the neighborhood court, enrolling himself as my attorney.

I was taken back by this display of celerity, so un-Russian, especially in matters of law. My head was ringing. Feebly, I agreed, signed some document, thanked him.

JANUARY 18   **PARIS**   **1910**

"Triumph for People over Nobility! V. I. Ulyanov (Lenin) Wins Bicycle Case! Bolshevik Leader Awarded New Machine!" Would these be tomorrow's headlines?

The French legal system at work is something of a revelation. It is not, as I feared, a court designed only to protect the property of the rich, to exert the authority of the state, to embody class domination. Equally it is not, as my advocate, Dr. Olivier, had asserted, an organ established by the Republic to protect the weak, the poor, the stupid from exploitation by the rich, the strong, the clever.

It was difficult to place the judge, at least for a foreigner. My lawyer assured me that he saw so many injustices brought before him for righting that he *must,* no! no! he *did,* consider himself an honorary member of the proletariat. The vicomte's lawyer, a fellow socialist (also, I gathered, a relative of my lawyer) offered a measly sum as settlement, advising his comrade-at-law/in-law that he should accept since the judge was a well-known *bourgeois arriviste,* a snob and social climber, whom everyone agreed always sided with members of the ruling class, particularly *les vicomtes.*

As we three were sitting together (a grave breach of etiquette already according to Russian legal procedure) at Les Trois Rongons, the café next to the court, the judge was pointed out to me. He was a tiny figure, weighing about as much as a large bird, with a face like a timid doodle, dressed in a mantle of dandruff and tobacco ash. In one minute, perfect claw, he held a glass of some green dye, in the other a battered, somehow pre-smoked cigarette.

Our case did not come up until the end of a long day. I could see the magistrate had expended the last scrapings of his attention and concern.

My own intuition? The side that told its story most simply and quickly would win.

Comrade Olivier dismissed the facts but maundered on about me being a radical, republican refugee from tsarist tyranny, leader of an illegal workers' party, living on the subscriptions of the poor, whose only means of transport was a bicycle. As a publicist, I have learned to watch my audiences' reaction to key words and concepts. The judge was registering "foreigner . . . troublemaker . . . underminer of status quo . . . no profession, no occupation, no regular income . . . sponging on the French taxpayer . . . causing traffic accidents with silly machine, not a serious conveyance . . . plea refused. Deportation?"

The comrade on the other side was shorter and more direct. The *vicomte,* he stated flatly, was a Frenchman, a nobleman, a patriot, former major in the Guards, a taxpayer, an employer of many French workers, a pioneer of the grand French sport of *le motoring.* Though his expensive machine had been assaulted by this subversive alien's children's toy, the *vicomte* was not the one who was wasting the time of this French court. All he requested was the dismissal of the case and the award of costs.

The judge would have granted it too, there and then, without further evidence, if I had not intervened.

I asked his permission, as a courtesy, being a fellow servant of the law, to say a few words on my own behalf. I was, I explained, a graduate in law from the University of St. Petersburg, called to the bar on the Samara circuit. I was not sure of the relevance of my politics, as introduced by both attorneys. But if public standing and background were to be taken into account, I had to point out that I was a member of the hereditary nobility at the court of the Emperor, holding a rank certainly equal, if not superior, to that of *vicomte,* and that this authorized me to the precedence and form of address somewhat above major, indeed major-general. I was not, admittedly, in trade, like the *vicomte,* but received an income, as a landed gentleman traveling abroad, from my estates. I was not, I regretted, overfamiliar with the French legal process, itself admired all over the civilized world, but I assumed that a small injection of testimony by eyewitnesses would not be inappropriate.

He was wavering. I only needed one more push, but what? Before me on the desk was the list of the ten witnesses, none of them, unfortunately, present. So I began very slowly to read out the ten names, occupations, and addresses in my Slav-accented French, stumbling all too convincingly.

I raised my eyes. He was sitting, like a dull gargoyle, at his much too large bench. So vivid was the manifestation, I could have photographed the longed-for chicken bone; the thirsted-after glass of red wine. He spoke: "His Excellency, nobleman Ulyanov, by his welcome intervention, has convinced me. I grant his submission as plaintiff, also full legal costs, compensation for loss of time otherwise spent enjoying the amenities of our capital, and whatever amount represents full replacement of his pedal bicycle. And I would remind *Monsieur* Profiterole the defendant, soi-disant *vicomte,* that this is a democratic republic where titles are unknown and no citizen is permitted to diminish the rights of another citizen through what I might entitle 'terrorism by automobile.' Court is adjourned."

FEBRUARY 20   PARIS   1910

Paris is a cruise liner. You meet the same people all the time. When it isn't French intellectuals making brilliant remarks that turn banal in translation, like seaweed out of the water, it is Russian exiles abusing each other in terms that sound as if they came from a special language designed for insults, Desperanto perhaps. Since the half-revolution of '05, life outside Russia has become for us a hundred times more barren and arid. Nothing but dusty scandals and scabby squabbles. Such are the occupational diseases of the émigré.

I have been in Paris for almost exactly a year—my annual ticket for the Bibliothèque Nationale has just come up for renewal. But I still cannot feel at home as I did in London after two weeks. I remember when Trotsky arrived there from France, his last leg from Siberia, he blabbed out: "Paris is nice but Odessa is better." Plekhanov creased at such naïve provincialism. Actually, Trotsky was wrong. Paris is *not* nice, and the Parisians are worse, particularly the intellectuals. It is as if they believe they are the only true adults in the world, the only ones to use words correctly and exactly. They are more interested in what things are called than in what they are. If it has a name then it must exist in its own right —like God. Once you have summed up a problem, preferably with an aphorism, then you have also solved the problem. Nothing could be more alien to my philosophy. I resent being surrounded by word-jugglers—"Look, six bright ideas in the air at once!"—when all around me living creatures are starving, dying, being beaten and robbed.

I thought nothing could change this considered impression. Then, suddenly, one morning Paris became a poster by Toulouse-Lautrec. What's the reason? There can be only one. Inessa!

MARCH 21   PARIS   1910

In an age like this, when all around people like you seem only interested in status and comfort, in shopping as an art-form, in moneymaking as a game, in gambling as a science, in buying things, there is only one satisfying alternative occupation for the revolutionary—editorship.

I like writing. I think I am a good reporter. But the role nature seems to have best equipped me for in the bordello of journalism is not the star attraction, or the specialist performer, but the madam. I am not seduced by the Yankee version of the editor, the slave driver everyone strains to please as the presses roll. My style is duller but much more rewarding in the end. A cross between a headmaster and a commanding officer. It is not a recipe for quick popularity.

When presented with "copy," I try to approach it in a balanced and impersonal fashion, almost as though I assume it had been assembled by an automaton. My eye is that of a critic, not a creator. I have made myself highly sensitive to the misspelling, the faulty transcription, the typographical error, the false logic; the good and the bad quotation, the dubious set of figures, the wrong historical analogy; the empty flourish of rhetoric; the cheap appeal to prejudice. I insist that all data be checked, particularly when it supports your own case, if possible against several sources. I point out that almost nobody copies more than a dozen words from another author without introducing at least one error. I make clear that the needs of the struggle take precedence over any hurt feelings, excuses for mistakes, omissions or accidental falsifications. What matters is the end product, the communal message, the printed version of the Party line. Least important is who physically put down the words, or whose name is on the piece.

Kamenev confirmed that I am effectively seeing myself as others see me this morning in the café when he recalled the fight over the editorial board of *Iskra* at the '03 Congress. He had been shocked by my attitude originally, but, reading carefully through the copies before and after I ran it, he had to agree that not only was my rule correct, putting principle before personality, but it made for a better paper. Lev Borisovich has almost everything a Bolshevik needs except his fatal desire to please. He irritated me by leaning over with watery eyes and saying: "*Starik,* I'd rather be grilled by the Okhrana than by you. But then I'd rather be praised by you for what I'd written than win the Prix Goncourt."

"I certainly wouldn't print that tripe. Exaggerated, over-emotional, too personal, sentimental. You make me think I didn't grill you enough."

There is, of course, the other side to editing, even more rewarding, when you come across new, inexperienced talent. Here my aim has always been to correct and improve their stuff without them noticing I was doing it. Nadya used to say—"Volodya, your straight line always has a bend in it."

I start before the piece is commissioned. I decide there is some talent in someone and begin discussing whatever the possible topic is. I expound my own ideas, suggest a few questions, get the prospective writer interested. After I have taken him all round the subject, I may say—"Well, you seem to have thought about this. How about writing us an article on it?"

The writer may not even have noticed how much I have helped him in this preliminary discussion. When he turns in a good piece, everybody is pleased, including the writer. I have failed if somebody notices that he has actually used any of my expressions and turns of phrase. If Nadya is the only one who realizes, then that is real editing.

APRIL 20   PARIS   1910

It is just over two months since Inessa Armand arrived here and my life has been transformed. For a while, I pretended to myself that no one else noticed. But this proved impossible because so many people remarked on the change in me, all favorably! Even Nadya, who is under no illusions about what is happening (though she has so far avoided discussing it directly with me), remarks on the improvement in my health, my personality, my work, even my manners, even my appearance.

Inessa has moved in next door to us, with two of her children, André and Ina. What has transformed my life is that Inessa and I are "lovers."

As I write it down, it doesn't sound right. I don't think of us like that, defined as if in some bureaucratic category. I love Nadya too, and Mother, and my brothers and sisters, and various comrades. I appreciate love's power but I realize that it is a purely subjective emotion. Amazing, how ex-husbands and ex-wives so quickly can feel for each other not even the ordinary courtesies of life. Friendship does not dissolve like that, or the ties of blood relationship.

What happened was that the first time I encountered Inessa, though she had her back to me bending over a child, I knew what she would look like, move like, speak like, be like. When we make love it has for me no element of conquest, of active against passive, but of equal completion, of two halves uniting, of resolution and synthesis. The first time it happened, I heard myself say as my head cleared—"*Slava bogu,* it's the dialectic!" Inessa rolled out of bed, laughing.

The first time *it* happened . . . More accurately put, the first time *we* happened, I did not notice what was happening! It was our second day, our first evening, together and we were floating on a torrent of talk. I saw, without seeing, that she was taking off her clothes, that she was turning back the quilt on the floor mattress, still talking. Still talking, I imitated her, slid naked under the quilt. It seemed a meeting arranged many, many years ago. For the first time since we had met, thirty-six hours before, we were silent.

Perhaps she takes after some relative of mine, glimpsed in childhood, shading her eyes in the back row of a family photograph. She certainly does not resemble me or my sisters. Indeed, I was something of a shock to her. Because of security, we try not to have photographs circulating. So she built her picture from what she had read by, and about, me. The hard man, the splitter, the aggressor, the leader of the fighting élite—somehow he was much taller, with beautiful eyes, graceful movements. Even hair. Instead she saw a short, bald, squat, squinting, ordinary figure, who might easily be (as comrades have said) a factory foreman or a farm bailiff. Yet she too, she tells me, knew this was her missing piece.

Nadya was out of town when Inessa arrived. She asked me the next day to describe her. I did so in some detail, which again is not unusual. In our life, on the verge of legality, often elbowed by spies and detectives, it has become second nature to be able to detail the looks of friend and enemy, passing on a description that others will be able to recognize. Not at all such an easy task as might at first be thought.

So I said she had a mass of chestnut hair, done up like a bird's nest. Large, dark-gray eyes, with a skeptically raised left eyebrow. A truly aquiline nose, in that it was really close to that of an eagle. A somewhat stern, set, headmistressy mouth. And a vivacity and sparkle that was positively theatrical. When Nadya did meet her, she turned to me. "Excellent listing of the items, Ilyich," she murmured. "But why did you not sum up by saying she was beautiful?"

"I didn't know she was," I admitted.

APRIL 28   LONGJUMEAU   1911

Our summer school at Longjumeau, a pleasant working village near Paris, has been running for nearly a month now and has two more to go. We have eighteen students, mostly Russian workers —these are apostles whom we will send back to spread the gospel, the good news, of man as the measure, the savior, of man. I doubt whether we could have started it without Inessa.

She went out ahead, naturally, since she is French, speaking fluent French and so got us a slightly run-down tannery at a knock-down price. If any of us had arrived with our Russified accents, the absentee owner would have charged a fortune. The French person outside Paris knows only two kinds of Slav—the fabulously rich, mad Prince or the penniless, mad Anarchist. Even with sober Social Democrats such as us (he reared back a little at Zinoviev's black golliwog flames of hair) the owner asked to be told whether or not we would be making bombs. When Inessa asked what he would do if she said "yes," he replied: "Treble the insurance, of course."

Inessa has also hired a house where the students can live together, dormitory-style, and cooks them one meal a day, which is all most of them eat. Inessa's food is almost the best I ever remember, a combination of most interesting, tasty and healthful dishes from England, Russia and France.

She is also the only woman among the Bolsheviks in France whom I would trust to give a course in any aspect of Marxism. She has chosen the bedrock subject of political economy and after sitting in on the first lessons Zinoviev told me it was the first time he had ever understood the equations in *Kapital*. I am giving most lectures, more than fifty in all, ranging over the whole spectrum.

The Zinovievs, the Ulyanovs and Inessa and brood share a woodman's cottage on its own just out of sight of the village. In the past, I had always (correctly) had the reputation of keeping aloof from the rest of the comrades when we were not working together. This is because I have little interest or talent for café gossip and storytelling. Life has not seemed long enough for our great task for me to be able to waste even minutes. So I would either be reading or writing or sleeping—and for these I needed to be protected from noise, commotion, even conversation.

But the arrival of Inessa has altered that. The best spring can be wound too tight. My work actually benefits from my not working. So I take, every few evenings, an evening off when I join the rest round the stove. We have borrowed a piano from the local schoolteacher and Inessa plays for us. I do not know much about these things, though Gregory tells me she is a virtuoso. I do know that when she plays Beethoven I feel that there is nothing greater in the world than the *Appassionata*. I fear I could listen to it every day. It is really fantastic, transcendental music. It is also a drug. If I had too much, I would melt away like a snowman in the sun.

MAY 5   **LONGJUMEAU**   **1911**

Inessa and I have been telling each other the stories of our lives. That is the advantage, I see, lovers have over spouses—the longer you have been married, the less of a separate existence you have to talk about. As it is, I am struck, as ever, by how much more interesting is the woman's autobiography than the man's. I put this down (largely but not entirely) to women telling the truth and men spinning fantasies. The truth is never boring, never pointless. Inessa's tale has more than enough for a novel by Balzac. I'm beginning to think I'll be lucky if mine stretches to a Chekhov short story.

"Inessa" is a cover-name. She was born in Paris in 1874, Elizabeth d'Herbenville. Both her parents, French father, Scottish mother, were on the music hall. Her girlhood was spent in the world of the popular theater. "The very first thing I remember is staring at a blinding light and feeling sick from the smells of flaring naphtha and melting greasepaint." Her father was quite well known as a comic mime and ballad singer performing under the name of Stéphen. Her mother would join in with a song and also taught the piano. "I was like a clockwork toy, an awful little show-off. I played several instruments, danced and did acrobatics, spoke two languages fluently. I loved being looked at."

Then Stéphen died, on stage. "Not only on stage, but playing a clown dying on stage. We were already gathered round him, wife and three children. He said his final line—'Hold the curtain'—and died."

Her mother kept the two boys and shipped Elizabeth off to Russia where her Scottish grandmother and French aunt were both governesses in the family of a millionaire textile manufacturer of French extraction, Evgeny Armand.

"Since there was no longer anyone for them to teach, they lived like ladies. Me too. I was the youngest person on that great estate at Pushkino, thirty miles from Moscow, and I had a tutor all to myself. I realize now that he had rather advanced, radical views. But I was too busy then making myself fluent in two more languages, German and Russian, becoming a communicant in the Orthodox Church, and pretending I did not know that the younger son, Alexander, had fallen passionately in love with me."

In 1893, both under twenty, Elizabeth and Alexander were married, to the delight of all their relatives.

Then there comes the part of her past, the six years that I find harder to imagine. An estate of their own, not much smaller than the father's, at Eldigino; a townhouse in Moscow; the round of parties, balls, country visits, like any upper-class couple. "I also had four children, two girls and two boys. I suppressed the twinges of tedium, the stirrings of ambition, worrying about whether this was all there was to life. I couldn't see what other way there was to fill my days, especially as a woman."

It was then that she began to notice that the elder son, Vladimir, her brother-in-law, was showing similar signs of discontent with a comfortable, undemanding existence. They coincided with an outbreak of unrest at old Armand's factories, one of which employed more than 2,000 workers. The men were beginning to demand the right to organize for better pay and conditions. Leaflets were being circulated, vigorously and eloquently written, elegantly printed, churned out seemingly regardless of cost. "Papa Evgeny brought one home and passed it round at a family dinner. I held it in my hand and in a flash of intuition I knew it came from Vladimir."

Such activity was a crime, and the police were hot on the same trail. "Volodya was suspected. I admired his Byronic arrogance. The way he proclaimed his solidarity with the workers but refused to answer any questions. Any danger was largely theoretical since his father simply bought off the detectives. But I protected him with the lies he was too noble to tell, the first I ever really told. Now I had someone to educate me. I read Chernyshevsky's *What Is to Be Done?* and modeled myself, like thousands of other rebellious young women, on the heroine, Vera Pavlovna."

Elizabeth quickly exhausted the kind of philanthropy thought suitable to married ladies of her background and station. "Interfering with the running of the home farm . . . raising funds for the hungry by attending banquets . . . teaching children whose parents couldn't afford to buy them boots to read books . . . discouraging the penniless from ruining themselves by gambling and drink. Then I discovered prostitution."

She had heard of this social evil but needed Vladimir to explain its mechanics. "I could scarcely believe him. I had read about it in Chernyshevsky for one, and in French novels, but somehow I had thought the actual practice had long ago been abolished. When I was assured that there were 'whores aplenty' just down the road in Moscow, I was as taken aback as if I'd been told there were cannibals. I wanted to leave immediately and save these unhappy women by offering the help of a purer, luckier sister."

Afraid that she would otherwise mount an individual mission on her own, the two brothers decided to arrange an elaborate safari into *Na Dne,* what Gorky was to call "the Lower Depths."

"It sounds like a huge joke now. But we took ourselves very seriously. Looking back, I believe neither of the two Armand brothers knew much more than I did. Certainly, they stuffed pistols into all their pockets. Enlisted a couple of gamekeepers with huge cudgels as bodyguards. And insisted I disguise myself as a young man. They also recruited a kind of dragoman in V. A. Gilyarovsky, a newspaper columnist who specialized in making suburban flesh creep by reporting what went on along those streets 'where not one Muscovite in ten thousand dares set foot after dark.'

"Our guide took us first, late in the afternoon, to Khitrovka. It is marked on the maps of Moscow as 'a market.' Actually, it is a kind of tented *souk* where human beings are bought, sold or rented. We kept to the far side of an open sewer—on the map, Yauza river. Gilyarovsky pointed out on the fringes such minor horrors as ten-year-old girls being auctioned for fifty rubles, even younger child-beggars, some hugging real dead babies, on hire for fifty kopeks a day.

"By comparison, the next sight, Yama, 'the Pit,' was almost salubrious. Stone buildings, paved road, some attempt to make the district look attractive with fretwork porches, lace curtains, lights over the door. There were only two streets here, the Big and the Little. On Bolshaya Yamskaya, high-class women—three rubles for a 'quickie,' ten for the night. One or two second-class houses—one ruble a visit, no lingering. On Malaya Yamskaya, the *tyotki* or 'scrubbers,' who kept out of the light and couldn't stand close scrutiny —fifty kopeks for anything."

Elizabeth struck up conversations with some of the women on the Bolshaya. They were pleasant enough when they thought she was a delicate-looking noble schoolboy, perhaps being given his initiation. But when she offered to take them away to the country, find them jobs on the farm, they grew affronted and angry. She removed her fur hat and shook out her rippling hair. "I'm a woman," she said. "I'll look after you. You'll be safe with me."

The response was even more hostile. "They called me a lesbian, a pervert, a freak. I didn't know what they meant. When Vladimir tried to explain, I was even more astounded. How many other things went on in the world that I had never heard about?"

The pimps began to stir. The porters woke up and asked what was the trouble. It was getting dark. Gilyarovsky handed round a few coins and the expedition retreated.

More than anything she read, or was told, this experience opened Elizabeth's eyes to the multi-layered exploitations concealed behind the façade of tsarism. "I made one last attempt to convince myself that these evils were due to individual sin, not the system of our society. I went to Tolstoy." The old hypocrite told her that nothing would change until there was a mass conversion to primitive Christianity. As for prostitution? "Nothing will come of work among whores," he said. "It was so before Moses, it was so after Moses. So it was, so it will be."

At the turn of the century, ten years, and four children, after her marriage to the millionaire's son, she decided to search for some more ordered, positive means of dismantling the corrupt old order and setting up a new world, here and now.

"I was very slow," she said. "Especially when I compare myself to Rosa or Nadya. I was attracted to the SRs, the glamour of direct action. Then I was attracted to Vladimir who was moving toward the Social Democrats. We read a book together called *The Development of Capitalism in Russia*."

By now, it was clear both brothers loved her, but she preferred Vladimir to Alexander. True to the laws governing free men and women among the new people of Chernyshevsky, the three of them accepted the new alignment. Alexander took the children and she left to help make revolution. Even then it was not until '03 that there came the final, open break. She joined Vladimir in Switzerland where she gave birth to his child, her fifth, André. Elizabeth had become "Inessa."

She was in Peter on Bloody Sunday, saw the massacre of the kneeling petitioners, and was arrested leading an attack on the soldiers. She was condemned to exile in Archangel, living alone reading Marx, until she escaped in '08 to be with Vladimir who was dying of consumption in Switzerland.

"I arrived with seconds to spare. He died with me kneeling over him, like my father. Now, I knew I was a Marxist, a Bolshevik, a Leninist. But I needed insulation from people as intimates so I enrolled on a course of socialism in Brussels. It took a year. I read all the back numbers of *Iskra,* everything you have written. I came to Paris for *you.*"

AUGUST 15   PARIS   1911

Longjumeau has been the one sunlit, happy stretch of what have otherwise been the ugly, quarrelsome, obsessive years since '05. I have had to drag myself off to fight for the Schmidt money. I hate money, but we must have it and it is ours. I have to keep telling myself to let the others be embarrassed. If they are not ashamed to shout out sums, and allot themselves percentages, why should we be? Nikolai Schmidt was a Bolshevik, like Vladimir Armand, and nephew of another textile magnate, Morozov. He died in prison for our Party, possibly tortured to death. But he made the mistake of leaving more than a quarter of a million rubles to the Social Democrats as a whole instead of specifically to the Bolsheviks. Since, at his death, we were still a unified body (ha!) the Meks have put in for their share. I managed to lift some of it for the coffers. But the mass remains in the hands of the German trustees, Mehring, Kautsky and Clara Zetkin. We are forced to behave like a set of squabbling bourgeois in a melodrama round the deathbed of a miserly uncle.

So it is with special nostalgia that I look back on the evenings there when we would all, students and instructors, children and mother-in-law, lounge about on the hay as the sun slowly sank on a really scorching day. Zinoviev would play his balalaika, Inessa would sing her mother's ballads, Lilina would dance with the children, Nadya would whistle (she's the best whistler I ever heard) and as darkness would come on and the heat still throbbed from the scraped earth I would do my party trick of reciting passages by the yard from the novels of Turgenev.

Last night was our last night at Longjumeau. The summer school has been a tremendous success, thanks to everyone, including the hard-worked students, but, above all, thanks to Inessa. It had seemed originally that I made a mistake, putting us all together so closely, including Nadya's mother, whose glances at her son-in-law's mistress would have skinned a less sunny personality than

Inessa. But, despite our ages, as Nadya observed, we were less like several families obliged to share a roof than a student commune.

I realize that what I say about Inessa can hardly seem objective even to me as I write and read what I write. Nevertheless, there is that in her, an absolute honesty and openness, that reminds me of Vera Zasulich—a crystal window on her spirit that is irresistible. This is not to say she is never unfair, never selfish, never sometimes cruel. But she never pretends that she has not been so and will never attempt to conceal her actions from others. She obliges everyone to be an intimate or a stranger. And this makes her, though thirty-seven and a mother of five, and the lover of a few men in her time, often look like a maidenly young girl, a pupil rather than a teacher. Especially when you see her alone, and, as she fancies, unobserved.

I have been seeking the right moment to talk to Nadya about Inessa. But there is no right moment, I realize. Nadya solved the dilemma by turning to me on one of our walks and asking, "Do you want me to leave?" I said, "No." She said, "I'm glad. So I'll stay." And that was it.

SEPTEMBER 23   ZURICH   1911

Meeting of the International Socialist Bureau in Zurich today. I bumped into Vladimir Burtsev, the Inspector Javert of the revolutionary movement, the exposer of master-spy Azev and who can count how many other Okhrana double, treble agents. He appears the mildest of men, as chubby as a nest of concentric circles. He has this habit which at first seems quite endearing, if a little tedious, but gradually grows oddly threatening. As you talk he begins to smile more and more broadly. He keeps up an almost unbroken cheery hum, as much as to say "yes, yes, quite interesting but that I knew already, tell me a bit more, yes, yes, that's what I thought, now just carry on and elaborate a little . . ." Police spies, against whom there was no evidence at all, and only the mildest suspicion, have been known to break down and confess all, at the end of such a jolly, encouraging, wordless interrogation.

So I always make a point of putting him on the stand in my best forensic manner. This reversal of his normal *modus operandi* makes him uncharacteristically foul-tempered, and likely to blurt out things he would not have mentioned. There is no question of his devotion to the Revolution in general, and his unique services to the cause. But I never forget that he is not a Social Democrat, let alone a Bolshevik. He is an old-fashioned SR, and a right-winger at that.

After I had refreshed his memory on this, put to him that and the other, and generally enfiladed him with a barrage of irrelevant, but worrying, questions, he changed the subject with relief.

"Did you hear that Stepan Ivanovich Radchenko was dead?" he asked. For a few seconds, I could not recall the name. Then up popped the picture of the birth-marked beanpole we used to call, behind his back, the Ace of Clubs.

"I'm sorry," I said. "He was one of the founders with me of the League of Struggle for the Emancipation of the Working Class. In Peter in '95."

"I know, and that's why I'm not. Sorry, I mean." He was now smiling and even humming a bit. Somehow he'd got me in his net. "He popped off just in time. For him. We were going to pick him up. Almost certainly an *agent provocateur*. He dropped out of political activity after the 1905 amnesty. Showed all the classic signs of the traitor within."

"Wait a second," I stopped him. "Amnestied? Then he was in prison before that. The Okhrana don't usually like their men to be sent to prison."

"Just the point. He was born a Cossack, you know. Father a bourgeois, a timber merchant. One spell of prison. Three months in early '93 just before you met him. That must have been when he was turned. Otherwise he was prominent politically, not to mention physically, for twelve years. From 1890 to 1902, twelve years, everyone he touched was arrested. Apart from him, *every* delegate to the First Party Congress in '98 was put behind bars. They had to salt him away for a little while in the end. In 1904, I had my hand on his collar.

"Then he vanished and I had only just found him again last month. You mean, *you* never suspected? You never thought he might have shopped *you*? You should look around. There are some other very fishy samples quite close. Must be off. See you in court."

And he was gone.

NOVEMBER 20   PARIS   1911

Only two months ago, Nadya and I cycled over to Draveil to visit
the Lafargues. I had met Paul first in '95 when I came to Paris to
research the Commune. Even then, he was one of the few survivors, probably the only leader, from that heroic endeavour of
twenty-five years before—"storming Heaven" his father-in-law Karl
Marx called it. At twenty-five, born just a year before this first
proletarian revolution of the nineteenth century, I felt in a silly
sort of way touched by destiny just to be able to rub knees in a
café with a man who could describe the events as he saw them
happen before his eyes, who had married Marx's daughter Laura,
who had eaten and drunk and fought and argued with Blanqui.
I imagined I could understand at last the experience of those
Grecian and Trojan warriors who found themselves temporary
companions of the gods. I even brought the pair flowers.

And I became shy and tongue-tied. Our opening conversation
went something like this:

P.L. "You say the workers in Petersburg are reading Marx?"

V. "Yes, and studying him in groups."

P.L. "But do they understand him?"

V. "Yes, of course. Why not?"

P.L. (*politely crushing as only the French intellectuals know how to
be*) "I'm afraid you are wrong. They understand nothing. They
do not know anything about Marx. Why, here in France we have
been explaining Marxism to the French workers for twenty years.
And even they still understand nothing."

I did not reply. But 1905 in Russia proved us right and the
Europeans wrong. The semi-Asiatics almost toppled the world's
most powerful autocracy, and even Father Gapon had read Marx
in the end.

Over the years, Paul and I became quite close, yet as two
couples we were never on terms of equality. Partly, it was the age
difference. Both of them were nearly thirty years older than we
were. Also it was a matter of temperament. Nadya, you could say,
does not have *any* temperament *at all*. She has dedicated herself
to the Revolution, body and soul. Nothing so trivial as personal
feelings, ailments, discomforts, dangers, up to and including fatal
disease and the death sentence, will ever discourage her. She will

go on serving the cause, getting older, slower, grayer, until she grinds to a halt, standing up.

I cannot claim to be quite such a hardened slogger. I do get depression, headaches, stomach pains, insomnia—failures of the flesh no doubt triggered off by weaknesses of the will. But I can honestly say I do not regard myself as anything other than Archimedes' lever looking for a fulcrum. I have no desire for any rewards, mental or physical, for myself. I do not want flattery, fame, money, luxury, even power—if I ever win power, I will keep it for what it can do for others, not for me. That is why whatever uncouth beast roars or whimpers within, I strive to tame it with whip and chair. I try to let no one see the nerve ever crack. I refuse to admit it is possible, save as a brief spasm.

That is why I did not know quite how to receive Paul's confession to me two months ago. While the women walked round the garden, he showed me his last will and testament and confided that the pair of them were determined on a joint suicide soon. My first reaction was that this was an act of selfishness, of childish aggression, of melodramatic play-acting, all too consistent with the streak of petty vanity that runs through so many of our British and especially French comrades (much rarer among Germans and Russians). It is as if life, history, the working class, the revolutionary movement had let them down by not bringing Socialism in their time, so in a burst of spite, they'll cancel this life and start another.

I said nothing to N. even when she asked me, as we were walking the bikes up the big hill outside Passy, what Laura could have meant by something *she* said. The two of them had stood for a moment listening to Paul and me niggling round some minor point of Marxist analysis. Then Laura had suddenly whispered— "Paul will soon prove the sincerity of his philosophic convictions" and flashed a smile to him behind my back. I went on hoping they would change their minds.

Today the funeral ceremony in the Père-Lachaise cemetery, the place where the leading Communard prisoners had been stood against the wall and shot down. Many of the milk-and-water socialists you always find clustering round such occasions were shaking their heads over the Lafargues and criticizing them for deserting the battle. One or two sought my support. But I sent them off, as we say in Russian, with a wasp up their arses. "What have you ever done for the working class that history should notice you are alive?" I asked. "The Lafargues spent seventy years each in the front line. Laura Marx was born there. Nadya and I would be proud to have achieved what they have. And if ever we could no longer work for the Party and for the Revolution, we too would look truth in the face and die like them." They looked abashed. But N.'s face lit up. I suspect she had been worried that the couple in the coffins under the red flags were being buried outside the Party line, like excommunicated Catholics in unconsecrated ground.

Nevertheless, I did not approve their action. Nor can I imagine myself following that path. Their usefulness was not at an end. They could still write. They could still talk. They could observe, study and advise others. It may be, as Paul hinted to me, that a kind of melancholia was gradually paralyzing them. Does it sound arrogant, or, worse, fanciful?—but I am convinced that it is possible to dispel such infections of the emotions by an act of the will. They can be cast out, as Jesus supposedly cast out the evil spirits. And if there are no Gadarene swine about to enter into, let them occupy the Mensheviks!

How can it be that the *thing* itself is so alive I can smell it— yet the words grow blurred and overfamiliar, "revolution," "revolutionary," "proletariat," "toiling masses," etc?

JANUARY 15   PRAGUE   1912

For our conference, I have chosen Prague, dodging unexpectedly sideways like a game bird, to throw off the spies. This is the furnace, I hope, that will finally burn away all the dross from our Party, melt down its impurities into clinker, leave us tempered and strengthened. How often have I said that? It has been a long haul to the new Party, the revolutionary organization of a unique type. "Workers of the world unite!" was the slogan of Marx and Engels's *Communist Manifesto*. So the call for "unity" always gets a good press. Those of us who cry "Let's split!" are easily dubbed pedants, or formalists, grammarians sticking to a Marxist holy writ. Even *saboteurs, provacateurs,* even police agents!

We must ignore the insults. Our aim is a squad of pared-down, muscular, professional, fighting specialists—the Jesuits, the Jacobins, the Praetorian Guards of socialism. And here in Prague, for the Sixth Conference, we seem on the verge of achieving our ambition. We will cast off and drive out the "Liquidationists." There is no room in our ranks for those who advocate disbanding and abandoning our illegal organizations, our undercover agitation, our dedication to the overthrow and destruction of the bourgeois state.

What they want is a Western-style labor party, grateful to its ruling class for those famous "three freedoms"—freedom to join together, without striking, in unions; to speak at crank gatherings, like London's Hyde Park Corner, without being moved along; to read, and possibly some day *publish*, one mildly radical paper that continually exposes injustices which are never righted.

Let them have their "broad church"—significant phraseology! —stuffed full of all those (and more) listed fifty years ago by Herzen in *My Past and Thoughts* (*Byloye i Dumy*): ". . . neglected artists, failed literary figures, students who never finished their courses, lawyers short of briefs, actors without talent, many people with huge vanity but medium ability, with great pretensions but no sticking power or devotion to work . . ." To which today I would add . . . sons of self-made merchants, punishing their parents for passing on an ability to spend, not make, money; ambitious scholarship boys from the upper working class, seeking to satisfy a taste for comfort without feeling guilty; provincial debaters after larger and larger audiences; narcissists wanting their names ever more often in print; good-looking doctors, self-deceived into an illusion of minor divinity, who imagine political prognosis must be as easily perfected as a likable bedside manner; biddable newspaper executives who count on their market price being raised by a reputation for modish extremism on peripheral topics; open-minded clergy who find the words of *vox populi* safer to interpret, and transmute into earthly rewards, than *vox dei;* trade-union leaders, who run their organizations like oversize employment bureaus, and consider it the essence of labor radicalism to greet every confrontation with the plea "Let's keep politics out of . . ." All in all, those my friends and I, when we were exploring the possibilities of any anti-tsarist movement based on the experience of the West in the '90s, used to dismiss as "wets" (*khlupiki*), "eunuchs" (*skoptsi*) and "milk-drinking softies" (*molokanya*). Who needs them?

The other deviationists, smaller, better ordered, more honorable as it may seem from a distance, come under the heading of "Recallists" (*Otzovisti*). They are more dangerous, because apparently more left, more doctrinally pure. I'm afraid I tend to refer to each (only among friends of course) just as "that twat" (*deezha*). They want us to "call back" our members from every exposed position—from the Duma, from the unions, from the insurance clubs, from the health committees, from the newspapers.

To be visible and recognized, they argue, is to give a hostage to the enemy. The powers that be would never allow us to show ourselves so prominently unless such exhibitions were to their benefit. Therefore, we should haul down the flag, put on our disguise, and vanish from sight.

What they refuse to understand is that we should then also *vanish from the sight of the workers.*

At the moment, we can swap roles, play one means of publicizing ourselves against another. If a speech is made at a demo, or even a semi-public meeting, only those who hear it know what was said. The press are forbidden to report us. But if we speak in the Duma, or at official sessions of authorized bodies such as health committees or insurance clubs, then what we say can be printed. Without these, if we withdrew as the Otzovists insist, we should be disarming ourself, throwing away our weapons. The Recallists are just the Liquidationists turned inside out.

The Bolsheviks (as distinct from the Meks) have only one desire in life—to lead the proletariat to power, peacefully if possible, legally when we can, openly as necessary; but also by armed force when we have no choice, without permission, license or approval of any other group or class, by violence, by crime, by any means we deem appropriate. That is why *we* will succeed.

JANUARY 20   **PRAGUE**   **1912**

Harosho, harôsho! Also, possibly, *hosannah!* as it says in the Bible (though surprisingly, if I'm right, only three times). We are triumphing. The *skoptsi* and the *khlupiki* are streaming away. The ship is lighter, more buoyant, more likely not just to remain afloat but to speed toward its destination.

As if to signal this turnabout in our fortunes, after the long dark years of reaction and suppression, I have found us a wonderful workingman, a genuine tribune of, for, from the people, someone who can operate independently for us inside Russia, perhaps even in the Duma.

(No, I mustn't rush too far ahead. Once more I must beware of "falling in love" with a comrade who fits almost too perfectly into the niche I have carved for him. Remember Martov! Remember Trotsky! Be on guard against "reverse-snobbery" as Inessa calls it. Still . . .)

Roman Vatslavovich Malinovsky arrived here several days late.

Nadya, our credentials secretary, has remained behind in Paris but writes to complain that his standing as a delegate is "somewhat murky." There are even doubts as to whether his Moscow group actually exists. Mikhail Kalinin, who agitated alongside M. in the Metalworkers Union, reports that he began as a Mek but has now graduated to the Bolsheviks. Mikhail regards this as tribute to his own powers of persuasion. He remains guardedly ambiguous about his *protégé*.

"He's too noisy and excitable. Always on a knife edge. Just talking to him makes me worn-out. Watch him among the other Moscow delegates. Why do they give him such a cool reception?"

Why? Possibly because middle-class intellectuals resent any worker bumptious enough to lecture, even hector, them (as I have noted) on terms of equality? On the other hand, I have to admit Kalinin himself has been a totally faithful supporter of my policies, the son of poor peasants, skilled craftsman at the factory bench— an impeccable pedigree. I feed all this into my running equation. Wait a minute, an extra bit. Stalin, who was jointly responsible with Kalinin for the great Tiflis railway strike of 1900, did tell me Mikhail liked to keep quiet about his first job—footman to the Mordukhay-Boltovsky family in Peter in '90! There is no formula for the perfect revolutionary.

I have to substitute for X (the unknown factor) my own in-tuition. Malinovsky is a genuine worker-agitator, full of natural gifts, self-educated against the odds; an instinctive orator who con-vinces because he describes what he feels and knows; a tough and efficient organizer. Exactly the type I would expect to sprout from the grass roots of the movement. I have commissioned an assess-ment of his career since he was demobilized from the army as a lance-corporal after far-eastern duty in the Russo-Japanese War. Unemployment in Peter. Then lathe operator Langenzipen fac-tory. On Workers' Committee, then secretary City Section of Me-talworkers. By 1907, secretary Directorate, full-time. Comments *made at the time* rank high as evidence. "Inexhaustible energy." "The soul of our Union." Also his pieces in the metalworkers' magazine I rate as not at all bad. A certain clumsiness (due perhaps to being a Pole writing Russian?) which is rather attractive. He branched out of strictly union affairs, appearing at various congresses on health and safety, presenting reports that impressed his profes-sional, often nonpolitical, audiences.

There was nothing much he could do to resist the brutal suppression of the unions during the gallows years when Stolypin was minister of the interior, say mid-1907 to end of 1911. There were criticisms, again made at the time, which must be considered—"rather vain," "quick-tempered," "extravagant with money." The police clearly thought him an asset to the workers' movement. November 1909, he was arrested, held for two months, ordered to leave the capital. During 1910 and 1911, he has been in Moscow. Here too I have personal reports, from comrades I can trust. (Both women—is that significant?) Cecilia Bobrovskaya: "Very intelligent, very experienced former metalworker, good command of language, able to debate; strong temperament, a little too self-confident, nevertheless a man who could not fail to attract attention; a commanding personality in all respects." I filed this away against the day and only retrieved it when, a year and a half later, my most trusted Moscow correspondent, Vera Lobova, wrote urging me to co-opt Roman Malinovsky to the new all-Bolshevik CenCom I had told her I was aiming for at this Sixth All-Russian Conference. I wrote back instructing her to get him delegated for Prague and sent here as soon as possible.

This is his "dubious party constituency" that so worries Nadya!

My own personal reaction, keeping a covert eye on him, over the last few days. Striking appearance. Tall, extremely well-built, almost the body of a crack athlete. Dresses with careless elegance, a touch of the dandy. Face deeply pockmarked, like Stalin's, as though he had not long since walked head on into a shotgun, or escaped from a burning house. Stalin's coarse, orange-peel complexion may have helped make him sly, oblique, avoiding open clashes. Malinovsky is fierce and fiery, a huge fox terrier, who leaps up at you so immediately you have little time to savor his looks. When you do look, he is hard to forget. Red, spiky, clumped hair like a bouquet of old paintbrushes. Voice of a steam-driven metal saw. Noble, slightly ruined profile. Yellow eyes (also like Stalin!) flickering round as if ever searching for prey or predators.

I wonder if the two are related? Ha!

JANUARY 24   PRAGUE   1912

The scum has gone. Now the cream should rise to the top. "Liquidationist" and "Recallist" scoundrels are out. We are our own Bolshevik Party. I have been elected as our spokesman at the International Socialist Bureau, controller of our central organ, *Pravda*, and member of the CenCom. My policy of utmost flexibility in tactics, with the creation of illegal controlling cells surrounded by a cordon of subordinate, legal cells, has been vindicated and backed almost unanimously.

A new CenCom, of whom the key members will be me, Ordzhonikidze, Zinoviev . . . and Malinovsky. Stalin and Sverdlov are also elected but nonfunctioning since both are in Siberian exile. Mikhail Kalinin is an alternate member. He is now unequivocal in his approval of Roman Malinovsky. "This is the rich soil out of which a real workers' party, rooted among the people, can now grow."

I had to canvass around a bit, finding ways of disqualifying early unfavorable ballots and rushing on to favorable ones, to raise a newcomer to such prominence. Was this rather devious of me? In my view, those who cannot stick to their considered position, when put under pressure, deserve to be manipulated in a good cause. (At least, my having to "sink to such depths" demonstrates how far I am from that Robespierre dictator pictured by Martov and Trotsky.)

APRIL 10   PARIS   1912

Malinovsky, CenCom member and our candidate as deputy in the Fourth State Duma for the Moscow workers' curia, lands on his feet like a cat. Napoleon used to order his generals—"Be lucky!" Of course I do not believe in luck. But it doesn't do any harm when it is on your side.

After his return from Prague, Roman Vatslavovich made trips to several Russian cities reporting back on the Prague Conference and gathering enthusiastic support for the Bolshevik tactics wherever he went. Last week he got a job at the Ferman textile plant just outside Moscow and put in his application to stand in October. There was only one obstacle. All (proletarian) candidates are obliged by law to prove they have been employed continuously in the same job for six months up to the election. Unfortunately, he quarreled with his foreman, a foul-mouthed reactionary Black-Hundred supporter, M. S. Krivov, who then threatened to dismiss him.

Advised of his dilemma, I instructed our smartest operator in Moscow, Vera Lobova, to find some way out. Vera, a direct activist in everything, offered to shadow Krivov on one of his nightly visits to some low brothel, a real *trushchoba*, in Yama, Moscow's red-light district, and shoot him down as he staggered back home. It was a tempting offer. But I felt it would not be too difficult to trace the connection back to us. Neither bribes nor threats were thought to be likely to work. We could engineer a strike. The workers have already sworn to close the factory if their favorite is fired. But this would still disqualify him by interrupting his employment. We were getting nowhere until a cable arrived today from Malinovsky in Moscow. Krivov has been arrested by the police and is being held indefinitely without charge.

SEPTEMBER 16   KRAKOW   1912

A note from Gorky soliciting an article for *Novaya Zhizn*—a New Year piece forecasting what will happen in the next twelve months. I have dropped a reply explaining that (apart from a couple of really piercing flashes of insight into the future by Engels) I think the pose of prophet unworthy of a Marxist. Anyone who announces that the new Russia will be built in this area or that, according to some estimation we have today about democracy, equality of opportunity, justice and so forth is soon lost in the trackless desert of subjectivity, misled by mirages on every side. What will shape tomorrow's Russia will be *the course of the class struggle,* flowing onward, always in the same final direction, but bounced this way and that by the boulders and rapids it encounters. Our own desires are irrelevant! However hard it is, we must learn to believe that. Attempts by publicists to create Utopias (Gorky's second suggestion for a piece) are even less in my line. I advise him that Utopia is a Greek word: *U* means "no," *topos* means "place." Utopia—a place that does not exist, a fantasy, a fiction, a daydream, a child's story. It will never be fulfilled, now or ever. I point out that, though supposed to be a realist, our Zola of the Volga, he is at heart a romantic. He already lives in Utopia, rent-free.

OCTOBER 2   KRAKOW   1912

Just before his name went before the joint Social Democratic candidates' committee (a mixture of Meks, Bolshies, Anarchists and floating Centrists) Roman Malinovsky sent a coded message containing a confession. During his early years (he was born in 1875) before he came to Russia, he roamed around Germany and Poland with a band of traveling tinkers. From time to time, between '94 and '99, he and his gang, driven by desperation, broke into the country houses of absentee gentry and stole food, clothing and occasionally money. He did not regard this as a real crime (nor do I). Rather it was a kind of revolutionary apprenticeship. (By trade, then, all he had ever learned was rough sewing, apprentice to the *portnoi,* a village tailor.)

What was worrying was not that he had fought back but that he had been caught doing so. In 1894, 1896 and again in 1899, he had been before the courts. On the last occasion, sentenced to three years' imprisonment. It was after his release in 1902 that he joined the Izmailovsky Guards.

At first, I could not see where all this was leading. There is hardly one among us who has not been in the Tsar's prisons. The offense is immaterial. And since, to enlist, he had been obliged to use his present false name from the passport of a distant, dead relative, who would know? Who would *care*? No election committee of *Socialists* would hold a prison record against anyone.

But I was still not familiar enough with fighting for socialism through the ballot box. I did not appreciate all the obstructions and pitfalls the authorities delighted in putting across the way of a worker candidate for Duma deputy. Roman needed, under Article Nine of the Election Code, a "Certificate of Good Standing." There were various places where this could be obtained. But all of them seemed likely to uncover his criminal record.

Vera Lobova, who had earlier offered to arrange an assassination for him, now suggests the use of bribery. A few rotten rich Moscow fellow-travelers (people, I always feel, who are really just backing all the horses in the race and no doubt also subsidize the Kadets, the SRs and the Tsar's favorite charities) pass over a few bags of gold. The German factory's foreman, Krivov, had been released on September 10. (No apology, no compensation, of course, just a mumble about "mistaken identity.") Not surprisingly, he has become somewhat more left-wing. One of Vera's bags completed the conversion, and he happily supplied our man with a leave of absence "on urgent family business." Roman went back to his home village in Poland. Vera was right—the further from the Tsar the slacker the regulations—and bribed the district clerk for a certificate.

The Moscow Okhrana have got no whiff of any of this. Roman's luck has held again. Let's hope, as all the signs indicate, that he will be chosen by his fellow electors in the curia as their choice for deputy on October 24.

OCTOBER 26   KRAKOW   1912

He's done it! Our magnificent Pole has been elected, with five other
Bolsheviks, to the Duma. He now has a platform, within this schoolboy parliament, to speak to the workers of Russia! Not that they
will hear him there, of course. But the text will be reprinted in
full next day in *Pravda* since reports of proceedings of the chamber
are free from censorship. And the way I write our deputies' speeches,
a lot of what they say will be picked up by other newspapers. He
also now has immunity from arrest, and permission to enter and
leave the country as often as he wishes. So we have gained a mouthpiece, a columnist, and a courier, all paid for by the Tsar!

From what Vera tells me, R. M. *is* rather a free-spender. Perhaps he had better keep all his salary, instead of passing over every
ruble above a workingman's wage, as the others do? Does it matter
if he drinks? If the others could do what he does, I wish he'd make
them all drunk. Nadya sent him a congratulatory cable, her own
idea. She has got over her initial distrust, a feeling that R. M. is
play-acting and talking falsities. I have urged *Pravda* to splash him
on the front page. I am slightly surprised, but delighted, to learn
that the Mensheviks *Ray* (*Luch*) has already done so. There are
now thirteen Social Democrats in the Duma, six of ours, seven of
the Meks. Ours are the only ones from working-class districts, true
representatives of the proletariat. Malinovsky has been elected
deputy-chairman of the joint parliamentary group which, I am
sorry to say, still clings to "unity." There is even talk of merging
our two papers. Disastrous! It's hard enough getting my line across
under the Bolshevik banner. Heaven knows what it will be like if
Luch and *Pravda* become one flesh, one spirit, in a shotgun marriage. But today is Roman Vatslavovich's day. *Some* things are going
well.

FEBRUARY 20   ZURICH   1913

These Europeans think of Russia as the winter-land of snow and
ice, a country frozen over for half a year. And it is true we tend
to scoff at their feeble blizzards where what falls from the air is
more like dandruff. It seems comical to us that foreigners, partic-

ularly the British, should get so excited about their "Dickensian" (really Germanic) white Christmases. What *we* call snow is an advancing curtain of fat, thick, floury flakes. Goose feathers sugared with ice that join together in a sort of furry pelt, wrap you round, weigh you down, cut off all sight and sound, smother you with a delicious bloodsucking embrace. Once, as a young man, I felt the temptation of this succubus, calling me away to another world as I sank down for a short rest onto a snow drift. No wonder anyone frozen to death—an entire family once in Siberia—often has on the face a seraphic, half-amused smile.

You might think then that Russians, when reminiscing about their homeland in exile, would summon up memories of these winter scenes. But no—I have never spoken to a fellow expatriate who even mentioned the word "snow." We yearn for spring or autumn. Summer, indeed, is much more the subject of our great Russian writers. I could find half a dozen passages, from Tolstoy, from Goncharov, from the poets, from Herzen's memoirs, within minutes. Above all, we all miss the smell of the countryside as it breathes like perfume out of sun-warmed earth. In our winters, the truth is you can only smell mankind.

This afternoon, I overheard in a café a new arrival from Russia describe his parents' old house in Tambov province. The ivy and the vines, the church bells, the singing birds, but above all the flowers in the garden . . . Just the names lit up Valentinov's face, as if he were holding up each in turn. He said he still had in his nostrils a scent mixed from the flowers, from the plants on the pond, from the hot sand around the beds when damped by the watering cans; all forming what he called "a kind of trinity." There was something about this unforced, unconscious eloquence that was totally disarming.

Just then, I noticed Olminsky had joined us. A former Narodnik, by temperament historian rather than journalist, he is even more opposed than I am to Bohemian individualism, the cult of personality, endless interlinked arias of self-indulgence around the marble tables. He had with him some papers we needed to work on, so he broke into the reverie of Valentinov in a very brisk, schoolmasterly way.

"Too sickening, don't you think, Ilyich? Listen to the country gent's son revealing his class instincts. Let them talk long enough and they always reveal their origins and allegiances. Here he is babbling on about his family estates. He moons away about flowers and their perfume like an adolescent schoolgirl. See how carried away he is about the loveliness of the limes and the beeches!

"Don't you agree, Ilyich? A revolutionary cannot permit himself to forget that today, along these lovely avenues of limes, landowners still *whip* their peasants and house-serfs. I suppose he would
like to return to these scenes of happy childhood. Happy for him,
perhaps. We must never give way to these daydreams of the past
if we want to preserve our revolutionary purity. It's too dangerous.

"We all know how it happens. You begin to pine for that idyllic
life. So you buy yourself an estate. Just a little one, of course.
Before long you are ordering the peasants to get on with their
work while you lie in a hammock with a French novel and fall
asleep looking down that lovely lime-tree avenue. Oblomov has
come home."

I agreed with a lot of that. I feel about nostalgia the way I feel
about music—it makes life too sweet, too idealized. But one way
a leader remains a leader—unfortunately, perhaps, but it is part
of our psychology—is by never being predictable. (Jehovah knew
that in the Old Testament.) So I took another tack. One that was
also true, one in tune with the thoughts he had interrupted and
dispersed.

"You surprise me, Mikhail Stepanovich, not Valentinov. So
we are to consider so many of the best pages of Russian literature
positively harmful, dangerous to our integrity, are we? You want
them to be torn out and burned? What you advise would make it
impossible to read Tolstoy, especially *Childhood, Boyhood, Youth,*
much of Turgenev, the first volume of Herzen's *My Past and Thoughts,*
and who knows what else. You must realize that until now, with a
few exceptions such as Gorki and Chernyshevsky, most of our
writers have come from the landowning class. It was precisely their
freedom from work, their lime-tree avenues, their ponds and flower-
beds, which allowed them to create works of art.

"You say there can be no charm or attraction even in the
thought, the memory, of these woods and gardens because they
were planted and tended by peasants who did not own them,
because serfs are still birched within them. This is an oversimpli-
fication, a sentimentality, a whiff of the old Narodnik. We Marxists
can look at these things with a steady eye and a clear head.

"If your argument were correct, we dare not admire the pyr-
amids of Egypt, or any of the Seven Wonders of the World. You
are a man of great learning. You do not need Engels to tell you
that the highest works of ancient civilization were created by a
society that rested on slavery. Valentinov may have been reading
Herzen, who was able, like Tolstoy, to write hundreds of pages

about growing up as a child of the ruling class. Such thoughts make us all homesick. We all ache to get out of this dreary Switzerland and its toytowns of clockmakers and pastry cooks and bank clerks. What is terrible about that? So long as he wants, like the rest of us, *to go back as a revolutionary*, not as a reactionary."

As I spoke I could feel the past, my Kokushkino days, rushing at me as if I were speeding back into them, riding on the cowcatcher of a steam locomotive.

"I too spent all my summers on a country estate which was owned by my mother's father. In that sense, I too was a sprig of the landed gentry. I have never forgotten those days, the lime trees and the flowers, the river Ushna. Am I in danger of betraying the Revolution that is still to come? I lolled about in the hay. I used to eat strawberries and raspberries by the handful. I crushed them against my palate, let the juice run down my throat like wine from trodden grapes. But *I* had not grown them. I loved fresh, warm, sweet milk. But *I* had not milked the cows. These fragments of our early life, properly understood, correctly interpreted, make us more determined to free our people and let them share what have always been—still are—the privileges of a few."

JUNE 27　　　　KRAKOW　　　　1913

Two terms of the Duma gone. Summer recess approaches. Malinovsky hailed on all sides as probably the most outstanding Socialist deputy ever to appear in the Chamber. Even the Mek paper, *Luch*, saluted him as the first "practical," that is, genuine shop floor activist, able to dispute with university graduates, members of professions, academics and cultured nobles, without embarrassment or awkwardness. No one had ever seen such enthusiasm among ordinary people for a parliamentarian. A mob of two thousand Muscovite supporters took over the railway station the day he left for Peter! And in his eight months there, he has developed himself as more than equal to any of his challengers, rivals or opponents.

Compared to the rest of our Bolshy six, he could be another species. He answers their letters, receives their constituents, even fixes their travel arrangements. Some of the Menshevik seven also prefer to consult him, rather than their own party officials, over parliamentary procedure. Last week, a whole workers' suburb of

Warsaw petitioned the chairman of the Duma to have Malinovsky as their representative instead of the left/liberal they had actually elected.

Of course the designers of the Duma have tailored the rules of debate to inhibit the natural talents of inexperienced opposition deputies, allowed for the first time possibly in their entire lives to stand up and contradict their "betters." Every speech must be made within the required time; stick close to its theme; avoid "strong language"; refrain from "insults" to the government or established society—in other words, be robbed of almost all spontaneity. If the workers' deputy then tries to compensate by constructing a rational argument in advance, backing it with facts and figures (usually mine), he is interrupted by the chair, ordered to stop reading from a text, invited instead to orate impromptu "like the great classical senators of old."

Apart from Malinovsky, none of our representatives has shown himself very dextrous at getting round these customs of the Chamber. (I hate to have to always write "himself"—if only women like Vera Lubova could be members!) Owing to the ingenious, anti-democratic weightings built into the election procedure, several of our nominees need the often decisive votes of some right-wing selectors. Many of these gang together to deliberately promote our most sincere, decent, honorable, typical wage earners. Unfortunately that also means our most simple, uneducated, credulous, timid, inarticulate candidates.

In future, I plan to circumvent this tactical voting, intended to recruit only those least dangerous to the bourgeoisie, by hammering out an advance list. Any of our weaker members who get so far will express their thanks but stand down for urgent domestic or health reasons. This will continue, name by name, until we reach one *we* want. Some comrades may be reluctant to agree. After years of illegality, after continually getting the shitty end of the law's nightstick for peacefully asking for the most elementary rights, it must seem wonderful, almost like passing over into heaven, to become a deputy. Dressed in sash and epaulettes, called "the Most Honorable," granted immunity from prosecution. Nevertheless, they will do as they are told. That is why we needed, and now have got, this centrally controlled Party. Here principles will always have priority over persons. Here efficiency is more important than sentiment. Imagine any flabby, egotistical opportunist in the German SDP, or the British Labour Party, standing down, once virtually elected, for the good of the cause!

Malinovsky more than makes up for the weaknesses of his fellow MDs. He is like a one-man battering ram against the fortresses of reaction. During this Fourth Duma's first session, he spoke twenty-two times, in the second thirty-eight times—more than the rest of all our Bolshevik faction combined. He also put down fifty-four written questions to ministers and then cross-examined them closely on their answers in the Chamber. He was responsible for five private-member's bills which, of course, had no chance of becoming law but made a brave splash right across the headlines of all the newspapers. This was more than twice the amount of exposure for socialist policies that was gained by the Menshevik fraction leader Chkheidze. No wonder that veteran publicist was visibly hurt when our newcomer, heading the minority of their Socialist bloc, was chosen instead of him to deliver the united party's opening address at the next session. Seconding, he praised Malinovsky as "an exceptionally active and energetic spokesman" who possessed an enviable power to "capture the mood of the whole Duma." In private, I'm told, he complains that Roman Vatslavovich is "extremely vain," with an inflated self-esteem that "borders on a mental illness." His summing up—"a careerist who will stop at nothing to reach the top of whatever ladder he is climbing." It takes one to know one. He totally fails to see how the counter-balancing virtues (by no means incompatible) of courage, energy, eloquence and intelligence, outweigh such minor flaws.

NB. No man is indispensable, or should be allowed to become so, in our Party. Badaev, Muranov, etc., etc.—the other five—must be flung into the *Sturm and Drang* of the debate, sink or swim. I have summoned them here for summer-school training—an intellectual assault course under fire from live ideas—to improve their fighting qualities.

AUGUST 13   PORONIN   1913

Last week was announced the death of the German Social-Democatic leader, August Bebel. At the age of seventy-three, he ends an era. He seemed to have been there forever—leader, inspirer, guide and philosopher of German Social Democracy. Yet he was its creator, and not so long ago. Son of the workers, a skilled turner, educated by the Roman Catholics, he became more and more closely devoted to Marxism the longer he lived. He was not deterred by the twenty years when Bismarck made socialist agitation punishable by hard labor.

With a cunning that seemed (to some) at variance with his open, honest, sincere, sunny nature, he utilized all the advantages and peculiarities of his country and his people. He aimed for a mass party, literate, skilled, used to a tradition of organization and efficiency, trained up in an atmosphere of optimism and progress, always expecting a new solution to new problems, a new hope for a new age. His Socialism sounded modern, sounded Germanic, sounded logical. He recruited half a million members, more than ten million voters. His army of followers now includes in its ranks police chiefs, guards colonels, bishops, businessmen, *minor royalty!* His SDP commands popular magazines and newspapers, insurance cooperatives, sports clubs and athletic teams, massed choirs, brass bands, chains of beer cellars and youth hostels. Nothing like it has ever been seen.

No other socialist leader anywhere in Europe or Russia has possessed Bebel's skill at speaking to huge audiences. He had a way of appearing, no, of *being*, at once intimate and universal, understanding, sharing, all his listeners' worries, confusions, fears for the future. And explaining he had discovered just recently, yesterday, or only a moment ago, the solution, the answer, the true way. What was it called? Er, *Socialism!* What only Bebel could have done was, after all that, to end up proclaiming that Marxism alone would produce Socialism.

We regret, as a Party, that he also resisted the pressure from Kautsky to move the movement bodily to the left, that he has kept German Socialism Marxist in theory rather than in practice.

Personally, I can say in this diary, he is not the leader I would have preferred. But he has forged that giant cannon only waiting for the right finger on the trigger, kept it oiled and primed. For this we must all be deeply grateful.

I have put most of this into my *Pravda* obituary. I ended with an excerpt from the official record of his last great speech in the Reichstag during the Morocco crisis:

What once happened between Japan and Russia can be repeated here. One day one side in Europe too will say: "Things cannot go on like this."

It will say: "Stop! If we wait any longer we shall suffer, we shall be the weak instead of the strong!" Then there will be a catastrophe. Then the tocsin will be sounded in Europe and sixteen to eighteen million men, the flower of different nations, will march against each other, equipped with lethal weapons. But I am convinced that this great march will be followed by the great collapse. (*Laughter.*)

All right, you have laughed about it before; but it will come. It has only been postponed. (*Great amusement.*)

It is not our fault that it will come, it is *your* fault. *You* are pushing things to a head. *You* are undermining your own political and social institutions. What will be the result?

After this great war, we shall have mass bankruptcy, mass misery, mass unemployment and great famines. (*Dissent from Right.*) Are you denying this? (*Right intervention: "After every war, things get better."*)

Better for who? For whom? (*Laughter.*) Better for you, for the moment. Better for us, for the century.

AUGUST 15   PORONIN   1913

For the last ten days, twenty-two of our leading Bolsheviks have gathered here on my invitation.

We—Zinoviev, Kamenev, Shotman, Troyanovsky, Ganetsky plus Malinovsky and all our five Duma deputies—have discussed many subjects. But principally tactics for splitting the Party in Russia, specifically in the Duma, and emerging as a Bolsheviks-only fighting force. Only one person, in my hearing, has spoken anything, except conventional regrets, about the death of Bebel. That was Roman Vatslavovich, whose impromptu obituary might have come from the same pen, even down to the same quotation. This is a man who someday soon undoubtedly will deserve the title the Menshevik press have begun to bestow on him—"the Russian Bebel."

And to think that I am still receiving denunciations of him as a police spy. From those, like Bukharin, who are in our corner, as well as from those who could have motives for unsettling us, like Lydia Dan, Theodore's wife, sister of Julius (Martov). She reports having been sent "anonymous letters" accusing Malinovsky from "inside the Okhrana."

Let me sum it up this way. If Malinovsky really is a creature of the imperial police, then the policy they pay him to advocate is, oddly enough, exactly the same as the policy I advocate. What

proceeds from this? That I too am in the pay of the Tsar? No
doubt they will say that too one day. Then I shall know I am on
the eve of success.

OCTOBER 29   KRAKOW   1913

Capitalism may be dying. But in its death throes, like the magician
in the fairy tale, it passes through various manifestations, takes on
new features and habits, in desperate attempts to avoid its fate.
We must not forget to note every new claw and tentacle.

Consider the homogeneity of the proletariat which is now
rapidly dispersing, and breaking up. Capitalism has given special
form to the ancient "migration of nations." Rapidly developing
countries raise wages at home above the average rate and thus
attract workers from the backward countries. There can be no
doubt that dire poverty alone compels people to abandon their
native land, and that the capitalists exploit the immigrant workers
in the most shameless manner. But only reactionaries can shut
their eyes to the progressive significance of this new movement of
the clans. And it is into this struggle that capitalism is drawing the
masses of the working people of the WHOLE world, breaking down
the musty, fusty habits of local life, breaking down national barriers
and prejudices, uniting workers from all countries in huge factories
and mines in America, Germany and so forth. It will not be long
before Britain, France and Italy will also be importing their own
colonial peoples to do the dirty work at home. Here is a field, ripe
for agitation, that we must not neglect to harvest.

DECEMBER 5   KRAKOW   1913

Even my closest collaborators, my most intimate companions, even
Inessa, now and then accuse me of pursuing some theme, the *same*
theme, round and round, in "a vicious circle." They do not
understand—*every* question runs in "a vicious circle." Political life
as a whole is an endless chain consisting of an infinite number of
links. The whole art of politics lies in finding and taking as firm
a grip as we can of the link that is least likely to be struck from
our hands, the one that is most important at the given moment,

the one that most of all guarantees its possessor the control of the whole chain.

DECEMBER 26   KRAKOW   1913

Wonderful Christmas present. If we were to indulge ourselves in such bourgeois sentimentalities. A tribute to me from a completely external, nonsocialist source, unfortunately one I cannot quote in public.

It is dated September of this year and written in Petersburg. Here are a few of its more salient comments:

> During the past ten years, the most energetic, courageous elements, capable of tireless struggle, resistance and constant organization have been the organizations and persons concentrating around Lenin. . . .
>
> The permanent organizational heart and soul of all party organizations of any importance is Lenin. . . .
>
> The faction of Leninists is always better organized than the others, stronger in its singleness of purpose, more resourceful in propagating its ideas among the workers. . . .
>
> When during the last two years the labor movement began to grow stronger, Lenin and his followers came closer to the workers than others, and he was the first to proclaim purely revolutionary slogans. . . .
>
> The Bolshevik circles, nuclei and organizations are now scattered through all the cities. Permanent correspondence and contacts have been established with almost all at the factory centers. The Central Committee functions almost regularly and is entirely in the hands of Lenin. . . .
>
> In view of the aforesaid, there is nothing surprising in the fact that at the present time the assembling of the entire underground party is proceeding around the Bolshevik organization. Indeed, this latter really *is* the Russian Social-Democratic Labour Party.

It is almost too embarrassingly flattering to enter, even in a secret diary. None of the few who have seen it has been able to guess its author. I certainly would never have done so. It is signed by the chief director of the Police Department himself, and photographed for us by our key agent in his office. How I'd love to be able to mark it "Copies to Martov, Trotsky, Plekhanov and so forth!"

JANUARY 10   PARIS   1914

Tonight I addressed two meetings here commemorating Petersburg's "Bloody Sunday" (January 9, '05). The first, small, packed, intent, a gathering mainly of Party members, and those largely Bolsheviks. I could feel the flow of a current, backward and forward, the way I suppose electricity must operate, between me and the audience as I emphasized that this had been the overture to a revolution that was not staged, but that did not mean it never would be performed. By this day next year, the tenth anniversary, I envisaged that we would have begun to complete its work. "Bloody Sunday" was not a defeat. It was an inspiration; a cause for optimism, not mourning.

The second, international, multi-party, was a large gathering loosely draped around the Grand Salle of the Geographical Society. Almost a fashionable *soirée* among the smart "Left-Set." Everywhere my gaze roamed, a careerist, a revisionist, a collaborator, a conciliator, a reformist, a parlor pink, a salon subversive. If there were a Museum of Revolution (and if this lot have their way, that's all there will be) then most of these would be in the case devoted to fakes and forgeries, false alarms and dead ends. Quite a few of them had come just to see me. I accept that I seem to them a curiosity, a genuine professional revolutionary, the *Blanqui des nos jours,* fit to curdle their blood. So with them I took a different tack—I used the commemoration solely as an example, one among many, of the tsarist autocracy as *an enemy of mankind.* By the end, I think I can say with certainty, they had forgotten about me. In their minds remained picture after picture of dandified officers ordering brutalized soldiers to fire round after round into crowds of ragged, starved women and children; of Cossacks slicing and skewering huddled Jews, dragging off their women for mass rape; of prisoners, sentenced for life for fighting for rights all Europe took for granted, cringing like dogs at the whips of their jailers. My listeners may not have ended up our allies (although there was a satisfying collection). But they can at least be classified as friendly neutrals.

JANUARY 13   PARIS   1914

Inessa and I attend an emotional two-hour lecture by Malinovsky about the work of our party in the Duma. He realizes, of course, that this is only the tip of the iceberg upon which we must impale our Unsinkable SS Nicholas the Titanic. As I said in both my Bloody-Sunday speeches—a revolutionary party that confines itself to legal, parliamentary struggle will never make a revolution. But parliamentary struggle remains one of our most powerful techniques just the same. Malinovsky has the knack of arousing his audiences (tonight all émigrés), whoever they are. Foreigners or exiles, Bolsheviks or Mensheviks, socialists or liberals, they boil to such a pitch of excitement they convince themselves that the majority of the world's inhabitants are solidly united against exploitation and domination of the many by the few. We have been on several such joint visits to centers abroad during this long Duma recess. Malinovsky's triumphs seem to grow with every opportunity.

I am on a (temporary, perhaps, but invigorating) upswell of euphoria—no headaches, no insomnia, no stomach pains, no skin itches. Partly, it is political and organizational. Malinovsky gives me new hope, new encouragement. Perhaps our power really does lie in the workers *themselves* forging *their own* instruments, not just for the overthrow of old tsarism, but also the new capitalists. I ask Inessa for her opinion of him—an intelligent woman's view is never noncommittal about a man. Either she is completely taken in and sees nothing but what she wants to see (the exception) or she sees right through him to all those things he wants no one to see (the rule).

"A man for business, not for pleasure. For the Party as a whole, but not for you, Ilyich!" she said, with surprising passion. "Keep him on the platform, out of your house. As a woman, I am all the time conscious of his closeness in a room. His eyes are never, what's the word, *impersonal*. They feel you! He's free and easy in a way that's not quite natural. Yet when he talks politics, well, he's transformed. Let him stick to politics."

Afterward, we had a drink with him. Or rather, he had several drinks with us. He loves the Scottish whisky. Half a bottle was poured to my one coffee and Inessa's single white wine. I could

understand what she meant. I twitted him about drink, making a
joke, but watching him closely while laughing and turning away.
He wasn't sure whether to share the joke or take me seriously. I
saw him concentrate on Inessa, gauging my mood through hers.
Then I could sense him riffling through several possible strategies,
like a good politician. Perhaps only a better politician would have
spotted him at it.

"I need drink, Ilyich!" he said, very sober, very sincere. "We
cannot all be like you, living for nothing, thinking of nothing,
except the cause." His eyes flickered for a moment up and down
Inessa. "Others of us are weaker. Or perhaps just different. No
one could say Engels was a black sheep. Yet he had two mistresses
at once, made a fortune and drank champagne in the morning.
Did you know he left a tidy sum to Bebel? With a message in his
will saying—'Don't let it all get into the hands of the Party, buy
yourself a few decent bottles.' Well, I hope our Party doesn't grudge
me a decent bottle or two."

"If I could only combine you with Yakov Mikhailovich (Sverdlov), I would have a human machine that could overturn Russia
tomorrow," I told him, squeezing his arm just above the elbow, as
Sverdlov always advises.

But he out-played me. "*Danke schön*, Baron Frankenstein," he
said, clicking his heels. He's gone off on his lifelong hobby—collecting (dirty) picture postcards.

Nevertheless, I am still floating. *I am with Inessa.* I see immediately, Roman Vatslavovich knows. How many others outside my
intimates? I feel a shiver of premonition, a parasite worm moving
through the guts. Yet at the same time I don't care. Indeed, it
gives me a thrill of excitement I have previously never found
anywhere else but in politics. With Inessa—pitiful admission!—
my least controllable impulse is a regular spurt of fury at the
thought that she could be with anybody else. Give her entirely to
me and I can remake the world. Pathetic!

She is not someone to be given, or taken. She will never be
possessed. She is herself as much as I am myself. Both would be
ashamed to exalt our silly little egos above the future of mankind.
I wish I had more time to explore this new psychology. That was
a tremendous insight of Marx when he said: "No one believes what
any society says about itself any more than anyone believes what
any man says about himself." I know I am speaking my truth when
I say that I have no jealousy or envy, no competitiveness or selfishness, about my role in making a revolution. If someone else can

do it better, quicker, cleaner, neater, then I will follow him or her. Because I know this to be so I do not find it at all surprising. But there are only very few to whom I can say it because it seems so incredible to others. Martov, Bogdanov, Krassin, Trotsky, Malinovsky—these I have loved. I have searched in them to find a leader better than I can ever be. With regret, I have to say, in vain. If they had been what history needs, I would have felt tremendous relief. No one wants to be cast for the role of Messiah, and believe it. Such altruism, such generosity in the dirty business of taking power over a sixth of the world! Such possessiveness, such heartache, such adolescent agonizing, over one woman. Yet we are too busy talking about the Party, about publicity, about expenses, about elections, about conferences, to really think about ourselves when we are together.

JANUARY 16   PARIS   1914

I am hanging on here—partly to be with Inessa, partly (or am I inventing, or over-emphasizing, the first excuse that comes to hand?) so that our Party expert on security, penetration by police agents and criminals, Malinovsky, can rendezvous with the SR sniffer-out of traitors and secret agents, Vladimir Burtsev. This is really an urgent matter—never have we been so moled by spies.

Our last notable catch was Brendinsky, spotted by Nadya just before the Prague Conference. He had been an exceptional courier—so it seemed—who operated out of Leipzig, ferrying Party materials backward and forward to Russia. He was one of the few with access to all our code-names. When Rykov was arrested, whole circles of our operators were hauled in. The rumor began that Rykov was at fault. It was said he had been carelessly carrying matching lists in his pockets.

Instantly, Nadya nailed this as a police exercise in black propaganda, putting up an absolutely watertight case exonerating him. Rykov was a man of meticulous precautions—before traveling into Russia he would have his entire body, clothes, luggage, wallets, etc. searched, cleaned and passed as new. He was as likely to be caught with a list of Party undergrounders as the baby Jesus.

But Brendinsky, who had first pointed the finger at Rykov, did carry contacts and pseudonyms *in his head*. He has lately been pushing to be given ever more details and displayed a strangely hysterical reaction when told that he was not accredited to Prague, crying out, "I'll lose my job!" Nadya, without giving a reason, has cut him off from all Party activity. Just after Prague, we discovered that he had himself now suspended all contacts with the socialist movement and retired to a 40,000 franc villa outside Paris, presumably paid for by his employers.

Brendinsky is by no means the only suspect. Many of them are much closer to the center than he ever came. For instance, Jacob Zhitomirsky. He was one of my Men of Confidence, in the years just after '05. My key handler in Germany of the "hot" money we were getting from the bank raids and train robberies carried out by the Armenian "Kamo" and the Georgian "Koba" (Ter-Petrosian and Stalin). Somebody was passing on the serial numbers of the notes, descriptions and aliases of those who would be changing them, when and in what cities in which countries. Somebody notified the authorities that "Kamo" was arriving in Berlin with a suitcase full of dynamite. Zhitomirsky was the only person who knew all this. Suspicion naturally narrowed down to him. I resisted the accusation just because it was *too* obvious.

Jacob was cleared by an investigation I ordered, unknown to him. For his own safety, after "Kamo," Litvinov, Olga Ravich, Semashko and a dozen others had been lifted, I transferred him to France. In '09, he called on me in Geneva to urge that I too move to Paris, arguing that in such a large city it was easier to avoid spies. I did not quite follow the logic, but we went all the same for other reasons. Two years later, in '11, Burtsev warned me that Zhitomirsky was a police agent, and an extremely clever one. "I hear he even got you to come to live near him, to save on his train fares."

Though a piece of advice about spies in your midst from the exposer of the infamous Azef, the government stool pigeon who rose to be head of the SR's terrorist action department, was not easily ignored, I ignored it. Burtsev, to whom counterespionage is what gambling is to others, a total obsession, had nothing to offer except hunches and intuitions and the occasional coincidence. However, last year, he kept bombarding me with more and more evidence, eventually in December threatening to publish the entire indictment unless I took some action.

I have never liked Burtsev. Thinking of himself as a hired player, Shakespeare noted that "the dyer's hand" takes on the colors it works with. There is about Burtsev the atmosphere of the interrogation room—sweating guilt, jumping pulses, masculine tears.

It frightens even the most innocent. I could not help smiling when I saw how Malinovsky blenched when I said that Burtsev was threatening to name an enemy within our top ranks. I indicated a passage in his most recent letter. "If my accusation is false," he wrote, "then let comrade —— summon me before a revolutionary tribunal of our fellows. There, once and for all, he can demonstrate his innocence and my error." I kept my thumb over the name. "What do you say, comrade?" I asked. Like most heavy drinkers, Malinovsky becomes bedabbled with boozer's sweat at any sudden exercise, mental or physical. He wiped his face with his big, rotatory hand, a typical worker's gesture when needing time to think. But he replied: "I'll go now, chief. Where is he?"

I removed my thumb. Zhitomirsky was the name.

"I want the quickest 'yes' or 'no' you can give. If Zhitomirsky is betraying us, I think he should meet with a sudden accident."

JANUARY 25   BRUSSELS   1914

Nearly ten days here—evenings at the good old boring Golden Cock where everyone has memories of the flour stains and the flea bites. But no letter from Inessa. I have written twice with the good news—the Fourth Congress of the Latvian SDs has opted for our Bolshevik policies, for the full Prague program. Splendid! How I wish I could discuss it with her, hear her voice praising or criticizing me. Is this going to be our life? Work, work, work—the occasional day together, like a feast day to an exhausted peasant. Should I leave Nadya and form a new partnership with Inessa? Then, at least, we should have days together at a time, and many nights. I should not be always on the boil, hot and steaming, like a railway engine left for a moment, when I came to her.

Nadya is no problem. Has not budged from her Longjumeau decision. She is faithful to the principles of Chernyshevsky. She sent me in Paris a quotation from Belinsky, one of the great pre-Marxist Marxists. I read it to Inessa, as we lay together watching the dawn come over the rooftops. Afterward we did not speak until I kissed her good-bye and left to catch the midmorning train. Belinsky writes: "A time is coming, I ardently believe in this; a time is coming when the loved one will come to her lover and say: 'I love another' and he will answer: 'I cannot be happy without you; I shall suffer for my whole life, but go to him whom you love'; and if through her magnanimity she then desires to remain with him, he will not accept her sacrifice, but like God say to her: 'I will have mercy and not your sacrifice.' "

Why has Inessa not written? Is it that she is too noble, too proud, too like God, to accept Nadya's sacrifice?

FEBRUARY 14   KRAKOW   1914

Is Malinovsky falling away from his late, high eminence? He never reported back to me about his visit to Burtsev over Zhitomirsky. Dr. Z. himself solved some of our problems. The same day that I dispatched Malinovsky, he left his apartment in Paris, fully furnished with all his books and antique medical instruments, and has not been heard of since. Perhaps Burtsev frightened him off by his letter to me. Though who told him I do not know. It certainly wasn't me. Still, I have instructed our resident Party presence in Paris to seize the flat, sell off whatever possessions are worth it and occupy it with some needy comrade, preferably plus ailing wife and numerous children. If Dr. Z. should return, he is to be told that he can renegotiate his claim either through V. I. Lenin in Krakow or V. L. Burtsev in Paris.

Burtsev has given me *his* account of the discussion with Malinovsky about Dr. Z. He says he passed over all his documentation, since this is a Bolshevik matter, retaining (cunning rogue) only photographic copies of the key originals. He says M. agreed the evidence was indisputable. Zhitomirsky was an *agent provocateur*. It will be no help to us to have this news circulated. So I'm glad Burtsev regards it as our business and Malinovsky has not brought it into the open. What I do not understand is why Roman Vatslavovich has not kept me up to date.

Burtsev also alleges that Malinovsky accounted for the prevalence of arrests among our leading people by asserting that not only was Zhitomirsky a police spy but that he was almost certain that M. E. Chernomazov, the new editor of *Pravada,* is another. Can this be true? *Two of them,* presumably working together! How did we succeed in achieving *anything* these last few years?

The logical conclusion would appear to be that the police, therefore the Ministry of the Interior, therefore the government, therefore the Tsar, want what we, the Bolsheviks, want. I reject no reasoning, no chain of cause and effect, that can be tested and proved. But I am missing a few pieces of the puzzle. Why on earth does R. M. not supply *me* with the facts he has obtained? I remember now, last year, it was Chernomazov, visiting me, who complained that when he was arrested in June the police interrogators betrayed a familiarity with inner Party discussions and developments that was actually superior to his own. Is that the way a *provocateur* would talk?

It is difficult for me to ask R. M. questions about this *en clair* in my letters, or expect him to reply openly. But there are couriers, codes, invisible writings—he could even telephone me from a safe instrument. It looks as if I will have to recall him during the Duma session. There is nothing worse for the balance of my mind, for my sleep and general health, than the endless circling inside my skull of questions that cannot be answered for lack of data.

MARCH 1   PORONIN   1914

I have not summoned Malinovsky, which might have looked rather odd. Instead, I have been able to get much of what I need to know from another source. However, as ever, new answers provoke fresh questions. Still, we are boxing along, progress is being made. That is what counts.

F. N. Samoilov, one of our Duma deputies, a nice, sweet worker of the totally uneducated, unskilled type—in fact, I think, a street-sweeper—has fallen ill. He was not high on our list, though a Party candidate, and seems to have been advanced by the right wing as a kind of joke, a piece of anti-Bolshevik satire. He is, though, no fool. He sees everything. He remembers everything. Even if it takes him ages before he can bring himself to draw any conclusions from this mass of detail.

When I heard he was suffering some kind of nervous complaint, and remembering him from the summer school, I arranged for Samoilov to be sent to the best (medically speaking) sanatorium in Switzerland. He has been there for a couple of weeks now and his bed is next to the telephone. So I ring up for ten minutes each day and he tells me bit by bit what he hears has been going on inside the Duma.

My end of the conversation runs something like this: "What you need is quiet, sunshine, sleep, *food*. Do they give you enough to eat? *You must drink more milk.* Be sure you do. You should also weigh yourself once a week and make a note each time of any change. . . ." I've become quite the doctor, waiting for Nadya to be operated upon for goiter. I went, page by page, at my accelerated reading pace, through every standard reference book, making notes all the way. Anyone who can get through *Das Kapital* would make an excellent physician. The only essential is a good, cross-referenced card-index system.

Samoilov's answer is a sort of unedited monologue, as if he were still actually sitting in the Chamber and giving me a running commentary. From this I see, what the papers do not report, what other comrades do not think worth passing on. *Malinovsky is becoming increasingly erratic.*

He drinks round the clock—large cups, not glasses, of tea. A preference for the opaque which permits him to dilute each one, half and half, with some brand of alcohol. He behaves when speaking in the Chamber as if his aim is *not* to deliver his speeches in full but to censor them as he goes along. Can this be so? Writing all his speeches, I know them practically by heart. I would spot a missing comma. What I had not realized is that the editors of our Party press print straight from my MSS. They do not check against delivery. Why should they? In the Duma, Samoilov observes, much is deleted, usually the more extreme and inflammatory stuff. This could be understandable. But I would still like to be consulted. At least informed afterward. We must leave freedom of tactics to the commander on the spot.

What I find strange is S.'s testimony that M. garbles these sensitive passages in a way that I know can only be deliberate while seeming accidental—dropping pages, mixing them up, being unable to read the writing, speeding up, slowing down, sinking to the inaudible, rising to a shriek, sometimes provoking a clash with the chairman so as to be disqualified. He is trying to fool somebody. *Who? Why?*

Burtsev had told me that Malinovsky was very tight-lipped. (Not such a bad idea—he *is* SR after all.) But seemed most keen to know all the sources Burtsev had inside the government machine, especially within the police or justice department. Burtsev was "too wily a bird" for that. Instead, he asked M. to provide him with specific information about a "shopping list" of named individuals he suspected. Since then, silence. The result is, all the SRs blame me for Zhitomirsky's escape before he could be nabbed.

Samoilov tells me a different story. And he is incapable of making anything up. He says Malinovsky came back from Paris with tales of what a hollow windbag Burtsev was. "He couldn't catch a nit on a holy man!" is the phrase he quotes. Sounds very Malinovskian to me! M. went on to denounce B. for poor security because he revealed his main source on Okhrana activities, a radical lawyer called Syrkin. Now Syrkin is my key source. A "sleeper" only awoken when he became chief legal adviser to the police department. Nobody knows this, except me.

And here is the twist in the tail of the tale. *Syrkin has just been arrested, tried in some secret court, and exiled to Siberia.* All this has proved too much for our poor street-sweeper deputy. His mind refuses to cope with the conflicting messages. Is Malinovsky going the same way? He begins to sound like a mental patient too. Either that or, as well as being the leader of our Duma fraction, member of our CenCom, on the editorial board of *Pravda*, my chief representative inside Russia, he is also *the key police agent inside our Party*. Not so much the Russian Bebel, eh? as the Bolshevik Azef?

Only joking. Still, we must get him out at the next recess before his nerve breaks and he deserts in the face of the enemy.

MAY 12   PORONIN   1914

Problems of correspondence: Samoilov, in Switzerland, has shown great improvement. So I wrote that I was planning he should come here, or to Zakopane (where there is a clinic) as soon as he was well enough to be moved. He'd asked about the problems he had heard the Party was having "over there" but I told him that, though we had political troubles "on the far side," they were not ones that should be shared by someone recovering from an attack of neurasthenia.

I also wrote to Inessa in Paris. This diary and my letters to her are the only places in which I can unbuckle and disarm, allow out on a leash various shameful emotions (self-pity, depression, egoism, irritation, boredom) that I normally pretend do not exist. Once I have exorcised them, allowed them a few bites and howls, they go back to sleep. Inessa knows this as well as I do, so she often doesn't bother to reply. Which is a pity. I ought to be able to open myself equally to Nadya. The trouble is, I have overtrained her for a secondary role, assistant, amanuensis, disciple. It is too late to cast her in a major part as major partner. She has not been well, really well, for years. Lately she has aged a lot. What keeps her going is her absolute faith in me, her conviction that I am never wrong, that I am a man of steel. If she lost this, she might not be able to carry on. (I say that, but then, somewhere inside, an intuition tells me she will see me out.)

To Inessa, I complained about being entangled in a cat's cradle of petty complications, part-policy, part-personalities, part-business, part-conspiracy, which seems designed to entrap me forever in its web. My enemies, even my friends, think I am the spider. Here at the center, I feel more like the fly, bound in sticky threads, waiting to be eaten alive. Am I even sure this *is* the center? How I hate all this bustle and buzzing and fussing and fidgeting—we might as well be little shopkeepers, country auctioneers, small-town lawyers! Does this mean, I asked her, that I am turning sluggish, and jaded, and tetchy? All my life I have liked my profession. Now I am starting to almost hate it.

Those letters were only two days ago, and already I had forgotten more or less what I had put in them, when both my correspondents contacted me—Samoilov this morning (by telephone) and Inessa this evening (by telegraph). Fyodor Nikolaevich, far from being this nerve-racked invalid who must be protected from the clangor of the real world, turns out much more closely in touch with "problems over there" than I am. He had been up all night in his dressing gown, hugging a portable oil stove, glued to the earpiece. His fellow Bolsheviks in the Duma have been calling him, one after another. Their news is—Malinovsky has, without warning to anyone, resigned his seat, packed his foreign passport and a revolver, then *vanished*! The rumor was that he was coming to consult me, may even have been obeying orders from me. What was I to tell his Duma colleagues to tell the workers who (understandably) had been thrown into confusion and dismay?

I cannot telephone Peter or Moscow direct from here, of course. There are only half a dozen lines across the border between Russia and German Poland. It's hell's own job to get connected through local operators, doubling back via Warsaw. Also, any conversation will be monitored by at least three sets of intelligence organizations. Samoilov, in twentieth-century Switzerland, has the choice of dozens of direct connections, almost certainly free from interception—who would tap calls to and from a madhouse (sorry, nerve clinic)? So I advise him to wait, listen, not talk, and keep *me* informed.

Gregory and I were not much nearer solving the conundrum of M.'s flight when a mule came snorting up the track carrying Inessa's cable. (I can see I shall have to get back to Krakow. Provincial and barbarous as it is, it has at least emerged from the Middle Ages.) This was an impromptu code, relying on our shared habits of speech, with reference to FAT SLEUTH, REDHEAD, COMIC PRESS, PEELERS, KHLUPIKI, REFIFFI. But it translated itself to say that the bourgeois press had been wiring and telephoning Burtsev, begging him to declare Malinovsky a police agent, while the Meks were asserting the case already proved by his known possession of huge sums of cash. What should she say to the "softs"?

MAY 22   PORONIN   1914

Seven days ago, I was pacing up and down the living room at Poronin—probably on tiptoe, thumbs in waistcoat armholes, one eye closed, since that is the way I am always mimicked in our *émigré* charades. I was thinking aloud to Gregory, who shares the house, and Jacob Ganetsky, also Haniecki, alias Fürstenberg, who lives across the road. Jacob is a Polish Bolshevist—the most agile, enterprising *homme des affaires* I have ever relied upon. Zinoviev is the worst, almost without exception, and can never be relied upon. However at the moment, as I glanced up and out of the window, they became my ideal combination.

"You have just been appointed to an informal three-man tribunal I am assembling. Brief—to investigate the allegations against Roman Malinovsky. Tribunal now convened. Jacob in the chair."

The pair of them stared at each other. "Where is Malinovsky?"

"Here I am," said the red-faced, red-haired figure I had seen in the distance sweating up the goat track, a gingerbread man, built on a scale at once lavish and careless, by a drunken pastry cook. "Do you have whisky here?"

"There is no whisky for you here. There is nothing for you here. You are a dead man. You are less than a ghost. You will never again be anything to this Party except a folder full of yellowing press cuttings. You will never be anything to me except a pencil that broke in my hand. Possibly, *possibly*, the bits that are left over may yet be of use to the cause you have sullied. We shall decide. At best, when we are finished, your reward may be that we agree to forget that you ever existed. At the moment, you are nothing but a piece of shit thrown at us in the street by people who hide their faces. Now, why are you *here*?"

I left him standing, for a while. Jacob sat behind the central desk in the small, rough-stone room. I took the darkest corner. Gregory prowled round, in and out of the sunlight. The rivulets from Malinovsky's hair must have been 100 degrees proof. "Well?"

He said the worst, most hopeless things. He said he had gone to ground with his relatives in Warsaw, fearful that the Meks in

Peter would flood the press with smears about his character. He said that he decided to surface again when he discovered that they had nothing to print but rumors and that the Bolsheviks were standing by him. Certainly, he understood he could no longer be on the general staff of the Party. But he hoped he could still serve in the front line as a humble private soldier . . .

"Tell him, Jacob." (A fellow Pole.)

"Look, Malinovsky. You are talking to three veterans who have been arrested, worked over, put up in court, by the best the tsarist police can afford. Our entire Party is a Party that knows more about forced confessions, forged testimony, double agents, et cetera than any in the world. You were one of our leaders, on the CenCom, on the editorial board of *Pravda,* chairman of the Duma fraction. Don't you know that what you have just said could only be said by a guilty man? An innocent man would not worry about anything the Mensheviks might invent. An innocent would not imagine for a moment that the Bolsheviks would desert him. What you are telling us is this—you are a police spy: but seeing that you appeared to have got away with it, you thought it worth coming here in the hope that we would back you up. Right?"

"Right!" said Gregory. "Right!" I said. We all stood up. We must have looked fairly menacing, though there was nothing much we could do. We were not equipped to eliminate traitors. Anyway, he was probably the only one who was carrying a gun.

"No, no, Ilyich," he screeched, practically giving off sparks. "I knew that was what you had to think, and what the police counted on you thinking. You see, I left the Duma because I *didn't* want to become a police spy. If I had wanted to be one, if I was one, I'd have stayed where I was, wouldn't I?"

Mmmmmmmmh? We looked at each other. There was a sort of point there. "Wait a minute!" Gregory might not be able to find his nose in the dark but his rabbinical mind was used to the small print. "By that logic, the other six Duma deputies are more likely to be government agents than you are because they didn't bolt. Why can't the police turn *them* into spies?"

"That's a point, the exact point." Malinovsky was tearfully grateful. "Because I am the only one with a past, with a record. I can be blackmailed."

Hmmmmmmh! His case was getting weaker. I'd told the others about his history of petty crime, his prison sentences, and we'd agreed that this would hardly put off the tough slum-dwellers who voted him into the Duma.

"I didn't tell the truth, Ilyich. It was worse than I pretended. Not just theft, but things I don't like to remember. I thought they had been forgotten . . . rape . . . more than once. Young girls, schoolgirls. It was dark. I was mad for a time. You might say you don't care. But Nadya would care. And Inessa. And your sisters. And Gregory's wife.

"And Vera Lubova. And Cecilia Bobrovskaya. The woman comrades care very much about honorable, equal relations between men and women. What would they feel if they learned that Lenin's confidant, his regular guest in Krakow, his companion of many trips, equal to Zinoviev and Kamenev, your security expert, had taken silly daughters of the nobility by force, in their maidenly bedrooms with a knife at their throat? Might you not have preferred him to be a spy?"

I made him tell it all over again from the beginning. We took turns at keeping notes. His story was that until the beginning of the year he assumed his worst crimes were unknown to the police; the lesser were known, but put aside as irrelevant, by us. Then, in April this year, there was a new minister of the interior, Dzunkovsky, who spent his first month combing through the files of everybody he thought his police might want to manipulate. Malinovsky's rapes were a gift they could not turn down.

Malinovsky was given a choice. Working for the police inside the Duma, and not being exposed as a sex-mad monster. Or refusing, and bringing shame and disgrace upon the Duma fraction. As a loyal Bolshevik, he could not accept the first offer, whatever the rewards. He did his best to mitigate the effects of the second by resigning and fleeing the country, attracting all the blame upon himself. *That* was why he had been silent. He had been waiting for the police to prime the press with the juicy details. *That* was why he had not contacted me. He was certain I would repudiate him.

When it seemed clear that no actual details were going to be made public, a dreadful suspicion hit him. Perhaps Dzunkovsky's proposition had been a bluff, and the authorities had intended all the time to force him to flee, arousing the inevitable suspicions, discrediting the Bolsheviks, splitting the left opposition? If so, then the move had been an unqualified success. The only countermove he could envisage was to come to me, convince me of his innocence, and have me announce to the world he had been cleared. Until then, he felt like Dreyfus.

We'd all three forgotten what a persuasive orator M. could be. Gregory gave him a whisky and sat him on a balcony overlooking the mountains while we put our heads together. There was no doubt that, with the addition of the missing piece about the rapes, his explanation fitted the facts better than any other so far. True, we had no corroboration of the convictions for rape, but it was extremely difficult to imagine anyone making that up about themselves. Either his was the authentic version, or, as crafty Jacob joked, the Okhrana had spent the missing weeks faking a convincing replica. Either way, we agreed, it would suit us to accept it as a working hypothesis while we invited evidence from all over to sustain or demolish the accusation of being a police spy.

M. we put under house arrest at Jacob's. For the rest of last week, we have been interviewing witnesses, taking depositions, studying letters, inviting informed opinions.

Most of the time I have kept an open mind, despite being blown to his side by the filthy breath of the Menshevik slanderers. Occasionally, I have felt a strong impulse to dismiss all the legalistic quibbles and queries and accept he must be the Bolshevik Azef. Only last night, I came to a halt on the humpbacked bridge and heard myself mutter aloud—"What if the accusations are true?" But Nadya, who has been keeping the log of the tribunal once the rape business was sidetracked, replied without hesitation—"Impossible!" and reminded me of some of the choicest Menshevik lies.

MAY 25   PORONIN   1914

We all know there are no such things as coincidences in underground, illegal work. One is enough to frighten you off, break the contract, send the danger warning through the entire network. Nevertheless, even a bundle of coincidences are not enough to justify condemning outright a valuable comrade without a cloud of suspicious happenings, like manifestations of supposed *poltergeists*, crowding around him.

There was one other strong charge against M. It was made by Troyanovsky and his common-law wife, Elena Rozmirovich. She came here and repeated her story. With her jet-black hair, chalky mask of a face, and scarlet lips, she looked like the *femme fatale* incarnate. Almost too much, I thought, to be safely dispatched on missions where to be unforgettable was to endanger everybody. I had sent her into Russia, March '13, to recruit promising pupils for my Party school in Krakow. She was picked up by the police as the train crossed the border. There seemed no doubts, they were looking for her. Her husband went berserk. Apart from the two of them, he asserted, only Malinovsky and I knew of her trip. Our lives stood forfeit if she failed to return! To flush out his prime suspect (even the mad lover did not think I was responsible) T. hit on an ingenious device. He wrote to her parents in Kiev a letter which began: "Elena has been imprisoned in Russia under obscure circumstances. If she is not instantly freed, then this for me is incontestable proof of colloboration with the police by one of our Party leaders whom I shall immediately denounce." Elena was freed—not quite instantly—but surprisingly soon. Troyanovsky, Elena Rozmirovich and Bukharin advised me of this in the spring of '13. The testimony was carefully considered then by a special section of the CenCom, and rejected as not decisive proof either way. The next witness was Burtsev. No friend of mine, or of the Bolsheviks, he remains undoubtedly the bloodhound with the most alert nose in the whole left-wing movement.

I don't quite know why, but I saw Burtsev as Malinovsky's most implacable enemy. Perhaps it was because our Pole had set himself up as a rival sniffer-out of *provocateurs* to the veteran spy-catcher. Certainly, B. was not complimentary. He wrote that M. was "an unsavory individual with a murky past" (the rape charges?); "a shifty scoundrel who does not fulfill his obligations" (failed to carry out missions for B?). But he went on to assert, in the strongest terms, that "Before Malinovsky's departure from the Duma, I had not heard even a hint of any kind of accusation of treachery. The thought never entered my mind that somebody someday would be able to attack him on these grounds." He repeated this to the Menshevik press, complaining that none of their critics had come up with any real evidence against the former Duma leader. When the right-wing press, typically, continued to proclaim that he still suspected Malinovsky, Burtsev forced them to withdraw the allegation. He emphasized that in his view no such charge could have the faintest validity.

That was about all. From our own side, nothing but rumors, many of which bore telltale signs of having been launched by the Okhrana. From the Mensheviks, similar rumors without any basis, except the sensational fictions from the bourgeois lie-machine. I did not invite outsiders to contribute as Trotsky and a few others thought I should, but I would have examined any facts from anybody.

But to return to Bukharin & Co. Gregory thought these anecdotes really weighty. I could not quite dismiss them but I had

an instinct that they were not as solid as they looked. It was Ganetsky, the conspirator-general, and our chairman, after all, who put
his finger on the weak spot. "I have always thought, *starik*," he said
in his slow, musing way as if speaking, dictating rather, to himself,
"that in these matters we should always look more at what the
accusers do and less at what they say."

We agreed that Nikolai and the Troyanovskys had indeed
come to me to point the finger at M., separately and together, once
in '12 and again in '13. But if they really believed what they said,
he asked, how did they account for their own later behavior toward
the master-agent? If Troyanovsky was so certain that his lovely
Elena had been betrayed, why did he not immediately publish the
story in the Party papers, or call for a Party court of honor? Why
did he wait ten months, leaving the supposed traitor still at work,
before approaching me? How could Troyanovsky continue to attend CenCom meetings in July and September '13 alongside this
tool of the Tsar? How could he bring himself to write a cordial
letter (M. brought it with him) in March this year to the man who
was responsible for his wife's arrest? Especially on the occasion of
her being arrested again?

We couldn't ask these questions directly of Troyanovsky since,
instead of appearing before the tribunal, and while still calling
himself a Bolshevik, he chose instead to trot out his oft-told tale
to our enemies among the Social Democrats. Elena did submit
herself (looking, as Gregory said, "as scrumptious as one of Inessa's
black and red currant tarts with sour cream"). She could not answer
for her husband. Nor could she explain why, since she shared his
opinion of Malinovsky, she had been willing to act as secretary to
the Duma fraction all this year, until the very moment M. ran off.
All she could whisper, licking her scarlet lips, was—"Discipline,
Ilyich. You trusted him. So he must be trustworthy."

Quite!

JULY 10   PORONIN   1914

The Russian press hung on for a while after we published our
verdict exonerating Malinovsky of spying. Whenever they unearthed
(i.e., invented) a suspicious tidbit, they would telephone, telegraph,
even dispatch their local "stringer" from Krakow, to demand my
opinion of it. Finally, I had to refuse to discuss the subject. I issued
a statement making clear that we were neither hiding nor backing

him: "We have judged and ruthlessly condemned the deserter. There is nothing more to be said. The case is closed." We have not been bothered since.

The Meks are not so easily discouraged. They are mounting a Commission of Inquiry of their own, issuing the transcript of the hearing in daily bulletins. It turns out to be little Bukharin writ large—more and more anti-Bolshevik Social Democrats suddenly recalling that they saw M. just before they were seized by the police; or that the Speaker often had surprising foreknowledge of some Duma fraction's speeches. A week ago, I hit on a tactic to stop them in their tracks. I challenged Martov and Co. to repeat these slanders in any country where there is a (relatively) free court and an independent (of the Tsar anyway) judiciary. There we would sue them for every kopek in their coffers.

Today I will be able to announce that not a word has been heard in answer. And their Commission has been abandoned. I think any fairminded comrades of any fraction, or none, must agree that there is something dishonorable and distasteful about blackguarding fellow socialists under a dictatorship yet refusing to publish your smears in an open society. I do not want to hear the name Malinovsky ever again.

Latest news—this afternoon three of our CenCom members visiting here reported they had seen M. *in the village*.

He was, they reported (I don't know why, but their phrase conjured up such a pathetic tableau) "sitting in a cart with a handful of peasants." They averted their eyes as they passed him, mostly out of embarrassment. But, a short way along the road, they turned to look back. At the same time, so did he. They all agree his face "reflected great fright." They concluded he assumed they were bringing news of a "guilty" verdict by the Meks' Commission, or from Burtsev, to be considered at the CenCom. And that he feared he would soon be liquidated.

I have asked Ganetsky to find M. and inform him for the second time that for us he is now a dead man. And to add that it is considered extremely unusual for anyone to survive a third such warning. In other words, the verbal equivalent of the Black Spot of the Camorra.

AUGUST 1   PORONIN   1914

Today we learned of Germany's declaration of war on Russia. Z.
and I argue over what will be the line adopted by the German
Socialists.

    Z.: "You will see—they dare not speak out against their war.
They will abstain."

    L.: "No, despite everything, they are not such rascals. Certainly
they will not *struggle* against the war. They will just vote against
the government, as is their custom, so that the working class does
not rise up against them."

AUGUST 5   PORONIN   1914

Z. arrives, puffing, at the house with collection of German papers.
On each front page glares the news that the SDP has unanimously
voted war credits to the German government. I cannot believe it.
For an hour or so, I was slightly deranged. What was the use of
anything, what future could there be for socialism, what significance was it to have a mass party that spoke for the working class,
if such a betrayal were possible? Unless it were false, my life had
been wasted.

    I looked in the mirror, something I rarely do. I don't remem-
ber, since I do not shave, having done so for months. What did I
see? A balding head, like a cannonball, dressed with a few wisps
of faded red hair. An unhealthy yellow-gray complexion, like old
lard, covered with a network of cracks. Tiny eyes, one almost
invisible and losing its sight, defensively squinting. A ragged shirt,
a crumpled jacket. I looked like an unsuccessful barrow-boy, or
rather barrow-dotard. By the time I was seventeen, at least one
school fellow took to calling me "Old Man." By the time I was
thirty, it was used by everybody who had ever met me. Now, at
forty-four, I look sixty-five. People bite their tongues after they
have said "Old Man" because it sounds too cruel. They pretend
they are saying some other phrase in which "old" is purely formal,
as "old boy" or "old chap."

    Will a class that dare not oppose a criminal war in which it
will inevitably suffer most ever have the guts to make a revolution?

I argued, and almost convinced Z. (not a difficult task, he is so *khlupiki,* and volatile as a fart), that the bourgeois press must be lying. How often had we read untruth after untruth, often self-contradictory, about us in the propaganda sheets of the enemy? I suggested we wait for the German Party paper, *Forward,* which arrives by a later train.

AUGUST 7   PORONIN, KRAKOW   1914

This morning, the quartermaster of the local gendarmes, "Big Fritz," came to our cottage to make a search. I know him well. As permitted resident alien, I have to sign in at his office once a month. We usually have a beer.

Now he refuses, because he is "on duty." The real reason is that he has had, in accordance with an admirable Austrian law, to bring along an independent witness. This is a local peasant who has always believed I am a spy of the Tsar. He carries a shotgun. While the gendarme and I talk, I have to keep extending a hand and pushing the barrel away from the side of my head.

The quartermaster takes me into the kitchen, closing the door behind us. He has a question to ask as a favor—what is he supposed to be searching for? I give him a (broken) Browning revolver, some books in Russian (Turgenev), and pages of statistics on the agrarian problem. "Codes, are they?" he asks. But he is pleased and back in the next room decides to poke fun at his witness who is sitting on the edge of a chair, looking embarrassed and worried.

The officer points to a jar of paste on the table. "That is an anarchist bomb," he says. "Get your head down and crawl out into the garden."

The witness crawls out, leaving his shotgun behind, much to the quartermaster's loud amusement. Now he has to decide what to do with me. Strictly speaking, since there has been a formal complaint from some locals that I am a tsarist spy, he should arrest me now. However, the nearest place with a cell is the military prison in Novy Targ ten miles away. He has another favor to ask. I am described on the warrant as "Baron Ulyanov," somewhat misleading translation of the Russian *dvoryanin,* hereditary nobleman, which follows me everywhere. Would His Excellency please catch the six o'clock train in the morning, on his own, and deliver himself to Novy Targ?

AUGUST 19   NOVY TARG   1914

Prisons are fascinating places, especially when you know you will
not be inside long. If I had been a tsarist spy, I would have learned
more in here about troop movements, worker unrest, failures in
delivery of rations, VD rates among barracks prostitutes, anti-war
feeling, etc. than in months of more formal espionage. Between
them, warders and convicts know everything.

Meanwhile, Nadya has been at work, using the three-in-one
firm of Jacob Ganetsky-Haniecki-Fürstenberg. He contacted Victor Adler, the leader of the Austrian Social Democrats, the man
who at a conference last year described me as a "crazed genius,"
to which I responded by calling him an "amiable moron." You
never know when such things may come in useful! Victor waited
upon Baron Heinold, the minister of the interior, eventually convincing him that Lenin was more of a threat to the Tsar than was
the Emperor in Vienna. Two other SDP MPs also spoke up for
me. And I am to be released tonight. Another fortnight's bureaucratic fumbling, perhaps, and I should be crossing over into Switzerland, some unconvincing documentation permitting.

SEPTEMBER 6   BERNE   1914

Arrest, imprisonment, deportation, more-or-less illegal entry—and
here I am, back in neutral Switzerland again, sitting out the war
to end war a paying guest of the Shklovskys.

Liberals, utopian socialists, revisionizing Marxists often ask me
why, if our philosophy of history is so scientific, we cannot even
forecast what will happen in the next five years. There are all sorts
of debating devices for meeting this silly query. Is meteorology a
science? If so, why are the forecasts often no more accurate, sometimes much less so, than the old wife's pinecones or the old village
elder's rheumatism? Are doctors of medicine men of logic and
reason? If so, why do we find hospital bulletins recording highly
successful operations with the postscript . . . "Patient died"? Who
does not know the patient who survived to be ninety despite being
told at fifty he had three months to live?

Nobody—thank God—believes in miracles anymore. But

Marxists have managed to use the tools of our profession to affect reality in direct, surprising, and sometimes shocking, ways. Consider the scoundrely Parvus, the Falstaff of '05, the bloated roisterer in the entourage of Trotsky's Prince Hal. I am assured by our people in Constantinople that he has made a million in gold. Using our politico-economic insights into the workings of capitalism, he managed to trick the system into rewarding him a thousandfold for telling it what it will do next.

But the most amazing prophecy, already coming true all around us, was made by Engels over a quarter of a century ago. If it had been made by some bourgeois pundit, we would have seen it reprinted, wondered over, gawped at, in every mass circulation newspaper in every European capital. Here is what he wrote on December 15, 1887.

> No war is any longer possible for Prussia-Germany except a world war and a world war indeed of an extent and violence hitherto undreamt-of. Eight to ten millions of soldiers will massacre one another and in doing so devour the whole of Europe until they have stripped it barer than any swarm of locusts has ever done. The devastation of the Thirty Years' War compressed into three or four years, and spread over the whole Continent; famine, pestilence, general descent into savagery, both of the armies and the mass of the people, produced by acute distress; hopeless confusion of our artificial machinery in trade, industry and credit, ending in general bankruptcy; collapse of the old states and their traditional élite wisdom to such an extent that crowns will roll by dozens on the pavements and there will be nobody to pick them up; absolute impossibility of foreseeing how it will all end and who will come out of the struggle as victor; only one result is absolutely certain: general exhaustion and the establishment of the conditions for the final victory of the working class.
>
> This is the prospect when the system of mutual outbidding in armaments, driven to extremities, at last bears its inevitable fruits. This, my lords, princes and statesmen, is where in your wisdom you have brought old Europe. And when nothing more remains to you but to open the last great war dance—that will suit us nicely. The war may perhaps push us temporarily into the background, may wrench from us many a position already conquered. But when you have unfettered forces which you will no longer be able to control, things may go as they will: at the end of the tragedy you will be ruined and the victory of the proletariat will either be already achieved or at any rate inevitable.

It was a vision unique in its time, and therefore ignored. So far only the first few lines of his remarkable piece of clairvoyance have come true, but I foresee each item he mentions rising in turn, like a specter in a play, when its cue is given. Surely any person of working intelligence and historical experience must feel the strong, solid cutting edge of Engels's analysis of things to come. Yet all around me they are still saying it will all be over by Christmas; that all it needs is for King, Kaiser, Emperor, Tsar, Prime Minister to get together and talk it over; that the whole thing is an accident.

I shall tuck this away in these pages. When I take it out again, I am as certain as I can be of anything—this is *my* prophecy—that the world war will be over and the proletariat in control in one, if not all, the capitals of the powers that have collapsed in chaos.

OCTOBER 19   BERNE   1914

In today's issue of *Sotsial-Demokrat,* a black box round the name of Roman Malinovsky, and a long and appreciative obituary. Here is an extract:

> News has reached us of the death in action in this accursed, imperialist war of a former member of the Bolshevik Central Committee and the editorial board of *Pravda,* once leader of their fraction in the Duma and head of their security bureau, Roman Malinovsky. What a cruel irony that so brave and dedicated a Polish revolutionary should die in the Guards Regiment of the Tsar seeking to conquer Polish Galicia!
>
> We owe it to him to insist on preserving his memory from malicious rumors and cleansing his name and his honor of disgraceful slanders. . . .
>
> Roman Malinovsky was an honest man and accusations of political criminality were filthy fabrications. He was not only an honest man, he was also a talented worker in proletarian affairs. He was no stranger to a thousand human weaknesses but he was noted for sparkling ability. He gave his talent—the talent of agitator and orator—to the service of our great revolutionary cause.
>
> Let us not remember only that he deserted the Duma, leaving his post without authority, exposing his fellow deputies to the ridicule and abuse of the enemy. He was in a deep depression at that time. He had lost faith, not in the proletarian struggle, but

in his power to serve it. He no longer had confidence in himself. He committed political suicide.

He offered himself willingly to the autopsy of his leading comrades. After the sentence of banishment from the movement, the harshest punishment for a true comrade, the old Malinovsky revived and he said: "I shall find myself again. I shall find in myself the strength to serve the workers' cause and in ten or twenty years I shall make amends for my sins against the Party."

And looking at this remarkably talented and courageous worker, we all hoped that this would be so.

I did not sign this—that perhaps would have been pushing rehabilitation too far—but everyone who needs to know who wrote it knows. I have been half-afraid that the next time I saw this name it would be in a situation where I should regret having met M. But he seems to have ended his life as he lived it, on the cusp between foolhardiness and bravery.

OCTOBER 28   BERNE   1914

Every newspaperman (I don't call myself a "writer") knows that as soon as you put down the first word in an article, you have already ceased to be objective. You have made a choice. For instance, if you describe a man as "well-built," we all know his enemies would call him "fat." To write that a woman has "beautiful hair" is a sign, at least to other women, that she is more correctly described as "plain." This is as it should be. The journalism I like is written by those with strong opinions who let them show.

So, Berne. To my Mother, to those I want to think of me as happily nesting (not always my friends), I say Berne is "a sleepy little town." Another way of putting it would be "a dreary little hole." Still, it's better than Geneva. And this last month we have been having a most glorious autumn—a season that does not exist in the same way in Russia.

I shouldn't complain. We have a pleasant couple of rooms on Distelweg, a small, quiet, tidy street running along the fringe of the forest. Just across the road is Inessa, up the road the Zinovievs (five minutes' walk), just beyond, the Shklovskys and their two lively daughters. (Georgy is an Old Bolshevik, escapee from Siberia in '09, who has become here a prosperous manufacturer of mineral

salts, thus our adviser on his favorite topics, medicine and money,
and also Zinoviev's nominal employer in his chemical laboratory.)

We all see a lot of each other. But the best times are when
Nadya and Inessa and I walk for miles along mountain roads,
paved with a padding of yellow leaves. We sit for hours, three, or
sometimes two, of us, framed on a sunlit wooded mountainside. I
jot down plans for speeches. Nadya is studying Italian from a
Teach-Yourself book and apostrophizing the ferns. Inessa sews on
a skirt or blouse. She has still not quite recovered from her last
spell in prison which led to an attack of consumption. When she
shudders, I know she is once again feeling the clammy gloom of
that cell.

NOVEMBER 22   BERNE   1914

It looks as though the name, R . . . V . . . M . . . , is still going to
haunt me for ill or good. At first, I thought I might ignore the
report. But we are not now talking about the words, constructs on
paper or in the mind, but about a real, flesh-and-blood person,
someone with whom I spent many enjoyable hours, whose abilities
interested, impressed and assisted both me personally and the
whole movement. So I have inserted in today's *Sotsial-Demokrat* the
following discreet but not obscure para. Without saying as much,
I have tried to give the feel of a minor "scoop."

> This publication has just received word from Petersburg that the
> information about the death of R. V. Malinovsky appearing re-
> cently in all Russian and most émigré newspapers is false.
>   Malinovsky is alive and active in one of the theaters of military
> operations.
>   They say that people who are erroneously declared dead
> often live a long time thereafter. We hope this is the case with
> R. V. Malinovsky.

And I signed it with my Party journalism name—N. (for nothing) Lenin. This is a convention that outsiders find oddly confusing. On the inside, it is immediately apparent that anyone who
addresses, or describes me, in print or in the flesh, as "Nikolai"
does not know much about me or us.

Where will Roman Vatslavovich surface next?

MARCH 5   ZURICH   1915

Letter from Koba. His nearest Siberian neighbor-comrade is Timofei Spanaryan. He's 125 miles away by sleigh. Koba must have
seen the "Seven Theses" I sent Timofei. Nadya's files show that
Koba was exiled after being rounded up at that disastrous Party
social-and-dance in 1913. I'm told he blames the arrest on Malinovsky who slipped out as the police broke in. Someday the incident must be properly investigated. If it should be Roman M., I'll
see he's shot within the hour. Meanwhile, poor old Koba is moved
ever northward beyond the Artic Circle every time he makes the
least gesture at an escape. He is due for release in '17. When I
met him in London, he barely spoke. Now he rarely writes. Anything that breaks that white silence is worth noting. I am copying
his letter here in full.

> February 21, 1915
>   My greetings to you, dear Ilyich, warm, warm greetings.
> Greetings to Zinoviev. Greetings Nadezhda Konstantinovna.
>   How are you? How is your health? I live as before, chew my
> bread, completing half my term. It's rather dull. But that can't be
> helped. But how are things with you?
>   It must be much livelier where you are. I recently read one
> of Kropotkin's articles—the old fool must have completely lost
> his mind. I also read a short article by Plekhanov in *Rech*. He's
> become an incorrigible old gossip. *Ek-mah!* and the Liquid-
> ators . . .
>   There's no one to beat them, devil take me! Is it possible they
> will get away with it and go unpunished? Make us happy. Let us
> know that in the near future a certain newspaper will appear that
> will punch them in the jaw. Do it again and again, without getting
> tired. Do you hear from Gusev?
>   If it should occur to you to write, do so at this address.
>   Your Koba

That tells us something of the courage of our people. Honest Koba,
all alone, still supports the revolutionary defeatist line. In his Baku
days, somebody told me, he was known as "Lenin's Left Boot"!
     I must reply at once. I've spent so much time and energy on

our Bolshevik POWs in Germany, sending them food, cigarettes, propaganda, that I've neglected our best fighters, imprisoned by their own government, in much more ghastly places. I can't answer, I realize, without his baptismal name, essential for open correspondence with Siberian convicts. I've forgotten it. How embarrassing! I'm sure it was Koba *Ivanov* in London. But then that's like Schmidt would be here—so ordinary as to be positively suspicious. Then he became "Stalin," a good Russian sound, like "Lenin," but hardly a real family name. And actually, of course, he's Georgian. It is Joseph Dj . . . something. We don't have it on file. I must get Nadya to ask around. *Very important!* Even our Steel-man might be hurt to hear we remember so little of him.

MARCH 20   BERNE   1915

"How many revolutionaries do you think traveled everywhere with their mothers-in-law and wrote home every two weeks to mother?" Radek asked me the other day. I suppose many cosmopolitan sophisticates do find the thought a little comic. It is very un-Western. But among Russians, all politics aside, the family exerts an attraction that seems as basic as the need to eat, or drink, or sleep. In this, we are of the East.

Certainly, it seemed quite natural to all of us that Nadya should bring poor, dear Elizaveta with her when she joined me in Siberian exile. I never hesitated for a moment to include her in our wandering, gypsy threesome around Europe. And she remained the center prop of our household until she died two days ago. My hands are still warm from the tin box of new ashes handed over to us just now at the Berne Crematorium.

I say "poor dear Elizaveta" but apart from these few last days she never needed anyone's pity. When we first met in Shushenskoye, she was quite pious, rather straitlaced, a sort of portable conscience that must speak the truth even if—especially if, I used to complain—it hurt. She had a face of rightly righteousness that was totally genuine, and over the years she increasingly used it to support our case. No one was better fitted to visit comrades in prison and carry in and out all kinds of contraband without being suspected. She could sit tight on illegal materials during a police search and never be asked to move.

Our two-person team would often have relapsed with fatigue if she had not been a bustling, organized, tireless third. Welcoming couriers passing through, fitting out their skirts or waistcoats with the sewn-in "armor" that concealed illegal newspapers and pamphlets, writing out dreary "skeleton" letters so that we could insert invisible ink messages between their lines. She became quite famous in the movement. Radek used to claim that the most sacred oath he knew was "by the pince-nez of Lenin's mother-in-law."

In early days, we used to fence with each other over God and Marx. But my own Mother could not have been more solicitous about my tiniest bout of illness. As for me, though I would sometimes decline to accept some domestic responsibility for Nadya, watching milk on the boil or such, when I was crushed by work, I found I never minded stopping everything to go out and find Elizaveta cigarettes when all the shops and most cafés were closed. (What a smoker! She could out-puff Martov.)

Later, I noticed she began to refuse to discuss religion, never attended church or kept holy days, never was known to pray. Suddenly one night, only a few months ago, she said to Nadya: "I was very religious in my youth, but as I have lived on and learned more about people and the world I see it is all nonsense. Please have me cremated."

She began to ache for Russia. Mother invited her to stay in the Peter flat but she refused, saying there was more than enough to do looking after young "Gora" with Anyuta and Mark, Manyasha and Mitya, under police watch and likely to be lifted at any time. She was waiting for the Revolution and our return. She sat on a bench in the woods on the first sunny day of spring for half an hour, then collapsed. The next day she was dead.

We have to move. Our landlady is very religious and she cannot let to those who cremate relatives who pass over. What will happen on Judgement Day? I told her the same as happens to those eaten by cannibals.

MAY 14   BERNE   1915

"Is it good for the Jews?" Trotsky told me once that this was his father's only guiding principle about anything that went on outside the family circle. I am inclined to ask "Is it good for the Party?" when asked to adjudicate on whether some action, or some person, is moral or immoral. I can't work up much indignation about "scoundrels" and have frequently found them very convenient and valuable agents for the Party. (Witness Victor Tararuta.)

Alexander Helphand, also passing as Parvus—the little one —is another sack of guts. Nobody knows his baptismal name. When he was a slim, young, ragged revolutionary, he was christened "Dr. Elefant" by Kautsky's children. They must have been clairvoyant. Even in the Munich days, when he was printing *Iskra,* no one could have rationally predicted the great tottering balloon he has become, with a nipple for a nose, and flappers for arms. Of all his old friends, comrades and, yes, admirers—for he had a brain like a searchlight—only Radek remains. And he circulates in émigré circles telling ever taller tales of Parvus the Casanova, Parvus the Midas, Parvus the Falstaff. Is he perhaps on a retainer as publicity agent?

It is difficult not to speak of him as a casualty of 1914. Indeed, Trotsky, having first thought up the Falstaff label (who is Prince Hal?), then listed him among the "politically deceased." Since he became a German, praised the Kaiser's war, and expanded into black-market profiteering, he has had the door banged in his face by Rosa Luxemburg and been publicly cut by Karl Liebknecht and Clara Zetkin. But his too, too solid ghost goes sweating on here, in Switzerland of all places.

For the last fortnight, Karl tells me, Parvus has been occupying not just a room, but a suite, at Zurich's most luxurious hotel, Bauer au Lac. Here he rules like a maharajah. It is said he feeds and houses a clutch of blondes as another might keep kittens. The butts of the cigars he throws away are bigger than any whole ones ever sold in ordinary tobacconists. He drinks a bottle of champagne each day for breakfast. He might be Baron Munchausen, though the money is genuine enough. He has reactivated a former mistress, current party member Ekaterina Groman, to distribute sizable sums of Swiss francs among the poor of our Russian colony.

Why is he here? A recurrent question. I think I know the answer. But I have no intention of going to Zurich. Let the man-mountain come to Mohammed.

MAY 16   BERNE   1915

I was almost beginning to think I was wrong. It is easier to convince yourself you are nearly always right when nothing much is going on. When you are in the thick of action, you just have to trust you won't be wrong. Events quickly prove or disprove you. This time I have turned out to be right.

At noon, I was sitting in the workmen's café with Nadya and Inessa, the sort of place that is much the same anywhere in Europe. Cleaner perhaps in Switzerland, but with steamy windows, damp tables, heavy smells, heat oppressive near the ovens behind the counter, nonexistent beside the door. Most of the nutrition seems to soak into your clothes. Once, in Munich, Parvus and I ate like this regularly. Here I for one still was, fork halfway to the mouth. And here he was, looming so overwhelmingly across our table, he actually cut off the daylight and plunged my food into darkness.

I dismissed comrade Ekaterina who was attempting introductions, failed to give the name of Nadya, whom he knew, and Inessa, whom I determined he shouldn't know, and offered him a seat I was sure he couldn't take. It was like getting a stuffed bear into a wheelbarrow. Instead we were driven back in his deep-sprung Mercedes to my rooms in Distelweg.

I was silent. He sold himself every bounce of the way. He was going to tell me things he had told no one else, that no one else knew. I must agree that tsarism was the enemy of all socialists, all democrats, all decent human beings, far more of an enemy of the people that the Kaiser. He was still a Marxist. We were watching imperialism military-style provoke the crisis of capitalism. Bolsheviks should take sides against the most absolutist of the combatants. There would be no revolution in Germany during a war. There would not be a revolution in Russia except during a war. He had a million marks in gold if I could engineer a general strike across Russia, double that for an insurrection, the sky's the limit if the new regime withdrew from the war.

The car stopped and I got out, holding the door half closed. He was left scrabbling like a spider in a plug-hole.

"You are too clever, Alexander, to imagine I can make any deal with you, especially as you have taken care to make yourself so conspicuous. I have only to look at you, like an overfed grub, to know you have chosen the more ignoble of the two roads we used to discuss, the route to riches. I have read your paper, *Die Glocke*. It is an organ of cowardly renegades and dirty lackeys, a cesspool of Prussian jingoism. In it, there is not a single, honest thought, not a single serious argument, not a single straightforward article. I shall say this in public tomorrow, in print next week."

Parvus's head filled the car window. He did not bother to argue a lost case. "What about my Copenhagen Institute opening next month? Condoms, salvarsan, Dutch caps for the Russian rich. Strategic materials, chemicals, rare metals for the German war machine. Huge profits both ways with a percentage to the Party. A ready-made underground railway. An office in Petersburg. Think what you could do with that. Give me a man of confidence, Bukharin or Shlyapnikov, say. They're both there."

Parvus was being open and direct, for him anyway. I was too. "No, Bukharin is a naïve intellectual. Shlyapnikov is too honest a worker. I'll send you Jacob Ganetsky, the cleverest fixer I ever met. Never heard of him? He's earmarked for head of the National Bank when the Revolution comes."

I clunked the car door and went inside before he could see the sweat gathering on my brow. A good day's work, and I come out smelling of roses.

JUNE 10   **SORENBERG**   **1915**

We have been in this ridiculous, picture-postcard village, a spot we discovered ten years ago when we did our foot-slogging, somnambulistic tour of Switzerland, since the start of the month. We are staying until the end of the summer at the Hotel Marienthal where once I polished the boots. We are a bit too old for that now, and anyway Nadya has developed a mild taste for tiny luxuries.

Not many tourists come to this handful of houses (plus post office) set at the bottom of a sort of funnel, rimmed by forest. You can hardly get your head far enough back to see the end of the trees and the white peak of the Rothorn peering down at you. It's ideal for working—the amazing Swiss libraries in Berne and Zurich send me free, at a special low postal rate, any book I need. And the hotel always has room for friends. Indeed, we have almost a lease on our corridor. I have invited Radek and Zinoviev to stay. Inessa is already here, in the next room. We circulate, *en déshabillé*, like family, without anyone taking the slightest interest. I have everything I want under my hand.

I am planning an anti-war conference at Zimmerwald in three months or so and I suppose this was what turned my mind to Plekhanov, now the most awful fire-eating patriot, lover of the Fatherland, hater of the Hun. What a lovely brain the old boy once had! Could age and failure do that to anyone, to *me*? I asked Nadya for our file on him, vaguely considering an article. I found there a piece already so good I couldn't have done better. I asked Inessa to read it out to me again as I copied into this diary.

The destiny of Plekhanov was tragic. In the theoretical sphere his services to the labor movement were very great. But the years of emigration were not without effect on him—they isolated him from the real life of Russia. The labor movement of the broad masses only developed after he had already gone abroad. He saw the representatives of the various parties, writers, students, even individual working men, but he neither saw nor worked nor felt with the Russian laboring people.

When any correspondence happened to come from Russia that lifted the curtain covering new forms of the movement, and made one grasp its perspectives, Ilyich, Martov, even Vera Ivanovna would read and reread the letters. Ilyich would read and pace up and down for a long while and could not get off to sleep.

When we moved to Geneva, I endeavoured to show Plekhanov correspondence of this kind and the way he reacted astonished me: he seemed to lose the ground under his feet and a look of mistrust would come over his face. Afterward he never mentioned those letters again.

At first, I was somewhat offended at this; but afterward I began to think of the reason for his attitude. He had long since left Russia, and he did not possess that gauge—fashioned by experience—which makes it possible to grasp the relative value of each letter, to read a great deal between the lines.

Workers often came to *Iskra*, and they all, of course, wanted to see Plekhanov. To get in to see Plekhanov was much more difficult than to see us or Martov, but even if a worker succeeded in seeing him he came away feeling confused. The worker would be enthralled with Plekhanov's brilliant intelligence, his knowledge and his wit, but somehow it seemed that on leaving him, he would feel only what a great gap there was between this brilliant theoretician and himself. Of the things he wished to speak about, or seek advice on, the worker could not say a word.

And if the worker did not agree with Plekhanov, and tried to expound his own opinion, Plekhanov began to get annoyed: "Your father and mother were still wetting themselves when I walked in the shadow of the gallows."

I dare say things were not like this in the first years of emigration, but by the beginning of the century Plekhanov had already lost all capacity for directly sensing Russia. In 1905 he did not go to Russia.

I am ashamed to say I had never realized that Nadya could observe, think and write like that. Have I underestimated her over these years? "Yes, you have," said Inessa.

What is the message here for me, then?

"When the moment comes to return to Russia, do not hesitate. What sapped Plekhanov's strength is what gives strength to you—the approach of the Revolution."

DECEMBER 4   BERNE   1915

Nadya is in active correspondence with guess-whom? She gave me five chances. Only on the fifth did I hit the right name—Malinovsky! Despite my obit, he went on to fight in eleven battles during the next year. "He was like a wild creature that had never understood the idea of death," according to the rather poetic citation recommending him for the Cross of St. George. He was captured on our Western Front and he is now in the German POW camp at Altengrabow.

From there, he has written to Nadya c/o the "Commission to Help Russian War Prisoners." This is one of our most successful front organizations and has been in action almost a year without being blown by the Russian government. They have gone so far as to grant us a small but useful subsidy (even though most of the cash gets stolen on the way) and, more valuable still, a respectable name. CHRWP now has reps in twenty-one camps spread all over Germany. As well as food and the usual comforts, we also pipe in loads of anti-war, anti-Tsar reading matter. Under the blind eye of the Germans, who imagine that a revolution in our country will win them the war against the Allies, we have already circulated *5,000 lbs.* of revolutionary literature.

Nadya exchanged a few letters before she told me. "I was sorry for the poor old fallen eagle," she said, "I sent him some underclothes, a few bags of flour, sugar and shortening. He wrote back desperately eager to help with the Commission's work."

I told her to keep him supplied with the Commission's newspaper, *V Plenu,* notes for courses on political economy, a few books for the prison library, and let me know how things go.

JULY 25   BERNE   1916

Mother died today in Peter—July 12, Russian calendar.

As those I love are picked off the board, first Father, then Sasha, Olga, then Elizaveta, now darling Mamma, I feel each time as if part of my brain is become waste space, desert, ruined land. She was in a family house, the steamboat flat of Mark and Anyuta on Shirokaya Street. Manyasha was there too, and the little marvel, Gora, the adopted son. In another world, another society, this amazing woman would not have had to live for others but have carved out a career of her own. With her skill at languages, her immense tact, charm, obstinacy and ingenuity, she could have become one of the first women diplomats, though she might have found that dull. The same talents would have served her well as an international conspirator or an international crook. I always suspected an appetite for adventure, danger, the thrill of the chase, which she was never able to indulge except through her children. We owe it even more now to her to succeed.

She was eighty-one and, Anna says on the telephone, "tiring of the race." If I live as long I shall still be around in 1951! That would not be a good idea, at least so far as I am concerned. I should have lost so many loved ones my brain would be all scar tissue. Be strong, be healthy, feed the will to survive, Inessa and Nadya, Anyuta, Manyasha and Mitya. You all feel flesh of my flesh. I would rather go first. But only *after* the Revolution, so hang on.

AUGUST 15 BERNE 1916

The experience of war, like the experience of every crisis in history, of every great disaster and every sudden turn in human life, stuns and shatters some, but it enlightens and hardens others.

AUGUST 22 BERNE 1916

On one front, at least, our cause seems to be advancing. Inside the German POW camps! Malinovsky works like a donkey-engine pumping out our propaganda round the clock. His prison library now contains a total of 1,011 volumes, all supplied by us. Nearly everyone carrying some radical message. M. has been giving my lectures on Marxism. Even the guards listen. Especially since he told them that Communism is a German invention!

Of course, I take all of this *cum grano salis*. We have our own sources in Altengrabow. M. is only exaggerating about 100 percent—a very low markup in the circumstances. After we started writing to each other about nine months ago, he remarked, "Now, *at last*, socialism has become my religion." What was it before?

But this is no time to rake over those ashes. His reports of the feelings of the (largely peasant) troops about land distribution, about the war, about the workers, about the Party, are invaluable. There is nowhere else I could learn their intimate, personal re-actions which bubble to the surface during enforced idleness in crowded spaces. He is also able to guide me as to the idioms, the images, the quotations, the jokes they use among themselves, which we so rarely transfuse into our prose.

OCTOBER 10   BERNE   1916

Gusev writes from Peter: the Tsar now spends almost all his time at the *Stavka* (Army GHQ). The generals ignore him and he plays dominoes. The Tsaritsa is in charge of the government. She re-mains in the capital with her degraded puppet minister of the interior, Protopopov, a syphilitic with all the clinical signs of gen-eral paralysis of the insane. Whenever they disagree, he insists his orders came to him from beyond the grave, transmitted by the dead Rasputin.

Other good news: the strike at the Putilov works, where the Party is at its strongest, holds firm. Contingents of police, a hundred strong, pistols drawn, make little impact on solid lines of workers. I wish I could see them—three deep, carrying two-foot spanners and wooden shields, mustering nine or ten thousand. Finally the army was summoned, ordered to disperse the pickets' blockade, by shooting them down if necessary. The soldiers first of all stood still. Then, very slowly, they raised the rifles in ones and twos. And pointed them at the police! The police scattered. The workers cheered. The officers smartly ordered their men to slope arms, quick march, retire. Gusev was there. Lucky man.

OCTOBER 15   ZURICH   1916

Strike situation still tense in Peter. Little goodwill toward monarchy and government from any class. Everyday law and order only preserved by constant resort to violence by the authorities. Putilov strikers are back at work. Their massive round-the-clock pickets broken up by repeated, savage cavalry charges from the Cossacks.

The soldiers who refused to shoot down their brothers at the factory gates have paid the highest price for their solidarity. Two hundred were arrested afterward, and court-martialed. This news has been censored from the papers. But Gusev writes that 150 were charged with mutiny, found guilty and executed by firing squad. Have written stressing it is this kind of story that must get into our Party's illegal newspapers. I will myself do a piece for *Social Democrat*. Something wondering whether our government may now be killing more Russian soldiers at home than it is killing German soldiers at the front. Just what everyone likes to whisper behind a hand—even the bourgeoisie. Can the Cossacks bear to go on acting as official death squads, licensed assassins, *forever*?

DECEMBER 22   BERNE   1916

I was just about to spin an article for *Social Democrat,* in an early January issue, around Malinovsky. This heroic agitator, despite a starvation diet and two lingering wounds, is turning his prison into a Party dormitory . . . etc., etc. Such stories not only encourage our faithful but help deflate such anti-Bolshevik parlor pinks as Martov and Trotsky. Just as I put pen to paper, I learn that M. is once again being attacked by those who aim to damage us, perhaps specifically me, through him.

Burtsev cleared him two years ago. What has happened to make "Fatty" reshuffle his files and come up with the conclusion, in a windy piece entitled "The Question That Demands an Answer," that we, the Bolsheviks, must now be required to prove him innocent? *They* cannot establish his guilt. So now *we* have to refute every silly piece of tittle-tattle. My inclination is to keep my mouth shut on these charges and only publicize M's positive achievement behind barbed wire. But Burtsev has anticipated that. "Silence is tantamount to a plea of guilty," he says.

Then there is the old Liberal, Markov. He used to barrack our deputies, after Roman's flight, with the repeated cry of "But where is Malinovsky?" Now he claims that he has been informed by "a high source in the government" that there is no doubt (1) M. was a police spy, (2) he decamped with metalworkers' strike fund, (3) he is now in the pay of the Germans, like "his puppet-master, Nikolai Lenin."

So I have had to rehearse the whole story all over again, winding up with the message that ought to stop all speculation on our side—"The Bolshevik Tribunal painstakingly investigated the public career of Malinovsky and unanimously confirmed that all charges of provocation against him were *absolute nonsense.*"

JANUARY 9   ZURICH   1917

The twelfth anniversary of "Bloody Sunday." At the Volkhaus lectured young workers' group on the lessons of '05 in Russia. Usual depressive mood from this ghastly Hansel and Gretel hall. A cuckoo clock for pterodactyls. It presses on my head like a migraine. The audience didn't look too cheery either. *Slava bogu!* If the next generation cannot be optimistic, then who can? *I can.* Even though I've been in almost continuous exile since the turn of the century.

So, after an analysis of what happened in Petersburg all those years ago, the forces involved, the mistakes and the achievements, deliberately scholastic, clinical, I announced as if it were a scientific fact (which of course, I believe it to be): "This was the prologue to the coming *European* Revolution." I could hear the question though no lips moved. Yes, yes, but now much longer do we have to wait for the curtain up, the end of the overture, the first act? Then I gave them my summing up.

> We must not be deceived by the present graveyard stillness in Europe. The continent is pregnant with Revolution. The monstrous horrors of the imperialist war on the battlefront, the overwork, underfeeding and exploiting of the working people behind the lines, are everywhere stirring up a mood of angry protest. The ruling classes, with their hired help, the reformed Liberals and Socialists, are increasingly backing themselves into a blind alley. They can only escape at the cost of tremendous upheavals.

Somebody asked about Russia. Surely "1905" ought to be ready soon to repeat itself? A good question. But one for me to worry about, not them. The task of young Swiss socialists is to concentrate their eyes on the tasks before them in Switzerland. And they must think less about learning at second hand from our older generation, and more about being taught by their own mistakes. "*We* may not live to see the decisive battles of this coming revolution," I concluded. "But I can confidently predict that you will not only take part in them, but win them." This brought a cheer. Actually, it is a thought that has been oppressing me lately—will I last out the long wait? But, as so often, by voicing a fear, you fish it out and it dies in your net. The drama may start sooner than any of us think. Overture and beginners please. The real worry is—are we ready?

FEBRUARY 23   **ZURICH**   **1917**

How boring, muddy, intractable are Swiss politics! They do not much interest me—but out of Russia nothing, and I cannot remain still. Yet it is hardly worth recording what is happening here. Leftist Nobbs and Platten swinging back to Grimm and the Right Socialists. Munzenberg, supposedly the young Danton *de nos jours*, afraid to print Radek's article denouncing Grimm. Nobody wants to appear to be "splitting the movement." As if all progress did not consist of throwing out of the sleigh those who are not going your way. As if I had not spent all my life split, split, splitting . . . honing, sharpening, pointing, steeling the revolutionary weapon, "the party of a new type."

But then, I comfort myself, reading up on Swiss history in the library in the old Preacher's Church, normal rules do not apply up here. Perhaps it is something to do with the rarefied air. I mean, where else, as in their great cantonal disputes of the last century, often leading to savage local wars, would you find that the towns were always conservative and the countryside always radical? It is positively unnatural. Also a warning against the dangers of pseudo-democracy, the delusions of the parliamentary way: that is, relying on the power of the ballot box when people's minds and votes are still controlled by bourgeois newspapers, schools and colleges, churches, employers.

In Switzerland, whenever any canton was granted universal male suffrage it promptly elected a reactionary government. Only the secular were expected to abide by the rules. The Jesuits, those Bolsheviks within the Roman Church, not only took to the streets more often than socialists or radicals, they actually led private armies into urban battle, and won! And when they won, as in the Valais, they made Protestant worship illegal. In Zurich, the Protestant clergy marched at the head of peasant mobs and seized power by force. The Swiss of the last century may have been perverse, but at least they got things done.

In this century, they plonk their backsides on the *status quo* and reject all change. Why? *Cherchez la ferme!* (Radek's joke.) Could it have any bearing on a statistic I plucked from the state archives this morning—out of half a million Swiss heads of families, 475,000 own landed property?

MARCH 14   ZURICH   1917

This morning N. recalled, for no particular reason it seemed, the visits we used to make to London Zoo. "Remember the white northern wolf?" she asked. "We always stood a long time outside his cage. The keeper told us once—'All animals, bears, lions, tigers, get used to their cages in time. Only the white wolf from the Russian north never grows accustomed to being imprisoned. Day and night he bangs his head against the bars.' "

She stared at the windows of our room, firmly closed all the year round against the smell from the sausage factory. I knew what she was saying, even if she didn't.

Throughout this raw, wet winter, I have been having more and more frequent attacks of what Inessa dubbed "Volodya's Mental Hydrophobia." I think I have savaged everyone—Zinoviev and Lilina, Rosa Luxemburg and Alexandra Kollontai (by post), Radek, Bukharin, poor devoted Olga Ravich, even Inessa, always Nadya. Once, after a fierce outburst, I caught my image in the mirror. My lips were lathered with foam.

My head will not stand much more banging against the bars.

MARCH 15   ZURICH   1917

It was exactly ten minutes before one. I know because that is the time I always leave our rooms to go back to the library after the midday meal. If I had just arrived from the library, it would have been exactly ten minutes past twelve. I double-checked my notebooks and pencils. Nadya had just started washing up the dishes.

As often these days, whenever I let my mind idle out of gear, I have the feeling of being at the bottom of a well. A tiny figure in a tiny roofless room, in some child's toy theater. The giant, normal world, outside and above, takes only occasional notice of me, looking down over the lip of the parapet at the bald midget shuffling around. Then Bronski came into the room. A very unusual occurrence. I have a strict timetable. No one interrupts my day. When I work, I work. When I pause, I pause. Evenings may have some free periods. But these too I prefer booked in advance. Oddly enough, revolutionaries do not like surprises. Bronski is not, as we say along the Volga, "the full ruble." He looked around, staring at everything as if it were all new to him, indeed new to anybody. As if he didn't expect to find us there, or being there, doing what we were doing, which was what we were always doing at that moment. Me checking my notebooks, Nadya starting on the washing-up.

Bronski was so excited he spoke in his native Polish. His emotion communicated itself like an electric shock. I understood him immediately without translating.

"What are you doing here?" he cried. "Haven't you heard the news? There's been a revolution in Russia."

Both Nadya and Bronski began translating what he'd said. "There's been a . . ."

"I heard, I heard. I'd know the words in Martian."

Yet I could not believe that I had heard what I had heard for a moment. Then the words were like a sorcerer's spell. I felt my veins turn to little pipes pumping molten steel. If it had been dark, they would have glowed white-hot. I felt I could walk through this wall, and the next. and the next. Across this frontier and the next and the next. Into Petersburg within minutes. Steady! There was no point in believing it because I wanted to believe it. Revolution is a science. Now then, what exactly had Bronski heard? This turned out to be little. His mind was so churned up. He had so wanted to cry "Revolution," he could hardly order his information.

He had seen special editions of the Zurich newspapers, rushed out on the streets, with reports from Petersburg. All the Tsar's Cabinet had been arrested—he was sure of that. Twelve members of the Duma had assumed power "on behalf of the people."

But what about the Tsar? I asked. He didn't remember. He didn't think there was anything about the Tsar. I stepped on a step that wasn't there. Unless the Tsar went, nothing would have changed except a few ornaments on the façade. But this felt like the first warning shock. Perhaps they weren't going to start without me after all. So long as they started . . .

The question—who/whom? Who must rule: Duma or Soviet?

Was it "1905" all over again? Would "Dual Power" be a slogan that could move control from the parliamentarians to the workers? Would a Provisional government dare to carry on this filthy war? I must know more before I could reach out and activate the party inside Russia.

We left Bronski rushing on, also with froth like sherbet on his lips. I never buy newspapers—they are far too expensive for our budget. I read them instead at the libraries and reading rooms this obliging republic supplies. But this morning's editions—I'd already read them—carried no such news. They must have been replaced with the new front pages. The latest headlines were in the display boxes that the publishers provided, under awnings, down by the Lake of Zurich at the Bellevue Platz. Or there must be a late news flash in the window of the *Neue Zürcher Zeitung*.

Nadya and I left the Old Town, hurried off down the cobbled hill together, taking short cuts through back streets. I have studied the map of Zurich well. I have walked almost every patch of pavement, estimated the width of every alley, the height of commanding buildings at important corners or overlooking useful squares. Even in Zurich, you never knew when the time might come for a street battle, an insurrection, a counterattack against the workers' demonstration. Though admittedly, in toytown Switzerland, it was more likely the bankers would bury the insurgents under an avalanche of banknotes.

There were quite a lot of people about in the rain, all the Swiss with umbrellas. They must get them issued from the Town Hall as they get rifles from the Armory. It's part of their uniform. There are exiles here, too, many Russians, but also French and German. An unsavory lot, mainly draft-dodgers saving their skins, confidence tricksters and criminals on the run, abandoned mistresses, stranded gigolos, entertainers and social secretaries and bagmen off-loaded by the rich as they fled home on the declaration of war. Exiles don't have umbrellas. Their clothes, like mine, have developed a glaze of old age, a patina from long use, which deflects the falling rods of rain. Anyway, it's hard to ruin clothes that were ruined when you got them.

So far the dispatches are all from German agencies. These *could* be lies. But what would be the purpose? Plenty of detail. Soldiers and police refusing orders. Ministers imprisoned. Crowds on the streets. It *must* be the Revolution. The first stage, anyway, the bourgeois overture to the Great Overturn. The Bolshevik Party has to be there. Uncompromising, intransigent, extreme, ahead of everybody and anybody, disciplined, drilled, aggressive, armed.

The spearhead of the proletariat, ready to take any risk, whatever it is that the others refuse. Which means I must be there.

MARCH 16   ZURICH   1917

This morning I wrote to Inessa, along the Lake at Clarens. "If the Germans are not lying . . ." I am beside myself with frustration at not being able to leave at once for Scandinavia and Petersburg. I will never forgive myself for not risking a trip after Bloody Sunday in 1905.

Also wrote to Alexandra K. in Oslo emphasizing that the Revolution cannot possibly be confined to Russia—Germany certainly, France possibly, next on the list. "Of course, we shall continue to be *against* defense of the fatherland, against imperialist slaughter. The defeat of Russia will be a lesser evil. *All our slogans remain the same.*"

Telegram to Gregory in Berne summoning him here immediately.

MARCH 17   ZURICH   1917

All through last night dispatches have flooded in with the newspapers. Our own messages, coded, garbled, written in circumlocutions, despite the cable costs, like a nursery word-game, arrive from our comrades in Sweden, Finland, even across Germany from Russia itself. It is clear: *our Revolution has begun!* I have not slept for twenty-four hours. But I want to savor *yesterday.* A small, sweet pleasure, a forgivable reward, like a nut chocolate bar after climbing the Zurichbergs. Everybody knows that the first time you meet someone who becomes part of your life, you see everything about them with a ghastly clarity, almost a kind of clairvoyance. Within weeks, days even, this has been lost and cannot be recaptured. You have forgotten what they really look like. The sharp, vivid, cruel snapshot becomes an altogether softer, vaguer, more sentimental, self-deceiving, formal portrait. That is the purpose of this diary. If I do not record instants now, with as near as possible total accuracy, a transfer direct from brain to paper, they will begin to rearrange themselves. They will harden into that kind of comforting fiction we call memory. Soon they will be myth.

Original impressions are always right. If I was wrong about Martov, or Plekhanov, it was because, *for other reasons*, I suppressed my first intuitions. Quite often, my assessment develops through various stages, favorable and unfavorable, friendly and hostile. Nearly always it returns through that same door from which it went. Was I wrong about Trotsky? No. He will be, I know, a Bolshevik. I think I am right about Malinovsky. Despite all the slanderers, he continues to agitate against the war even in his German POW camp. Only yesterday morning, I was getting up, doing my exercises, eating my breakfast, folding my bedding, dressing and leaving for the library, working there until lunchtime. It seemed I might do this forever, until retired by the Party with a long-service medal and a clock. But now that we must, we will, leave for revolutionary Petersburg within days, capitalist Zurich is already beginning to fade.

Yesterday, I had slept the night, though fitfully, dreaming of wolves. More and more, I have felt caged by this cozy little menagerie of money changers. Marx complained that, slice it where you will, England was bourgeois through and through. Like the poor whites in America's South, its workers would never rise against their oppressors so long as they kept a lower class beneath them. The Irish are England's blacks.

Marx should have tried being an émigré in Switzerland. They regard all Europe as beneath them. Being shopkeepers, they take care not to show their scorn. They are confident they will never be overthrown. So much so that their laws not only require every able-bodied man, that is every proletarian, to be trained in arms but also to keep his guns at home with him!

While most of the world are killing each other, the Swiss sit on the sidelines taking a percentage, making a profit, from every ounce of war *matériel*. We should not hesitate to exploit the exploiters as much as their fellow exploiters exploit them! Not even the Swiss make as much from the belligerents as double-dyed, triple-agent Parvus, Marxist-millionaire, agent for Prussian intelligence, lord of the international smugglers.

When he came here last year, offering me a million gold rubles if I could cause enough chaos in Russia to take the Tsar out of the war, I sent him off (to use a soldier's phrase Malinovsky has taught me) with a red-hot needle up his prick. Now there's somebody I ought to have seen through at first sight like a windowpane, if my theory is right. Today the Red Falstaff looks more like a bag of washing. Still, no one knows better how to walk the backs of the imperialist crocodiles. If the worse comes to the worst, I know

enough to dish him ten times over, and I could make him buy us
our way round the world to Peter.

Is it possible I have functioned these three Swiss years like an
automaton, one of those "robots" (good Slav word) Parvus used
to argue electricity will allow socialism to use to free humanity
from alienating, repetitive labor? Throughout that time, now a
long day ago, my exercises were what kept my will from cracking.
Who would guess that I made the pumping of the blood a metaphor for the struggle? That inside the mechanical routine, I pretend I'm striking, dicing, grinding down our enemies? No one, I
hope. But this adolescent fantasy has kept me fit and strong as few
other exiles are, especially at age forty-seven. Nonsmoking, non-
drinking; reading, writing, thinking; walking, climbing, shadowboxing—bang! wallop! smash!—I'm training to be a champion of
Revolution.

And yet how dull, depressing, how lacking in salt it all has
been until now. Something inside has saved me. I never noticed
the room, the food, the march up and down the steep, cobbled
Spiegelgasse, the clothes I put on—the baggy trousers like the
back half of the elephant in the pantomime, the bowler hat, the
leatherette shopping bag, the overlong coachman's coat, the concertina boots. What a joke I must have looked—the bookworm
Bolshevik, the pen-pushing pyromaniac, the agitator of the archives hoping to overthrow the world's most powerful autocrat,
ruler of one sixth of the earth's surface. The burghers of the city
could have set their watches by me, if any burgher ever had a
watch that was so subversive as to lose or gain.

And yet I *knew*. I knew at midday this was the moment, the
message I had been waiting for. After all, timing has been my
métier. I have made a profession out of analyzing the symptoms
and portents of social change.

Marx, the paterfamilias, clowning with his soon-to-die children
on his back, clinging to his boil-ridden neck, in squalor and poverty,
always used the metaphor of childbirth. Labor is a pun (if no joke)
in every language I know. Men labor only in the first degree, work
for their living, sell their ability to create wealth (for others). Women,
not only in capitalist society, in every known society, labor twice.
They produce not only the wealth of nations, but more future
producers of the future wealth of nations. And this extra task of
theirs is more dangerous than digging coal underground, going
to sea, certainly than serving in a peacetime army or police force.
Women are the slaves of proles, the exploited's exploited, the workingman's colony, the pauper's servant, the whore who dare not ask

to be paid. This is not a model—a torn, bleeding body giving life
to a weak infant—that appeals to me. Any more, I suppose, than
it did, in any deep sense, to Engels. He wasn't much interested in
wives and children, the bourgeois holy family. I recall Marx's son-
in-law, Paul Lafargue, telling me in Paris in '95, just after Engels's
death (I could have met him) that the Old Gent lived throughout
the secret, rackety life of a radical bohemian and bachelor. By day,
Manchester businessman, riding to hounds with the local hunt,
secretary of the Club. By night, and at weekends, international
socialist, carousing at home with his two mistresses, Lizzie and Effie
Burns, sisters even, and Fenian terrorists. Engels's metaphors were
taken from the army, from the battlefield, from the insurrection
and punitive expedition, from the strategy and tactics of warfare.
They called him "the General" because of his (I have to say) not
very extensive or particularly successful diversions into actual fighting, as in the German rising of 1847. His later writings, ranging
around from the Peasant Wars in Germany to the American Civil
War, the Franco-Prussian War and the defense of the Paris Commune, are well worth reading. But I prefer Clausewitz. Also Marx
himself. Marx's rules for escalating a rebellion into a revolution
can hardly be bettered. I have them in front of me now.

Marx's old age was made comfortable (he even sent his surviving three girls to schools for gentlefolk) by Engels. Engels's old
age was made comfortable by Engels. They were both revolutionary philosophers, but still philosophers. The noun is more important than the adjective. I am a philosophical revolutionary. The
world will change the world. *The revolutionary's task is to be as revolutionary as life itself!* Rosa was right.

My picture of the forces of history at work is different from
that of Marx or Engels. Not obstetric, not militaristic, but meteorological. Inside my head, I have been listening for a sound. It
is a sudden fragile-boned crack—no, that's not the word. More
like a scream. We used to hear it some early mornings on the Volga
as the sun rose. We would rush down to the river, yes, about now,
the middle of March, always somehow a time of portent. Nothing
seemed changed. The trees, plastered with snow, unshaken as the
wigs of the Ancien Régime on the eve of July 14. The ice still as
thick as paving stones. Yet we had all heard that screech, like trains
skidding with locked brakes. And we knew as I knew at midday.
We knew that within the week the whole landscape would shiver,
serrate, fall apart, turn to strips, chips, dust, melted slush. A new
countryside would be unveiled from under the old.

That is what happened when Bronski spoke those words in

Polish. Though I pretended to doubt it. Though I refused to celebrate without evidence. Though I counseled calm and patience. Inside my head, I had heard the noise in the dawn.

MARCH 18   ZURICH   1917

Nothing now matters but getting my instructions and myself to Russia. I sought out Bronski again. Pigeonholed in my memory, confirmed from the file which Nadya keeps for me of all "useful" people, was a fact about Bronski which could be of help now. What was it? Ah, yes, as I saw him with his soft, crumpled face like a new dishrag, still passing on the latest news, still getting it wrong, I remembered. He had boasted in a rather childish way about a couple of friends of his who were smugglers, moving across the border (he claimed) and back again like ghosts. Perhaps I could replace one of them and glide back to Petersburg? When I drew him aside and offered him this chance to do something active for the Party, he went gray. He would be no use. Anyway, it was not a practical proposition—his smuggler only did Berlin and back. And Berlin was the last place I wanted to be dumped. Though, I don't know . . .

When Gregory turned up, he had a better objection. However I return, it must not be in secret. Too excited to go back to the hole at Spiegelgasse, I spent another night awake walking the streets this time with Zinoviev. Pauses at the *Neue Zürcher Zeitung*, much to their irritation, every few hours for more news.

Despite Gregory's advice—I saw it instantly as sensible and incontrovertible—I cannot help canvassing any scheme to get me out of this accursed Switzerland. Perhaps it is because of lack of sleep, but I consider stratagems that are scarcely more than daydreams. What about an airplane? I find myself already feeling the shaken body of the plane like a dog throwing off droplets. The roar of wind past my cheeks. The whole wound-up, canvas-strained, flying toboggan pushing against the chocks which hold it in restraint. Then *whoooom*, I am off, an arrow in the blue. I have seen an occasional machine from the Swiss Army Air Corps—I'm told the total of planes is only four—buzzing about below me when I have climbed one of the Zurichbergs. I have never been in an airplane. But such is my desire to fly from here that I feel it as though I experienced it every day.

Nothing must be neglected. I have written to Kaprinsky in Geneva suggesting he sound out through Allied diplomats the possibility of Russian exiles traveling incognito through France into England, across the Channel to Holland, then on to Sweden and Russia. To do this, I could travel as him, photographed wearing a wig, possibly also clean-shaven. He will have to go into hiding until I arrive. I will be arrested in England if I go back there under my own name. After all, I am a "defeatist," plotting to overthrow all warring governments. Particularly reprehensible, from their point of view, my main enemy is the Russian government, their ally.

From the objective viewpoint, the country most likely to allow me passage is Germany. I am a greater enemy of the Russian government, any Russian government which supports the war, than Ludendorff. If they would give me . . . No, no, it must not be me alone. Give me and other *bona fide* Russian socialists *and* democrats returning to their newly free country. Give us safe conduct to Sweden. Then I shall be quicker than any other party leader back from abroad. Why wouldn't they provide . . . what, a railway coach? After all, as an uncompromising defeatist I am just what Germany needs.

Ah, I have it! I have been writing these thought to Inessa. My mind always works well when touching hers. Probably, I so want to impress her, to justify her absolute faith in me, the gray matter fairly boils. So this is it. What we need is some Russian social patriot, or some moderate, "decent" Menshevik, to front the scheme. Are there any pawns in Geneva suitable to the purpose? What about, this would be rich, what about Martov? So I have instructed Inessa, Radek, anybody to start spreading the rumor that Martov has thought up the idea of a German train. Then begin congratulating him on his inventiveness and clear sight. So much more in the real world that that revolution-obsessed Lenin.

MARCH 19   ZURICH   1917

Continue to explore a variety of ways of reaching home. Some are bizarre and improbable—though you never know. But the point is they help to put everyone off the track of the German train. I take no one here into my confidence. If all Zurich and Geneva and Berne believe I am serious, though mad, all the better. Wrote to Inessa outlining the worst outcome: "What if *no passage what-*

soever is allowed either by England *or* by Germany! And this is possible!" As usual, by being pessimistic released my native optimism.

My next proposition: a *Swedish* passport. Surely not too difficult for Stockholm comrades to arrange and smuggle across. As a neutral, I could travel to Sweden through any territory.

A bit fanciful? N. points out that I do not know a single word of Swedish. I counter by betting I can learn a vocabulary of 600 words in a night. N. protests that it would still be easy for me to give myself away. She begins to laugh and laugh so much she cannot tell me what is so funny. (One of ten infallible signs of lack of sense of humor.)

"You'll fall asleep," she sputters at last. "You'll see Mensheviks in your dreams. You will start swearing and shouting out 'Scoundrels, scoundrels!' and give the whole game away."

She keeps describing "Lenin's plans" and her own comment all round the cafés, laughing just as much the tenth time as the first. (Another infallible, etc.) Marvelous security! Thanks be to providence, it *is* only a cover story. I decided to test how far the café-gossips could be gulled into thinking I had taken leave of my senses. So I suggest all objections could be met if I travel as a Swedish *deaf-mute*. Later today I overhear some ass whispering to another under the usual oath of secrecy—"Lenin has a brilliant plan. He and Zinoviev are traveling under false passports as *two Swedish deaf-mutes*." Pretend not to have heard, leave café. But outside, almost burst a blood vessel. Cream of the joke, Gregory has never been silent, except when I am talking to him, for more than two minutes in his entire life!

MARCH 20   ZURICH   1917

Wrote to Party Sec. in Geneva a noble letter for all to see: "Martov's plan is excellent." However, in my view we Bolsheviks "cannot take part, either directly or indirectly. Our participation would spoil it all for the others." I end up: "But the plan, in itself, is very *good* and is *very* right." (Fools and women in love adore underlinings. For them, all important things in life are written in *italic*.)

Just in case whoever is reading our mail is keeping a dossier on our travel schemes (and naturally I never put anything on paper that it would be damaging to find repeated in public) I telegraphed to Ganetsky in Stockholm: "Please check whether British government would permit some distinguished neutral say Secretary Swiss Social Democratic Party Fritz Platten chaperone passage via England Russian group returning émigrés in locked railway coach."

How do you seal a coach? We must afford absolute proof we have not been contaminated en route. Platten to be in charge, take all responsibility. Coach to have "extra-territorial" rights. I am not sure, nor are they, what I mean by this. But it sounds proud and independent. "Tools of the Kaiser" would not have "extra-territorial" rights. No control of passports or persons either entering or leaving Germany. Extra thought—might as well try it—"no names at all." Just numbers written on pieces of paper like entries in the bran tub at fund-raising parties. Agreed, agreed! Someone must be pulling Romberg's strings. Might as well try one more. "Excellency, we insist on paying our own fares, no German gold." Afterthought—"Third-class only, of course." He tells us that Martov and the Mensheviks have definitely withdrawn from the plan, refusing to move until they get permission from Petersburg. Damn! The more we were, the more *mixed* we were, preferably with a few rich, apolitical exiles thrown in as well, the less the journey could possibly be called treason. "Traffic with the enemy!" Ha! Never mind, this is the only way, the direct route. Trotsky had already been in New York for ten weeks when the Revolution broke. (What was he doing there? Someone says he was playing small roles in "motion-pictures." I can imagine that.) Now we hear he has been lifted off the neutral freighter that was taking him to Russia by the British. They have stuck him in a Canadian concentration camp. So we'll beat *him* home by weeks.

MARCH 23   ZURICH   1917

Kamenev and Stalin have reached Peter from Siberia ahead of me. K. is "Comrade Sweet" and a collaborationist by instinct. He'll always want to split responsibility by working with the Mensheviks, the SRs. Koba is more my man, "Comrade Bitter," really a man of steel. Kollontai writes that his exile was no soft option, "as with some." No, Koba had been for four years in the Turukhansk region, fifteen miles inside the Arctic Circle. There native villages no longer existed. Nothing but a prison commune. Winter, from October until March, they lived in almost total darkness. The temperature fell to 56 degrees below zero (Celsius). Fires had to burn continually, otherwise human life would have ceased. During snowstorms, no one dare go out for days. In the brief summer the prisoners, allowed only fifteen rubles a month by the government, could earn a little extra cutting firewood for the passing steamer. The only crops, potatoes and moor berries. No wonder so many comrades killed themselves. Dubrovinsky leaped into the icy river. Within minutes he was a crisp, dead shell, like a prawn fried in batter. Leo Gallin locked himself in his cabin, set it on fire. As they tried to break in, he was heard to cry out that it was the first time he had been warm since 1912.

Alexandra says dreadful conditions have only strengthened Koba. He became an expert hunter and fisherman, trapper and logger. He lived alone and relied on no one. He was, and is, his old, rude, rough, self, "prickly as a fir tree." He rarely attended meetings with the others. Politicals and common criminals were mixed there. The authorities hoped that the crooks would terrorize and dominate the revolutionaries. When Koba appeared, he rarely spoke. When he did, what he said was hardly designed to make him popular. Our chief Bolshevik there kept complaining about Koba to the Center. When a thief was found robbing a peasant and brought before the commune court, Koba defended him. "Capitalism makes thieves," he had argued. "We should recruit him to fight it with its own weapons."

His only friend, some had complained, was the resident policeman. They wanted to try Koba for this before a Party court, but he brushed them aside with his hunting rifle. "I 'consort' with him," he's supposed to have said, "because he's a man. Not like the rest of you milksops. And he knows what you should know. That if he comes up against me on the barricades I'll kill him as I'd crack a nit." My marvelous Georgian is unique. I see he has also dented Sandra's heart! If we could reproduce a hundred of him, I could capture Peter with them alone.

MARCH 25   ZURICH   1917

Shall I die with the name "Malinovsky" on my lips? He haunts me like the ghost of Banquo (Shakespeare). Only five days ago I wrote to *Pravda* enclosing yet another article defending him and our record in exposing police spies in our midst. Crossing this in the slow post via Scandinavia comes a copy of *Russian Word (Russkoe Slovo)* in which the unspeakable Burtsev lays out a what must be admitted looks like a very damning case against M. He has been able to obtain testimony from the tsarist archives that could not be available to our Swiss tribunal. And, of course, our verdict would have been different if we had had these allegations before us. Through really impressive detective work, he has tracked down P. K. Popov, former chief of Peter Okhrana. Popov admits that he was the official deputed to tell Malinovsky that the Okhrana had retired him, pass over 6,000 rubles and advise a quick exit. Burtsev has also found S.E. Vissarionov, former deputy head of the national police department. Vissarionov confirms that M. had been a paid police informer until the arrival of a new minister in the Home Office. This alone would not be necessarily enough, for me anyway. Policemen testifying against revolutionaries! But Burtsev promises hard documentary proof—handwritten reports of our CenCom meetings, signatures for cash advances. I'm afraid I shall have to drop Malinovsky!

One fortunate turn of events. *Pravda* had already decided to "spike" my article in his defense (even though for not very good reasons). So it did not appear anyway. It would have been disastrous in the issue of the day before the revelations in *Russkoe Slovo*.

I'm afraid Malinovsky will now go down in history as "the Bolshevik Azef." He should count himself lucky he is beyond my reach. As if I did not have enough wormy frustrations here, eating at my will, as I pace my room knowing that we are getting it *all wrong* in Peter.

APRIL 5   BERNE   1917

The train leaves Zurich in two hours! Nadya sets about liquidating our household effects—a few fires will burn brighter these crisp evenings. I can't imagine many people regarding what we are leaving, our two beds, two chairs and a table, as furniture. Though perhaps the sewing machine will be worth a few francs. She also settles up with the Kammerers. Meanwhile, I fulfill what I have always regarded in our many moves as the basic debt of honor, breached only when your life is at stake. That is, the return of the library books.

Of course, as half of me knew, this was a false alarm. The train will not leave for days. Still, once my steam is up I cannot bear to step down from the driver's cab. So we came anyway here to Berne where comrades and not such comrades will be gathering ready for the actual departure of April 9. I shall have time to call in at the police station to engineer the return of the hundred francs I deposited as a surety against my "good behavior."

The fourteen months with the Kammerers have, I must now admit, been something of an endurance test. Looking at 14 Spiegelgasse, no one could believe so many separate entities were plugged in there without it bursting like a cardboard box. The old shoemaker and his wife and three children spread themselves across two rooms. Then there was the wife of a German soldier and her two children in one room, two Austrian actors in another, an Italian alone in another, and us in the fourth. Outside, were we foolish enough to open the window, there was stench from the sausage factory.

Yet I warmed to this cross-national, polyglot hive, allies, neutrals and enemies all rolled together. Nadya kept on saying that, for the same money, we could rent a much better place. I agreed, and was tempted. Until I once heard Frau Kammerer exclaim to the various wives gathered around the kitchen range—"The soldiers should turn their guns on their own governments." After that, I could really not bear to move.

Another bonus: the skills of old Adolph K. He presented me last year on my forty-sixth birthday with a pair of climbing boots. Handmade, needless to say, crafted and tailored through several fittings to fit better than gloves, these hobnail marvels walk on their own, eating up the miles. As we left this afternoon, he shook my hand, pulled me close and whispered in my ear: "I hope you won't have to work so hard in Russia, Herr Ulyanov."

APRIL 8   BERNE   1917

Everything is ready! Well, so we all tell each other only to find at that exact moment we have forgotten something so obvious that its omission in any other circumstances would be accepted even by your mother as unmistakable proof of feeblemindedness. The Russian Revolution has begun. We are going back home to join it. Excuse enough to throw any comrade into disarray.

The calmest of us is Nadya. I have been sending off cables in all directions, internal and external, many of them contradicting each other as the plan keeps changing. First this date and time, then that. This number of travelers, then that. Martov and the Mensheviks refuse to move without official approval from Peter. According to foreign press reports, the Russian Foreign Office has assured its British and French allies that any of its nationals traveling through enemy territory with enemy aid will be arrested on arrival and tried for high treason. This means any SRs now also drop out. I will have to make do for cover on half a dozen Jewish Bundists.

Every now and then what seems for that second a genuine intuition, possibly a premonition, strikes through my skull. Could this be a trap? Is it not all so improbable that, after the trap is sprung, I will be kicking myself forever for believing it? To distract my mind from unworthy fantasies this morning, I started sorting through a box of old newspaper cuttings Nadya has included among our luggage. (What am I saying? That *is* our luggage. Along with another box of Party documents, a basket of books, and—smallest of all—a basket of clothes.)

The first cutting I unfold is from a German daily of August '16—three German officers and thirty-two other ranks, arrested on the Western Front, have been brought back to Berlin, courtmartialed, found guilty, and executed by firing squad. Their crime? Circulating my Kienthal Manifesto which called on workers in uniform to cease killing comrades from other countries and turn their guns on enemies at home. "Live bombs" is Radek's name for international revolutionaries. Like bombs, we can explode on both sides of the frontier. In Germany as well as in Russia.

So, fighting fire with fire, I determine to deposit a farewell letter to the Swiss workers which will make clear that I am agitating for the overthrow of *all* ruling classes. The best moment may be the lunch given for us by our Swiss comrades at the Hotel Zahringer Hof in Zurich at midday tomorrow. It will make an interesting *ave atque vale* before the train leaves at (being Switzerland) exactly 3:10 P.M.

Now my mind has something to grind on, a calm descends. I accompany Nadya on her final inspection of our fellow travelers as if I were a tourist courier. It is really rather impressive, I have to admit, the speedy efficiency of these barnacled exiles. "True Bolshevik discipline!" Nadya keeps on saying to everybody as if minor royalty awarding a medal.

Last look over our baskets and boxes. I *have* forgotten something. Our portable Swedish paraffin stove. We might have had no tea!

APRIL 9   ON THE SWISS TRAIN   1917

I read out my good-bye letter to the Swiss labor movement over luncheon as planned (more of that later) and assumed this would probably be the anticlimactic day. Instead it was only the beginning of an operatic, emotional display, part farce, part demo, which continued to build almost until we had steamed out of sight.

First, Oscar Blum was among the few guests from the local SDP branch. Gossip, loudmouth, journalist, *entrepreneur,* and in my view almost-certain police spy, "Dr." Blum is in no doubt of my hostility. But then I was not the host. After our host, little Fritz Platten, had handed over to me traveling expenses of 4,000 Swiss francs, a present from the Swiss Union of Co-op Societies, and revealed that a further gift of ten days' supply of food was waiting at the station, he announced that Blum had asked permission to travel with us. Most of our group hardly seemed to care one way or the other. A minority were strongly in favor. I suggested a ballot.

I could hardly influence the electors by calling Blum an enemy agent—Swiss laws are hot on defamation of character. So I cast my own opposing vote on my feet, waving a hand, glaring around, before anyone else. It was the best I could do to get a message across. And I only just won—eleven for, fourteen against.

Around 2:30 P.M., the thirty-two of us wandered in a straggling crocodile down to the station. You might have thought we were off on a picnic in the woods—we were carrying cushions and quilts, also the awkward, lumpy baskets and bundles typical of a spring outing. Instead we were embarking on a wartime train journey of two and a half thousand miles north from the heart of Europe, almost touching the Arctic Circle, to Peter the Great's capital on the Gulf of Finland.

I was bent over, at the rear of the procession, hanging on to my English "trilby," in the knee-high wind from the lake. Glad of my old ankle-length raglan which neutralizes all weather; raised above the watery grid of the cobbles by Adolph's many-clawed mountain boots. This poor gentlefolk's street-armor seemed less out-of-place when I trailed the rest round the corner onto the station forecourt. I raised my steel-tipped umbrella in front of me, bayonet-fashion. Around a hundred fellow Russian exiles were rushing about with banners and placards on sticks. They were not there to wish us a pleasant journey.

"Traitors! Saboteurs! Enemies of Russia! Friends of the Kaiser! Spies!" Breath sour with hatred, spit flying, eyes rolling like marbles. Our path was walled with distorted faces. Gregory wrapped his great, floppy head in his cape, abandoned his luggage to his wife, Zina, and charged for the nearest carriage. Inessa arched her neck, her smile seeking for a spotlight floating in the air above the engine, began singing the "Internationale." Nadya looked closely at every protester, nodding and speaking each name, reducing them from a mob to a collection of individuals, all of whom she knew in detail from our files. "Tsk! Tsk!" she said. "No, no! That's silly! You don't mean that!" I marched on, carrying the flag, ignoring these irrelevances, sliding past them as if they were fish in an aquarium. Despite the noise, the threats, the clenched fists and thrusting placards, no one I could see was touched. We climbed aboard and closed the compartment doors. Only then did we glimpse the center-piece of the demo—Fritz Platten fighting an apoplectic Swiss socialist twice his size and driving him backward into the crowd.

While we sat inside, our faces waxed with a shine of benign forgiveness, Radek danced about, popping his head out of windows like some puppet demon. He too had his dossier on almost everybody. But he used his inside knowledge to infuriate not soothe.

"Spies, are we? When did you collect your last two hundred francs from the Japanese Embassy?" Or . . . "Who's a traitor? Who came here to avoid service in the Russian Army paid for by his father's profits on leftfooted pairs of Army boots?" (Dangerous stuff from an Austrian subject wanted for desertion.)

I pulled him in, and leaned out. 3:07 A.M. I would distract (and attract) the mob's attention during our last minutes in Switzerland. Some beat on the sides of the coach. A few began the "Internationale" again. One shook my hand: "May you return safely here, old 'un," he babbled foolishly. "They'll hang you," pleaded another. "It's a mistake, think again." "Hanging's too good for any of you," said another. And yet one more whispered: "Take care, Ilyich, you're all we have!"

The whistle blew. "Dignity, calm, quiet," I hissed over my shoulder. Radek's face was creased with chuckles. "Oscar Blum's on board!"

The train was moving. It was public transport. Anybody who cared to could take a seat to the Rhine border town of Schaffhausen. I had no right to grab Blum by the neck, boot his behind, and project him onto a receding platform. But I did.

I sat back, warmed by a glow of self-approval. Nothing so satisfying as a good deed well done. My right big toe throbbed happily.

I reread my letter to those Swiss workers who would most likely never learn of its existence. I was aiming at a much more scattered, esoteric group who, for their own reasons, felt they needed to keep tracks on the coming Revolution. I could picture these experts, all over Europe (all over the world?), searching my words for clues, deciphering the code, reading into it their own prejudices, their own wishes.

This is not *folie de grandeur*. I have spent too long conscious of my own week-by-week insignificance. A small fish in a pool that is little more than a damp patch; minority leader of a minority party which proclaims itself the Majority; a comic figure, poor, shabby, underfed, little known, a wandering anti-Pope of the slums, forever expelling, exorcising, beatifying a few among his handful. But now I am become a key figure known to Tsar and Kaiser, Prime Minister and President. Without me, the door of the future may not open. In peacetime I preached, like so many other socialist prophets, that capitalism inevitably meant mass poverty. The ruling class smiled, bought off one or two of the more dangerous worker-leaders with a few large crumbs. But now I am preaching, almost alone, that capitalism inevitably means mass murder, and all around the war is proving my case. This is a crusade that transcends national barriers. "Bread for the People" may be a powerful slogan. It does not compare with "Peace." I trust the foreign office consultants, intelligence chiefs, political editors, party committees, ideologues of right and left, followers, rivals, opponents, enemies, will notice various points planted to catch the eye though not *too* prominently.

In Peter, the Provisional government, all capitalists and liberals, except for one shop-window "socialist" (Kerensky), are parading themselves as patriotic radicals faithful to the national revolution, while the CenExCom of the Soviet, all Meks and SRs plus a show-window "bolshevist" (Goldenberg), are masquerading as responsible Marxists faithful to revolutionary nationalism. Let them make what they can of my gratitude for the "great honor" history has bestowed upon us of overthrowing a tyranny that has long ruled over one sixth of the earth's surface, one twelfth of its peoples. My repudiation of the idea that the Russian masses are "the chosen proletariat among the workers of the world." Our peasants, the majority, are backward. Our workers, still unorganized. "The reason for the Revolution is simple—*the imperialist war*." It is a coincidence of historical circumstances. We are in the vanguard only for a definite, *probably very short*, period. For the imperialist war is everywhere about to become a civil war. "Long live the proletarian revolution which we can see it starting in Europe." (A jolt for the Allies, Britain and France.) Special mention must be made of the German workers—"the most trustworthy and reliable ally of both the Russian, and indeed the world, proletarian revolution." (Make them sit up in the Wilhelmstrasse.)

My task, when I reach Peter, will be to make ours the prologue, the first tottering step toward a socialist planet.

APRIL 10   ON THE GERMAN TRAIN   1917

Last night, this diary fell from my hand, my pen jabbed in my knee, sleep covered me like mist round the Jungfrau, while I was still writing. To bring the journey up to date.

After we had left Zurich, chuffing through the hills to the frontier, Fritz Platten appeared, a model of Swiss propriety. You could have taken him for a ticket-inspector—idiom of high praise in Zurich. You would not think he had been giving a bloody knee-cap to a giant challenger only shortly before. He dished out a numbered slip to each of us—total thirty-two. This was to be our only identification. We had to promise various things, like contestants in a folktale. *Never* to leave our "sealed carriage" after we had once entered it, and *never* to speak to anyone outside. It is assumed these are German rules. They are not. They are mine. I had to be able to swear we had not a second's contact with the enemy. "I'll never be able to do it. I'll be turned into a pillar of salt," protested Radek.

The first warning that our trip might not be all jokes came at Schaffhausen. Swiss customs officers asked us to transfer to platform four and line up beside our possessions. We were told to declare all food, most of which was then confiscated. "You Russians have forgotten there is a war on," sneered the officer in charge. "It is an offense to take anything eatable out of the country without a license." He then also seized the provisions the Co-ops had packed for us, mainly chocolates, condensed milk and tins of biscuits. "We could never afford to eat such things anyway," Zinoviev observed sourly, his sweet tooth obviously itching to bite the nutbars the

customs men were shuffling like playing cards. We were handed
back the bread rolls we had purloined from the Zahringer Hof.

On the German side, at Gottmadingen, the station had only
one platform. No one was on it except two German officers, shining
from every button, belt, toecap, and peak, military totems painted
on glass. They announced themselves, Captain von Planetz and
Lieutenant von Buhring.

Once more we were lined up by the side of the railway line.
Most of us had become highly sensitized to uniforms, associating
them with arrests, searches, questioning, if not actual pain from
beatings or wounds. The atmosphere grew blacker and bleaker
when we were herded into two groups, men and women, one at
each end of the waiting room. Despite my checks and double-
checks, precautions and assurances, was it to be a trap after all?

I put my back to the wall. My Bolshevik Men of Confidence
ringed me round. Radek fumbled away at reassembling a Colt
lady's revolver he'd imported from America and carried in his
tobacco pouch. Zinoviev had a nosebleed.

It was all right. They were simply counting us, making a rough
test of our general description by ensuring the sexes matched.
Then they collected from me twenty-eight full and four half third-
class single fares from Gottmadingen on the Alpine slopes to Sassnitz on the Baltic. It wasn't cheap, eating up most of the cash Fritz
had given me. But then that was why he had given me that amount.

When we came out of the waiting room, there stood a heavy-
breathing locomotive linked to a gray-green coach with eight compartments, three second class, five third. Our lodgings for the next
three nights.

"What do you say, Ilyich?" asked Radek. "The final solution
to the Bolshevik Question?"

I look round at my fellow passengers. Since I have forbidden
a list of names, protection against any reprisals in Russia, I am not
certain about everyone among the thirty-two numbered ticket
holders. Four are children. A pity only two turned out to be Bundists, i.e., non-Bolsheviks. Rosenblum and Aisenbud is it? A pity,
too, in a way, Sokolnikov, one of the ex-stars of the Menshevik
paper *Nashe Slove*, along with Martov, has recently crossed over to
our side. I may still have to count him as a Mek when testifying
to our mixed makeup. Otherwise, unfortunately for my cover story,
almost all the others are Bolos, mostly close colleagues and
friends—Gregory and Zina plus nine-year-old Stepan; Inessa and
Olga Ravich, the young woman who was arrested in Munich chang-

ing the stolen money from the Tiflis bank raid for me; Radek, chimpanzee of genius; George Safarov—he and Inessa used to be a brilliant smuggling duo, perhaps more, but now traveling with his wife, Valentina; Ussievich, and his wife Helen Kon, daughter of the distinguished Polish leader, Felix. That's enough . . . With some fairly obvious exceptions, a good lot "to go tiger hunting with." Who was it used to say that now? *Slava bogu!* Malinovsky— one gun bearer who was on the tiger's side!

There was some talk of casting lots for seats. But it began to rain and it was quicker for me, standing on the far side of Platten from the Germans, to allot places according to numbers. I accepted the second-class compartment at the front with Nadya, under some protest, until I realized that there was work I must do. So this was an office, not a sitting room. It seemed reasonable that the two other compartments with padded benches should be for wives and children plus husbands. The bachelors and the young happily spread out across the hard, bare wooden seats of third-class.

More vital, how were we to ensure efficient segregation? I waited until all the others were aboard. Then with our chaperone, Platten, our armed escorts, the captain and the lieutenant, I traversed the coach from front to back. There were four doors on the platform side, one at each end, two in the middle. I witnessed the locking of the forward three. On my instructions, Fritz pasted across each keyhole a strip of paper on which was written "sealed" in German. That was all that was to keep the rabid dogs of Bolshevism from breaking out and infecting Germany or the German firing squad from breaking in and executing the opponents of all militarism. A washroom at each end, so we did not need to share any facilities. Only the door next to the two officers was kept "unsealed." A chalk line across the floor signified the barrier between our two kinds of passenger.

After this was over, there was clicking of heels and saluting. I said quietly to Fritz: "There's a gob of crap on the captain's boot." His Russian was too polite to understand me. The captain showed less concern than if I had been clearing my throat. But lieutenant von Buhring started, flicked a glance at his superior's feet. *His* Russian was fluent and idiomatic. Good. It showed the Wilhelmstrasse was taking the operation seriously. I could arrange that the lieutenant heard what I wanted his masters to hear.

The engine hooted. A bell rang. The train began to sway slightly as it moved off downhill. I walked back down the corridor to my compartment at the front, taking pleasure in the way my thigh muscles kept me vertical. I went the length without ever needing a hand to stop me bumping the walls or the windows. Fritz came pounding after. "You realize the Germans haven't locked the other compartment doors, the ones that don't open onto the platform? Does it matter?"

"The train is *sealed*," I advised. "You did it yourself. That is all that concerns you."

The first leg of the journey had been quite short. Over and over, our third-class sang "The Marseillaise." The light was almost gone. The blinds were drawn against the flickering dark. We might have been a Party sing-song in a windowless Zurich beer cellar. But by the time we were shunted into a siding outside Singen, almost no one except me and the children were still awake.

I could not sleep. Nor could I find an appetite around midnight for the beer and sandwiches our escort handed across the chalk line. Stepan, and four-year-old Robert, son of a Jewish Bund woman, tucked away more food than seemed possible by anyone. Except Radek and Zinoviev who woke up to eat even more.

That was all Monday, April 9.

Tuesday began early, around 5 A.M. Platten passed on the news that it was to be a long, devious route, with a change of engine for each state railway, via Stuttgart, Karlsruhe and Mannheim, to Frankfurt, and our connection for Berlin.

I have already sent ahead of me to Russia a series of five pieces for *Pravda*, straplined "Letters from Afar." They contain my snap diagnosis, and prognosis, for the Revolution so far. Only the first has been published, and then in a garbled, attenuated form. The others must be on the office spike, though I had assumed that when Stalin and Kamenev took over the editorship my stuff would appear uncensored. Something odd is going on there. No doubt when I arrive, my propositions will be out of date. At least I had the right to expect some reaction from comrades supposedly such close supporters of mine. Yet nothing from anyone, except Sandra Kollontai—from her, passionate agreement.

There are only two real men in the socialist leadership. One is Sandra. The other, Rosa. Gender is, of course, a comparatively trivial distinction. By "men" I mean worthy representatives of humankind. I mean those in whom nature and nurture have combined to inspire the masses to break their chains, physical, symbolic, psychological, which have enslaved them throughout history.

Odd that it should so often have been comrades in the bodily guise of the female who have so clearly seen that my harshness and hardness, my aggression and "extremism," balance an almost equal overplus of their counterweights. Only they sense how often I am flushed with subterranean waves of concern and pity, flooded by indiscriminate torrents of a love for this earth and everything on it that is positively mawkish. I should have cracked and broken, ground myself to dust, without Inessa, Sandra, Rosa, Essen, Nadya of course, Marguerite Fofanova, all my sisters too, and, yes, Mother.

I must mount a new onslaught on the backsliders and compromisers. "Letters" are not enough. These will be "Theses." If one man can stop and divert the flow of history, I must do it. Luther, Cromwell, Bonaparte, something of all three. But I must prepare with some hard work, and for hard work I need *quiet*.

"*Quiet!*"

Somewhere approaching Stuttgart, the cork popped. Next door I had apportioned to Inessa and Olga Ravich, Valentina Safarova and her young, studious, engineer husband. Three serious women and a sedate male. But I had overlooked Radek, who ought to have been in third with the single men. I suppose they were not audience enough for him. Inessa, Olga and Valentina—as well as being quick and bright, they are also three very attractive women. That ought not to matter, but I know myself it does, unless suppressed by an act of will.

Olga's voice was the highest, her laugh the most penetrating. The others rarely spoke loud enough for me to know they were there above the bassoon gurgling of Karl Radek's monologues. I folded back the door, took her by the hand, and led her along the corridor to the compartment shared by the Zinovievs, Stepan, Robert and his mother, and Helen Kon. I put my finger to my lips and left her.

On the way back, Inessa, who has scarcely spoken to me, or anyone, since the lunch in Zurich, handed out a book as I passed. It was a collection of short pieces by Turgenev and her finger held it open at "The Story of Kolosov." I knew it well. Nadya and I had translated it together into German in Shushenskoye.

I sat down again with the Turgenev on my lap like a desk lid and tried to make notes. Karl's voice had sunk to a whisper. There were five minutes of near-silence. Then almost all the men were in the corridor at once, not just chatting and laughing but *smoking*! I'd forgotten about smoking. With all the windows locked against the chilly night air, the tobacco fumes seemed heavy along the floor, surging into my compartment like a gas attack.

Some of my enemies picture my role in the Bolshevik Party

as that of the self-appointed field marshal. In practice, I am more often condemned to take the job no soldier wants. What I believe is called "orderly corporal"—the pettifogger who makes all the piddling decisions no one can be bothered to fuss about.

"All right!" I shouted. "No smoking at any time anywhere!"

I could see in their eyes a faint glint of mutiny. There are some commands even a field marshal must hesitate to utter.

"Except," I said, "except in the washroom."

I went back to my notes. But only for about fifteen minutes. Karl put his head in. He'd been elected as spokesman.

"Ilyich. *Ilyich*," he wheedled. "It won't work. Gregory's been in there twice already. Valentina Ivanovna says it's embarrassing to queue outside when everybody knows she doesn't smoke!"

"All right. Smoking only in the washroom. Take turns according to the numbers on your pieces of paper. Try to combine all your functions on the same visit. When the last number is reached, *sleep!*"

Bolshevik discipline prevailed. I inspected the coach at 9:30 P.M. Everyone had obeyed orders, or anyway closed their eyes, even the children.

I sat down to work.

APRIL 11   ON THE GERMAN TRAIN   1917

Half-past midnight. Stuttgart station. The first sizable German city at which our train has stopped. Parts brilliantly lit. Sections in total darkness. Strange, unreal atmosphere as of a giant nursery. We look out on nobody. There is nobody to look in on us.

The Swiss customs officers had been right. We exiles did not know there was a war on. We were used to buildings, machinery, institutions operating on the demands of civilians, of anybody with money in hand. Stuttgart station was responsive only to military necessity. No troops were using it. Therefore no newspaper stall, no buffet, no porters, no noise, no steam. The state ruled all.

We had been told originally that we must always keep our blinds drawn. But even I, determined that there should be no disputes with our escort, could not stand this. It was like being in a submarine. Besides, the officers (a) could not know we were looking out, or (b) exert any control, when the train was moving. As they saw themselves, there was nothing to see. Empty countryside with only the rare boy or old man. Empty villages with only women. We were given permission to gaze on the scenery of total war.

Platten came to me through a coach in which our people were gradually stirring, roused by the silence. And hunger. Most had only the few bits and pieces of food left us by the Swiss officials. Lieutenant von Buhring had explained there was no surplus at any of the halts where we stopped to change engines. (Curiously inefficient system.) Fritz said the Germans were now hinting we might find some fodder here if I agreed to talk to a visitor, Wilhelm Hanson.

"Tell Hanson I'd rather we starved. If he comes over the chalk line, I'll kick a hole through him. We have extra-territorial rights and I mean to exert them."

"Just a few words, Ilyich. Why not? Charge a fee in sausage and cheese. What does everybody think?"

Zinoviev's childish greed was curiously endearing.

"Everybody but you knows," I said, "that we might have to pay for those few words with our lives. Hanson is a social traitor, a trade-union leader who sold out with the SDP. He voted for this war. A press picture, a news agency story, just showing me touching his hand would be taken to prove I am leading a troop of the Kaiser's agents. Back to bed. No one must look too fat when we reach the Finland Station in Peter. And Radek, quick! To the baggage van."

I had just seen Hanson slowly patrolling the platform, in a musing pose, but snatching a quick inventory of each compartment. There was nothing he could do to harm any Russians, so long as we ignored him. But Radek was a Polish-born Austrian citizen. The two had often clashed at prewar meetings of the German SDP. And Hanson might retain enough malice, or pique, to denounce him to the authorities.

It was also too good a chance to miss. I locked him in with a supply of newspapers, "fraternal gift" c/o Hanson to us all. And I somehow forgot to open up until we were well on our way again. He didn't notice, so deep was he into what he calls "my survival kit."

When dawn came, we watched more dead landscape sliding by. Karlsruhe. Mannheim. Next stop Frankfurt.

At one station with no name sign, presumably a busy junction where we guessed reinforcements were going west to the front, armaments going east to the stockpiles, we stopped unexpectedly.

For once the platforms were packed with soldiers and workers. As with most of those marched around by war, they barely glanced to right or left. Then one stopped by our coach, tripping the rest. More stopped. A crowd gathered to stare. But only at one of us. At Sokolnikov.

It became rather frightening. Gregory Yakovlevich is not easily shaken. In '05, after the autocracy defeated us in the towns, he led a band of guerrilla saboteurs in the forests. He was seventeen. But now he looked down, fidgeted with odds and ends on the table.

"What is it?" he whispered, as though they could hear.

"You're playing with some stale white-bread rolls from the Zahringer Hof Hotel," I replied. "They haven't seen anything like that in three years."

We had become more careful . . . Correction, all but one of us had become more careful when we drew into Frankfurt. This was the busiest time of the early evening. We would never have a chance to observe so many Germans at once.

"What a sad sight," said Robert's mother. "Poor things. Eyes so worn and tired. I've been watching for five minutes. Not a single smile."

There's a Jewish Bundist for you.

"Most cheering sight I've seen so far," I said. "What is making them weary and worn is the imperialist war. I take it as a sign that the hour for the German Revolution to follow ours may be at hand!"

That's about as near as we would have got if Platten hadn't taken it into his head to go off and visit some long-neglected German girlfriend. Well, that is his privilege, he's the neutral. And I can hardly complain at his thoughtfulness in stopping off at the buffet and buying us some beer, sausage and cheese. The mistake he made was in tipping a couple of German soldiers to carry the food and drink across to "the strangers on platform ten."

When they saw how strange we were, they asked where we came from. I had nearly made them believe we were Turks, allies they had heard about but never seen, when Radek burst out from the baggage. In fluent German, full of soldiers' slang, he told them we were Russian communist revolutionaries going home to hang the Tsar, shoot the profiteers, strip the generals naked, proclaim "peace, bread and land!" for all workers and peasants. We gathered half a regiment asking us questions, above all one question—when will the war end?

Before I knew what I was doing I was pointing to their guns—"When you use them against your enemies, not your friends." The first of the privates was just about to cross the chalk line, when (fortunately) the captain and lieutenant awoke to what was happening. In a fine display of aristocratic dominance, they prodded the rankers back onto the far side of the platform by the power of their beastly blue eyes. Within minutes, we were being shunted once more into a siding for the night. We had missed our connection for Berlin.

I found the contact even more encouraging for the prospects of a revolution in Germany. These were ordinary soldiers, typically loyal and patriotic. But the slogan "peace," even from red Russians, filled them with enthusiasm. I asked Gregory Z. what he thought of the incident.

"Wonderful, marvelous! I never heard Karl speak so well. And those soldiers' words! *Braune auge*, 'brown eye.' What a wonderful insult! What a marvelous way of saying 'arsehole'!"

"No, no, as propaganda?"

"Oh, no," he said, looking worried. "You couldn't say that to Russian soldiers. It's against the *Pravda* line."

APRIL 12   ON THE GERMAN TRAIN   1917

Fourth day on the German train. I'm beginning to feel it really is sealed. I no longer bother to watch. All my energy is directed toward thought. Some hot food has helped to speed round my circulation. We have a little Army galley on wheels tagged on behind and a little Army cook who seems inured to being all on his own, far from the firing line.

Incidentally, our two Junkers were not very pleased with us. They officially protested against our fraternization with their troops, also objected to the third-class men chorusing "The Marseillaise" over and over again. It is an insult to their fighting men, says the captain, though how they can hear us in these wastelands I can't imagine. I imagine the pair are really worried about how they will explain Radek's speech in their daily report to the War Ministry.

When no one was about I took the lieutenant aside and assured him, in Russian, that I was the only person authorized to represent the trainload. Senior Russian officer, so to speak. And I promised that in my account, for my own protection after all, I would not mention any such trivialities. We will have proceeded from Schaffhausen to Sassnitz without speaking to a single German—witness the rejection of Wilhelm Hanson. He looked very relieved and thanked me in beautiful Russian.

Berlin sooner than seemed possible. It looks as if we shall be out of Germany by this afternoon and on the ferry to Trelleborg for Malmö before nightfall.

Fourth night on the German train. My celebration was premature. We have spent all day here in some marshaling yards. Through his folding rubber-coated binoculars, more of his comic spy equipment, Radek reports on the behavior of our two officers. By the time I had ordered "lights out," they had been three times to telephone, four times to the telegraph office, six times to the bar.

APRIL 13   ON THE GERMAN TRAIN   1917

Yesterday we were restricted to the train and a view of a brick wall, as if we were prisoners, though with decent food—lamb cutlets, cabbage, beer, fresh milk for the children.

I know Berlin well. First visit must have been in '95, twenty-two years ago—I studied in the Staatsbibliothek, bathed in the Spree, wandered round the markets, cabarets and beer halls. In '05, on the way to the Fifth Congress in London, I gave a guided tour to Maxim Gorky. Berliners remain very much *sui generis,* that flat, metallic accent like chinking coins, those flat-fronted, bony faces masking quicksilver thoughts.

Of all the cities in my European travels Berlin has the most distinctive, unmistakable, penetrating . . . what? Damn politics! It depletes your vocabulary. I suppose I mean something like atmosphere, though more of a cross between aroma and aura, *essence* perhaps. I know you smell it and taste it every minute you are there, the whiff of a strong, spicy, fatty stew that must be eaten quickly before it goes off. Or is that an association with the dinner party with Rosa in '08 (I think) when Nadya and I were laid low with food poisoning?

At first, we saw only Potsdam station, tied up in barbed wire. At dawn this morning, we moved on to Stettin station, more barbed wire. Then in order to escape north from the besieged capital, our train took a circular route through the inner suburbs. We all agreed it looked as if the inhabitants had just fled to avoid some invading horde of pillagers (the Huns perhaps?). It was the first time I had ever seen Berlin streets dirty.

After twenty hours here (unexplained) our officers who left us at Potsdam rejoin us at Stettin, slightly tipsy and reeking of almost Slav gloom.

APRIL 13   ON THE SWEDISH TRAIN   1917

At last, I keep the date but change the heading. At Sassnitz, ferry port for Denmark and Sweden, our Germans were glad to let us go. I never thought I'd see one of the Kaiser's border guards, the harbor chief no less, in bucket helmet and carrying a sword, accepting as proof of identity thirty-two torn pieces of paper scrawled with numbers.

On the Swedish steamer *Queen Victoria*, their immigration officials refused to allow us to sail without a list of passengers. There seemed little reason for us to conceal who we were. But the first up the gangway (Zinoviev) gave a false name, out of habit perhaps, and all the others followed suit. I became "Petrov" which could have been a mistake.

After the dead air on the train, its washroom often leaking smoke like a coffin on fire, its space cramped for compulsive walkers like me, the prow of the *Queen Victoria* seemed a mountain peak after a week in the sewers. The sea was very rough, hurling up great lacy bundles of green spit that exploded like joke water-bombs. Only a handful of us remained in the spray. "The first revolutionary wave from Russia," joked somebody as I got a bucketful in the face. It wasn't much of a joke, but we laughed like drunken hyenas.

I was still chuckling when one of the ship's officers approached. "Mr. Petrov," he asked politely, "which of your colleagues is Mr. Ulyanov?" There was, of course, no such person on our list—why would the captain want to find him in the middle of the channel? I was silent.

Fortunately, he went on: "There is a radio message for him from Trelleborg." I looked toward Radek, egging him on to take up the narrative. He did. "Ul-*yan*-ov, did you say? Sorry, that's me. It's my stage name." Karl flashed him a simian grin, yellow gap teeth exposed like footlights and gave an actor-laddy bow.

The message was from Jacob Ganetsky, Polish socialist inter-

national man-of-business, transliterated in the West from "Haniecki," known here as Fürstenberg. He had probably been meeting
the ferry for days—as of necessity, my cables had been rather
cryptic and contradictory. His one, to Ulyanov, was to the point
—how many in party for trains and hotels—as was Radek's answer.

Jacob was on the quay as our ferry nudged in through the
creeping dark. Along with him, elegant in sporty English-style
tweeds, the white finger of the lighthouse illuminated at dramatic
intervals some fifty demonstrators waving flags and banners. Also
portly pontiff wearing a gold chain and top hat who could only
be the mayor. I let the others, green with seasickness, staggering
still to the motion of the boat, go down the gangway first. They
hardly noticed there was a reception committee but collapsed where
they stopped in front of the customs shed. Radek, Zinoviev and I,
too keyed by excitement to feel how wet and tired we were, smiled,
gripped elbows and palms, and said the right things to the Swedish
Social Democrats. They seemed genuinely approving and
sympathetic—but then who knows what Jacob had told them?

He whispered in my ear, "Bustle along. Train for Malmö
leaves in fifteen minutes!" I whispered back that nobody got through
customs in less than fifteen minutes, well, not twice on one day!

"Watch me!" And he handed over to the customs boss a copy
of Sweden's best-selling opinion magazine, *Politiken*. On the cover,
a squat, squinting figure like an old-clothes man, with a caption,
so far as I could guess my way through, that read: "LENIN—the
genius behind the Russian Revolution." I autographed some copies
of *Politiken* and we were all on the train to Malmö with two minutes
to spare.

"Who writes this rubbish?" I asked.

He smiled. "Parvus, of course. He says he must talk to you in
Stockholm."

I scowled, and spoke in my gritty, dictation-speed tones. "That
will not be possible. It would be as bad as speaking to Ludendorff.
Indeed, it would be exactly the same as speaking to Ludendorff.
No contact is possible. I will make that point to the press myself."

Malmö. Really, nobody can beat the Swedes at painless, pleasant efficiency. They are like good Germans, grown-up Americans.
At a little restaurant by the station, four tables of what we call
zakuski, the French *hors-d'oeuvres*, the Swedes *smorgasbord*. I think
theirs is the best—*gravlax*, sides of salmon "cooked" in the frozen
earth; sweet herrings stitched with onion; quail eggs in mayon-
naise; bear, reindeer, goat *pâté;* seal in aspic; boned roast game,
stuffed with a kind of caviar, and sliced. I did not see any of this

myself as I was busy pumping information out of Jacob. But Zinoviev showed me a sample of each dish before tipping it down.
Radek, too, flung himself with the rest on the great shining spread.

"I've got more on my tie tonight," he shouted "than I could
afford in a week in Switzerland. Thank God, they don't know
there's a war on."

Jacob smiled. "Oh yes, they do. That's how they make their
money. Wait till you see our accounts. Parvus is making a fortune
exporting rubber goods, cures for VD, pills for women's troubles,
dressings, prosthetics, to Russia from you-know-where. And another importing into you-know-where vital metals, industrial gems,
special oils and fuels from Russia. Don't worry, the Party gets its
share."

From the tables, our group reeled onto the night train for
Stockholm. Everyone but me looked the way I suppose a Strasburg
goose must feel when they take the funnel out of her mouth and
untie her. I too was in the business of cramming, myself and these
three intimate fellow-conspirators, with everything we knew that
would help the revolution move from its rut. I locked the door on
Ganetsky, Zinoviev, Radek and me in a four-bed *couchette* and
pulled down the blinds.

"Ah ha! Sealed again!" yodeled Karl.

I learned a lot. I taught them some too. I warned of the danger
of Kerensky, the balalaika of the left, a nasty combination of rabble-
hater and rabble-rouser, nationalist-socialist, jingo-pacifist, a radish
radical, red outside, white inside, who would communize the workers for the benefit of the bourgeoisie. I also stressed the need for
a Bolshevik Bureau in Sweden. We must always have a back door
for clandestine operations—the ideal operators, Ganetsky and Radek. There was more, much more, until four A.M. Then, once
again, dropped off a cliff into unconsciousness, pen and pad in
hand.

APRIL 14   ON THE SWEDISH TRAIN   1917

Another day of this endless, clattering, swaying life. Or rather, the
same day since I fell asleep at four this morning and I was woken
at eight A.M. An enterprising pack of newspapermen, alerted by
messages from Malmö (Parvus? Ganetsky? Radek?) announcing
my approach to Stockholm by the night train, had driven out to
intercept me and get ahead of their rivals. How flattering to be

the object of such public attention! How unfortunate that I have
to frustrate them! I am a journalist too—it's what I proudly put
on my documents when I'm telling the truth, and using my real
name, as today. I've never forgotten the thrill of my first *scoop*. I
published the secret decision of the Russian Orthodox Church
council that, once Tolstoy was safely dead, they would refuse him
burial in consecrated ground. It was printed round the world!

But I am not some financier, entertainer, or parliamentary
politician about whom lies and distortions are painful only to a
few individuals. What I am about to say and do in Russia may
affect the future of socialism for half a century. So all I state is:
"I will not, repeat not, be seeing Dr. Helphand here or anywhere.
Everything else I want to tell you will be in a written communiqué
and handed out to all the press in Stockholm. I regret there can
be no interviews and no discussion."

I posed for endless photographs, the lesser evil. I expect they
will make up the rest. But I cannot risk being a collaborator.

Stockholm station. The receptions are getting bigger. Nine
A.M. and red flag over the waiting room door. Two Swedish MPs,
Nerman and Lindhagen, anti-war campaigners who backed us at
Zimmerwald, speak in brisk, measured but cogent praise of the
Bolsheviks. Then we moved on to the Hotel Regina just down the
street, snapped all the way by press photographers, even by what
Radek assures me is a motion-picture newsreel camera. Inside, the
press, including some from France and Britain as well as Germany,
seem fairly under control. I see Ganetsky discreetly circulating with
a bottle in each hand promising, what the bourgeois newspapermen like even more than free drink, some tangible bit of evidence
with facts, dates, figures and signatures on it. I had a lot to do
today so I produced a nice thick bit of prewar paper upon which
I inscribed the testimony that none of us on the German train had
ever exchanged a word with anyone outside. I then called on my
fellow-travelers to sign it after me. This gave the reporters a chance
to quiz one or two of the passengers for "human interest"—I notice
Inessa, Olga and Valentina, next to little Robert, were the most
popular interviewees.

I announced that I was shortly expecting to meet a delegation
of Russian exiles in Stockholm, a real mixed bag of Meks, SRs,
Bundists and Anarchists. The press were welcome to hear my
advice which would be short and simple—"Come home!" I added
that I had also been pressed by a former Russian revolutionary, a
hero of '05, now a German, a millionaire, and a supporter of the
war, Dr. Alexander Helphand, once called Parvus, for a private

meeting. I had refused to remain in any room where he was. I
called the two MPs, the local Social Democrats, the exiles or indeed
any of the press, to witness this declaration. Until moments before
the press conference, I announced I had still been unsure of my
own welcome by the authorities. Now (sensation, hot news) I had
here in my hands a telegram from the Provisional government
spokesman declaring that supporters of the Revolution would be
admitted so long as they were Russian citizens.

Stockholm is familiar territory to me. I stopped over on my
first trip abroad in '94. I was the Petersburg delegate here for the
RSDLP "Re-unification" Congress in '06—what a round of back-
breaking work that was! There were twenty-seven sessions, and I
chaired thirteen. I spoke in five. And I was not inactive behind
the scenes. Still, I got to know the map of the city center by heart.
After a day of debate and maneuver, I would walk the empty streets
in the early hours cooling down the overheated engine of my brain.

But Stockholm to me means September, let me concentrate,
September the *thirteenth to the twenty-fifth*, 1910. Congress of the
Socialist International. The details of the politics have gone. What
remains, though, is as vivid as if it had been played out by the
Comédie Française—backcloths fresh as new paint, people large
as actors in center stage. On the thirteenth, Mother was there, and
it was the first time she had ever heard me speak in public. An
audience of about sixty. I was determined to show my control over
them. Perhaps I over-did it! Sister Marya, tactful nurse to our
vigorous matriarch of seventy-five, told me later of her reactions:
"She became tremendously excited and kept whispering 'He's so
impressive, so *skillful.*' But then, afterward, she started to worry.
'Volodya is too worked up. Why does he speak so loudly? He's not
looking after himself. Nadya should tell him to sit down in a nice
chair and just *talk.*' "

Then, on the twenty-fifth, she and Marya sailed back to Petersburg. I watched them dwindle toward the horizon, gradually
filled with a mounting melancholy which has never really dissi-
pated. It was the last time I saw her. I knew then that she would
be dead before I came back to Russia.

I left the others all milling about at the Regina in what was
turning into a party. I was off to indulge my own private, sensual
pleasure—buying books. The word reminded me. I took out the
Turgenev that Inessa had given me. Standing under the unfurling
green shoots of the fruit trees by the river, I read what I expected
to read. It is the passage in which Kolosov, the uncommon man,
questions himself about his way of separating from the woman he

once loved. Many men failed to end a relationship because they fear not the reproaches of the former mistress but the bad opinion of some stupid bystander. "Oh, gentlemen, a person who breaks with a woman once loved at that bitter, great moment when he involuntarily realizes that his heart is no longer completely filled with her, that person, believe me, understands more deeply the sanctity of love than the fainthearted who, from boredom or from weakness, continue to play on the half-broken strings of their flabby and sentimental hearts."

What a scene in a sentimental-sophisticated romance! Maupassant could make something of the tableau. But he might be wrong, Zola would be better. His short stories are much underrated. Zola would understand that Inessa is not suggesting that *I* am Kolosov. She is describing *her own thoughts* after she has separated herself from me! "How many of us have been able to break with the past in good time?" She is going on to Moscow. Some day there will be an opportunity to talk of all this. For the moment, I need all my nerves screwed to the sticking point.

"Ah, we knew we would hunt you down here! You cannot escape!" I looked up from the books I had piled round my knees in the old shop on the quayside, automatically checking each exit. Radek, Zinoviev and Ganetsky were frowning down on me.

"We are in revolt, Ilyich. You are going back to Peter where nobody has seen you for ten years. We cannot permit you to return dressed in such a fashion."

There had also been other visits to Stockholm. Enough for a fat nest egg to pile up in our Bolshevik secret account. I have left it here for just such a moment. The founding of a Party bureau, that is—not a trail round the shops. I had already handed over a check to Ganetsky, obliging the others to countersign the invoice. (I want no rumors about "secret funds.") So I ignored the silly proposition. "All right, now we catch the train for Finland."

But Radek went down on his knees next to me in the bookshop. (It must have been a good party. NB—keep the receipts!) It was sight of the Swedish comrades, all so beautifully formal in clothes, not to mention Ganetsky's snappy suit, that made him, made them all, experience "a strong desire that you, Ilyich, should *look more like an ordinary person. It's not much to ask, is it, comrades?*"

I indulged them to the minimum. At one moment, there was a pile of stuff a foot deep along the counter. I swept it all off. "Who do you think 'Lenin' is? A haberdasher on the Nevsky Prospect? I settle for a hat or a pair of trousers. Nothing more."

My Stockholm thoughts, memories, premonitions, personal

and political, are somber. I am writing this early in the morning on the fifteenth—it must be within minutes of the end of the Swedish leg of our odyssey. Tornio is the frontier post. As a Finnish village, part of territory newly freed from the Tsar's imperialist tyranny, its officials are likely to be sympathetic to revolution in Russia. But Ganetsky believes their officers are English, patriots all, who could regard a Slav communist agitator as deserving no better fate than a Teuton U-boat commander. Have we come 2,000 miles to end up in a lake with a bullet in the back of the head?

APRIL 15   ON THE SWEDISH TRAIN   1917

The trip to the northern border is much longer than the station master led us to expect. Or else the engines are becoming slower. We left last night at 6:30 P.M., Easter Friday. Now we decide it is almost breakfast time though still dark; our famous paraffin stove is brewing tea for the whole corridor; Nadya shares out the open sandwiches (excellent) from the Stockholm station buffet. The trees click by, dull as telegraph poles.

I have read all the papers, Russian and European, we could collect. *Pravda*, edited by Kamenev and Stalin, is worse than any Menshevik rag. I remark to the person nearest me on my bank of this three-bed sleeper: " 'Social Democrat' has become a shameful name. They're just liberals who are worried that soon all the workers may have the vote. They want a better world but without all the dangers and struggles involved in creating it. They want a bourgeois society without a proletariat. Until then the bourgeois will remain a bourgeois—for the benefit of the workers. Marx said it all in the *Communist Manifesto. That*'s what we should call ourselves—Communists!"

There is a sweet, languorous hum of agreement from my neighbor. It is Inessa. She has been in the bed across and above, while Nadya has been in the one across and below, all night. Strange feeling. Stranger perhaps that I have a slight sense of disappointment that my companion is not Radek. He has been left behind as a non-Russian. I need his special qualities.

At this moment, the train skidded to a halt. I had only just time to summon our contingent to a moment's briefing—nobody must apologize for traveling across Germany, or indeed behave as though it had to be defended. If asked why via Germany, they should attack the Provisional government for failing to make arrangements with England or France so that the exiled victims of the deposed Tsar could return sooner to their native land.

The frontier is the Torniojoki river, frozen solid between Swedish Haparanda and Finnish Tornio. Snow, and white umbrellas of trees. It reminds me of a spring picnic at dawn in the Kindyakov Forest of Simbirsk, the "lovers' kingdom" of our courting couples. We cross in two-person sleighs, the *veiki,* pulled by horses in fur bootees. Under the rug, Inessa and I are together, holding hands, silent.

Before we get to the far bank, the younger ones of our pilgrimage are leaping out and running for Greater Russia, shouting, waving, weeping, singing. The Russian and Finnish border troops are so moved they too break ranks and embrace the returning natives. Only the English officers stand aside, cold and stiff as corpses, while old and young, men and men, women and women, kiss and hug.

Most of Easter Sunday was spent being passed under the Anglo-Saxon microscope, one by one, by these foreigners. Most of us were stripped. Some, like Zina Zinovieva and Valentina Safarova, naked. Every piece of clothing, every item of baggage, was turned over, often with a stick. We were made to feel like idiot carriers of a loathsome disease. But our discipline held. Almost all of us had been through far worse.

The English could find nothing. We were Russians returning to Russia. At last, around 6 P.M., we were free to climb aboard our final train, a wonderfully rackety, third-class, branch-line conveyance. Before we left, I asked the Russian senior officer to send me a telegram to Petersburg and watched his signaler tap it out. It was to sister Manyasha: ARRIVING MONDAY ELEVEN PM STOP TELL PRAVDA ULYANOV.

My hand is too heavy to do more than jot down impressions of the next five hours, electrifying though they would have been to any man not paralyzed with fatigue. The compartments and corridors were crawling with Russian soldiers. Like most Russians, they had no concept of privacy, no idea there were times when even agitators do not want to talk. They kept asking me how I would stop the war as if expecting I would show them a secret weapon or a magic wand. Would the Germans go home if we did? What would happen to me in Peter? How many Bolsheviks were there in the world?

Like a dying man, I sat supported by Zinoviev. (After Radek at Stockholm, I had lost Platten at Tornio, the Russians-only policy was being strictly observed.) Together we answered even the stupidest (especially the stupidest) questions. The two officers i/c the soldiers were more easily convinced than their men. Their only objection—but will the workers follow you?

They had an answer at Byelo-Ostrov. It was nearer eleven, and I cursed the expected half-hour delay for Russian customs. Instead, poking my head out for a gasp of air I saw the little station was solid with workers. Then there was sister Manyasha—impossible! Even more like a dream, a grayer and sterner Kamenev, Shlyapnikov, others I had forgotten, or never met, but all with the unmistakable stamp of Bolshevik. When the workers saw me, they became something near delirious. I was hauled out like a soldier's kit bag. I was carried shoulder-high, passed on from group to group. The night was black, the platform slippery, the hands rough as bark—I began to fear I should slide off and vanish in the crowd like flotsam on a flood tide. "Steady, comrades. Gently there. Take it easy!" I kept saying. At which they all laughed, and tossed me in the air.

Back at last inside the compartment, Kamenev explained that Ganetsky had once again been a telegram ahead of me and alerted Peter. The Bolshevik network then aroused the cells in the Sestroresk munitions plant just outside Byelo-Ostrov. They insisted on being the first to welcome me back. I suppose I made a speech. I remember saying—"Comrade Gregory will expand on these points." I know I pushed *Pravda* under Kamenev's nose and shouted—"I really curse you for your feeble compromises!" And Kamenev laughing and saying to the young sailor next to him— "You have to know Ilyich to realize how occasions like this drive him crazy." And I'm certain the young sailor, Raskolnikov by name, boasted that the February Revolution had been near-bloodless, except in Kronstadt where his men had executed an admiral and forty-three other officers.

I know I made an excuse to retire to the conductor's cubicle and bring this diary up to date. What I really wanted was rest. Everything is going too well. Will I be arrested at the Finland station? I have just asked that of Lev Borisovich, Alexander Gavrilovich, and the rest, all sitting smiling and jolly together under one flickering taper with their arms round Nadya. Their smiles have become even broader. "Wait and see," said Marya. I must rest. Honestly, I no longer care. Let them hang me so long as they don't wake me.

V

THE OCTOBER REVOLUTION

April–October 1 9 1 7

So. I settled back in my seat. I've no need to worry about Prince Lvov's firing squad greeting me at the Finland station. The frontier welcome committee, despite my having emptied a bucket of abuse over some of them about *Pravda,* look too cheery for that. I haven't been on a Russian train for ten years, but I recognize the familiar downhill slide we always hit just around this distance out from Peter, the sudden, friendly, excited chatter of wheel on rail.

I look at my watch. I had taken the fat glob of gold, with its spring lids like beetle's wings, from Father's waistcoat pocket just before they screwed down the lid of his coffin, and the rest of my life it has been worth a good deal more than all my worldly possessions put together. And yet here it is still, despite being worn up the Alps, during Moscow street fighting, through London street markets, on the ferry to Capri (twice), in several prisons, around the cabarets of Paris (once at the Folies Bergère), in Berlin beer cellars, across the Stockholm ice, in Siberia and Lapland, on the beach at Biarritz, in the cafés of Vienna, around the docks of Marseilles, not to mention Malmö, Prague, Copenhagen, Brussels, Amsterdam, Warsaw. How many of these monoglot international statesmen who dismiss me as some kind of Tatar savage, briefly intruding upon the European stage, have themselves traveled so far and for so long around the continent? The occasional *grand luxe* hotel, or first-class *wagon-lit* perhaps, a youthful glimpse of their own lower depths, is all I can imagine for Lloyd George, Zimmermann, Clemenceau, Woodrow Wilson, Kerensky. I speak all *their* languages. But I was looking at my watch—11 P.M. Now I have another worry.

"It's very late on Easter Monday. Do you think we'll be able to get a droshky to take us to Anna and Mark's steamboat flat on Shirokaya Street?" Too boring, comrades. Not another school-kid fit of guffaws? I *have* been away too long.

At last, Kamenev, still purple and spluttering. "No, Vladimir Ilyich. I can promise. There will not be a droshky within miles. This is a *new* Peter."

I would never have guessed what he meant before our train pulled in to Petersburg at exactly 11:10 P.M.

Not any New Year's Eve, not the Coronation, not the opening of the first Soviet during the '05 Revolution, not the day this war was declared, not the day the Japanese War ended, not all put together, prepared me for what was waiting this chilly evening, with flakes of snow floating, on a rare public holiday.

Our coach was the fifth back from the engine so the impact came in waves, in slices, in scenes. There was a noise that blanked out the fat, fizzing engine as of a giant fairground, beyond the ticket barrier, where half a dozen steam organs competed—except that fairground music doesn't usually run along the lines of the "Marseillaise," the "Rote Fahne," the "Internationale" and I recognize massed military bands when I hear them.

Another reception committee came at us the way I realize they always do, like some kind of hockey team, arms held low, knees bent. Only that the Nordic war-goddess, blondest of blonde Earth Daughters, Sandra Kollantai, moved ahead of them at full stretch, her six-foot frame almost hidden by a huge stook of long-stemmed red roses. I prayed she was not going to unload on me. But she did.

I saw this was how tonight was going to be—my idea of a homecoming for the Bolshevik turned inside out. You would think they had actually had our Socialist Revolution. I determined then it would make no difference . . . well, that's not quite correct. It would not alter my view of what's to be done. But it may make a difference to them because the message I have brought is not what they expect, or want, least of all against this sort of theatrical background. So, comrades, pour it on! I have survived rejection, isolation, disappointment, defeat, nothing unusual in our business, since a revolutionary, almost by definition, is someone whose revolution has not yet succeeded. I can outlast admiration, applause, oratory, massed bands and flowers. You are the ones who face the test!

Secure in this protective gear, I slung the bouquet over my shoulder like a sack of washing, and took on the first of several guards of honor. Nadya was close by my elbow.

"Take a note of what's said," I hissed.

"What everybody says?"

"No, no, I don't care what *they* say. They haven't come here to say anything. What *I* say. I'm the one who'll be misquoted."

"All right, but don't gabble. If in doubt, say twice." Whenever did I hesitate to repeat myself?

The guards of honor, sailors, soldiers, civilians with red cockades in their hats, were presenting arms. "Salute!" said Bonch-Bruevich, out of the side of his mouth, "*no, right* hand."

Of course, I'd seen the Grand Dukes and Field Marshals do

it often enough. It was a coincidence but it seemed I'd pressed the button. All the shouting and music died away as if a curtain had dropped. Somebody played a single trumpet. A silence of a tenth of a second, then a "Hurrah!" that shook the whole of Vyborg, a cry more stirring than any I had ever heard.

Everyone had come to a halt. I was standing in front of the Kronstadt sailors. For a moment, I couldn't even open my mouth. There is a kind of shock which jumps you back five seconds in time. I remember Kamo, Stalin's friend, telling me about an experience in Turkey when the air shook like water in a bottle, sides of buildings slid into the road, the pavement came agape in ragged cracks, and he said to himself—"Good God, for a moment there I thought it was an earthquake." I thought to myself: "Good God, for a moment there I thought half a city shouted 'Hurrah!' " The Kronstadters stared with hungry eyes. All right, might as well start here.

"Sailor-comrades, I greet you. I don't know as yet whether you all agree with the Provisional government but I know very well that when they give you sweet speeches and make many promises they are deceiving you, just as they deceive the whole Russian people. The people need peace. The people need bread. The people need land. And they give you war, and hunger while the land remains in the hands of the landowners. Sailors, comrades, I am glad to see you are armed. Because you must fight for the Revolution, fight to the end. There are no half-victories. Long live the worldwide Socialist Revolution!"

I turned quickly and bumped into someone I once knew well, Ivan Chugurin, star pupil of our Longjumeau summer school outside Paris. His face was shiny with tears. "In honor of your return home . . ." he muttered and gave me a new Party card. It was No. 600 and issued by the Bolsheviks of the Vyborg district, Peter's "Red Fortress," which flanks the Station. I wiped his eyes with my cap, "Consider this is your postgraduate course."

But B.-B. was nudging me on in the manner, at once discreet and dictatorial, of an experienced old courtier steering an awkward, untrained young "royal." I was being invisibly urged toward what was once the Tsar's personal waiting room. I'd often wondered what it was like inside. Behind me crushed in a cross-section of the capital's left élite, mainly Bolsheviks—but also waverers and half-committed, fellow-travelers and those waiting to jump aboard, a whole crop which had ripened in the ten years I had been away, and not known to me by face.

I almost knocked down someone I had known too long,

Chkheidze, now chairman of the Soviet Central Executive Committee, a Menshevik and active collaborator with the bourgeois Provisional government. He had been sent as the official greeter, one Social Democrat to another. And I might have accepted him on those terms, touched as I was by the Vyborg card, a gift somewhat more appropriate than the bush of blooms I was hoisting from one shoulder to another. But I had in my pocket the latest copies I had picked up in Stockholm of the London *Times* and the Paris *Le Temps*, unashamed mouthpieces for English and French finance capital. Both, coincidentally, with long articles praising the Soviet's CenExCom. So far as I am concerned, the key sentence in *Le Temps* leaves our chairman indicted for treason—"The leaders of the workers' parties, particularly M. Chkheidze, are exercising all their influence to moderate the wishes of the working classes."

He had started his address, delivered with the gloomy mask of a preacher and the tones of a funeral sermon. "Comrade Lenin, we welcome you to Russia but . . ."

Five words into a welcome and already a "but."

". . . *but* we think that the principal task of our revolutionary democracy is now the defense of the Revolution from any encroachments, from within or without. We consider that what this goal requires is not dis-union, but the closing of the democratic ranks. We hope that you will pursue these goals together with us . . ."

So I *had* got them worried. Now to worry my own side, even more. Probably Chkheidze monotoned on, I don't know. After a first glance, such as you might give at a potted palm or other ornament, I made a point of giving him no more attention than the rest of the decorations. Gilded bas-reliefs of bears, wolves, reindeer, foxes, salmon and other Finlandish fauna. Had the Tsar ever been to Finland by train, or used his waiting room? My aim was to reproduce the air of someone who had just dropped in out of the rain. I did not reply, or acknowledge the CenExCom's chairman's presence. The crowd outside hammered on the great, bending, plate-glass windows, baying for a speech. I had a speech all right. A more extreme, and steely, epitome of my "Letters from Afar" fired off out of exile as soon as the news reached Geneva from Peter. *Pravda*'s shifty editors, Kamenev and Stalin, only printed the first of the five, and that so heavily cut it was practically castrated. I am saving the expanded text for the assembly of Bolshevik district and factory committees I am certain our CenCom must have arranged at whatever is our HQ now. The heart of the matter is easy to sum up.

I spoke first to those packed into the waiting room with me. This is what I said (according to Nadya's notes):

> Dear comrades, soldiers, sailors, workers. I am happy to welcome in your persons—no "buts'—our victorious Russian Revolution, and greet you as the vanguard of the worldwide proletarian army . . .
>
> The piratical imperialist war will soon become a civil war flaming across Europe. . . . The worldwide Socialist Revolution for which we have all been working has already dawned. . . . Germany is seething . . . any day now the whole of European capitalism may crash. The Russian Revolution accomplished by you has prepared the way and opened a new epoch. Long live the worldwide Socialist Revolution!

"What about all the dots? The bits you've left out?" I asked Nadya. After all, this may be the most crucial entry in this diary. Nadya laughed: "Sorry, I was too busy watching their faces. I got down the main bits. But you should have seen them, Volodya. Like people locked in a cellar coming out into the sunlight. You blinded them. *They* had made their kind of revolution without you. And *you* return from stuffy, middle-class Switzerland, the voice from afar to explain to them what they had done and what they had still to do. They found you strange, harsh, upsetting. But then— I'm being silly. *You* saw all that too." But I hadn't, and didn't until later.

At the time, I was edging my way round the fringe of the crowd to get out and away. When I encountered the square beyond, I would have reeled back if there had been a tenth of an inch to reel. Gusev had told me that Podvoisky and Nevsky, commanders of our Military Organization, had also become brilliant impresarios of the mass demo, spectacular choreographers of the revolutionary pageant. Opponents who came to jeer found themselves participators rather than spectators—when there are 150,000 performers, there's not much space for an audience. Outside the Finland station, I was facing at least that number. They were jammed so solid I could have walked across on their heads. These acres of people had been there since the afternoon, an Easter Monday, lured in by bold, brusque posters everywhere: LENIN ARRIVES TO-DAY. MEET HIM.

Now, it was dark. Faces were litter scattered everywhere over a deep, blue-black lagoon. In a constant sequence, torches made of flaring tar-balls smoked and sparked. It was like a gigantic firework display just waiting to erupt in dazzling disaster. First here, then there, this field of restless cabbages would be exposed in a sudden patch of marquetry, pale humans in deep shadows, as half a dozen mounted searchlights swept over the scene at random. Cut-out silhouettes of angular household equipment, pots and pan on wheels, were revealed as armored cars, machine gun barrels swiveling. Over all hung a net of interwoven wires, threaded with slogans, banners, flags, streamers, emblems and portraits. And lining its extremities, all round the square, two stories above the rest of us, like an overcrowded rookery, were windows, roofs, chimneys, penthouse gardens, with Peterburgers perched on every grip. And the bands played on.

I made a bolt for a Renault taxi tucked away behind the royal tradesman's exit. But the citizens at the front of the crowd were quicker. Politely, rather impersonally, they prevented me from opening the car door, murmuring that they had come to hear Lenin speak. I climbed on the bonnet. (Nadya's notes here are even briefer—obscene imperialist slaughter . . . every side, lies and frauds . . . capitalist thieves and robbers . . .") How would this all end? Would I be marched round from stump to stump, repeating my message, after the fashion of the American poet, Edgar Allan Poe, who was dragged from ballot box to ballot box drunk, exhausted and dying?

Then Podvoisky was at my elbow, Party activist since '01, perhaps the most outstanding street fighter of '05, he elbowed me free and into the Renault. It was noisy there too and almost pitch-dark as the bodies piled up on us. Nikolai Ilyich gunned the motor. But it was just as if the wheel had never been invented.

"More your type of transport anyway, *Starik*. Think of the press pictures!" he shouted as he hauled me up onto the turret of an armored car. Nadya, B.-B., Zinoviev, Kamenev and all the rest had been swallowed up. I was alone on a hot, throbbing, metal platform with nothing between me and more people than I had ever seen in my life. I spoke, no longer thinking, but spilling out what was deepest in my thoughts—this must become the Revolution Russia has been waiting for this hundred years. Nothing shall stop us, none of the mistakes of '05. The armored car edged out of the square like an icebreaker, opening up a path by the heavy, knocking sound of its clockwork heart.

We left Vyborg, crossed the Samsonievsky bridge, nudged through the narrow lanes of Old Petersburg, and on to the Kshesinskaya Palace, years ago the ivory-white love nest of the Tsar's ballerina mistress, since March the Bolshevik citadel. People joined, and left, but we were always a rolling crowd. Every time Podvoisky stopped, I stood up, held onto the muzzle with one hand, waved my cap with the other and spoke. We must have done it fifteen or sixteen times. "Long live the Socialist Revolution! Down with the collaborators!"

All the way, I had been followed by giant spotlights of the Peter and Paul fortress which kept me continually illuminated like the star of a musical comedy. Or perhaps the performing bear in the circus?

Inside Kshesinskaya's, I was reunited with Nadya, Zinoviev and almost everyone of the other Party members from the train. They had all been looking forward to some kind of celebration. But none of us had ever envisaged anything so grandiose, and triumphal as our Finland Station Show.

"Plekhanov arrived back three days ago. First-class travel courtesy of the French," said Kamenev. "Not much of a fuss. About five hundred people. *He* was pleased, though."

"Still, it's only fair to tell Ilyich, since he's the great realist, that Peter today will turn out fifty thousand to honor a cat having kittens," said Podvoisky. "I think the record was a million, last month, when we buried the victims of the Revolution. Very simple, very dramatic, red coffins, total silence, half the population of Peter filing past the common grave on the Champ de Mars. But two or three times a week some group stages a marching demo—even the liberals and the bourgeois."

"What about last week?" asked Kamenev. "That would have interested you, Ilyich. The March of the Aged, it was called. Peasants with beards to the ground and banners saying things like SEND THE YOUNG TO THE FRONT LET US GET ON WITH THE HARVEST. Don't get me wrong, though. Tonight has never been equaled for any Welcome Home. In fact, there are thousands outside in Alexandrovsky Park now, at one in the morning, waiting for yet another speech."

I went on to the first-floor balcony. My lips moved, and a small army of soldiers and sailors cheered and stamped. My energy level was dropping. I was saving the last few pints for the district and factory committees due in soon. Looking down, I saw dozens of long-unseen old comrades having their cards checked at the front gates. Only Inessa is not here but on the night train to Moscow.

I decided it was time to reassert my authority as leader of the Bolsheviks. The most radical, militant, emotionally honest, intellectually rigorous, physically adventurous, socialist party *in the world* has allowed itself to become a hesitant, slothful, timorous, self-deceptive, compromising, old-pals club. My first task must be to bring them back to themselves. After that, converting the proletariat and peasantry should be child's play. The speeches I have made so far in my first six hours here are for outsiders, for the masses, for those untrained in Marxist analysis. They are the work of an agitator, not a propagandist. They contain a skeleton of argument—that is the only key I know to oratory—but they are basically slogans stitched to a single thread. It should not be possible that anything I am saying will come as a surprise, let alone a shock, to a mature Bolshevik. Yet Nadya has been right about the reactions of the comrades. (She so often is.) Even senior Party members have clearly not heard anybody speak like this since the Tsar abdicated. That is a scandal!

While I was running these thoughts, like typewriter ribbon, across the platen of my brain, sipping a glass of tea, I noticed there was a rather factory-canteen sort of "banquet" going on. Well, enough for Gregory to have a sausage in one hand, an eclair in the other, while being poured a vodka. Enough for a succession of committeemen to be making passionate addresses, officially in honor of me, but really anecdotes about each other. Without a second's consideration, I found I had risen. I was beginning my most important speech, while some pompous idiot was still in full spate.

"Revolutionary intoxication has gone far enough, comrades. It is now the day after. We have done enough congratulating each other on the Revolution. Especially as we haven't had one."

There was no mistaking their unease. It might almost be fright. They had been so pleased with themselves—was Lenin going to spoil it all? Hadn't I just been buttering up the demonstrators, soldiers, sailors, Red Guards, for incarnating our victorious Revolution?

I put aside the unpublished "Letters from Afar," suppressed by *Pravda*'s editors. I moved on to the program I had compiled on the "sealed" train. What I now called my "April Theses." Both of these were ahead of all but a handful of Bolsheviks whose opinions I knew. The Party had still not caught up with the cable I'd sent to Alexandra Kollontai, as she left Stockholm for Petersburg, within a day of hearing that the Tsar had been toppled: OUR TACTICS ABSOLUTE DISTRUST. NO SUPPORT NEW GOVERNMENT, KERENSKY PARTICULARLY SUSPECT. ARMED PROLETARIAT ONLY GUARANTEE. IMMEDIATE ELECTION DUMA. NO ALLIANCE OTHER PARTIES. I am amazed how right I was!

I spoke for two hours. I am not an orator in the traditional sense. I give no aesthetic pleasure, as of an operatic aria or a dramatic declamation. In Shakespeare's *Julius Caesar* (a political play I recommend to all comrades), I would speak with the blunt tongue of Brutus, not the honeyed tongue of Mark Antony. Trotsky (perfect casting for Antony) said to me, in a lull in our duel, that he dared read anything I wrote but he resisted listening to me in debate. Because too often I radiated "the physical sensation of truth" which his honor would not allow him to reject. If that were ever so, and I suspect the gamey whiff of romantic phrasemaking, then it was so that dark morning under the burned-out chandeliers of a ballerina's ballroom.

I gave my theses to them, block by block, conclusion by conclusion, review notes for an examination already too close.

Central reality of Russia today—the *War*. No Marxist could doubt it was imperialist still, waged by puppets of international finance. ProvGov no more than Petersburg office of Anglo-French Enterprises & Co. Burglars' quarrel over loot. Secret treaties not exposed, renounced, still intend divide up colonies, agree spheres of influence, annex border states. Our war policy—stop the war! Words no use, action. Fraternize! Refuse shoot! *Desert!* Two million Russian soldiers already deserters, wandering between front and home. Two million potential recruits to our cause. After all, they are executing our policy. Let them know it! Not one more dead worker or peasant to protect foreign investors, native profiteers and greedy landlords.

Dual Power. Not a fact, a phrase. No society can have Dual Power, any more than child have two mothers. Originally, the masses were in control after dismantling tsarism. The liberal bourgeoisie did nothing to make February rising successful. Then strikers, demonstrators, street fighters, mutinous troops who refused fire on them, handed government to Duma rump, misled by Soviet leaders. ProvGov will carry on gaining strength, confidence while promised Menshvik, SR, even Bolshevik support. What people's revolution would appoint sugar baron with eighty million gold rubles its finance minister? Sole Soviet reps compromisers—Kerensky, right-wing SR opportunist, Napoleonic careerist; Menshevik Chkheidze, believer workers' best friends are their bosses. No revolution can half-succeed, any more than anyone remain half-virgin. Our Revolution has been artificially interrupted by Soviet. Nevertheless, the *Soviet* is our instrument for democratic, peaceful revolution, backed by majority workers, peasants, soldiers. Best future form of government superseding bourgeois parliamentary republic. Weakness, control by Mensheviks, SRs, simple-minded Bolsheviks, who still insist iron laws Marxism decree feudal structure always gives way to capitalist with socialist only in distant future. We must assume leadership of Soviet and push it to single total dominance over society under slogan: "All Power to the Soviet."

The worst thing possible for the people of Russia was this unnatural unity of the ProvGov and the Soviet against the militant working class. Our Bolshevik Party had allowed it to happen, had *helped* it to happen. This must cease if I am to remain leader of the Party. That was my policy. Perhaps the comrades would let me know their reaction in due course?

By the end, the faces had altered. Many were rapt, and rapturous, cracking open into cheers. A large minority applauded, but stared ahead the while, as if nerving themselves to go home and break the bad news. Quite a few staggered as they rose to their feet, as if their legs had gone to sleep. Or was it their brains? One stopped me by the door. "You're right, *Starik*. Now I hear it, I know you are. But I feel as if I have been beaten about the head by flails."

I felt fairly bastinadoed myself. My body still shuddered rhythmically to the motion of the train. I could feel, whenever my lids closed, the noise and warmth of the crowds at the station, the brain-illuminating glare of the searchlights, the thump of the bass drum. "Masses" would never be just a word anymore. I went to the Shirokaya flat, with Mark, Anna and Nadya, led like a blind man. My lids too were "sealed." The last thing I thought as I fell into the double bed beside Nadya was "Mother slept here." Last thing I saw, handprinted on a streamer across the headboard, was—WORKERS OF THE WORLD, UNITE!

APRIL 4   PETERSBURG   1917

Awoke early, but not early enough to find Nadya asleep. Noises from the kitchen, even better, smells, fried sausage, and waffles, and real coffee. They live better, here in wartime Peter, than we ever did in neutral Zurich. But then Mark is director of a thriving insurance company, and Anna has a maid.

My first full day, for a decade, in Russia is about to begin. A Russia free from tsarism. A Petersburg that has begun the Revolution, or rather "revolution." At last, I am in the correct place at the correct time. Six days to my forty-seventh birthday. If this isn't it, then I'll retire, like Plekhanov did after '05, and collect my works.

But then, why am I still somehow disquieted?

Well, my throat is extremely sore. Not just the speeches. I remember now that, even though I drank only tea, I became infected at the end with the euphoria I criticized in the others. I insisted we sing some of the great rallying songs, and some of the satirical ones too—"Varshavianka" and "Muzykanty" had us all heads together, arms flung wide. I had to teach them the "Internationale." The orchestral parts arrived only a few weeks ago, and the army bands had been hoarding them ever since. I love singing, becoming an instrument, letting the melody surge through me like an Aeolian harp. But it's not often I get such an opportunity. Not since Longjumeau . . .

Well, perhaps I can skip speeches for a few days. I want to read up on the press, on the party minutes, on the correspondence from the country members. I also want to listen. What are they saying in the factories and the barracks? I revere statistics, but there is nothing like the warm breath of human testimony. One person can tell you volumes. I remember that peasant I overheard talking to George Gapon in Zurich, that *muzhik* in the First Duma in Peter—just those two and I knew there was no point in trying to negotiate. They want *the lot*! My policy is: give it to them!

Getting dressed now, I tripped something that disturbed, depressed—what could it be? Such a routine, refined to eliminating every unnecessary choice or decision. That's it, my hand should have gone from the little heap of pocket furniture under the bed to various pockets without pause. Well, *that's it*. Somewhere, on that great evening, floating on a tide of bangs and shouts and applause, guarded by the crack troops of Bolshevism, I had been relieved of Father's watch. The rest of the chain is here, nipped off a few links from the top. That must have taken some nerve. But then as Koba Stalin, who has holed up with outlaws in the Caucasian mountains, used to say—crime breeds more heroes than law and order.

But that isn't it. Nor yet a groveling letter from Kamenev saying he forgot to tell me in all the excitement last night that there is a joint Bolo-Mek discussion meeting this afternoon. Subject—"Party Unity to Advance the Revolution." Speaker—Lenin. His hand gets a bit shaky here—"Would I like to give them the benefit . . . Very much anticipated . . . Great disappointment . . ." I look forward to *that*. After the sausage and waffles and real coffee, not chicory and chestnuts, the breakfast that Mother always gave me.

This was the last sight she saw, I suppose, nine months ago. The room, wide behind the bedhead, narrowing away to the width of a single window ten feet beyond the foot, like the prow of a ship. The cracks in the ceiling your eye can't help turning into islands, skylines, instruments of war, faces, animals. The balcony beyond the window from which it is possible to see the gilt spires of the St. Peter and St. Paul fortress-prison. Where Sasha was held for trial. Where, only a day ago, I still thought I might be taken from the Finland station.

I breakfasted alone from the giant helpings in the stone bowls on the stove. Manyasha and Anyuta had gone off to work at *Pravda* taking Nadya with them. Mark was at his office. My eleven-year-old foster-nephew, Georgi Lozgachev-Yelizarov, a child prodigy adopted by Anna and Mark, and known as Gora, was at school. I'd been warned every one did everything, work, shopping, visiting, traveling as early as possible in run-down, half-ruined Petersburg. You could usually count on light, power, trams, food and whatever giving out around midafternoon.

B.-B. arrived as I was doing the washing-up. Waiting below was Robert Matisovich Gabalin, my official driver, courtesy of the Soviet, a perk awarded to all top people in the left parties. He is a handsome, young, athletic fellow. I suspect he doubles as bodyguard. Possibly trebles as informer. Anyway, as I climb into the Renault limousine, I note that some luxuries are more corrupting than others. Capitalism would never soften me with luxury hotels, food and drink, clothes or jewels, beautiful countesses, palaces or estates. But transport? That really is tempting. No more queues in the rain for trams that never come, no more endless walks. Instead a magic carpet, at pavement level, that ferries you from appointment to appointment. I see it also begets its own justification. I am persuading myself it is an essential working tool, a necessity, a legitimate expense that will double my work load and the car hasn't moved an inch yet. Perhaps it is just as well the privilege will be withdrawn when they read my "April Theses" in *Pravda*. This time there will be no cutting or censorship.

"Volkovo, if you please, Robert Matisovich."

"Where?" asked B.-B.

But my driver, indispensable already, had let out the clutch, or whatever it is drivers do, and we were purring through thin traffic to the cemetery.

I left my companions by the gate and found my way to the area where Mother and Olga lie next to each other. Nowhere to sit, so I leaned on Olga's cross as on a shooting stick. There is only one form of immortality. I spliced together all the memories I had of Mother in the chronological order of a family photograph album, or, since they were usually moving images, of a motion-picture production.

Under a gray sky and dripping boughs, eyes closed and senses drowned by the fruity smell of decaying flowers, my biography of her became a vivid charade. She seemed to act with free will, taking on a willful personality of her own, the way Gorky told me a novelist's characters sometimes do. I was enormously refreshed after it was over.

I had to ask B.-B. the time. He said I had been by the graves for an hour.

Our appointment in the Grand Hall of the Tauride Palace, home now of both Soviet and ProvGov, was not for several more hours. I asked B.-B. to give me a guided tour, touching on what happened where and when, while I flipped through some archives I had acquired.

Just being on the actual spot, I find, immediately clarifies muddy patches of any story. The overthrow of the Tsar was the work of the masses. What's more important, they did it independently, spontaneously, without any organized political leadership from us, or Meks, or SRs. "Hadn't the workers read *What Is to Be Done?* Didn't they know the proletariat are not supposed to act alone?" B.-B. is a stony-faced joker whose sense of humor would survive the guillotine.

APRIL 17   PETERSBURG   1917

Ever since I got back here, the covert Right and the self-styled Left, the Kadet majority in the ProvGov, the Menshevik SR majority in the Soviet, all the newspapers, have been demanding more and more details about my journey across Germany. You would think I had just won some Blue Riband in an international steam locomotive race. Thousands of other political refugees from tsarism have flooded back from all over the world—according to the official returns of the Foreign Ministry, to be exact, 18,782 between February 27 and March 31. Many of them must have had strange, marvelous, comic, heroic stories to tell if anyone had asked them. But no. It was as if I were the only one.

None of the newspapermen is interested in genuine information. They barely listen to their own questions, let alone my

answers. The object of the exercise is to keep the name of the
Bolshevik leader in the headlines, in the chatter in the clubs and
the queues, around the factory canteens and the communal wash-
houses, but always associated with Germany, the country's enemy.
Lenin spent the night in *Frankfurt* . . . Lenin spent another night
in *Berlin* . . . Lenin travels to Petrograd by courtesy of the *Kaiser*
. . . Did Lenin meet *Ludendorff* . . . ? Could Lenin have dropped
in at the *Wilhelmstrasse* . . . ?

Nadya tells me she overheard a housewife in the Old City
shaking her doormat and asking her neighbor, genuinely puzzled
and seeking advice: "What should be done with this Lenin who
came from Germany? Should he be drowned in a well, or what?"

I keep on repeating that I was only one of thirty-two travelers
on the train, several of whom belonged to other parties than the
Bolsheviks. That none of us left the train wherever it stopped, or
had contact with any one outside the train. That we had insisted
on paying our own fares and bringing our own food. That the
plan had been originally suggested by the Menshevik leader, Julius
Martov, and that he himself with 256 former exiles will soon be
returning by the same route and under the same conditions. No
matter. Stories keep on circulating which vaguely hint that I must
have been involved in some dishonorable or treacherous transaction. They are justified by a self-fulfilling logical trick—these
rumors must be more than rumor, otherwise how could such rumors have been started?

That reminds me of an anecdote about the power of suggestion. I was told it by Camille Huysmans, secretary of the International Socialist Bureau. In Paris in, I think, '09, he was collecting
signatures appealing against the death sentence on a Spanish anarchist who had been found guilty of bomb-throwing on the most
feeble, untrustworthy, and probably forged, evidence. The police
had simply wanted a scapegoat. Camille hit on the idea of canvassing Captain Alfred Dreyfus—I think I may even have suggested it. The Jewish captain had been cleared, pardoned and
rehabilitated three or four years previously, after a shameful, per-
jured trial. The ISB had been one of his most staunch defenders.
Camille came back from his call on this famous martyr of anti-
Semitism almost in tears, past despair, past reluctant laughter.
Dreyfus had unhesitatingly refused to sign. His reason? As he put
it: "There's no smoke without fire."

The smoke is getting thicker and thicker round here. I have
just been summoned, along with Gregory Evseyevich, by the ExCom
of the Peter Soviet to render our explanation of our journey across

Germany. They kept us waiting in an anteroom of the Tauride Palace for three hours. Messengers popped in and out every fifteen minutes or so to explain that their masters were "preoccupied with urgent matters of paramount importance."

Gregory was all for storming back to our HQ in Kshesinskaya's Mansion, half Chinese pagoda, half English Botanic Garden. "Let them push through *our* gun-toting sentries." But there is a time for wrath, and a time for calm. I was going to be neither prosecuting nor defending attorney, but dispassionate judge. When finally some drop in the fever-heat of affairs of state allowed us in, I presented a roll call of indisputable facts, one by one. They quickly abandoned what turned out to be their main item—that we had fraternized with German SDP officials who were supporting the war. Finally, they could not but agree that the two of us had broken no rules of socialist honor, explicit or implicit.

I asked them to register this decision formally, and in writing. When this was done, I dropped my judicial pose and lashed into them for their own breaches of revolutionary decency. I could understand that a capitalist Provisional government, though publicly inviting all banished rebels to come home, might secretly order its diplomats abroad to obstruct the legal return of any Russian opponents. But that the ExCom of the Soviet, in effect the Cabinet of a Workers', Soldiers' and Peasants' government, should have connived at this and not forced their bourgeois partners to change the policy, was despicable. The ExCom found it hard to disagree, though of course they pretended they did not know what Milyukov and Co. were doing. It was a total victory. Tomorrow I publish an article making all the same points, "How We Came Home," in our *Pravda*. And the day after that, it will be reprinted in *Izvestia*, the Soviet's own official mouthpiece.

APRIL 21   **PETERSBURG**   **1917**

I have also dropped round at *Izvestia* an exhibit that I suggested they might like to run in their columns. This is just one of the hundreds of poison-pen messages I get every post. It declares itself to be a proclamation by "The League of Struggle against Bolshevism and Anarchy," is addressed to "Mr. Ulyanov." Its latest meeting had unanimously resolved: "(1) Ulyanov who calls himself 'Lenin' be killed. (2) The printing presses of the paper *Pravda* be blown up. (3) This verdict be executed in the event of Lenin failing to quit the country within the fortnight and the *Pravda* failing to cease publication. Execution of the verdict to be the duty of the League members. (Signed) Chairman Bulgakov, Secretary Yazykova."

Probably the "League" is only a sacked gendarme and his trollop, a former Okhrana spy, with a knackered police horse to give the casting vote, but our MilOrg takes them all seriously. I pointed out I was living in a safe house, at an address known only to a picked handful of close colleagues.

"Oh! Where is it?" asked our martial mastermind, Gusev. "I'll send you round a dozen or so of our riflemen to mount guard."

"Thank you," I said. "That will certainly keep my incognito incognito."

"Don't mention it!" he said.

Still, the death sentence from the League has had one good result. Today's *Izvestia* rallies round to our side (again) in a leading article headed "What Do They Want?" This is the best part:

> For several days now smears have been circulating in Petrograd that will embarrass and dismay all involved in the Russian Revolution. Certain shady characters loiter in the streets, markets, bathhouses and shops, gathering crowds and everywhere inciting the gullible to violence, urging them to arrest Comrade Lenin, to beat him up, to ransack the editorial offices of *Pravda*, and so on. This dishonest, repulsive persecution of Comrade Lenin is used by dark and sinister forces, and is supported by their newspapers, as a means of initiating the hounding of Socialists generally, before assailing the Soviet of Workers' and Soldiers' Deputies. After this, they hope to revert to the old, hated system.

It is reassuring that at least some of the "center-left realize that "counterrevolution" is not just a word. Why would the privileged not seek to undermine and destroy us? They have everything to lose.

Another curiosity I wish I had time to investigate. I found this small flyer posted all around the old city, not far from the steamboat flat:

> *At the Bi-Ba-Bo cabaret, 19 Italayanskaya Street,*
> Tonight at 10:30:
> Medicine for Girlish Ennui.
> A song about Lenin.
> A Scene by the Seaside.

A Song about Bolshevik and Menshevik.
The Story of the Grandfather and the Turnip.
The Sealed Politician.
And many other attractions.
Admission 10 rubles.

APRIL 23   PETERSBURG   1917

I suppose every English schoolboy knows—"Untune *that* string, And, hark! what discord follows." This, so far as I can discover (and I admit I am no expert on English literature), is the basic political message of Shakespeare. He was the greatest writer who ever lived, in my opinion. (Marx agreed with me, and he *was* an expert on *world* literature.) There is a schoolboy part of me that goes on hoping that someday it will be discovered that Shakespeare really was a revolutionary. But there is little doubt that he wasn't even a democrat. He was in favor of the *status quo* that had looked after him quite well. He wanted the middle road, the golden mean, a place for everyone and no one in *his* place!

Shakespeare is not easy to read, especially for a foreigner. No poet ever packed so much into so small a space, quite often saying two, three, or even four things at once, pleading most eloquently when he is arguing against his own prejudices. But, no doubt, continually he stresses the horror of what we can only call "revolution." It is a time, he shudders to mention, when the baby beats the nurse, the son evicts the father, the subject topples the monarch. What could be worse than the world turned upside down?

This interests me a great deal. I seem to be one of the few observers of the February uprising who believes that what the people wanted then was not just peace, bread, land—though I back these demands as the simplest, strongest, most widely spread. They wanted, and still do, *much* more than that: nothing less than a New World.

Kerensky understood that. He said as much in a speech in March, pointing out that the entire country has been infected by "a sense of unlimited freedom, a liberation from the most elementary restraints essential to every human society." The difference is, as can be deduced from his phrasing—I applaud it, he is afraid of it.

What else than a topsy-turvy world was being envisaged by those students in Odessa who switched their lecture room round and made their professors sit and listen to the pupils' view of how history should be taught? By those actors in Petersburg who locked up the theater manager in his box office and told him that in future *they* would choose and direct their own plays? By those workers in Moscow who dragged their boss to the shop floor to see how they made his money for him amid the dirt, the drafts, the stink, the noise, the danger, the boredom? By those troops in the trenches who captured the military chaplain when he paid his weekly visit, roped him down night after night during enemy bombardments, asking him what spiritual consolation he gave himself in the face of death? And, my favorite example—those fourteen-year-olds in Kiev who refused to enter the schoolroom unless the headmaster promised them boxing lessons which would equip them to extract a little respect from older boys?

If all these had united behind a common slogan it must have been—*Nothing Must Ever Be the Same Again!* It remains the only one under which the people of Russia can advance and complete their Revolution. Though our Party ship may veer and luff, stand still in the doldrums, even put back to port until the storm passes, it will always continue to steer toward a New Socialist Commonwealth while I stay at the helm. The old world must be entirely destroyed, before the next one can start to be constructed. This is the message that now underlines every speech I make, every article I write.

APRIL 29   PETERSBURG   1917

The first all-Russian Bolshevik Party Conference since the February Revolution began here on April 24. I had been in Peter exactly three weeks. Every day as I do my exercises on the balcony of the steamboat flat bedroom, I have said to myself—Revive the Party! Recapture the Party! Re-arm the Party!

Two out of the three seemed possible even on the opening day. Membership is 80,000. Their delegates have almost always rallied to my extreme and unwavering line. My total rejection of Prince Lvov's capitalist Cabinet was given a standing ovation. I had the majority behind me when I stated flatly that we are no longer interested in setting up a liberal bourgeois, parliamentary republic. Anyway, the Kadets in the ProvGov are too inadequate to attempt it; the Meks and SRs on SovExCom too cowardly to suggest it.

My program for Russia is rule by a network of Soviets of

Workers, Soldiers and Peasants. I scorned to conceal that this would begin as a dictatorship: "It would rest, not on law, not the formal will of the majority, but on direct, open force." History demonstrates that we have no other choice. One great mistake of the Bolsheviks in February was to resist arming the striking masses. An oppressed class which shows no desire to have weapons in its hands deserves to remain in slavery. "In every class society, the ruling class is always armed." But that is not to argue that *at the moment* we should attempt to carry out the transfer of control to our democratic proletarian-peasant commonwealth by violence. Unless, and until, we are attacked, we operate through peaceful propaganda, and patient persuasion.

Today, I summed up by saying: "Comrades, you cannot ignore the people. They are our ultimate weapon. Only dreamers by nature, conspirators by temperament, think we few can stamp our will on the masses. So long as the majority refuse, because they do not yet understand what is happening, to take power for themselves, no minority, however brave and clever we are, can impose our desires upon them."

After that, I was elected to the CenCom, topping the list of winning candidates. "The most revolutionary of Russian parties now has the most revolutionary of Russian leaders—watch out!" I am pleased to say this handsome tribute was paid in an interview with an afternoon paper by the other lawyer from Simbirsk, Alexander Kerensky. I have regarded him, since the murder of Rasputin, as the most dangerous obstacle in our path. It is reassuring to discover that he returns the compliment. We can only hope that our masters, the people of Russia, may someday also interpret that as praise! Amid the boiling enthusiasm of our militants, it is easy to forget the chilly, suspicious distrust of us that still rules 90 percent of the rest. Talking of Rasputin, I must include here a priceless remark made by Badaev, a Bolshevik deputy in the Duma. Luckily for him, he was convalescing in Switzerland when war broke out so he avoided being sent to Siberia. I had shown him a picture of Rasputin, popeyed and blood-boltered, after the *Starets*'s corpse had been recovered from the frozen Neva. Badaev looked at that face for a while, then he said: "You see what happens, Ilyich. One of the people gets to have the ear of the Tsar, and the nobles kill him." I wrote it down because I thought it probably conveyed much better the general feeling of the masses than my own joy at the flushing away of another piece of monarchist filth.

MAY 4   PETERSBURG   1917

Podvoisky has certainly been doing a marvelous job promoting our recently launched popular paper for troops in the fighting line. My name for it was *Soldatskaya Pravda* (*Soldiers' Truth*). Somehow, it didn't go down as well in practice as it should have done in theory. Then Nikolai renamed it *Trench Chat,* overprinted in red, with the message running round the border—IS YOUR LETTER HERE?

This puzzled me at first. "But if practically no soldier is reading it, how many will be writing to it?"

Nikolai thought that quite a joke. "You've got to prime the pump, *Starik*," he said. "We wrote all the letters here. We competed with each other to find out who could think up the most dreadful anecdote about bad food, hopeless officers, poor equipment, wrong orders and so on."

"We've overdone it," I told them all afterward. "Nothing can be so hellish as that." But anyway, the issue was due and we couldn't hang about.

"We didn't get any response. A couple of weeks passed. We geared up to go to press again without any genuine letters. Then, sacks of them started to arrive. The men in the trenches had taken all that time spelling out their own stories. They were staccato, like telegrams. And almost every one began—'You think *that* was rotten? Wait until you hear what went on here . . .' " And there followed stories of corruption, brutality, cowardice, squalor, privation, no propagandist could invent.

"We print the most impressive. And we write back to every single one—thanking him for writing, giving our sympathy, passing along the latest Bolshevik slogans. I've got twenty women down there, including your Nadya. Most of them do nothing but answer readers of *Trench Chat* fourteen hours a day."

Not all Podvoisky's brainwaves are as effective as that. In fact, if a really wild and weird project comes floating along the corridor for my backing, I call it a "Podvoiskyism." And half the time I've even got the author right. Still, it's better than being what I call an "Early Bolshevik"—a term Kamenev and Stalin and a few others here have taken to regarding as a compliment. More often I mean somebody who tries to deal with the new realities of an actual revolution by repeating formulas learned from books.

What I need now is a way to infiltrate a thousand agitators

into the canteen and dormitories of the Peter garrisons to explain what our policy really is. "They need not be Party members who can make long speeches. The longer the speech, the more issues it will raise that can cause argument. A soldier's attention easily wanders. After five minutes, he'll be angry or asleep. All he needs is a few words he can understand."

Nikolai looked slightly embarrassed. I suppose he didn't want to point out that the Party—and particularly me as the leader most targeted by the yellow press—was not widely popular these days. Any of our known militants going into Army squares and huts might be torn to pieces. There was no way we could get one single speaker inside. Where would a thousand come from?

I let him shake his head for a while. "Soldiers aren't the only fighters in uniform," I explained. "Why not send *sailors,* Bolshevik sailors from Kronstadt? No soldier will refuse to listen to a fellow serviceman. Our man will only have to repeat this line from our program. On land, on bread, on peace. All these must come under the control of the *people.* This is our main point."

MAY 9   PETERSBURG   1917

Our man in the traffic office at the Finland station reports: arrived 4 A.M. this morning, no press, no welcome committee, no bands, a trainload of Russian émigrés who had crossed Germany in "sealed" carriages. Passenger list: responsible person in charge, Martov; other "names," Lunacharsky and Manuilsky (Bolsheviks), SR leader Natanson. Total: 205 persons, officially categorized as 58 Mensheviks, 48 Jewish Bundists, 34 SRs, 25 Anarcho-Communists, 18 Bolsheviks, 22 non-party.

Will all, or any, of *these* be denounced as agents of German Junkerdom? If so, please note Bolsheviks clearly in minority. Perhaps I can get *Pravda* to print a prominent article congratulating them on their enterprise and printing all the names.

MAY 11   PETERSBURG   1917

Glad to see *Trench Chat* is becoming a genuine people's paper. The soldiers really feel they are *writing* it. Thanks to Podvoisky's device of inviting letters it now consists of almost nothing else. It fulfills

my intention, as founder, of making it the only publication in
Russia, perhaps the world, today which prints what the soldiers
are really talking about among themselves. We hardly need to
scatter a sweetening of left-wing politics over the newsprint. What
we want to say, they often are already saying.

I have suggested two other props to our campaign among the
troops. First, we have asked them to appoint some reader in every
group to collect money for the paper's fighting fund. This is not
strictly necessary as our income is now high enough to support
such a legitimate propaganda expense. But it gives soldiers the
feeling that *Chat* belongs to them. And nine times out of ten, the
collector is turning out to be a working-class militant. One of the
strikers the government unwisely exiled to the front, or a former
socialist or anarchist. They are becoming an informal chain of Party
agents. They send us invaluable information on the mood of the
troops, the behavior of the officers, the state of food, weapons,
ammunition, the progress of the fighting, while also passing round
our leaflets.

My second thought was—why should only middle-class sentimentalists and patriots set up tearooms, newspaper libraries and
the like for "Our Boys," usually at the price of them having to
listen to a government orator or join in a few jingoistic ballads?
Our soldiers are very much like any peasants or workers away
from home, I suppose. The uniform gives them a certain extra
solidarity, but what they want to do is buy each other beers, cadge
an occasional vodka, complain among themselves, boast away to
outsiders. So I have opened up "The Trench." It's a kind of proletarian nightclub in the basement under Kshesinskaya's, where
troops can do exactly that. Entrance is (almost) free—well, a cut
price subscription to *Chat*. And those nice civilians "Our Boys"
meet here, middle-aged, fatherly chaps and sisterly, sweet girls?
Well, they could all just happen to be Bolsheviks. This *is* our Party
HQ as well.

MAY 26   PETERSBURG   1917

When I first got back, I was continually whipping on the comrades.
Urging them to abandon compromise, passivity, procrastination,
adopt a revolutionary, aggressive, Bolshevik course. Yet I could
not help also feeling that in practical terms, we were in danger of
running too much in advance of the masses. Now I think we must

be aware of lagging behind. So I'm glad to see that the program of training up and turning out our thousand Bolshevik salesmen in the guise of Kronstadt sailors is booming along. Nikolai Podvoisky is president of the Party's Military Organization. He still walks with a limp from the wound he got charging the Cossacks in '05. This helps give him a real war-veteran look when he takes charge of all activities with a martial flavor.

The first volunteers sent us by young Raskolnikov from Kronstadt seemed hopelessly unfitted, Nikolai told me today. Barely half-literate, often with vocabularies of around six hundred words, they simply did not comprehend the existence of abstract concepts.

"Fine," I said. "A real challenge. I will try to give a speech without any of them—only Peace, Bread, Land. It could even be all negatives—No Tsar, no war, no moneylender, no hunger."

"Please," begged Nikolai. "You are the one speaking in Podvoiskyisms. Think what that actually means. We are talking of a sailor who wrinkles his brow when you ask him if he knows what 'Revolution" is. 'Do you mean the Red Cock?' " asked one."

I know what the Red Cock is—it is what peasants call setting fire to the landlord's house and farm. I must bring it back into my vocabulary.

"I remembered a folk-saying from the Volga you once quoted—'stone polishes stone.' " *Now* I understand what it means. I was about to give up trying to give a shine to your Kronstadt rough diamonds. Then I hit on the scheme of letting them polish each other. We put them in separate rooms, bunches of twenty, with no more than five questions each, and closed the doors. The questions may have been a bit loaded—something like 'Why must the war stop?' and 'Why must the peasants have the land?' But when they came stumbling out at the end of the day, exhausted with thought, they had all the answers and all the reasons. They had reinvented our program on their own. What's more, they thought nobody else had helped them. Which was true. They left very pleased with themselves. They didn't need Bolsheviks to put words in their mouths. If they had problems they couldn't solve, they'd come back and consult Lenin himself."

JUNE 4   PETERSBURG   1917

Second day. First Congress of Soviets. The assembly is to discuss its relationship with the Provisional government. A key subject:

for until this dangerous farce of dual power is ended, the Revolution will remain semi-paralyzed, a man at the crossroads undecided which one to take. Tseretelli, the Menshevik leader, and most of his choir, have been singing the praises of Coalition, with Soviet leaders in the Cabinet. All Russia's responsible, respectable, decent elements in a broad front. That is what we are gradually forging, apparently. And it has supposedly justified itself over and over, if only because it has established that *there is no alternative.* (How often have we heard that phrase recently. Why is it never churned out on the hurdy-gurdy when there really is no choice, but only when the better one staring us straight in the face does not suit the organ-grinder?)

This line did not go down well, even though most of the audience were on the Tsetse Fly's side. Catching the eye of Ivan Smilga across the aisle, I mimed a man vomiting into his hand. He laughed, and in reply held his nose. Someone tapped me on the shoulder—it was Sukhanov, one of the many diary-keepers around Peter today whose ambition, presumably, is one day to have a diary keep them. He publishes edited and buffed-up extracts in *Novaya Zhizn.*

"Glad to see you come out of your underground cave into the light of day from time to time," he whispered, already noting down his own witty phase in case he forgot it. "But, remember, it is not just the Bolsheviks who find this blind and vulgar bragging deeply nauseating."

But Tsetse was buzzing on, spreading a sleeping sickness around the Tauride Palace with every soft, soporific bite. "At this moment in time," he crooned, "there is not a political party in this hall which is ready to say: 'Give *us* supreme power.' " There is no such party in all Russia."

I was on my feet, by a conditioned response, like a fighter who hears the bell for the next round despite being out to the world. I shouted: *"There is such a party.* No party has the right to refuse supreme power. Our Party certainly will not. We Bolsheviks are ready at any moment to take over the government." There was a silence. Then at least a quarter of the delegates stirred, as if suddenly woken, and still unsure whether the disturbance had been inside or outside their dreams. Others had been dozing with eyes open. They initiated elaborate displacement actions, shaking themselves, stretching themselves, as if to demonstrate that they often listened with head back and mouth wide open. Meanwhile, almost everyone explained to everyone else what they thought they had just heard. I slowly lowered myself back into my seat.

I was halfway there when from the massed ranks of the Right came a few artificial guffaws, done for effect, at dictation speed— "Ha, er, HAHA, *heah!*" Then some genuine amusement bled in, grew cresendo, took on a full-blooded, hostile baying.

Laughter is a response, warming, invigorating when invited, but chilling and painful when unwanted. So I rose again.

This time I felt like the prizefighter when the icy water hits his face. I knew I had to box on and strike back as hard as I could. I was leader of the smallest party in the entire assembly—105 reps, out of a total of 1,090. We Bolos could be dangerous to the majority way of life, but only as a pickpocket briefly threatens a rich man who is carrying too much money in his back pocket. A taste of the whip, a few hangings, wonderfully discourage such folk—the "Stolypin neckties" had shown that. We were just a gang of agitators. We could start strikes, mount demonstrations, plot insurrections, squabble in the streets. But take over power, become the government? They couldn't help laughing.

"Tsetse" had not been going to call me, or any of our Party. But now, like the chairman at a music-hall entertainment, he took the temper of the house. He realized that they wanted to see the wild beast Lenin on show especially when unable to do much damage, so outnumbered by hunters and spectators.

"Sharpen your pencils!" I hissed to Sukhanov. I looked round, like a stump orator at Durnovo Park, for the heckler who would provide me with the peg I wanted. I saw a face of the kind I've always disliked, the handsome, power-hungry charmer, a touch of debased Romanov. His saw-teeth were buzzing with spite. It was "Little-Shit" Kerensky, the poison dwarf from the Volga. "So you found a policy on the train, did you?" he jeered.

"We do, indeed, have an economic program," I said slowly, trying to recall what specifics had been agreed at the April Conference. My opponents within the Party would not forgive much off-the-cuff policy-making from a democratically elected leader. I was slightly thrown by the discovery that there were ranks of these deutero-Kerenskies, shop-window dummies ironed into stylishly simple tailored uniforms. I forced myself on.

"This is to arrest fifty . . . No, no half-measures. To arrest the one hundred richest Russian capitalists, our hundred fattest millionaires. Why? *Pour décourager les autres.* Why else?

"Since '05, your bourgeois friends have assumed that any trade unionist must be a revolutionary—how I wish they had been right! So they lost him his job, his liberty, often his life. Now, in 1917, we friends of the workers reserve the right to assume that any financier, factory boss, big businessman, must be an *enemy* of the Revolution. So we'll slam the prison door on him."

I sat down to give way. The bait was well-laid. Kerensky's teeth plowed toward me through a sea of froth. "What remedies are these? Where does Marx encourage such a Mexican bandit vendetta? These are games of evil children—arrest, kill, destroy! What are you—socialist statemen or tsarist policemen?"

I had to reel him in, otherwise "There is such a party" would be dismissed as an arbitrary, individual cast into the wind. The problem was: I had been angling for very different fish the last two months, on street corners, at dock gates, at the bottom of mine-shafts, in the glow of Bessemer furnaces. I had nothing in common with these history professors and literary editors, men of letters and weekly essayists, minor novelists and anthology makers, many of whom had emerged from petty-bourgeois obscurity, festooned with red cockades, and laid claim to youthful victimization or even student martyrdom. They emerged from the cool quiet of studies or libraries, where they lived, even in "Red" Petersburg, lives protected from the intrusion even of their own children. Their idea of political debate, of policy-making, had an academic pedantry alien to someone who was on duty round the clock at the Bolshevik HQ, days and nights. Mine was an existence stained by lies and threats, heated by anger and dispute, burdened by that ever-repeated smear of the German connection. In the first heady March Days, workers had expropriated the capitalist press, awarding papers to their staff, to good causes, to liberal institutions. The Soviet was persuaded to give most of them back, in obedience to the imperative of press freedom, in favor of overpaid hacks and rich proprietors. Within hours, they had mounted an anti-Soviet campaign of abuse, mockery, slander, misrepresentation which has never slackened. The SovExCom regard this as a natural phenomenon, like rain in spring, snow in winter, irritating perhaps, inconvenient, depressing, to which socialists and the like must learn to adapt and adjust.

This flashed through my mind, as Kerensky went on heckling. My only alternative was to speak over the heads of the Soviet to the workers, soldiers, peasants who could read me, at least in our press—after all, *Pravda*'s circulation daily is approaching 400,000. *They* would not think it just a bad joke to suggest arresting millionaires. Factories were closing. Unemployment was soaring. Real wages had dropped, this year alone, from 19.3 rubles a month in January to 13.8 rubles in May. Every mention of a strike was met by an instant lock-out. When employees had to be made redundant, it was always the leaders of the February uprising who were dismissed first. Both sides were paying off old scores. But only one side was featured in the newspapers. The statistics of profits from supposedly bankrupt firms, never before revealed, were sensational by any journalistic standard. But of no interest to our sensational, millionaire-owned press.

I thought I had become hardened in '05, above all watching the last hours of the Moscow insurrection. My carapace is thickening much more rapidly in 1917. A week ago, the Volynsky regiment, one of the first rebels in February, marched into Alexandrovsky Park, outside the windows of my office in Kshesinskaya's, and stood for a day chanting demands that I be shot as a traitor. Yesterday morning I walked out early for a snatch of the sea air pushing in along the Bolshaya Nevka. When I got back, I found I had missed the Organization of Russian War Cripples hammering on the gates with crutches and tin arms, circulating the walls with white sticks and seeing-eye dogs, blocking the pavement with wheelchairs, to publicize their proposition that Lenin be sent back to the Kaiser on a stretcher. They are spread across the anti-socialist press this morning. There is a photograph of one on the front of *Izvestia*. "Sorry, comrade," said its picture editor. "It makes for such a dramatic effect."

These images must be all over Russia. Inessa telephoned last night on an awful line. "Ah, Volodya," she sighed. "I love you because I know you will not let this hurt you. Somebody has to be indestructible. It is your fate that we have chosen you. We hate tsarism, and capitalism. But not because they oppress the good, and the wise, and the brave. No, we hate these autocracies because they distort humanity. They eliminate, they make almost impossible, the survival of any good, wise and brave. It is amazing that not all the masses have become as multilated in mind as those were in body. Imagine a sane person, victim of war, blaming not the munitions millionaires, the bloody generals, the lying politicians, but Lenin. Lenin, who has risked everything he holds dear to abolish capitalism which breeds war, to make armies lay down their arms, to create a future where people dare love each other . . ."

The connection broke before I could assure her I was listening.

So I let them have it— "Tsetse," and "Little Shit," and Chernov, and every face I recognized. When we got power, we would smash the intrigues of the war profiteers, unchanged since the fall of the Tsar. Without their liquidation, all talk of peace is phrasemaking. We would inform the workers of all countries, over the heads of their rulers, that we regard every capitalist regime everywhere as a conspiracy of thieves and plunderers. To me, to any Bolskevik, the new "liberal" foreign minister, Tereschenko, since he collaborates with Anglo-French moneylenders, remains on the same debased moral level as his predecessor, the dismissed Kadet, Professor Milyukov. The only thing to be said in favor of Tereschenko is that he is much, *much* stupider.

They were howling like baboons, which is what I wanted, as I left.

JUNE 9   PETERSBURG   1917

Our man in the traffic office at the Finland station further reports: arrived 4 A.M. this morning, yet another trainload of Russian émigrés who have crossed Germany under special arrangement with the enemy. (Does Parvus get commission on tickets sold?) Official passenger list summarized as—total 187, including 29 Mensheviks, 25 Jewish Bundists, 27 SRs, 26 Anarcho-Communists, 22 Bolsheviks, 19 non-party and 39 "others."

Once again, note, we are in the minority. It looks as if the Zurich-Finland station journey is becoming quite a routine outing for the non-Bolo left. Book here for the Sealed Train! Sit in seats once occupied by Lenin, Martov, Natanson!

Once again, of course, no mention of this suspicious, treasonable operation in any of our capitalist press. What about those "others"? Are we sure they did not have spiked helmets and *sauerkraut* on their boots?

JUNE 10   PETERSBURG   1917

Despite everything the SovExCom and the Cabinet of the ProvGov keep on telling each other about how the country is rallying behind them, how we can forget the class war and concentrate on winning the "real" war, all the information that comes to us from all over contradicts them. Seizures of large estates, burning down of mansions, occupation of state buildings, mutiny of isolated government posts, setting up of peculiar "independent republics." The people are taking the law into their own hands. The generic term for all this, in upper circles of Petersburg anyway, is "Anarchism."

It proves a very handy label. It denotes almost nothing—a black cloud of destructive mania. It connotes almost anything the timid, bourgeois-liberal fears—the raping of nuns, the freeing of criminals, the blowing up of public monuments, the abolition of money, the outlawing of marriage, the bastardization of babies and disappearance of inherited wealth. It is a name at once vague and potent, fanciful and vivid, appallingly modern and horribly prehistoric.

The only ones who love reveling in this evil notoriety more than the yellow press are . . . the Anarchists.

Even before most citizens had taken in that anything was happening in late February, the Communist-Anarchist association set up a power base at Durnovo Park in the heart of Bolshevik Vyborg. The owner, Durnovo, is almost forgotten now, though he takes up quite a few pages of my archives. Sometime minister of the interior, typically choreographer of anti-Semitic pogroms, wholesale hangman and retail bribemonger, he was still a big shit in a small privy—the Council of State—when he died last year. He was temporarily famous as front man for the rising commercial class whom he exhorted, borrowing Guizot's phrase—"*Enrichissez-vouz!*" Few proved reluctant to make the trip to the bank. And one outward and visible sign of his own success at this policy is the vast and rambling Villa Durnovo, itself almost lost inside its even more vast and rambling Park. The Park's great iron gates are in the shape of a pair of giant dung-beetles, each juggling its solar ball of rolling manure—a quaint relic of D.'s late-life interest in Egyptology. No one doubts the sincerity of his admiration for a society which managed to remain unimproved for three thousand years. Through this hive-entrance, today at almost any hour, can be seen issuing and returning the soldier ants of Anarchism—attired in black leather tunics, black Cossack boots, often black motoring helmets, with earflaps and smoked glass goggles, wreathed round, like Laocoön, with bandoliers of cartridges, two or three belts of holstered revolvers, and an occasional string of bronze hand grenades.

This genuine self-raised workers' militia is far more stirring to me than the drums and fifes of any Guards regiment. It is not a view shared by the inhabitants of Peter's city center. To them, the Villa Durnovo is the ogre's hideout, Satan's Den, an urban Brocken where the enemies of mankind gather for a perpetual Walpurgis Night. Here, many will tell you, are tortures beyond the ingenuity of the Spanish Inquisition, orgies Rasputin had not imagined, cells containing many of those prominent folk who have vanished since February from their usual haunts, and large stocks of every kind of weapon, shell, bomb and explosive.

So far the Durnovonians have done little to threaten the rest of the city. From time to time, they mount a quick sortie into another district, seize a house, kick out the occupants and set up a little Durnovo. These outposts are nearly always the town dwellings of the rich. And where the authorities have objected, serving an eviction order, the squatters have obeyed the law and retreated. This does not stop rags like *Rech*, the Kadets' hypocritical scandal sheet, comparing this activity to "the spread of cancer cells."

But earlier today, it seems, Durnovo mounted a more ambitious foray. Nearly a hundred Anarchists, even by their standards heavily armed with mortars and mobile machine guns, invaded the newly built, ultra-modern printing plant of one of our most vulgar and degraded dailies, *Russkaya Volya*. They declared that it would in future be used to publish only the truth. Which, being interpreted, means, of course, Anarchist propaganda.

But all news in Peter of 1917 is out-of-date by the time you've heard it. At midday, it was leaked from the Justice Ministry that government troops had surrounded the paper, disarmed the occupiers (mostly, as it turned out, young ones in fancy dress) and ordered them off the streets. This conformed to the usual pattern. I was just pointing out to a few cronies, in a corner under the stairs at the Tauride, some quirks in the sociology of class behavior. When representatives of the workers take over, for instance, a newspaper, this is an instantly visible act. It occurs out there in the open with a lot of noise, probably a bit of a scuffle. Such street action is very disturbing to the timid, obedient and law-abiding, even among radicals. Whatever its merits, any mass sit-in tends to look extreme and arbitrary, and therefore to be deplored by the moderate center. Things are very different, however, if your rich man takes over the same paper through some undercover financial fiddling, secret acquisition of controlling shares, or the like. Then nothing need obtrude at street level to draw the public's attention to the change. The same staff may carry on under the same title. And it could be some months too late for any organized protest before the readers realize that they are being indoctrinated by a different proprietor.

But I was interrupted by an update on the Anarchist affair. Perevertsev, the justice minister, is accusing the *de facto* tenants of Durnovo of criminal consipracy, a threat to public order, possession of illegally acquired arms, harboring of wanted persons, stolen goods and prisoners detained against their will, all amounting to conduct likely to cause a breach of the peace. These charges require no urgent countermoves from the left. But the minister is pushing his luck with a demand that may easily set off a short fuse to that famous powder keg—he has ordered the Anarchists to get out of Durnovo, and hand it back, *within twenty-four hours,* or face the wrath of the state.

Chief Procurator Bessarabov, with a lot of modest huffing and puffing, proclaims that he will go to Durnovo himself, in person, to serve the writ alone, by hand, tomorrow. I was in earshot when various pink-faced, breathy Meks and SRs begged him not to risk this foolhardy enterprise. Did he not realize that these were not just Anarchists, but *Leninist-*Anarchists? Durnovo was a Bolshevik concentration camp from which no opponent of theirs ever emerged alive. A few nervous glances were then cast in my direction.

"The chief procurator will get the shock of his life," I said. "I think I'd better be there to guarantee his safety."

JUNE 11   PETERSBURG   1917

Bessarabov tried not to look *too* relieved when I introduced myself by the left-hand dung beetle. He saw what I had often seen and what I knew he would see. Either side of the looping drive leading to the Villa, old men sleeping on benches in the sun. Children shrieking around statues and fountains, up ornamental steps, and along flowered arcades. Entwined lovers, laid out in the shadows under bushes like corpses. Kiosks selling tea and *kvass,* giving away papers and pamphlets. The occasional orator idly addressing a handful of strollers. This was my—and Vyborg's—favorite pleasure garden, an amenity that did not diminish Anarchism's popularity in the neighborhood.

The Villa itself, thickly overdecorated in that marzipan style beloved of the jumped-up favorites Inessa once christened "Nouveau-Richelieu," was in perfect museum condition. Most of the furniture had gone, it's true—but then the Villa is surrounded by some of the worst slums in the Western world. Only the chairs are preserved and herded into a large room used for lectures or debates. No Anarchist representative was around. On a point of honor they were continuing their daily agit-prop safaris. Not that their presence would have much assisted the procurator in his inquiries. On principle, I find, no one Anarchist ever takes responsibility for the opinions or actions of any other.

What surprised the chief procurator was the discovery that the Villa had other tenants—an entire wing occupied by that most

clannish and pacific of trade unions, the Amalgamated Association
of Bakers, Confectioners and Cake-makers, also a top floor largely
taken over by the Woman's Support Group for the Factory Militia.
There were no signs of caches of explosives, ammunition, bombs
or shells.

As it became known that Bessarabov was the procurator of
the Ministry of Justice, he was mobbed by friendly visitors. Those
not entirely sure what a procurator is asked him to pencil his
autograph on anything they happened to be carrying. An occasional camera crank ordered him to stand still for three minutes
and have his photograph taken with the baby. Those who thought
they knew what a procurator might be pressed on him small pieces
of paper across which some family grievance had long been la-
boriously copied, and carried about for just such a fortuitous eventuality. They were much like members of the Peter public anywhere.
I suspect he was faintly disappointed.

Even he could see that the Villa Durnovo was no sinister threat
to Civilization As He Knew It. He apologized in the direction of
the Bakers and Woman's Support. The ProvGov had no objection
to the presence of those who had nowhere else to go. Action was
only ever proposed against certain "criminal elements" who had
infiltrated the Anarchists and were giving them a bad name. At
least, this may have been the message he intended to leave behind.
While I was at his side, without exception, all those the procurator
spoke to replied that they were strangers here themselves.

Early this afternoon, the minister issued yet another statement. His ban did not apply to the *Park* in any way. Inside the
Villa, he condemned only those same "criminal elements" (i.e.,
Anarchist-Communist militants) and those irresponsible "political
extremists" (i.e., me and my friends) who were using this now dead
issue to stir up trouble. That is to say—his order had been quietly
rescinded.

The authorities are back-pedaling fast. But now it may be too
late to stamp out the fuse. To the surprise of almost nobody else,
Peter is in an uproar, verging on an uprising. One or two of the
more left SRs, and harder Menshies, have been taking aside members of our Party to whisper the question—Is this what Ilyich meant
by *"There Is Such a Party?"* In other words—are we Bolsheviks
planning to seize power, using Durnovo as our pretext?

It is a question we have to ask ourselves. Most of industrial
Vyborg has rallied to its Anarchist neighbors. Twenty-eight factories promise to strike tomorrow if armed eviction proceeds. Durnovo has become the bristling fortress of bourgeois fantasy. Its

wireless transmitter has broadcast appeals asking the sailors of Red Kronstadt to join them in street protests. The All-Russian Congress of Soviets, meeting at the Military Academy on Basil Island, is thronged with would-be demonstrators.

From the Congress balcony, I look down on Anarchist envoys bustling about to enroll supporters, black and thrusting as stag beetles in rut. They receive a much warmer welcome from the spectators than from the delegates. For the Workers', Soldiers' and Peasants' Parliament is once more siding with the bourgeois politicians. The Anarchists *must* obey the rule of law, they cry. Instead of acting as (at worst) loyal opposition, the Soviet leaders are taking on the function of the vanished police. How long before we have to label them the class enemy?

Without our doing anything very much, the balance of support among the proletariat of the capital is swinging back toward us. Only the Bolsheviks refuse to compromise, decline to support ProvGov policy. Regiments come to Alexandrovsky Park now to cheer Lenin. It is about time we did *something*.

JUNE 12   PETERSBURG   1917

Peter is gradually, but perhaps unstoppably, coming to the boil. That neutralizing of the "Communist Commune of Kronstadt," this abortive operation designed to "fumigate the nest" at Durnovo—these are only excuses. The unrest sprouts from one real, deep-rooted injustice—the miserable lives led by the mass of poor workers in the towns, the poor peasants in the countryside. They want to express bottled-up feelings in a way that cannot be ignored. And all their complaints are linked together. None can be solved on its own, or piecemeal by an installment plan, without a complete change in society.

What the masses want, I am certain, is really to hear such views put simply and forcefully. When I denounce the "ten capitalist ministers" and suggest the arrest of "the hundred richest millionaires," an audience of Mensheviks laughs. When I say that, if the Mensheviks do not agree, they will have to be taken out as well, they laugh again. But I think I notice a faint bleat of alarm in that last, self-satisfied, amusement. The only point is—who laughs last? I know the workers and peasants who did manage to hear me, at a distance, and through others, nevertheless felt a bond of agreement. Most Peter plebs I meet are a thousand times to the left of the Chernovs and the Tseretellis. They may even be a hundred times to the left of most Bolsheviks. Every party, so far, which has claimed to speak in the people's name has deceived them. Millions are starting to understand this. Few of them are very surprised at the crookedness of politicians. But do they realize *There Is Such a Party* which is not a fraud? I doubt it. They have to discover that *we* stand for what *they* want above all else. And we have yet to realize how powerful we can be when we have their strength behind us. We must start a two-way flow. We must find out who the masses really are, and they must find out who we really are. We have nothing to fear from each other.

Take the question of war. We are not against it simply because we want to stop soldiers killing, or being killed. We are not pacifists. Nothing great has ever been achieved in history without force. Violence is the midwife of change. Every recruit understands it is the job of the soldier to kill, or be killed. We too know that at our moment of truth, we must all be willing to fight or die. This imperialist war lies at the heart of all today's conflicts and crises. The bourgeoisie must keep the war going in order to stop the advance of the Revolution. For the proletariat, the best way to end the war is to keep the Revolution going. It is as simple as that.

JUNE 13   PETERSBURG   1917

All last night, until early this morning, I chaired a meeting of the entire Bolshevik leadership in Kshesinskaya to decide on our tactics. Our Military Organization reports that emergency plans are ready. Maps of key points to be occupied—railway termini, postal and telegraph offices, bridges, telephone exchanges, power stations—have been printed in dozens on the *Pravda* presses. Nikolai (Podvoisky), Ivan Tenisovich (Smilga), Sergei (Gusev) are our main experts and have studied the art of "urban guerrilla" fighting very closely. I think Gusev popularized the term—certainly I had never heard it before I came across it in one of the papers he read to our Party CenCom. I remember it had to be explained to me.

How easy it is to remain stuck in the past. How comforting to assume that the problems of seizing control of a twentieth-century metropolis like Peter will still be much the same as in even the Haussmanized Paris of 1848 and 1871. I'd studied the works of General Cluseret, veteran suppressor of the workers at the barricades on that first occasion, minister of war for the Communards on the second, in between a staff officer in the American Civil War, at the Geneva Library in '05. This is no longer sufficient. Giving a briefing to Ivan, Nikolai and Sergei last month, I advised them to get out of the city architect's files the plans of the Tauride, the Smolny, the Marinsky, the Winter Palace. They exchanged smiles. "Whatever for?" they asked.

A spasm of irritation jumped in my guts. It was a rather inventive suggestion, getting a monopoly of the blueprints. "What for?" seemed a childish retort. *Because* these were the centers held by our opponents, the Provisional government, the ExCom of the Soviet, the top civil servants. To defeat them, we would have to storm their buildings, winkle them out and occupy the sites with our own people. That's "what for . . ." They smiled again. Then Gusev, theorist and historian of war explained.

"True, that's where the powerful *people* are. But in a modern capital, it is not where the power lies. To exert their authority, these people need to send messages to their underlings. We will cut their telephone lines! We can stop, censor, rewrite or merely monitor, whichever suits us, their cables and telegrams! They need to move troops, or bands of armed volunteers, around the city? By raising the Nikolaievsky, the Troitsky, the Dvortsovy, the Liteiny bridges, we can isolate Basil Island, Old Peter and Vyborg from official, bourgeois Petersburg! Or from each other, as we choose! They will need to import troops, to divert supplies, to escape even? We will control all signal boxes! Whenever we want, as it is most convenient to our plans, and most damaging to theirs, we can plunge the whole city, or any section of it, into total blackout!

"A place like Peter these days no longer operates by ranks, titles, chains of command, orders and counterorders. In this new age, it works by machinery. Machinery that we workers, engineers, electricians, technicians, train and tram drivers know more about than all those bureaucrats, pen-pushers, office *chinovniki*, former professors of history, teachers of grammar, courtroom baritones —sorry, Ilyich!"

Of course! As soon as I encountered the basic idea, I could feel it was right. That is how revolutionaries must function in a modern age. But still, I wanted to know what about fighting in the streets, barricades, sniping, and demonstrations of workers with guns? We would never be able to keep the citizens of Petersburg in 1917 at home. After all, we had seen plenty of street battles here, and in Moscow, in '05. Here, once again, during the "April Days"? Surely it wouldn't all be pulling plugs and switches? (Was there a note of regret in my voice?)

Smilga was quick to reassure me. Ivan Tenisovich looks like a first-year student not yet used to living alone and taking care of himself. His hair is thinning at the front but below his collar at the back. His goatee beard is hardly more than a piece of fluff left over by someone who cut himself learning to shave. His overlarge spectacles are like those given to a primary-school swot yet seem to have remained one size ahead of his face as he grew up. He is the most precocious rebel I have ever met.

He startled me the other day when he remarked that his revolutionary consciousness was awoken when the SR Karpovich shot the minister of education, Bogolepov. I keep an index of such things in my head, especially dates and figures. I could not help totting up the sum—"But that was in '01. And you were born in 1892?"

"Yes," he observed, with a hint of apology. "I held strong religious and monarchist views until the age of nine or ten. It was '04, perhaps '05, before I was a complete atheist and communist."

"Then you were . . ."

"Oh, twelve or thirteen. It wasn't until January 1907, when I was fourteen, that I joined the Party."

I did not doubt him. He has been a member of the Party's CenCom since April. And he is just about to celebrate his twenty-fifth birthday.

On another occasion, he made some passing reference to Sasha's death. I turned away, without comment. Everyone who knows me knows that I do not open such private corners of my life, and I thought him more sensitive than most. He noticed the sudden chill, and put his freckly, boy's hand on my sleeve.

"Forgive me, *Starik*. I understand. My father was hanged with a Stolypin necktie in '06. Arrested, tried, condemned and executed within the hour. For the crime of being a landowner who chaired a Committee of Socialist Peasants."

So I was content to be teased by him over the future of urban guerrilla warfare. At his age, I was standing, like a gauche sixth-former, being icily patronized by the great headmaster, Plekhanov.

"The Revolution—or so *we* think—will still begin and end with the clash of arms on the streets. But the deciding factor in this new situation, our heavy artillery, so to speak, will be the ability to manipulate the technology of the city. It will be the greasy hand of the mechanic that gives history its final push. Appropriate, don't you think, that the proletariat should win or lose through its skill with a proletarian weapon?"

Nevertheless, this evening I questioned our MilOrg on how

our Red Guards are progressing. I am told they are drilled, disciplined, psychologically and politically prepared for action, nine out of ten equipped with some kind of weapon. Liaison with the forces also goes well—especially the Baltic Fleet (Smilga), Kronstadt (Raskolnikov), the Peter and Paul garrison (Gusev), the key Machine-Gun Brigade (Podvoisky). We are ready. But for what? All our informants are warning us of a massive protest, possibly violent, that workers and soldiers all over the city are muttering has been prepared for the fifteenth, the day after tomorrow. But who can be organizing it, if it isn't us? And it isn't us. Can it be a trap? I propose: *it should be us*. We will simply take it over. There is much dispute. But finally it is agreed—as the clear white of a long illuminated Petersburg night melts into the misty white of a Petersburg morning. We will accept the risk. The date: two days from now, at 2 P.M. A fire is lit in the furnace of the locomotive, the engine begins to roll. Slowly though, with the brake half on.

I chose a bedroom at random for a few hours' sleep. It was small but exquisite, a tented gondola, with mattress upon mattress of swansdown, a basket of luxury I had never pictured. I asked who used to sleep there. Smilga laughed—"Far above our station. It belonged to the former Tsar's former mistress's secretary's maid."

In the afternoon, I sat in a curtained retiring-room off the Grand Hall collecting the good news. Enter left, a stream of messengers who had been out on horseback, motorcycle and bike to monitor reactions to our decision among the workers and soldiers. All bring back reports of solid enthusiasm, promises of massive support.

Enter right, around teatime, Kamenev with the bad news. All yesterday he had been sighing "premature, rash, impulsive . . ." Eventually I had to stop him and point out, win or lose, few revolutions had ever been so planned, down to the last detail. All that was in doubt was the timing. Anyway, all we had on our official menu, at the moment, was a *peaceful* demo. Not even a small street brawl, let alone an armed insurrection.

Now he was off again. The ExCom of the Peter Soviet had learned of our decision and immediately denounced any public gathering for June 15. The assembled Congress of Soviets is to be asked to confirm an order banning it. The government has announced that any resistance to the order will be suppressed with "all the power at our disposal."

A roundup of our CenCom members available this evening —a quorum of ten—finds no backing for Kamenev. We will go ahead. We have little choice. To go into reverse could leave us isolated. Most of our new followers would desert wholesale to the Anarchists. Still, I do not order full-steam, but keep, so far as I can, one hand on the brake lever.

JUNE 14   PETERSBURG   1917

Brake or not, when Bolsheviks move, they move. I woke early, took one of my early-morning walks round the Old City and across the Grenadersky bridge into the workers' Vyborg side. Everywhere here our posters are already up, ink still wet, lumpy paste dripping. It is a proclamation signed by our Central Committee, endorsed by the Central Bureau of Factory Committees. It calls on the proletariat of Petersburg to take part in an orderly manifestation against the threatened counterrevolution at 2 P.M. tomorrow. There is a short, measured summing-up of the situation—nothing inflammatory. (I dictated it myself.) But the most important part is the list of slogans under which we Bolsheviks intend to march. There is a well-tried formula, understood by all parties, by the government and the Soviet, even by the newspapers and the foreign diplomats, to measure which section of the political spectrum is currently favored by a changeable populace. This is done by counting the numbers who carry placards and banners supporting the slogans advertised in advance by each party or faction. As our Choice for the Day, we recommend the following:

1) "Down with the tsarist Duma!"
2) "Down with the 10 Minister-Capitalists!"
3) "All Power to the All-Russian Soviet of Workers', Soldiers' and Peasants' Deputies!"
4) "Long Live the Control and Organization of Industry!"
5) "End the War!"
6) "Neither a Separate Peace with Wilhelm nor Secret Treaties with the French and British Capitalists!"
7) "Bread, Peace, Freedom!"

Myself, I would endorse 1, 2, 5 and 7—not least because, as well as being direct and extreme, they are the shortest and easiest to copy. Still, I do not reject the others. Something there for almost everybody on the Left.

　　Another afternoon and evening at what everyone now calls just "Kshesinska's." It begins to look as if there will be more guns being shouldered through these streets toward the Champ de Mars than on the battlefields. What can go wrong? I always answer rhetorical questions. I answer myself. What can go wrong is . . .

(1) Kerensky may pull a couple of divisions back from the battlefront (a popular move among trenchies) and launch them on the home front. Here, they would be invited to make mincemeat of our lightly armed greedy workers, a few Bolshy spies in the pay of the Kaiser, and the barrack-room layabouts who have never sniffed a firework thrown in anger. (There is a report that these divisions are already on their way. But Gusev has just rung our *Pravda* correspondent at the forward HQ, a sergeant in the Pay Corps. He has extracted a denial from Supreme Commander-in-Chief Kerensky. "Little-Shit" is not content to say "No" but puts his arm in a sling, mounts a saluting rostrum and prates: "I give my solemn oath. Soldiers of Russian democracy marching out of the factories and homes of revolutionary Petrograd as we now call it, to fight the war against the reactionary powers invading our great Fatherland? Yes, and again yes. But democratic warriors of our great Fatherland marching toward revolutionary Petrograd to combat the workers? Never, ever." So that's all right. The life of a solemn oath is about a month.)

(2) Kerensky could mount an offensive in the field to coincide with our offensive in the streets. If he won some early victories, captured a few prisoners—enough of a triumph anyway to look good in the photogravures of the Sunday papers—he would stir up a lot of ghastly patriotic emotions among the bourgeoisie. Also I'm sorry to say, among many thousands of the masses. No sign of this yet. If it does happen—and why is K. at the front otherwise when all the medals are to be won here?—then I am afraid we can only wait for the attack to fail, the public's rapture drain away when they read the casualty lists. Our most opportune moment might be during a *heavy German counterattack*!

Kamenev has reverted to muttering about "hotheads" and "intellectual hooligans." I had authorized him to join the Cen-ExCom of the All-Russian Congress of Soviets, believing he could do no harm there. Hoping he might even be able to bring us back a little useful intelligence. All that has happened is that they so outnumber and overwhelm him that his Bolshevik spirit—always very dilute—evaporates.

He says CenExCom have heard tell of our renewed determination to proceed with Sunday and are foaming with hostility. Chkheidze personally quizzed him about the operation—"I refuse to confirm or deny," squeaks Kamenev, pouring sweat. The debates of the Congress were then interrupted for yet another motion on the Bolsheviks, this time specifically banning unlicensed demonstrations in the city for three days. It was passed *nem. con.*

Kamenev now insists I call *our* CenCom together again and ask them to reconsider. This time sixteen of us meet, the arguments are once more rehearsed. On a vote, all except two (Kamenev and Nogin) reauthorize the demonstration.

The pair then leave for the Tauride once more. Kamenev turns at our heart-shaped, frosted-glass doors to utter a tiny roar: "When this disaster becomes Party history, your names will be on the wrong side of the page!"

JUNE 15   PETERSBURG   1917

As yesterday shaded into today, the planning staff of our Party—CenCom, MilOrg, Peter Exec, FactComm reps and SoldierSpokes—were still threading among the giant palms at the Crystal Palace end of Kshesinska's. We had just about pegged out and pinned up on our maps and bulletin boards everything that should be arranged for 2 P.M. By 2 A.M. most of the members had drifted off to find beds nearer to their positions on the route.

I was sitting alone on a little gilt chair admiring the almost mathematical elegance of the arrangements. I was particularly pleased with the march formation I devised to meet some tactical problems we had experienced in '05. Then, spontaneous overflowing rivers of our people, unknown to each other, moving to no timetable, possessing no objective, had wandered across the city like spilled milk across the kitchen table. When the government order was given to attack them, most did not even know they were being sprayed by machine guns, raked by massed rifles, sliced by the sabers of Cossacks and mounted-police "Pharaohs," sniped at by plainclothes agents and Black Hundred groups with revolvers, until much too late. Their fat, wriggling columns were stopped ahead and behind, cut up from the sides, the way I once saw a blindworm segmented and devoured by soldier ants.

Never again. Each section of the marchers is to be equipped with marshals and stewards, clearly badged, who will steer and pace them. In front and rear are small, well-trained bands of armed escorts, ready to protect the column. Along parallel streets to right and left, there will move Red Guards from the factories as volunteer soldiers and sailors, under Bolshevik officers. These will flush out any pockets of danger.

Then Kamenev and Nogin reappeared, bearing yet another message from Soviet CenExCom. If a single marcher crossed Petrograd today, the Bolsheviks would be instantly expelled from the Soviet, declared enemies of the Revolution, deprived of the right to bear arms, and evicted from any state property seized from tsarist supporters. Kamenev did not believe our CenCom would want to defy that anathema.

Only five of us could be found on the premises. There was no sense, I had decided, in trying the case before the full body of the planning staff, a score or so of whom are still somewhere around. So the quintet adjourned to the former bedroom of the former Tsar's former mistress's secretary's maid. In this lacy intimacy knee to knee, we chewed over, for the second time in six hours, the depleted pros and increasing cons of continuing with today's great parade.

Kamenev had always been anti. And Nogin had always been pro-Kamenev. In minutes, Zinoviev, the great pendulum, swung to their side. The demonstration was therefore canceled by a majority vote. I pointed this out, and rose. Kamenev and Zinoviev bleated a joint protest. It was not fair. History should not be left registering their opposition without also recording that Sverdlov and I had advocated proceeding with "the adventure." "That is not correct," I replied. "I will not be written down on the wrong page. I *abstain*." "So do I," chimed in Sverdlov, with what seemed some relief.

But then our work really began. We had to set about summoning back the rest of CenCom, MilOrg, etc., etc. and get them to call in their teams. It was the worst organizational task I have ever attempted. We had to ask our cell-leaders, block-captains and roving agitators, who earlier had been straining like greyhounds in the slips, to go round sticking CANCELED over our posters, calming down their followers, explaining our change of mind.

"Coitus interruptus" was the entire cabled message we got back from Fyodor Fyodorovich, better known as Raskolnikov. The Bolshevik leader of the Kronstadt Soviet was touring the big ships of the Baltic Fleet on a warming-up mission for us. His answer seemed to me unduly crude, if unfortunately accurate. Though I was grateful for the easing of tension through the laughter it caused. Smilga even went on to argue that it was not a metaphor. Fyodor had just yoked himself to the fiery Larissa Reisner, that young poet and orator whom Trotsky once identified to me, swearing it was no exaggeration, as having "the mind and body of an Olympian goddess"! Apparently, her new partner, Fyodor, was half hoping for an excuse to be summoned home to her.

This decision of ours will be easier for our activists to understand than to justify. It has been taken to protect the Party, not to assist the workers. Once again, our short-term tactics will appear at variance with their long-term aims. The CenExCom of the All Russian Union of Soviets had heard the same rumors we had: an imminent stormy eruption onto the streets by masses of angry workers and soldiers. But they assumed *we* must be behind it. And when they saw our posters they felt sure they were right.

As I see our situation, we are caught in a cleft stick. The masses have begun looking to us to lead them. Yet clearly the only prudent, indeed the only rational, course is for us to refuse that role. *This time!* There are several good reasons for inaction. There always are—that is the worst of politics. This is *not* the move we should play in the game. Growing evidence suggests that the balance of forces on the board is advantageous. Forced to pretend it is our move, we would have been blamed for any ill results. It might then have provided an excuse for our suppression. However, by giving way to the Soviet, I calculate we can wriggle out with the least damage to our reputation, and the minimal threat to our survival as a legal party.

After all, I think it was this argument that shifted the balance in that scented boudoir. We can hardly keep chanting the slogan "All Power to the Soviet" and then refuse to obey the Soviet when it exerts its power. As I had stressed at our All-Russian Conference of the Bolsheviks in April, as I often stress, there is no more dangerous mistake for a revolutionary advance-guard than to base its tactics on its own subjective wishes. Nevertheless, I will inform the full CenCom that I, for one, do not intend to go on refusing to take the opportunities presented to us by increasingly frustrated and suffering people. We will cry "Sheep!" once too often.

For the moment, the scales are not quite ready to tip in our favor. This is always our hardest period, the waiting. It calls for maximum calmness, caution, restraint and organization. No pretext must be given for the reactionaries to attack us. Very soon, we will need to attack them. For this, no pretext will be necessary. It will be simply our next step in the ascent to real Revolution.

JUNE 16   PETERSBURG   1917

Professional revolutionaries usually assume that the hardest part of our job will be to concentrate the maximum number of the exploited into one place at one time, thus showing them that, though weak as individuals, their strength is irresistible when united. I have never before come across the opposite problem—how to disperse your own supporters; damp down the fires you have lit; turn back home the forces hurrying to save you. When straining to raise up the aroused masses, you at least have history on your side. We are struggling against the current, defying nature, attempting to reverse gravity and force water to fall upward.

Yet we have done it.

In the end, the working class citizens of Peter obeyed our instructions. Our agents managed to reach *Pravda* before it "went to bed." They wrenched out a peppery recipe for potential insurrection and substituted a thin, watery plaint about the imminence of counterrevolution, the need for the Left to prop up the wavering Congress of Soviets. At *Okopnaya Rech* (*Trench Chat*), egged on I suspect by some firebrands of the MilOrg, the staff refused to reset their front page. For two hours, their presses continued to roll off copies with the banner headline YES, THERE IS SUCH A PARTY! while editors and printers stood guard together with Brownings cocked. They only stopped the run when they found I had already seized their distribution vans, and removed the wheels. At Kronstadt (so Raskolnikov complains) he was only able to divert the mutinous wrath of thousands of rifle-brandishing sailors by standing at the head of the pier with a bayonet in his hand while Larissa floated by, distracting them with a performance of her latest cycle of satirical songs. "Even then it might not have worked," he said, "if there had not been so many Anarchists in the front ranks. As everyone knows, Anarchists can resist anything, except a bit of drama and a beautiful girl."

Even the Soviet leadership had to admit that yesterday we kept the streets rather emptier than usual by scaring off the middle-class Sunday strollers. In the late afternoon, its CenExCom staged a postmortem on the *putsch*-that-never-was—significantly far away from the crowded, unruly galleries of the Tauride in the almost-unfindable Naval Academy. I had warned Kamenev, our man on the ExCom, to insist on making a preliminary statement, and always retain the offensive. So Lev Borisovich probably feeling a bit guilty at having been "the midwife who dropped the baby" (as the saying goes) was in fine, ironic form. We Bolsheviks had arranged a peaceful parade, a right guaranteed all parties by the February Revolution, and never before denied. When this time it *was* denied, we instantly canceled the event. We had advised our people to forgo their freedom to protest in public against "the capitalist ministers" and "the imperialist war," even though this made us distinctly unpopular. We, the dissident minority in the Soviet Congress, had bowed to the authority of the ruling majority. For this, we had been slandered with accusations of adventurism and near-treason. We had acted throughout like democrats, like comrades. Wherein lay the evidence for a charge of illegality in our first move, or disloyalty in our second?

The fanatically anti-Bolshevik faction (led by Tseretelli, Dan, Leiber, Chkheidze) had hoped to isolate, then excommunicate us. Chkheidze opened by denouncing us for a breach of the political peace, an attempt to topple society into Anarchy. "In future," he insisted, "demonstrations by individual parties ought to be permitted only when licensed by the Soviet. None, except those arranged by the Soviet itself, should ever include armed detachments. Those who break these rules should be expelled from the Soviet and lose all the privileges membership conferred."

Everybody there with an ounce of political *nous* knows what this means. This act of almost papal control could be directed at only one party—the Bolsheviks. No other party's followers live so much on the streets. Since we are a minority and our opponents, the SRs and Mensheviks, the majority, it would mean we could never demonstrate again. Like Antaeus lifted away from his mother Earth, cut off from our umbilical connection, we would shrivel and die.

It took only a bit more *nous* to understand that the decree might have other effects, perhaps not always so pleasing to the parties presently in control. Kamenev, a decent tactician when he lets his brain rule his stomach, sat still, waiting to see who would spot the self-inflicted wound. It was Bulkin, a reactionary Mek (and, I'm sorry to say, an absolutely genuine, horny-handed proletarian) who got there first. In his nasal, Vyborg whine, he demanded to know whether *"Professor"* Chkheidze had considered that the few sometimes become the many, and *vicky-verky?* Did the Mensheviks want to give a warrant to the Bolshies, should they ever park their arses up there on the platform to kick all non-Bolshies off the streets? To throw behind bars any who poked a

nose outdoors to protest against majority policies? These new masters would be able then to point out that their opponents had
willingly voted away their own prerogatives. And what would be
the answer?

Zinoviev intervened: the Bolsheviks would very soon be the
majority, probably already were the majority. either way, we did
not advocate dog licenses for those who disagree. Bulkin "Esquire"
need not worry. In a true socialist state, he would be so rare, he
would probably be protected. In a zoo.

Tsetse could not stand this. These criminal Bolsheviks were
somehow escaping from the dock and jumping down into the court
to mock their prosecutors. He had already forgotten how he had
laughed in my face when I said we were ready to take power. Now
he claimed to have known all along that Lenin was only waiting
to trigger off a deep-laid conspiracy.

"It failed yesterday only because we caught him in the act,"
he shouted. "But he will try again tomorrow. And the next day.
And the day after that. The Bolsheviks are determined upon a
coup d'état, not a revolution. They know this is the only way they
will ever get power. The Bolsheviks claim in today's *Pravda* that
counterrevolution had lifted its head. Where is this monster? The
only force rearing its head against the Revolution belongs to the
Bolsheviks. They have gone beyond propaganda. The weapon of
argument has been replaced by arguments with weapons. We too
must find other methods. Their private army, the Red Guards,
must be disbanded. Every Bolshevik must be disarmed. . . ."

Kamenev had another good moment. Above the uproar, he
could be heard on a point of order. "Mr. Minister, former comrade! If what you say is not just verbiage, why stop at words? I
insist you produce your evidence, arrest me here and now, and
put me on trial for plotting against the Revolution!"

Tseretelli remained silent. So the Bolshevik contingent walked
out, as I had often suggested, at the exact moment when the feeling
in the assembly was running strongest our way. Long experience
of public rows has taught me that this confers a striking psychological advantage. The others cannot help feeling that you must
be *very, very sure* of yourselves to withdraw when you are poised
for a knockout!

I wish I had been there—I feel I was! This is what I call politics
in the highest form, true revolutionary debate, so different from
the empty, sterile theatrics of the Duma, or even more so the
schoolboy ruderies and posings of the Reichstag or the House of
Commons, so much shadowboxing. At Party conferences, among

all groups of Social Democrats, even in the Soviet Congress, phrases, slogans, proposals, questions are as much *things* as thoughts. They refer to real actions in an actual world outside. We are playing a sort of three-dimensional chess where each piece throws a giant shadow beyond the hall, beyond the city, often across country, and beyond the frontier.

I have collated various versions of the reactions to yesterday by our enemies and rivals. The Congress debate went on after our delegation strode out and I have a report on this too—a carbon of the article Sukhanov has submitted to Gorky's *Novaya Zhizn*. According to this, Tsetse was only grazed by Kamenev's dart. But he collapsed under the rapid fire of someone who is in some ways a far more dedicated opponent of ours. Perhaps because his views have frequently been parallel and often close. Of all people, Julius Osipovich (Martov), my first comrade-in-arms in '96, my former *fides Achates*. Julius's mind can move at the speed of a bullet and grasp the most complex situation in seconds. His weakness is that he is, as I dubbed him in London in 1900, "the archetypal journalist," always willing to talk or write rather than do.

He took Tsetse's speech apart, though, phrase by phrase, idea by idea, demonstrating step by step that it was an artificial edifice which would collapse at the door slam of reality. This Bolshevik *coup d'état*—did the government have any proof that it had been timed for yesterday? If so, could the evidence be laid before the Soviet? If there was no actual evidence, then wouldn't the minister agree that it was the measures he advocated which were unlawful and uncomradely? Then, what about this "band of conspirators"? If that was all that Bolshevism consisted of, why not let this handful of the heirs of Nechaev and Bakunin have their lonely parade?

Surely anyone who had ever taken a walk outside the marble halls of the Tauride knew that we were talking about a mass movement of unprecedented proportions, much of it aligned with the Bolsheviks. If even one in three workers and soldiers were inclined to an armed uprising, then no suppression of conspirators, no banning of parties, no licensing of marches would stop them. If this really were about to happen tomorrow, or the next day, or the day after, then the Soviet and the government could only combat it by setting up a capitalist dictatorship, introducing martial law, and drowning the revolutionaries in blood.

Then he turned to the "disarming of the Red Guards." Did the minister think there was some governmental monopoly, some municipal ration, of weapons, that could be forbidden to the Bolshevik CenCom? Did he not understand that today three-quarters of all proletarian men and the soldiers on reserve already had guns? And possibly half of them were beginning to follow the leadership of Lenin? To disarm them would be to disarm a people. Who would do it? The minister was advocating rule by direct force but he did not possess the force. There were no "other methods."

Tsetse seemed to have been flattened. And it looks as if we will live to fight another day, even if temporarily dashed. What a speech, though! I know how much it must have hurt, having been exposed to many such onslaughts by Julius myself. Yet I think Tsetse has understood us rather better than Martov has. Very much depends on our next step.

First, I have to appear before an augmented Special Commission of my own Party to explain myself. *They* will not be put off with tricks of logic and historical illustrations. I may even have to resign. (Stalin and Smilga, fierce partisans of turning yesterday's march into a frontal onslaught, tendered theirs and had them refused!) But I have learned, it would seem, more than they have from the enterprise. I also think I may have a surprise up my sleeve.

JUNE 17   **PETERSBURG**   **1917**

My appearance before the Commission did not begin well. I had arrived early and taken a back corner seat so that few of the members realized I was there. I do this at meetings. It gives me a chance to take some soundings of the temperature, test it with my toe, rather than throw myself off the top board in a belly flop. This time, the water was *icy*. And I was not encouraged by a little pantomime staged by one of the firebrands from MilOrg. He upended a sack on the platform table and indicated the torrent of cardboard pieces clattering out. They were, unmistakably, torn-up Party cards.

"And that's just from the Putilov," he announced. "At Kronstadt, they'd have torn us up," added somebody else. Most sat silent and grim. I was not just a witness, I was the accused at a court-martial.

Sverdlov bawled the meeting to order. "Comrade Lenin will be here at any moment to lead a discussion on the cancellation of the demonstration, and deal with your criticisms. But I do not have to remind you that our Party operates on the principle of democratic centralism. The decision was taken, after several sessions, by all available members of the CenCom. The voting, as usual, was not secret. And you will see, in the summary you should all have on your seats, that the final change of plans was made at the insistence of Comrade Kamenev while Comrade Lenin abstained."

Yakov Mikhailovich, his skin pale as milk, his turban of hair, moustache and little beard so black they could be dyed, is just becoming known to a wider Party membership. His highly Jewish appearance causes some confusion at times because he looks so much as if he might be Trotsky's smaller, younger brother. He is our best organizer, "fixer" might not be unfair, carrying in his head a continually updated roll call of key members, each entry complete with potted biog. He was already exercising this talent on my behalf, recognizing and exchanging chat with a string of delegates I had never seen before. However, his buttering did not much oil and relax these frozen types. One of them, the same who had brought in the sack of cards, interrupted—"Comrade Chairman, we are not a bunch of schoolkids. I've been a Bolshevik since '03. Do we have a leader or do we not? And where is he?"

This gave me the cue I might have written into the script. My voice from the back caught almost everyone off balance (though Yakov did not seem too surprised) and they all had to turn to see me.

"Yes," I said very calmly. "There Is Such a Person!"

It brought the house down! The kind of laughter, reluctant but convulsive, which sometimes seizes people at funerals, followed me down the aisle, up onto the rostrum. A lot were irritated with me for shattering their lovely, superior mood of righteous censure.

"Correction," I went on. "There Are Such People! Our Party has a team of leaders, courageous, experienced, self-critical, determined, without equal in any revolutionary movement in the world. Yet none of us is indispensable. Our Party constitution guarantees that any of us can be recalled, and replaced. That is why I am here. You have your opportunity. However, while your choices are there on the CenCom, or on any other of our organs, they have the right to be trusted. They must be backed and, in emergency, obeyed. When the final decision to cancel our show of power was taken, three in favor, two abstaining, don't you think it was just possible that some of us knew something you did not!"

I strolled my eyes along the ragged hedges of heads. There were many bovine eyes staring with slow, surly willingness to be convinced. When this lot does finally stampede, the Golden Horde of Temujin's Mongols would be wise to stand aside! I identified Kamenev and his cronies, on their faces comical expressions of wonder and incomprehension. Yakov Mikhailovich, most reliable of my fellows, ever at my right hand, had no more idea than K. & Co. what this "something" might be. But he flashed confidence, "That's *right*, Ilyich," he announced. "That's absolutely *right!*"

"Why do you think Kerensky, the balalaika of our Soviet, the roaming minstrel of our ProvGov, remained at the front when all Peter knew the pot was boiling over? Why has he been hawking his patriotic song-and-dance all around the country during the run-up to the demonstration? I can tell you. Kamenev, Nogin, Zinoviev, and Sverdlov can tell you." I paused to let the first two stew a little, as if I were about to call them to testify, and noted how hard it was to catch their eyes. "Kerensky was, and is, still planning a June offensive. When we put off ours, he put off his. *Now* do I need to explain why we canceled?"

Nobody said "Yes," but what matter? I was going to tell them anyway.

"For the benefit of the newer recruits"—I gave a long glare at that supposedly veteran bag-carrier—"I *will* labor the obvious. Suppose our activity on the streets of the capital had chimed with the early days of a government attack which, I predict, would initially have been extremely successful. Would we not have been buried under a gusher of jingoism? What I called in '05 the 'little-yellow-monkeys' effect. The bourgeoisie would have been delirious with hope because a battle won against the former Tsar's cousin would encourage the troops in their battle against the Tsar's former subjects. And there is always a section of the masses which regards fighting the German masses as a glorious crusade for the honor of the Motherland. Our slogans about war, our calls for the soldiers to come home and share out the land, our skirmishes with the capitalists on the home front—all this could easily have been dubbed 'treason.' On the other hand, suppose our activity on the streets of the capital had coincided with the second phase of that attack when, I also confidently predict, our army would be defeated, rolled back, since their heart is not in this war? Then paradoxically, the swing against us would have become *even stronger*! The generals and the ministers could claim, as they have throughout history, that they were not defeated in the field. They were stabbed in the back by subversive, criminal elements, that is—Bolsheviks or Anarchists."

It was not exactly a lie, what I had just said about Kerensky. The worst that could be alleged was that I did not *know* it to be true. The evidence for his projected attack was almost exactly as strong as that for our projected uprising. Neither of us was against the gambit, in principle. But neither was sure *this* was the moment.

Both were waiting, hoping, the weight of events would give us the necessary impetus. What the Bolsheviks did was—we did nothing. Kerensky's offensive must be launched soon, that I am sure. We Bolsheviks cannot allow it forever to preempt our own. That I am also sure.

I broadened to a general point. "The road to Revolution," as Chernyshevsky used to say, "is not the pavement of the Nevsky Prospect." It was more like climbing a mountain, a pastime in which I had gained some skill. Only a fool thought that the best way was the shortest way—straight up. You had to take a winding path cutting from side to side. Revolution was *class*-warfare. Our attacks too had to be postponed sometimes, moved to another section of the front.

As for our relationship with the CenExCom, it was clear that their revolutionary feeling was leaking out of their boots. Soviet leaders dare not attempt to govern alone, secure in the backing of the workers, soldiers and peasants. They missed their old masters, the capitalists and the landowners, the generals and liberals. The present leaders were less and less reliable allies. Our slogan should now take a small, vital change in grammar. Not "All Power to the Soviet" but to the "Soviets" in the plural. In other words, to all the organs of mass strength, wherever and whatever they may be. Even if SovCong were to take all the powers we had been urging on them, we could not allow its CenExCom in future to instruct us where, and when, to demonstrate. We would always agitate as we wished. Rather than give up those rights, I would want to take the party underground again. I would operate illegally, and to hell with persecution.

This brought cheers, as I guessed it would. We have many romantic revolutionaries, in love with clandestine operations, who cannot believe revolution can ever succeed if we stay in the open air. But now for my surprise.

Zinoviev had slipped out toward the end of the speech as arranged. He was to visit the CenExCom of SovCong and bring me back news of their final decision. I could only hope I had guessed what that was. It should be the one I would have made in their place. Zinoviev came up to the front of the hall. He nodded.

"Ah," I said. "It seems that Comrade Zinoviev has something to show us. Pass it over, Yakov Mikhailovich. Thank you. I see. It is a proclamation from the All-Russian Congress of Soviets which is going to hold its own peaceful mass parade. Banners and bands in three streams, joining up at the saluting base on the Champ de Mars. Date—June 19. All groups supporting the Democratic Revolution are welcome. Well, comrades, what do you say to that? *Shall we be there?*"

The *postmortem* investigating Lenin's retreat in the face of the enemy broke up among cheers and whoops and shouts. We *would* be there!

JUNE 18   PETERSBURG   1917

Though N. and I are notionally sharing a room at the large, three-cornered flat of Anna and Mark, we have seen little of each other this last month. Perhaps longer. Night after night, I have found it easier to sleep at Kshesinska's so as to be on the spot for an early start next morning. The attraction of small, dark, cozy retreats, the human equivalent of the fox's burrow or the bear's cave, also revived. (Agoraphobia, I suppose, your Viennese mind-doctor would jargon it, possibly even utero-philia! Ha!) Anyway, I find that maid's room an ideal night-nest, a silken, cushioned womb, in which to seal myself off like a cocooned chrysalis, recharging my cells for another bright, blinding day.

I must admit as well that a gap has been growing between Nadya and me since we got back here. Over the last ten weeks she has "dwindled, peaked and pined" (*Hamlet?*), grown older and duller. It is as if the Revolution had outgrown her, a forty-eight-year-old who has thought of little else since her girlhood. About a month ago, she woke me in my little camp bed (it's like sleeping in splints) to whisper—"Ilyich, I'm *bored!*"

Well, I blew up—afraid, depressed, confused, almost anything, but bored! I was about to launch at her one of my rockets.

I had hardly said more than a few words when I looked closely at Nadya's face and my heart jumped as if it had been kicked. How long since I had really seen her?

She wore the expression Anna, with feminine precision, once likened to that of "a widowed cod." But that was not it. Curiously, that had always moved me, for even as a girl she had a strange, aquarian, mermaid gaze. Now I scrutinized her with that clinical exactitude that only twenty years of loving cohabitation can authorize. Her whole body had melted, like a waxwork in a fire. Her face was a mask about to slide off, her hands badly wrapped tubes. It was as if she were dying on her knees by my bed, the last little flame just rattling out.

And I knew I had been the one who almost killed her. As on

a lantern slide, I saw the past illuminated in bright colors. Of course, I had always prided myself on complete absence of any philistine prejudices. Jew or Greek, black or Tatar, proletarian or prince, man or woman, it mattered as little to me as brown or blond hair, so long as the person was a fighter for the cause. Yet I had exploited Nadya as callously as any vulgar husband, worse perhaps, since at the same time I was congratulating myself on being one of Chernyshevsky's new men, the salt of the salt of the earth. Without thinking I had allowed her to specialize in boring conspiratorial routines, coding and decoding letters, keeping an up-to-date card index of *klichki*, noting each change of Party-name and address of safe house, balancing the books, copying articles into a fair hand—all the jobs that more valuable comrades, many of them women, had not time to bother with. I had never stopped to wonder whether she had other talents, other ambitions.

Now, here we were in the rebel capital of our Empire, the autocracy once more gathering strength as we delayed the second blow that should destroy it, in the First Year of Revolution. And I had left her untrained, and unequipped, for any role in the final struggle except filing letters, making tea, taking orders from men and women who had been my secretaries, messengers, acolytes and office boys.

Even the triumph of true people's democracy over a sixth of the world cannot justify such personal behavior. My brain raced, flipping page after page of agenda. Then, I had it. "No longer, my darling, must you hang around Party HQ waiting to pick up dropped envelopes. As member of CenCom of the Bolsheviks, I instruct you to take charge of the elections to the municipal Duma on the Vyborg side due to be held on June 18. And I expect to see you as one of the victorious councillors."

For a moment, I recognized in those dear fishy eyes fear, doubt, self-pity, the collusion of the slave in the master's low opinion. I took her hands, and we both stood up. "No 'ifs' or 'buts,' " I said sternly. "That is an order. Now off to Vyborg to fight your stretch of the battle line. Don't you know there's a revolution on?"

That was nearly a month ago. And I don't say I had forgotten my instructions and her task. But when she woke me this morning in my stretcher bed I could not at first decipher what this grinning, rosy hoyden could be saying in such an authoritative voice.

"I *said*, I'd like to introduce you to Comrade Councillor Krupskaya, leader of the majority Bolshevik group on the Vyborg Municipal Duma, also president of the Vyborg district branch of the Committee for the Relief of Soldiers' Wives, also author of an article in *Trench Chat* entitled "A Page from the History of the Party" mainly about one Vladimir Ilyich Ulyanov, known as Lenin, the Revolutionary from Simbirsk." And she waltzed out like a schoolgirl.

At this season of the year, Petersburg might have been designed by nature to be the city of constant dispute and debate. By day, it is as warm as the isle of Capri. In the crowded tenements of Vyborg and Basil Island, body heat inflates the indoor temperature to tropic levels. Nonworking workers flood the streets seeking some coolness simply by stirring the soupy atmosphere. Over-worked workers among squealing lathes and roaring belts in the factories long for the shifts to end so that they can get out and join their neighbors in the open air. Since the sky hardly darkens through the long "milky hours," so that you can read a poster at midnight, there is plenty of time for everybody to do the rounds of beer crate preachers, park-bench philosophers, *al fresco* community singsongs where hymns, music-hall ditties, patriotic arias and satirical ballads overlap, formal and informal slanging matches between rival local mouthpieces.

I have got into the habit of tapering off my day by appearing on a flowery mound at the bottom of Kshesinskaya's garden. Here I conduct a question-and-answer session with any of those who collect just over the wall. These tend mostly to be hostile, bilious, spoiled intellectuals, but I find it relaxes and unwinds me to give them back in double helpings all the verbal garbage they throw at our speakers. It has got to be quite an event of evenings in old Peter and (I'm told) more than a few of former "Society" drop by to round off their day with some lively polemic. If I suspect they may be there, naturally I make my points even more provocative. Mostly, I forget afterward what I said. But B.-B. sits, out of sight at my feet, back to the wall, and he takes a note to stop misrepresentation in the scandal sheets. Last night so he tells me this morning, I said this, among other things!

So, imbeciles, braggarts, idiots, you thought that history was made in drawing rooms where upstart democrats fraternized with titled liberals! Where miserable provincial pettifoggers learned to kiss the gracious hands of their Eminences! Imbeciles, braggarts, idiots! History is made in the trenches where the soldier, possessed by the nightmare of war-madness, plunges his bayonet into his officer's stomach. History is made behind the lines, where the soldier, clinging like grim death to the buffers of a train carriage, escapes to his native village there to set on fire his landlord's manor.

You don't like such brutality? Don't bother to complain, answers history. You are getting your share of all I possess. What happens today is simply the result of what went on before. Do you truly imagine that history is made in these parliamentary commissions? Nonsense, childish babble, schoolboy games, fatheadedness.

History—as all will soon see—for the moment has chosen as its workshop-laboratory the palace of Kshesinskaya, the ballerina, onetime mistress of the former Tsar. Here, inside this wedding-cake edifice, so symbolic of the old Russia, history prepares your liquidation. The death rattle of your monarchical, bureaucratic, courtly, landowning, and bourgeois corruption and squalor. To this palace of the former imperial ballerina flock sweaty factory delegates, gray and haggard, and also lousy foot-envoys from the trenches, and from here they carry throughout the country our prophetic message.

Well, I can't pretend it's quite Cicero. But off-the-cuff, impromptu, in the face of snarling barrackers, I'm not ashamed.

I am positively proud of N. I've always believed in the genius of the ordinary person—"every cook should rule the state . . ." and so on. And yet I can hardly believe the transformation of my own wife once she is given the little push which starts her running her own life. Tonight, after my over-the-wall session, we snatched an hour for her to bring me up to date with her new career. Her Bolsheviks swept the board in the Vyborg local election. A few Meks scraped in too, but are in a sulk and never turn up. She is very impressed with the soldiers' wives, smart, independent, even well-dressed, she says. They take no nonsense from anybody. N. runs self-help sessions, men and women together learning the law, finance, history, politics, also shopping, plumbing, cooking, even sewing on buttons. One of the men, a Bolshevik too, protested at the needle and thread. That was for wives, he said, that was their job. The women were indignant and ready to scrag him. "The wife sew buttons on trousers?" they demanded indignantly. "A revolutionary upholding the slavery of women? The wife is the husband's comrade, not his servant." Even they, she reported, were at first surprised and incredulous when she told them that Lenin mended his own clothes!

I like the sound of this lot. An idea is sprouting at the back of my mind. What do they do to earn money while the husbands are at the front?

They take their baskets and hawk sunflower seeds, cider and *kvass*, occasional baps of hazelnut bread, Nadya said.

Yes, yes, but *where?*

In the factories, where the machinists work on through their brief breaks—a heroic sacrifice for the war effort!—or outside the barracks, where the soldiers are so badly, drearily fed they snap up any goodies.

Ah-haah! I have it! Since our earlier aborted demo, we have been finding difficulty contacting soldiers and workers who do not attend meetings. The Kronstadters are so annoyed with us they are no longer much use as infiltrators. But *women!* Soldiers' wives! Politically aware, attractively dressed, bearing pleasant little snacks? They might have been made for the job of Bolshevizing the non-activists. Even if they only pipe on one note—"Join our Parade! Join our Parade!"

I made her promise she would drop everything else and start early tomorrow sending them out like the Salvation Army girls we used to see accosting drunks and villains in the East End of London. I cannot think any other Party has the variety of outlets for its propaganda that we have.

JUNE 19　　　PETERSBURG　　　1917

Tomorrow is the Grand Official Authorized March of the Supporters of the All-Russian Congress of Soviets. The radical majority in SovCong, like all politicians, cannot imagine that the views of the electorate that put them there can possibly have changed since the election. It suits them to believe that once a ballot is dropped in a box, the voter wants the *status quo* to carry on carrying forever—certainly until the next election.

In between, the ruling power might stage an occasional, carefully orchestrated pageant of popular will. This will use all the instruments of mass persuasion—flags and banners, drums and trumpets, strutting boots and glittering uniforms, salutes and speeches—such as were patented in the last century by that first suffragan emperor-dictator since Roman times, Louis Napoleon. And tomorrow will be such another. It will be seized upon by a bought press as proof that the nation approves Dual Power and trusts the Soviet to merge eventually with the Provisional government.

Does it look as if I were preparing our side to be swamped? Certainly, this is what everybody at the Tauride and the Marinsky, in and around official Petersburg, is telling everybody else. Sukhanov even writes in *Novaya Zhizn*, supposedly the organ of the moderate, law-abiding left, that we have "conceded defeat." Lenin, he writes, takes care not to show himself but guides all from behind the scenes "like a great noble." This shows how much he gets around. I may not have been where he's been—the Tauride, etc. But I have been almost everywhere workers and soldiers gather. I have never contributed less than five pieces, made fewer than ten speeches, every day for the last fortnight. Is that how "great nobles" behave?

And I have found increasing solidarity behind our policy and our program. I know canvassers must beware of hearing what they want to hear. Still, I would give us heavy odds on emerging ahead in any tests of public opinion, so long as two unpredictables do not break the flow.

These are, *first*, the course of the war, and *second*, the actions of the militants to our left, the Anarchists, the Kronstadt sailors, the Machine-Gun Brigade, perhaps our own Bolshevik Military Committee.

The war is crucial. Kerensky has been spinning round the country, spouting from one end of the front to the other, spraying huge meetings in opera theaters and palace ballrooms in a dozen cities, like a singing top or a whirling dervish. There is no doubt that he is a spellbinder in real theatrical style, on the level of a Trotsky or a Lunarcharsky. But with a battery of cheap conjuror's tricks neither of them would ever adopt. Kerensky wears the most expensive, court-tailored, officer's uniform, though without badges of rank, like the Unknown Soldier Resurrected. He tends to put one arm in a sling (bursitis, in fact), encouraging popular belief it is due to a wound from a German bullet on a secret mission in no-man's-land. He also cultivates the air of one who has only months to live—rumors are carefully spread to this effect, though a state secret—and comes on pale and nobly suffering, supported by a pair of well-decorated genuine war heroes, one Army, one Navy. At the climax of his speech, or earlier if an audience's attention starts to wander, he throws a fit, collapses and is caught just in time in their arms.

Much as I hate to believe it, I have to accept our agents' reports that he really can send troops into paroxysms of excitement and martial fervor. While among bourgeois audiences, in white tie and tails, and sparkling ball dresses (who would credit such folk still exist?), his evening often ends with men pelting him with pocketbooks and gold watches while women release a downpour of diamond bracelets and necklaces.

Quite a change from my style which is argument, repetition, example, analogy, figures and dates; logic, logic, logic; dry, severe, straightforward. I try to do it as if I am hammering in nails. "Little-Shit," the other lawyer from Simbirsk, does it as if he were pinning on medals or even presenting bouquets. To think I might scupper him with one piece of information I will never reveal—my old schoolmaster's wife, Alexander-the-Balalaika's mother, was a Jewess.

JUNE 20   PETERSBURG   1917

I feel literally exhausted, sucked empty like a deep-sea diver with a leak in his air pipe. My feet seem laced in leaden boots. My body moves as if wrapped in a thick canvas suit against the weight of waters. My head could be riveted inside a steel ball, the view restricted to a glass window ribbed in brass. And I am finding it harder and harder to breathe.

I can only stay upright for the moment because I am buoyed by the triumph of the day. Even as I gasp, I savor the sweet juice of revenge.

Today began with a breath of mist and a dabble of dew soon polished away so that the city *shone*. In the morning it was the kind of sparkling *diamanté* Sunday you think you remember from childhood when you were expecting some special treat. The afternoon would be hot and the people of Peter would come out as if to celebrate Day One of the Brave New World.

They came late. At midday, the advertised rallying-time, I was in my office waiting for telephone reports from my monitors. They were spaced out along what now had expanded to four routes—from Basil Island in the west, from Old Peter in the north, from Vyborg in the northeast and from Narva and the Putilov Works in the south. All were to join at the saluting base on the Champ de Mars. Yet the time crept on nearly to 1 P.M. and still the first telephone bell had not rung.

When it did, it was Gorky. He'd heard tell there was nobody at all around. The whole thing was going to be a failure. It would be a message of no-confidence in our Party. So he was staying at home, with the rest of the citizens of Peter. I told him not to be a defeatist. Why would that not be a message of no-confidence in the Soviet? Then I hung up. Because my other bells were ringing now.

Dead on 1 P.M. the calls started to come in from all over. . . . The suburbs were jammed, as if choked by refugees. But these crowds were pushing to get *in*, not out. Everyone was nearly sober. Experienced mob-measurers put the capacity—they had an algebraic formula for the exercise—at 350,000. Most were in organized groups, people who trusted each other. No vandalism, no disorders, participants seem almost too businesslike. No sign of arms being carried by significant numbers. Revised estimate, nearer 400,000. All this, and yet our observers with telescopes on the Kshesinska's roof cannot see more than a few hundreds on the city center streets.

I have a battery of telephones, five in all. They are kept numbered and nailed to a desk bookshelf, with long flexes. This gives me a mobile contact post. I am able to take it out onto the balcony, where ironwork writhes like lace, overlooking a crystalline river Neva. I too could spot few demonstrators on the opposite bank. But just then I saw them. To my left and right, the swollen heads of two marching caterpillars which had just begun to cross by the Trinity and Liteiny bridges. My eyes could distinguish the rippling lines of the marchers but not identify the particular detachments. For all I knew they might be the Soviet's famous tame stage army: messenger boys, cleaning women, gardeners, commissionaires, redundant *flics*, concierges, janitors and caretakers (the *dvorniki*), convalescent members of the forces, lesser bureaucrats and the like. Then I realized that running commentaries were being piped to me by wire, like those in London's gambling *spieler* which tell the punters who is winning. This would keep me posted on who was ahead in our race.

It was a strange effect. I asked those whispering voices in my ear, varying with the strength of the electric current, drowned occasionally by cheers or music, to describe what they saw in as much detail as possible. "Pretend I'm blind," I said. "Give me the obvious. What everyone knows. The grass is green and so on."

So, though to my eyes they were two-legged dots, through my ears I heard about the color of the soldiers' uniforms ("pale clay," "faded beige," "almost sort of off-white"). In answer to my query as to why they weren't khaki and olive, I was reminded these were barracks soldiers. "They love washing their clothes every day and drying them in the sun." It was a while before I took in that at least twenty regiments, many almost at full strength, were taking part. I saw on a screen in my head a visual interpretation of the buzzing words—clouds of sailors, blue caps and white blouses, also newly laundered and ironed, teeth flashing, so unused to strict goose-stepping as to be almost dancing; the cavalry, blue and silver, scarlet and bronze, traditionally the most loyal troops with the arrogance of the man-on-the-horse for those under its belly, curvetting and rearing sideways and in circles, partly because the beasts are more unnerved by the sweat of the crowd than by explosions of gunpowder, partly because the riders are showing off that they have come here of their own free will and not under orders; nurses caped in bright, unnatural blue, like so many strutting Virgin Marys; mill girls, laundry girls, shopgirls, schoolgirls, flowery faces, flowery dresses, aglow with the excitement of being touched by men's eyes; factory workers, militants more disciplined than most soldiers, in short black tunics more military than most uniforms, also more determinedly in step. The word is passing along—mob-measurers must be using logarithms by now—the total is almost *half a million.*

What about the red, the redness I can see blooding the marchers? Apparently everyone has something red, a flower, a streamer, a scarf, a waistband, a neckerchief, a hat. No. The solid red that seems brushed thick along Shpalernaya Street and the Embankment, piling up at the Champ de Mars where the Soviet CenExCom will take the salute?

"The banners, Ilyich . . . Of course, *Starik,* the banners . . . Our banners! That goes without saying!"

The CenExCom of SovCong had decreed their own slogan. Typically something that would appeal to everyone without offending your granny—"Universal Peace," "Democratic Republic," "Soonest Possible Convocation of the Constituent Assembly." Stuff you can hardly add an exclamation to, since no one would ever exclaim it! But when studied, basically counterrevolutionary, or perhaps just meaningless.

There had been a few of these Soviet messages about every quarter-mile. But then rank after rank, riding above the heads, in gold and scarlet, *our* slogans "Down with the Ten Capitalist Ministers!" (They know who they are!); "Down with the Offensive!" (Must get that in before war hots up, any day now); "All Power to the Soviets" (Not just this one, but the new ones, the Bolshevik ones, being set up every day); "No Separate Peace with Germany nor Secret Treaties with the Anglo-French Capitalists!" (A mouthful, favorite only of those who love printing and painting); "The Right to Life Is Higher Than the Right to Property!" (Must be a

condensed version somewhere); "Peace to the Hearth, War to the
Castle!" (Rather archaic, I'm afraid). Half a million Petersburgers
have taken the opportunity Tseretelli and the Soviet offered them.
Then they have backed us, overwhelmingly! Now the telegraph
machines are clacking. Other parades have been held in a dozen
provincial cities, including Moscow—all are behind us too!

Despite a lethargy, like chloroform in my veins, I must be
there for this peak of triumph. There was some attempt to dissuade
me for my own good.

"It's all right you just wandering about the streets on your
own, *Starik*," protested one of Nevsky's deputies. "Nobody knows
you are you. I mean, you're ordinary. Well, that is, not the popular
idea of what Lenin should look like. But if you turn up marching
under our CenCom's banner, that could be dangerous. There's
always some holy fool looking for martyrdom by killing Antichrist."

We crossed the Neva by naval cutter—temporary unofficial
loan—and landed at the quay under Trinity bridge. The Red
Guards knew who I was and a bunched wedge of them planted
me in the front row just opposite the plinth holding Soviet top
brass. Immediately, as if in a dream, our CenCom materialized
round the corner, and I fell in step with them. They were holding
aloft an enormous, gold-embroidered, twenty-feet-wide swath of
scarlet silk. It could hardly be said to be provocative. All it contained were the letters announcing who we were—"C.C. R.S.D.L.P.
(B)" Not even an exclamation mark!

The other delegations had been allowed to dip their flags but
keep marching on. I led the CenCom around and beyond the
assembled SRs and Meks and ministers, not stopping until we
reached the graves of the February dead. Here, we bowed our
heads quietly and I said: "Long live the worldwide Socialist Revolution." (No exclamation mark.)

Some kind of majordomo or master of ceremonies tried to
protest. But the crowd were cheering, swaying, stamping for us.
We were the victors of the big parade. Who could stop us now?

I am writing this at Anna and Mark's flat. I should be asleep,
as Nadya is. But my flesh resists rest, quivering as though I had
just had an electric shock. I find it steadying to update my diary.
For this may be (haven't I written this before?) the most important
day so far in the history of the Russian Revolution, and of my life.
They are the same thing.

Afterward, when we have won (as we will) or instead when
we have been hunted down and exterminated, either way, *afterward*
everything will look clean, clear-cut, simple enough for schoolkids

to understand. Whichever side of the barricades they are on, historians will establish that the evidence shows, if we succeeded, then it was impossible to fail, or if we failed, then it was impossible to succeed. By tracing here the zigzags of history, more accurately the whims and fads of a bemused and battered proletariat, I aim to leave behind a record of how muddled, misleading, unpredictable and frustrating it was here and now, even from week to week. That is the sole reason why I permit myself the thought that another person may read this. I may have already arranged that it cannot surface for a lifetime, three score years and ten from now, which ought to be the seventieth anniversary of our victory. On that socialist, cooperative, productive, peaceful egalitarian planet, these will seem naggings and nigglings from the Dark Ages.

Only if our Marxist timing has slipped a few cogs, if humanity has not been brave, honest, selfless, self-critical, straightforward enough, and the 1987 world still encourages and rewards aggression, exploitation and greed, will one man's struggle against this future without hope be of value to comrades yet unborn.

As I reread this entry by swaying candlelight, I realize that I must get out of Peter. There is just too much in my mind. But I will complete the point. Of course, learn from my mistakes. You will have the advantage over me, I am not sure *what* they are. You will have no doubt what they *were*. I know I was encouraged, not depressed, to learn from letters and journals of my predecessors in 1847 that they then remained certain of approaching victory. So am I. So should you be.

Nadya has worked even longer hours than I have preparing for this display. She loved leading her Vyborg Soldiers' Wives on the march. Now she sleeps. She has always been able to sleep. On her sleeping face is that healthy, smackable flush only the good get when they are rightly admired for their goodness, and a big, big smile. . . .

What would I not give for a pause, for news that history had stuck and will stay that way—just for a few days, just for twenty-four hours. But every solution breeds new problems, every answer fresh questions. That is dialectics, I know—thesis, antithesis, synthesis, ever spiraling upward. Sometimes I wish I didn't.

JUNE 21   PETERSBURG   1917

Yesterday's victory is curling at the edges. The bought press pushed our demonstration to the bottom of this morning's inner page.

The lead story, in banner headlines, is the Kerensky offensive—how hateful sometimes it is to be right! I take our communiqués with a pinch of salt, but the information coming through Stockholm from the Other Side confirms that Russian troops may really have made some spectacular advances. They have breached the German line in two places. While the newspapers are stirring it up, a mercenary army of ruling-class lackeys and Soviet camp-followers is emerging from the wings to mouth patriotic slogans. It is another period for us to hang on to our advantages, keep our guns oiled and our mouths shut. Personally, no difficulty! I feel I could live happy if I never heard the human voice raised again, at least in rhetorical mode.

As I sit here, clutching the molten turmoil of my guts, I am condemned to hear yet more bad tidings. Yesterday, while almost 500,000 supporters passed before us in procession, a Roman triumph in front of our eyes, a second piece of ill fortune was dropping, like a snapped chimney stack in a gale, across our path. Kerensky's army is beating back the Hun, creating an image of gallant, battle-scarred veterans advancing the cause of freedom on our borders. Set this against the other image of skulking, battle-scared apprentices, safe in town, advancing only the cause of Bolshevism. Look here upon this soldier and on that! At the same time, a task force of Anarchists from Durnovo has mounted an armed raid on the Kresty prison, near them in Vyborg, and rescued seven prisoners.

Since the February Revolution, Peter's jails have been notoriously leaky. Most of the Tsar's staff have disappeared (those that were not murdered). The new warders are an odd mixture of penal reform cranks, petty criminals, ex-convicts too institutionalized to leave and a few devoted civil servants. Nobody would have much noticed if a couple of Anarchists had quietly sprung a friend, while carrying perhaps a Browning and a crowbar; 460 common criminals escaped last week from two other prisons without any fuss from anybody. But our Anarchist friends turned up 2,000 strong, over-weaponed as Pancho Villa, ready to dynamite any door whose knob was slow in turning. And the only liberated prisoner anybody had heard of just had to be F. P. Khaustov, well-known as a leader of *our* MilOrg.

The result is that we instantly have some of the basic ingredients of successful counterrevolution: (1) Forces operating in the name of democracy and moderation, winning golden opinions fighting the country's ancient, foreign enemy but also willing to display their selfless courage suppressing subversive conspiracies at home. (2) A subversive conspiracy conveniently at home, caught red-handed freeing its firebrands, possibly in German pay. (The one card so far flourished but not played.) A plot using Bolsheviks and Anarchists combined.

Both sides are warming up and some players have already appeared on the field. The government sent an even larger striking force of Guards before dawn today to surround the Villa Durnovo. They carted away sixty residents they took by surprise. It was an operation that made a lot of noise, a bit of spectacular damage to property, but almost no harm to any person—just like the rescue at Kresty. And so things should have ended: in a draw.

However, one Anarchist (who was hiding in a broom closet) got his gun arm caught in the slammed door and fired by reflex. The bullet went in one ear and out the other of a fellow Anarchist named Asnin. The Kresty-Durnovo Affair had gained what all such affairs need to survive the fleeting mythology of the hour— a martyr. One of my afternoon visitors arrived bearing a placard on a stick—REMEMBER ANSIS!

One set of crowds are building up along the Nevsky Prospect—SAVE MOTHER RUSSIA! TRUST KERENSKY AND OUR BOYS! BERLIN FIRST, THEN SOCIALISM!—showing once more how much we have always underrated the proof spirit of nationalism. Very different crowds are gathering in Durnovo Park to tour the wrecked Villa and weep over the corpse of Asnin, birthmarked with blood. Then they depart Vyborg over the Sampsonievsky bridge and pile up outside our HQ. They have no prepared message. It is part of the Anarchist creed to claim—"We let the streets decide our slogans!" In other words, a policy of opportunism and adventure.

Meanwhile, here I am, still sitting at Anna's table in the steamboat flat, like a doctor in his surgery. How strange—all my patients suffer with the same ailment. All want the same prescription. It is not the one I intend to give them. Like many of the most effective remedies, mine is exactly the opposite of what their instinct tells them is best. They all want a tonic. They get a sedative. Incredible as it seems to them, for this complaint the best treatment is—wait and see. Time *is* on our side.

JUNE 22   PETERSBURG   1917

At midday, on the pretext of taking Gorusha for a stroll, I slipped out of Anna's flat, my escape bag in my other hand, determined not to go back if I can find some other place to lay my head. Georgi

Lozgachev-Yelizarov (that's what he prefers to be called, rather than Gora or Gorusha, but I sometimes forget) is my foster-nephew or whatever is the right title for your sister's adopted genius. He could read and write at three, memorized the classics at five. Just turned eleven now. Anna says he's amazingly like me at that age. She may be right. I honestly think highly of him as a companion, warming to something about the surface smartness, rudeness and almost bruising boisterousness, with tact and sensitivity hidden underneath.

Among all the memories of that night of April 3, nothing is more touching than that of our collapse onto the bed Marya had vacated for us to find the pillows decorated with hammers and sickles cut out of gold paper. While above the headboard, where the conventional hang GOD IS LOVE, Georgi Lozgachev-Yelizarov had suspended that streamer reading: WORKERS OF THE WORLD UNITE! Next morning, I thanked him for this fraternal welcome.

"That was when I thought you were only 'Uncle Volodya,'" he said. "If I'd only known you were also 'Lenin' . . ." And he made a marvelously eloquent gesture somehow incorporating popping corks, saluting guns, exploding bombs and eating cake which conveyed his view of Revolution. Since then, he has learned a lot more.

I'm flattered to be the only person in the family he can bring himself to listen to. I use him as a sounding-board for my philosophical ideas, though these have been growing a bit thin lately. (Metaphysician, heal thyself!) Otherwise, *he* talks all the time. Occasionally I take him with me to Party HQ where he serves the purpose of a small, fierce dog by keeping the bores away.

The other day I said to Anna, "Your Gorusha's outspoken, isn't he?" "He *is*?" she asked. "Who by? Please tell me."

I do not imagine that I am so fascinating to him just for myself. I tell him that revolutionaries are not rare. Soon they will be in the majority. His adopted mother and father, his Aunt Marya are all revolutionaries. Why, he insists, do they not have escape bags? And each morning he checks mine for me, trying hard to think of something that should be there that I have not thought of.

A Browning and six bullets. Opera glasses—specially useful since I learned to lip-read. A pair of blue-tinted specs with side blinkers—for quick disguise. Razor and brush—ditto, but more permanent. A couple of false internal passports—no longer obligatory by law, but backup to new identity. Half a dozen visiting cards—ditto. Simulated gold (brass) pectoral cross—for misdirecting the nosy. Flask of bisongrass vodka—in case of shock, or as bribe, the best. Three portraits, Marx, Engels, Chernyshevsky

—sentiment, possibly poor security, but framed like family pictures, rarely recognized. Small pillow—worth all the others on long journeys, except one of two classics—either Engels's *Anti-Dühring* or Marx's *Civil War in France*. Surprising how little space this all takes up in my battered old "Gladstone"; usually there is room over for a spare shirt, socks and so on.

Our usual trail-blurring—sudden reversals of direction, entrance on one street and exit on the next—simply as part of routine since any shadow would guess I'm bound either for the *Pravda* office across the river, or down the road to Kshesinska's. Gorusha is first rate at this, knows Old Peter like his bedroom carpet, and is always suggesting new refinements. Then I left him. And this time went instead to Elena Stasova's flat with the key she had given me.

Elena is director of the Party Secretariat. The membership files of the Bolsheviks are mimeographed inside Sverdlov's head and nowhere else. All other documents are padlocked, five times over, in Elena's famous steel cabinet which stands on the bidet in Kshesinskaya's old bathroom (present site of the Secretariat). It (the cabinet not the bidet) is said to be lined with dynamite which will blow up half the palace if the locks are not opened in the correct sequence.

Spent the afternoon dozing on the sofa with the curtains closed. Awoke to the sound of a key in the latch. It was Elena. A comrade from the earliest days, I knew her presence even without seeing her in the light. By the rhythm of her step, by her outline, by the way she breathed. After twenty years living underground, you get to know your political partners like lovers. My gripes seemed to have stopped. But now my head aches as if it were one mass of bad teeth.

Elena said that every kind of cell leader on the left, inside and outside the Party, had been calling at Anna's and finding me gone, camping out around her door. Nerves were strained at every level in the organization by the latest news from the Front.

K.'s original offensive has slowed down. But he is now busy dealing with 10,000 prisoners. A second Russian offensive has opened up further south in Galicia. It seems to be moving forward as fast as the Austro-Hungarians can retreat. There is to be a service of thanksgiving in Peter's Kazan Cathedral, an open-air banquet in the gardens of the Tauride, and the combined Soviet and Duma have sent a message of congratulation to "Supreme Commander" Kerensky.

JUNE 23   PETERSBURG   1917

After two days at Stasova's (alternating pains head and guts) a visit
from a young officer, a secret Bolshevik who has been instructed
to remain a "sleeper" until we need him. A lieutenant on the staff
of General Kornilov, he reports it is common knowledge that I am
hiding out here. (I am also said to be Elena's lover!) No official
action is contemplated, but he overheard a colonel in Intelligence
discussing a plan to break in, murder me and throw my body into
the Karpovka Canal that flows under the window. He suggests
Elena sleep in the office (perhaps in Kshesinskaya's bath?) for a
few days and me leave the city tonight for a month or so. He
confirms my view that both Russian offensives will peter out very
soon. Once the artificial euphoria has subsided, would that not be
the best moment for us to mount an armed rising? He believes
that, by October, less than a quarter of the troops now at the Front
will still be there, while those left behind will be fraternizing. Wouldn't
it be ideal for us, if the Germans laid on a large-scale attack in
September–October?

I cautiously agree. But it is a cardinal rule never to trust
anybody—*anybody*—unless you must. Elena and I take his information seriously. But I have to bear in mind we have no independent corroboration. It is just such a tale as would earn our
gratitude, and provoke confidences in return. So I thank him,
assure him I will leave tonight. I have very good contacts with the
Other Side. It does look as if their next push *will* be around that
time. Is this too much of a coincidence?

Tomorrow Elena must start staying over at the office. I will
move into the backroom of the Central Trade Unions' center on
Furshtadsky Street. It is still thought to be a haunt of Meks though
our lads took over in force last weekend. As to leaving town, that
remains my intention. But I will put it off for a couple of days. If
the lieutenant *is* a double, his agents will already be screening all
immediate city departures.

JUNE 24   PETERSBURG   1917

Not much better at the CTU office in the peace-and-quiet department. I have a little place at the back, its door hidden by a

bookcase. On the face of it a perfect bolt-hole. Most of the staff, almost every one of the visitors, are unfamiliar with this layout. Only a handful suspect there could be extra room there. I spend most of my day wandering about among the factory delegates, the union secs, the shop floor stewards, who call in for a smoke, a spit and a gossip. There are almost no chairs but a surplus of tables. Most people sit on these—a curious effect, rather like a huddle of flood refugees floating down the river on a convoy of furniture. The result is that the person you are talking with is usually at an awkward, acute angle. Quite often over one shoulder or the other, if not directly behind you. Somehow, this closeness without confrontation leads to an unusually relaxed intimacy. Everyone talks honestly, and personally, about problems, failures, successes. There is a general feeling that we are all learning together. These informal chat sessions, known as *vechera*, have become so popular everybody hates to break them up and go home.

Around nine at night, I find I am becoming rather groggy (I try to speak at least once to each visitor). But my CTU friends cannot open the entrance to my bedroom until they can get the outer office cleared. It is not even as if this were the sliding panel of crime melodrama. I'm fairly strong but I need a couple of burly smiths from the Putilov welding department to help me hump the false front off and on again. So the four nights here have been rather a strain, with me praying for the last caller to depart.

Still, I enjoy the daytime. I discover much I did not know, much not mentioned at Bolshevik HQ, where every proletarian, like an English milord in August, talks only of guns. I had thought our campaigns in the workplace ought to be most often about poor wages and bad conditions. Now I realize they should increasingly be angled to deal with rising unemployment. We must take more thought of this. The tide of approval for us stands ready to overflow into a flood—more than we deserve, as I have admitted to hundreds of the union activists.

The prospects from this point of view seem almost glowing. Our resolution (moved by Zinoviev) at the "Workers' Section" of the Soviet that all power should be taken by the Soviets has been carried by 173 votes to 144. In the municipal elections in Vyborg which made N. a councillor, 37 Bolsheviks won seats out of 63. The latest test of mass feeling, taken since I came here, has set everyone talking—our demand (again expressed by Z.), at the Peter Conference of Factory Committees, for workers' control of industry. It was backed by 335 out of 421. The latest news from Moscow is almost as heartening—on June 20, the elections to the

Moscow Soviet returned 206 of us, a clear victory (if not an absolute majority) over 172 Mensies and 110 SRs. Yes, *There Is Such a Party!* I'm assured by the comrades who now run the CTU that just by making my appearances I have raised the workers' morale.

There is an agreed fiction in the office that I am unrecognized, like Haroun al-Raschid on his night-walks. If I am asked, I say my name. But I rather think most of them like "the Man from HQ" to use some *nom-de-guerre,* a harmless romanticism. They tell me they never meet even the most obscure Menshevik councillors. These gentry are too busy in-fighting at the Tauride, carving their niche in history, climbing the greasy pole, hoping to become deputy, assistant undersecretaries to ministers. Here at CTU, I am with the workers' workers. Here I more often listen than speak. But afterward I feel I have conveyed what I truly believe and so, I sense, do they. Sverdlov, the D'Artagnan of political organizers, would probably tell me I waste too much time on each individual. He claims that he has scientifically tested his techniques: and every minute over two minutes, you risk losing a supporter, not gaining one.

Yakov Mikhailovich has perfected a way of greeting the largest number of comrades in the shortest possible time that Gorky christened the "Ekaterinburg Twirl." It consists of pressing the palm of person no. 1 with right hand, while also enfolding the shoulders of no. 2 with left arm, and meanwhile smiling and speaking to no. 3. It is amazing how well it works. You might think that one, if not two, of the trio would be offended. But apparently each thinks *he* is being given the real greeting, and hopes the others don't mind. After all, everyone knows "Baby" (S.'s Party name) is an important, busy professional. We've all got to share him—squeeze, squeeze, wink, wink.

JUNE 25   MUSTIAMIAKI   1917

I'm writing this, not in my sealed room, but at the villa of Bonch-Bruevich in the Finnish waterland. I arrived here at 6 o'clock this evening with little sister Manyasha who also needs a break from being an editor on *Pravda.* Also, she is good cover on a train journey. The semi-official snatch squads, encouraged by the patriotic upswell to go Bolshy-bashing, will not be looking for a man with a woman. Nevertheless, I wrapped up like an invalid, displayed the brass cross, and let her feed me her peculiar dietary concoctions as if she were still a nurse. (Truth to tell, but only here—she may make a better nurse than editor!) At Mustiamiaki, we made a diversionary detour by station coach to the house of my favorite poet, Demyan Bedny, who also has a *dacha* among the lakes. He walked us across to Neivola by green satin backways. I have rarely seen two faces fall open so far, like a pair of letter-boxes, when Demyan pushed his ginger head through the beaded curtain and said to B.-B. and his wife, Vera Mikhailovna—"Hey, look what I've brought you!"

JULY 1	MUSTIAMIAKI	1917

Not since Kokushkino have I found myself so able to live a completely pagan, animal life, sensual but innocent. My insomnia has vanished. I take naps in the sun, whenever the desire for sleep falls, wrapping me round like a cloak, as easily as I gulp a beaker of hock-and-seltzer. My head has cleared. My brain has been hosed down. Once a dirty vegetable in a colander, it has returned, glossy clean in a fresh new dish.

I am intensely fit, muscled as a Roman statue. B.-B. and Demyan grow quite irritated. They claim the whole point of coming to this salad world, where even flowers and the trees look eatable, is to relax. Take it easy, move slowly, fall into the rhythm of the seasons, try to make the days stretch out like weeks. Not to rush about like a pink steam engine, stamping footprints in the turf, hitting the water like a chunky torpedo, shaking the cottage with gales of breath.

I'm sorry but I cannot help it. I have reverted to the young Volodya who wanted to out-hoot the Volga steamboat whistle. I should have brought Gorusha along. He's taller than I was at his age, already almost as tall as I am now. He's a real Western boy, with none of our Tatar blood, skinny, freckled, gap-toothed, Huckleberry Finn on a raft on the Neva. But he would know how to enjoy himself in the open air.

B.-B. is rather apprehensive about me and the lake. Keeps telling me how deep it is, how cold, how full of dangerous currents. I see he really is a city-merchant type, ideal fellow to run a bookstore in Peter but no empathy with the great outdoors.

So far I have contented myself with using the lake as exercise pool, swimming backward and forward not far out from the sandy beach until I am exhausted. Then collapsing on a leather mat in the sun. But today there was quite an audience, not just Marya, B.-B. and his wife Vera, Demyan and some of his friends, but one or two people from the village in search of cool breezes to cut the baking July heat, and even a few summer tourists from the city.

B.-B. took it into his head to give me a lecture about the number of unwary visitors who had gone out toward the silvery hub of the lake, now hidden in a filmy gauze of mist. And never returned! It wasn't that I wanted to be the center of attention. Though after years of competing for the leadership of a group with the most grueling tests of intellectual ability and psychological stamina, it is a relief to be able to impress a random crowd by something so simple and uncomplicated as physical prowess. I just felt a holiday urge to put an old chum in a mildly embarrassing hole.

"Well, I'm undrownable!" I called out and dived in from a rock. I started slicing my way straight ahead using what we used to call as a boy the Volga Crawl, a powerful, fast, overarm technique much flashier than the discreet, gentlemanly breaststroke almost all Russians are taught by fathers and schoolmasters. When I turned on my back to give a wave, I found I was much further away than I'd expected. The watchers on the shore were barely distinguishable as people, more like a collection of insects, nits perhaps, strung out along a blond hair that was stretched across the metallic mirror of lake and sky. Land seemed a forgotten element, canceled out by water and air, except for this faint, disappearing streak. The mist was now moving toward me blown by a soft wind. Soon I was inside it, able to see only a couple of feet in any direction, though light was all around me as in a sun-warmed tent. I wondered how far I could get beneath the surface.

I have been an amphibian for so many years I tend to forget how you move vertically in water. I seem to alter my buoyancy, like a fish, just by wanting to do so. I could feel the bubbles streaming out of both corners of my mouth, looping up round my ears, in long pearly necklaces. I was digging my way deeper and deeper, like a man excavating a pit in soft, wet sand, with easy, giant handfuls. I was soon approaching a slatey, polished bottom, with few plants and no mud, illuminated like an aquarium.

In all my swimming days—in the Volga, in the Rhine, in the Seine and the Serpentine, in the Mediterranean off Capri, the Atlantic off Biarritz, the North Sea off Brittany—I never ever felt at all endangered by another underwater creature. Here, my heart gave a lurch as I came eyeball to eyeball with some sort of eel or lamprey, though not one I'd ever seen on a fishmonger's slab. It was huge, around five feet long. Its teeth were as trim and regular and precise as a pig's. The fluted tail wagged and it moved backward and downward as though inviting me into what looked like the entrance to a man-sized black pipe.

Then it advanced, still wagging its tail, and smiling. I was smiling back until I realized its jaws were stretching so wide they were about to unhinge. My feet and hands were as heavy as a jousting knight's gauntlets and boots. My lips, my nostrils, my eyes were swelling with blood. Yet I was floating in a trance. It sounds impossible now, but for a second there came a strangely seductive wish to give in, give up. If it was going to seize me, to let myself be towed back to its larder. But no, no! The idiocy of the thought galvanized me. The Revolution frustrated by some misshapen freak, half-snake, half-shark? Never!

I closed my eyes. I told myself I was holding my breath and doing my morning exercises. I passed into a half-conscious dusk where all nerve endings were switched off and few sensory messages reached the brain. I had as little connection with my body as a first-class passenger with the paddles of his Volga steamer. Miles away there was a tiny thought, a pinprick, a dot on the horizon—was this the way the heroic rebel angels, defiers of God's despotism, felt as they fell across an endless heaven . . . ? Then the pinprick, the dot, expanded into a great, blinding, hot, breathing world. I rose in the water like the bounce-back of a stick thrown for a dog. I was ready to fly.

Only yards away was the far bank of the lake opposite B.-B.'s beach. I crawled up the grass. I looked at my underwater watch, a present from the Kronstadt sailors, formerly the property of a tsarist admiral. I had tried to give it back to him in the naval prison, but he refused: "Just use your influence to stop the *matelots* kicking open my cell door when they come back drunk and shouting, 'Wake up, Gold Stripe, and show us your bum!' "

It was only noon. The sun was at its height, burning through the thin, well-rinsed Finnish air. When I awoke, it was getting chilly. I looked up into the embarrassed faces of B.-B. and Demyan. They had rowed across in an old dinghy, worried that I had been five hours missing in the now-melted mist.

"I'm responsible for your security to CenCom," complained B.-B. "Everybody was so impressed with your swimming, I had to think up some explanation. So I said you were a sailor on leave from the Baltic fleet. Now they want you to tell them some heroic tales of war at sea and whether you have ever met their cousin in the Navy, Ivan Ivanovich Ivanov."

So I had to promise not to show off to the populace anymore. And I also decided to keep quiet about my encounter with the Lake Neivola Monster.

"Everybody knows sailors can't swim," said Demyan.

JULY 3   MUSTIAMIAKI   1917

Two more days of the sun rising over the fringed horizon like a searchlight. By noon, the bone-white cobbles of the forest paths feel hot even through boots, while two steps into the coniferous dark is like walking into an icehouse. B.-B. is right. I was becoming too prominent doing my Sandow act by the lakeside. Demyan even went so far as to tell me—satirical poets make a virtue of being tactless—that he heard what I had hoped was an awestruck young beauty asking her mother: "Do they really have sailors in the Navy as old as *that?*" I have to take into account that I had just beaten him, fifth game in a row, at chess. So now I burn away the tensions by lonely walks across a tableland almost as empty and flat as Siberia. Only when I have put eight or nine miles between me and my nannies, do I settle down to read by a pool or stream. Not difficult—half of Finland is water. I still refuse to look at the Peter papers. There is only one piece of news I am waiting for—one event that will dynamite the logjam. This will reach us faster than papers can be printed. Instead, I take with me from B.-B.'s shelves, stuffed with his old stock, a foreign novel or two, mainly English, but sometimes French. I find this a satisfactory compromise: the strange languages give the mental muscles something to work on while the content would not strain the intellect of a Tsar's mistress. Reading *Russian* popular novels—now that *would* be too much like a breakfast of bon-bons! (That reminds me, I have not come across a decent chocolate since I left Switzerland. Even before the wartime shortages, Russian confectioners did not understand that the essence of chocolate is not bland, milky sweetness. It should have a sharp, ebony tang, somewhere between coffee-bean grounds and orange-peel oil, with even a speck or two of saltiness.)

I feel the long, rippling back of the revolutionary surge rising under my feet and gathering to rear up, wave upon wave. What is the physical sensation it reminds me of? Ah, yes, ocean-surfing. That South Sea island sport which in Europe seems only to have become naturalized at Biarritz. Inessa and I came over there from Arcachon, that marvelous week. Both of us were sensitized, *gal-*

vanized almost, by the electric currents of our passion. The excitement of the great, tumbling, chuckling breakers, after the mild, treacly ripples of the inland sea, sucked us in. We rode, hand in hand, twin Mazeppas, in charge after charge across the glassy plain to the beach, while Inessa yodelled Wagnerian noises from *Die Walküre*.

Then it was I trained myself to know the false ocean wave from the true one, gaily gliding off any which were doomed to melt away and rolling into the hammock of their trough. Just so, now I feel no guilt about taking this vacation into emptiness between breakers. We have had the April Days, then the June Days. Mass energy is concentrating, growing larger and stronger, but so far still stumbling over the same premature dissipation into foam. My antennae tell me that unless overwhelming forces outside the country strike into us with determined ferocity (an untimely Ludendorff offensive, say) then this patch of doldrums may be the longest. The September Days may be the ones that will make the Revolution.

So I turn with justified frivolity once more to such as Arsène Lupin and Sherlock Holmes. It is not easy for a reader with dissident views about bourgeois society to find light, holiday fiction where the heroes are on his side. Even with historical novels, my occasional self-indulgence as a student, I had to search hard for a "great man" who measured up to the standards of my own rebel heroes.

Mine were more or less restricted to the captains who also led my armies of toy soldiers on their campaigns across the tiled, weedy battlefields of backyard Moscow Street. Lincoln aided by Sherman and Grant; Cromwell (with Fairfax and Ireton); Napoleon and all his marshals. My friends, even where they inclined to my mild nonconformity, found romance, glamour, the magical touch of the irrational, linked with destined defenders of the *ancien régime*— English Charles II and Rupert of the Rhine; American General Lee and his Southern colonels; the anti-French Allies, Wellington, Blücher, even Tsar Alexander!

I remember with what a sense of betrayal, somewhere between schoolboy and university entrant, I found out that *Les Trois Mousquetaires* had a sequel, *Vingt Ans Depuis,* and the author was clearly on the side of Charles, the Man of Blood, and not Cromwell, the People's Warrior. True, Dumas split the four inseparables ("All for One, and One for All!") equally between the opposing sides. But the nobler, more idealistic, less ambitious pair, Aramis and Athos, declare for royalty. In the end, once more united, they attempt to rescue him from that death on the scaffold he richly deserves—unsuccessfully, of course. And I have never quite come to terms with the thrill that stirred my guts, almost a sexual throb, as the tyrant's blood drained through, while they crouched hidden beneath the executioner's block, wetting each one.

Between Arsène Lupin and Sherlock Holmes there is not much for a socialist to choose. I remember thinking that, even in Paris in '08, when A.L. was the season's literary sensation. Lupin is a rabid nationalist, a staunch conservative, a defender of private enterprise and private property, a supporter of the *status quo*—in other words, a typical professional crook. Holmes is also a reactionary, under his carnival mask of eccentricity, who admires the monarchy, the landowning aristocracy, the City gent, the upper classes everywhere. His character is nearer that of the secret-service agent than the private-inquiry agent—I would picture him today as rather resembling the chief Allied spy in Russia, Captain Bruce Lockhart, of the British Embassy.

If I have to make a choice, it is for Lupin, particularly in books like *813* and *Les Huits Coups de l'Horloge*. Most British and some French novel reviewers, while praising these, found them far-fetched. In Paris or London, few would credit that a public enemy like Lupin would ever really manage to pose for a couple of years as Commissaire Lenormand, Chef de la Sûreté, and lead the hunt for himself, or that as M. Victor of the Special Branch actually contrive to arrest "Arsène Lupin." But no educated Russian would blink an eyelid. We are quite used to such double/treble operators, revolutionaries holding high positions in the tsarist security apparatus or tsarist *agents provocateurs* on the central committees of many left parties, including, I'm sorry to have to admit, the Bolsheviks. Even in Europe many people now know the story of Azef. But that is only one of dozens of chases through the hall of mirrors, hunter and quarry often not certain which is which, who is posing and who is posing as posing. When Savinkov decided to revive the SR Battle Section, battered by many defeats, arrests and persecutions, he called for Twelve Heroes, fearless, incorruptible, ready to give their lives to assassinate oppressors of the people. Twelve volunteers presented themselves within days. Three were in the pay of the Okhrana. Then there was Malinovsky, our own Party leader in the Duma. I might now still believe in his innocence—after all, in his German POW camp, he continues to woo his fellow Russian soldiers with our propaganda! That is, if I had not seen, in the newly-opened archives of the Peter police, the accounts of his government salary and his regular handwritten reports on us.

But this is what I half-feared. I try to cut myself off from my comrades, and our deadly struggle, by retreating to somewhere where I cannot be observed. I settle down with a sack of books which bear only the most tenuous links with real life and, before I know where I am, my train of thought has puffed back to the terminus from which I began my holiday.

Ah well! There is always sleep!

JULY 4 **MUSTIAMIAKI** **1917**

Like most insomniacs, I am a sound sleeper. It is when I remain awake that I become uneasy and distressed. Unlike most sound sleepers, I awake instantly at any change which would put me on the alert when not asleep. It is as if inside me there is stationed a sleepless, twenty-four-hour-duty guard who hears everything but arouses me only when the unusual is detected. Thus, if I heard a cow at any hour in Petersburg I would sit up immediately. Here, Vera's two milkers, those straying pieces from a black-and-white jigsaw, can sound their throaty foghorns whenever they like without any of us noticing.

But at 6 A.M. a scratching on the louvered shutters, as if a burglar were picking their locks? I had my feet on the cool, birch floor and was crouching, Browning in hand, behind the chest of drawers before I recalled that the *dacha* had no locks. Indeed, now I thought of it, none of the cottages of rural Finland ever closes its doors day or night, anyway during the summer. B.-B. was talking to Shotman, one of the most resourceful of our Party messengers, and turned to me his long, academic face—"There's been an uprising in Peter," he said. "And they want you."

That's the wrong way round for a start, I thought. It should be me first, then the uprising. *It is absolutely the wrong time to do it.* How many false starts can we afford?

"What do you mean 'the wrong time'?" asked B.-B., startled. "You just said it was . . ."

"Never mind," I explained. "When is the early office-workers' train to Peter? That's the time you should be worrying about!"

"Six-forty-five express. Get you at your desk by eight A.M." interjected Shotman.

"I've kept the droshky. Both ends."

The 6:45 from Mustiamiaki was packed with *petit-bourgeois* self-made businessmen, middling bureaucrats who had come down in the world, their typewriting daughters, officers in mufti with uniforms in their briefcases, officers in uniform with civvies in their briefcases, B.-B., Marya and me. I had to work out who the other passengers were from their lower halves alone. Their uppers were hidden behind their newspapers. This was lucky for me since my only disguise was a mahogany tan and the blue-tinged glasses from my escape bag—a combination B.-B. said made me look already so suspicious, like a black-market farmer, that nobody would imagine I was a political. We too had our share of the morning's press, as many as B.-B. would allow. "Nobody who reads *that* would read *that*," he kept instructing me out of the side of his mouth. "That's enough. Take any more and you have to be revolutionary or a police agent." Eventually, we settled for eight between three of us. No copy of *Pravda* on sale here. The one Shotman had brought me burned like contraband in my pocket—all I'd been able to see was a large white hole where the CenCom had pulled out some message and not put in another. I couldn't settle down with the capitalist press at first. Partly because the shading of the lenses of my specs was so dark it was like trying to see by a wax match in a coal cellar (bad staff-work! Ilyich). But mainly because I was fascinated by some fellow-travelers, a breed I had never examined at such close range. These were the upper-middle-middles, the eight-to-five regular shuttlers between white-collar office and that pocket-handkerchief country seat, that nail-scissored, private, grassy plot that all aspiring climbers seem to need to prove they have passed the halfway mark on the greasy pole.

It might have made what they call a "number" in a revue at the Bi-Ba-Bo cabaret—two rows of papers facing each other across the compartment like Zulu shields, then each folding down in turn to reveal a single face, either purple (male) or chalky (female), which utters, staccato, "Damn Bolsheviks!," "Filthy Reds!," "German spies!," "Guttersnipe traitors!," leading on to a chorus, when all simultaneously lower their defenses to repeat in unison: "I know what *I'd* like to do with *them!*" It should be set to music.

It is not easy to gather from the press quite what precisely happened in Petersburg to cause such fury, or require my instant presence. After all, I have trained myself to bring into focus, often from afar, through the distorting prisms of foreign languages, hostile ideologies, journalistic invention, the stupidity or cunning of official spokesmen, complicated by the screens of governmental or proprietorial censorship, what finally inks the page. Even then, I expect only a workable, rule-of-thumb approximation to the truth as I would have seen it myself. Say about as near as the printed prison menu is to what the convicts really eat. What can they know, those who read only one paper? I suppose each chooses the one that will tell him what he wants to believe in the way he prefers. "Unconsciously," as Radek would say, readers may know that they are being fooled, entertained rather than informed, manipulated. And semi-consciously, if there is such a word, the hacks and the capitalist publishers milk a fat living out of indulging them.

We shared the eight, marking key stories with a thumbnail, but showing no reactions. B.-B. gave me the side-of-mouth advice to pretend to be reading only the City pages and the horse-race results—"You look like a gambler, gamblers can even read *Pravda* without being suspected, but not leading articles." In the serious publications, most of them fairly superficial by Marxist standards, the news was conveyed either in abstract, Latinate prose, enlivened by an occasional figurative invocation of the Muse of History or the Spirit of National Honor, which gave the impression that *all* events take place in some remote past, possibly at Rome: or it was presented in businesslike, detailed terms, rather like the instructions on an architect's blueprint, with a lot of improbably precise items such as "exactly at 7:18 A.M." The yellow press also have two styles, though these tend to overlap. Some of them record just the bare bones of any event, in its most simplified form, and then wrap it round with wreath after wreath of rhetoric, woven from feeble puns, bad verse, threadbare proverbs, familiar quotations, outlandish superlatives, all printed in large, italic capitals. This is the most profitable method since even a very short article can stretch to a page and a half, and the writers have no need to leave the office to find their material. Others, with a bigger budget, supplement this mixture with firsthand reports from their fearless correspondents, men whose prescience is such that they frequently manage to be on the spot several hours before the news happens. They also then sometimes get their accounts back to the office, printed and sold on the streets, in advance too. In times of editorial stringency, it has been known for these ace reporters also to operate without leaving the building. It becomes clear (eventually) that there has not, anyway so far, been an uprising, or even real violence on the Peter streets. The First Machine-Gun Regiment, correctly described as the Petersburg force most loyal to the Bolsheviks, has been variously ordered to send half/all/one in ten of its strength to the Front. In the absence of almost all of its officers, said to be either murdered or waiting at home with their uniforms hung in the closet, it is under the command of Corporal Mashenko/ Ensign Shamenko. (Presumably our friend, Lieutenant Semashko, one of the fieriest of the Party's young hotheads.) The Regiment did not wish to march to war, especially since Kerensky's victorious heroes are rumored to be in full retreat. (I take *that* to be indisputable since all six papers deny it.) But the Regiment had to do something to work off its ill-feelings—so it began to parade about the city. Semashko, not liking to see such rebel energies go to waste, gave the Machine-Gunmen some rallying cries: "Down with the government," "Power to the People!," "Let Soldiers and Workers Rule Alone!" After a day of marching and countermarching, they called on the Kronstadt sailors and the factory Red Guards to join them. All the papers say the Bolos then *ordered* them to seize control of the capital, afterward the country. However, when the press bother to quote any of our Party statements—e.g., speeches by such of our MilOrg chiefs as Nevsky and Podvoisky—it is clear that they have been imploring the masses, military and civilian, to keep calm, make their demands peacefully and not use firearms.

However, I have to admit that the speeches, which sound for once reported with reasonable accuracy, are pacific only on the surface. I can well imagine that in the real world they can be construed as fairly obvious nudges to the insurgents to get a move on. The gap in *Pravda* when at last I got the chance to examine it in the washrooms, looked to me a sure flag of indecision. I would guess that the original message had been, as in the June Days, a two-way bet. If the demonstrations continue massive, militant but orderly, we Bolsheviks can afford to be seen as the *mahout* on the elephant. But if the creature turns rogue and tramples the obstacles in its path, then of course we also must seem behind it. At least not in front of it! Again, as in the June Days, I would imagine that CenCom must have been forced to issue another manifesto requesting the forces of potential revolt to rein back. This, alas, is once more not the moment.

From my readings between the lines, I would write down yesterday as a draw. All depends on today. I am not exactly recovered. But the Neivola holiday has got the process off to an encouraging start—the music of battle rolling nearer has always steeled my sinews, recruited fresh blood.

What remains somewhat unclear is how much actual *fighting* has already taken place, if any. Only *Russkaya Volya* reports any violence. Its typical standardized account is dispensed to a basic formula that hardly ever varies. Perhaps the editor keeps it set in type, with only a few gaps left where dates, times, the proper names of people and places can be inserted later? A pity the Durnovo Anarchists were ever forced to hand back this shoddy rag to its appalling owner!

Here are typical paragraphs:

As I write this dispatch, a hail of bullets sweeps over my head from either side of the Nevsky Prospect. A child like a broken doll lies almost within reach of my hand. My words, scrawled with a stubby pencil in a bloodstained notebook, may never reach you. But I must make the attempt. The readers of *Russian Freedom* deserve to know how the Bolshevik shock troops are terrorizing our capital city's most famous boulevard.

The Red Anarchists, a mob of work-shy laborers, stay-home soldiers and street-brawling party bruisers, bristling with weapons, began the battle. On their way to the Marinsky Palace to murder the Supreme Commander, carrying a banner, "The first bullet for Kerensky," they stopped to loot our world-famous Nevsky stores.

Not many would blame shop owners and managers, former guardians of law and order, or just patriotic, honest citizens, if they repelled these gun-toting robbers. But no one could swear to the identity of those who fired back on the Red Anarchists.

As always, the innocents in the middle suffered most. Flame spat from muzzles poking out through hidden loopholes, from the tiles above, from the cellars below. Leaden gusts swept backward and forward scything down spectators and passersby. Women and children slipped on pavements that had become ice rinks of blood.

German agents had earlier been seen handing out 15, 10 and 5 ruble notes to hired trouble-makers. Now they reappeared to urge the Bolsheviks to capture and hang the government, cow the decent citizens of Petrograd, and open the gates to the Hunnish hordes.

In the lull in the killing, I managed to bring my notes back to this office. But I can scarce transcribe them, so sickened am I still by the foretaste of Hell I witnessed last night.

"How can anyone believe that stuff?" Marya asked me as we took the droshky Shotman had booked for us from the station forecourt. "They will see for themselves today that the Nevsky Prospect is perhaps boarded up but otherwise untouched. . . . Won't they?"

I explained to Marya what few reasonable, honest, straightforward people, unfortunately, understand. In a fluid situation, changing every hour, what matters is not what happens but what is believed to have happened. No one can check everything firsthand. Few even dare, or want, to try. *Russkaya Volya*'s story would now have been lifted by all the other papers and adapted to fit their later editions or tomorrow's issue.

Thousands of people who never look out of the window in times like this will have read about the supposed looting, killing and attempts to wipe out the government. Then, even more convincing, they will meet those who swear that they know such things occurred because they were told about them by a friend, or relative, who was actually there. Because so many (on our side as well as among neutrals or enemies) already think this is what *may* have happened on July 3, then it becomes that much more likely that it will happen on July 4. By July 6, nobody will be in any state to wonder which came first—the report or the deed. The version will be authorized by the side which wins.

B.-B. said he preferred to walk across the city to his flat. But in his most elder-brother fashion, just before he left us, he gave me a little reproof. "A good job after all you didn't go diving in the middle of that lake, Ilyich. Since then peasants have told me that it is famous as the haunt of a giant water-worm that has been known to drag down dogs, even deer."

He looked so concerned, I couldn't help laughing.

"You don't believe those hayseed yarns, do you? There are more frightful monsters waiting to eat us alive in Peter than in all your Finnish fairy tales. Take care."

Marya and I climbed into the droshky. I was already at work, sorting impressions, testing theories, collating what I had picked up on the train, recording what I could see from the cab window, preparing the questions I would ask.

Most of MilOrg, some of CenCom, some of PetroCom (the city's Party bosses), were waiting at Kshesinskaya's. I was pleased to find that their report of yesterday more or less matched what I gathered from decoding the capitalist press, though the papers had misunderstood some rather important details. There *had* been a group dedicated to arresting, probably liquidating, Kerensky, dispersing the government and Soviet, smashing the state apparatus, summoning the people to rule themselves. (They missed him by twenty minutes.) But owning to the inability, or reluctance, of pressmen to distinguish between different brands of revolutionaries, we Bolsheviks had been saddled with the plan. The originators, of course, were the Anarchists from Durnovo.

It also seems likely that there *was* quite a lot of shooting. As usual, the evidence is not really firsthand. Weary experience as a revolutionary leader has taught me that often both your allies *and* your opponents, particularly the extremes of Left and Right, collude in telling the same lie. Each wants an excuse for opening fire as soon as possible. What better excuse than the report that the others have already started? I determine to reconstruct a timetable of the situation.

Semashko has nose-led his Machine-Gunners around all morning and early afternoon. For "something to do," they had occupied the Finland station, roadblocked Troitsky and Liteiny bridges, patrolled Nevsky. Afterward, Semashko claims he tried to persuade them to return to barracks with help from our MilOrg boss, Nevsky. I called N. to give his version. He admitted that, though S. and he had indeed "advised" the troops to disband, this was just for the record. "Only a fool would get the message that he really should not demonstrate!"

But around 2:30, CenCom issued a direct order to all Bolsheviks not to take to the streets. And a statement was sent across for *Pravda,* today's issue, asking its thousands of sailor readers not to obey any Machine-Gunners' appeal to march on the city. Poor old Stalin was dispatched to assure the Soviet chiefs that our Party leaders were totally opposed to an uprising and trying desperately to defuse one. With his harsh provincial accent, his pockmarked scowl and bandit moustache, not to mention his reputation as bank-robber and train-wrecker, the elusive Georgian (Sukhanov in his color pieces in *Novaya Zhizn* nicknames him "the gray blur") is hardly the Soviet CenExCom's favorite politician. One of them brought out a file of cuttings from our papers in which I am frequently quoted (correctly), as arguing that a real socialist revolution is only a matter of time. "You ought to get your chief a new watch," said one. "What he needs is a perpetual calendar," shouted another. There were a lot of such jokes, some of them quite sharp (I think). But Stalin, who is not afraid of anything, is afraid of ridicule. Like many unlikely sensitives, he tends to suspect that people are always laughing at him—even people at tables over on the far side of the room, even people in the next room. I imagine he stumped out looking like the Third Murderer.

For the rest of yesterday, July 3, it was crescendo.

5 P.M. Raskolnikov telephoned to say he would not be able to stop all Kronstadt storming into Peter.

6 P.M. Call from the Narva. Something like 20,000 Putilov workers will march on the Tauride Palace that night. Another 15 or 20,000 wives and children are behind them.

7 P.M. 10,000 armed workers from Basil Island have begun a trek to the Tauride. A second installment, same strength, same route, plan to follow today.

8 P.M. Machine-gunners, who had gone back late afternoon to barracks on Vyborg side, now reported returning early evening over Liteiny bridge, reinforced by Red Guards from our proletarian citadel.

Around this point, our CenCom's nerve broke. Now Kamenev took the Stalin trail downstairs to the Soviet leadership. He begged them to join us in giving official sanction to a display of strength in order to avoid it turning into an exercise of strength. There was something absurd about this. K. would have noticed if he had not been in such a panic. Hundreds of thousands of demonstrators were demanding that Soviets stop holding hands with capitalist liberals and seize power for themselves and the masses. How could Soviet CenExCom support such a demo even if they had wanted to? It would have meant marching in the front rank of a deputation to *themselves,* which would then demand that they *themselves* carry out a policy that they *themselves* oppose! They refused, rejecting K."s plea with many a jibe at the expense of the Bolsheviks. I must say, I find it hard to blame them.

9 P.M. to midnight. Huge processions of troops and Red Guards and lightly armed workers gathered in Alexander Park across the way from Kshesinska's. The first speaker from the balcony was Sverdlov. I suppose in an Anarchist black-leather three-piece, with boots. (This has become his hallmark.)

His message: "Shout all the slogans you want, Comrades—*but stay north of the river!*"

More arrivals. I can see Podvoisky and Nevsky taking turns on the balcony. Nikolai Ilyich Podvoisky, chairman of MilOrg, tall, skinny, hair and beard black as soot, has a hard, cold look. Speaks as if reading from a text written on the horizon, though he never uses a note. In public, he is rational, unhurried, down to earth, reminding everyone, even if he does not say it in so many words, that guns have bullets, bullets make holes in flesh, life bleeds away through bullet holes. Comrades, *this is not a game!* If you want to fight, we will lead you to battle. But some of you shouting now will be lying dead on the cobblestones tomorrow. . . . I don't know how he does it. Without quite scaring the hell out of you, he gives you the feeling you have just survived your first day under fire.

Vladimir Ilyich Nevsky, short and squat, with a round, flattened face common as a chamberpot. The last man you would expect to beguile you with epic rhetoric. He starts with a roll of papers to help him, then gets confused and stuffs them back in his pocket or throws them away. (This is a deliberate, rehearsed routine, like the act of a cabaret comic. I picked up one of those sheets once—it contained a list of the materials needed to make a chicken coop.) Then he takes off on a simple sequence of thoughts which he elaborates, decorates, plays with, juggles and bounces, like a composer devising variations on a theme. I can't explain how it works, any more than I can explain why an aria from *Faust* is so different when I sing it and when Chaliapin, sings it. Final effect spellbinding, oratory of the kind you can almost fancy prodded on the Greeks and Trojans across the windy plains of Ilium. Occasionally, N. will stumble. The whole theatrical artifice could disintegrate in a second. I remember he assured the Soviet Congress that if they took power we would support them to the death in their struggle. "Working like Trojan horses . . ." was how he phrased it. Luckily, there was so much shouting and interrupting only a few really heard the words. In B.-B.'s view—he likes that kind of joke—Nevsky meant what he said and was correctly describing my policy.

The pair are a great agitational team, working on the platform like the nasty gendarme and the nice gendarme of the police interrogation cell. What is more unusual, they operate even better in tandem when the struggle needs deeds rather than words. Podvoisky is best behind scenes, indoors at a desk, taking the overall view, making the command decisions. Nevsky is the leader who thinks on his feet, shows himself everywhere, the physical fighting man, truble-shooter and morale-booster. They balance each other as Trotsky and I must learn to do, since he has become a Bolshevik. What a crew! P. and N.; beery, barrel-bellied Gusev; tiny, ferocious, half-blind, ratting-terrier Antonov-Ovseyenko; gig-lamps bookworm Smilga: these are marshals Bonaparte might have envied. And just under them, leading their personal hordes like Mongol khans, Raskolnikov and his not-so-jolly-tars, Semashko and his itchy-fingered Machine-Gunners. The leader who cannot make a revolution with such Men of Confidence should . . . what? (Join the Mensheviks?)

But, as we had already found in June, our people are like an avalanche, easy to start moving, impossible to halt. It may be, now as then, ours is the only party that can divert the stampede without being trampled to gristle. Yesterday P. and N. did not succeed. Now it's my turn to try.

It would be pointless to blame them. Even Nevsky could only hold his audience rapt and dreamy for seconds. Then a voice shouted: "Give us another tune, mate. We want a march, not a love song!" The regimental band of the Machine-Gunners struck up the "Internationale." Section upon section, in their thousands, they fell in behind and started off, to the southeast, across the Troitsky bridge and past the Field of Mars, along the Nevsky, and the Liteiny, to the Tauride.

They were joined, halfway along the Nevsky, by the Putilov contingent tramping northeastward up from the Narva suburb.

Shortly after this, so far as I can make out, just over the Fontanka Canal and near the corner of Liteiny, the now mixed and disordered columns were fired upon by a handful of invisible attackers, lurking like bedbugs in the cracks of alleyways. This part of the press reports ran briefly parallel to the truth. But our fearless correspondents cannot have been looking very hard since nothing else that they describe occurred. Contrary to what those who have never seen street fighting may think, it is not a very daring or dangerous act to shoot bullets into a passing column, even one containing a lot of armed men. And if it should happen to be dark, the marchers pressed into a solid, hobbling queue, inching along unfamiliar streets, deafened by their own chants, numbed by internal pressures, blinded by too many heads—such brave assassins will have an even better chance of killing, and not being caught, than they would have . . . what? Rolling boulders down into a valley packed with sheep?

The soldiers, workers and Red Guards spread out, like stooks of wheat, over the Potemkin gardens, across the wide pavements and walks around the Tauride Palace. Only then did the white faces and bloody clothes of the dozen wounded, the two or three dying, glow like waxworks in the chandelier radiance from the palace lights. Only then did the great moving camp realize it had been cruelly savaged on the way. Instantly, the mood soured, grew childish and sullen, a queasy mix of brutality and self-pity. Wounds are contagious.

Soldiers hacked off branches with their bayonets, built themselves fires around which to sprawl, drink and gamble. Civilians, many worn out by a ten-hour day and an eight-mile walk, slept under bushes. Some swore never to leave the places they had staked out until the Soviet agreed to make itself the ruler of the nation. The Soviet's CenExCom was now alarmed too by this unchained giant squatting on its doorstep. Its best speakers tried vainly to catch the ear of the monster. The stars of our Party, old Bolsheviks like Zinoviev, new recruits like Trotsky, dramatic figures who often attracted audiences simply as theatrical entertainment, were also ignored.

2 A.M. this morning, July 4. While I slept, our CenCom, now only too familiar with the pattern, guessed what would happen

next. The barometer of the masses had swung its finger toward a spell of storm and hurricane, riot and upheaval. Where else should Bolsheviks be, but clearing the way ahead? Whether we were pulling, or being pushed, we must be *seen* to be leading. So Zinoviev and Kamenev hammered out a new manifesto for *Pravda*, replacing that appeal to the masses NOT to take to the streets in any way by an appeal to the masses to take to the streets but in "a serious and responsible fashion" under Bolshevik guidance. But there had been far too much debate. By the time the messenger arrived at *Pravda*'s expensive new presses on Moika Street, it was still early enough to pull out the first message. But just too late to insert the second. The result was the paper that Shotman had brought me, with the white, empty box on the front page. This device also had its drawbacks—many people, not surprisingly, assumed that the hole had once contained a Bolshevik call to arms, censored at the last moment by the Provisional government or the Soviet!

They also decided to call me back from B.-B.'s Finnish *dacha*. The reason they gave seemed slightly odd. Admittedly, I had slipped off like a thief in the night, on impulse, leaving behind instructions to send me no newspaper, memos, resolutions, letters or other Party business. And I was grateful for the holiday. But does it really make sense to keep your leader exiled in the quiet provinces for a day after the capital city has become clamorous with tumult? And on the grounds that so long as he is absent no one will believe his Party is sponsoring insurrection? Because then, when Lenin does come steaming back to the Finland station, summoned at dawn ... won't our enemies think the insurrection is on? Did someone want me out of the way?

By the time I had established this sequence of events. I was ready to start entering the events of today in my notebook.

9 A.M.: Podvoisky joined Nevsky and me and most of the executive of MilOrg in the best bedroom. They had shrewdly anticipated the CenCom *volte-face* of the early hours of this morning. So last night, they put into action those first contingency plans we had outlined together centuries ago in May and June.

Every regiment, factory, civil service department, tenement block, workers' organization, that had ever shown a response to our political line has had its Party cells activated. Unwieldy bodies are split into handy, compact groups—companies, workshops, branches, staircases, floors or whatever—and guided by a local Bolshevik, known to all their members. MilOrg agitators from HQ, recognizable by their bowler hats and padded sleigh-coats, each with a pair of revolvers in his belt, will be attached to larger sections.

During the weeks of waiting, they had been trained by a couple of disabled, disaffected Guards officers in the orchards behind Kshesinska's. Going over assault courses under fire from live ammo; learning marksmanship, the maintenance and repair of most kinds of gun; making hand grenades and fire bombs. Finally, the professionals passed them out as fit to be awarded sergeant's stripes even in the Preobrazhensky Guards. In the evenings, when too many flares, explosions and gunshots would have attracted unwelcome attention, they sat down in the ballerina's private theater to study Marxism, party history, the art and craft of urban guerrilla war, how to debate and give orders. Most had been promoted from the ranks of our illegal citizen army, the Red Guards. And Gusev had worried that, by sending them ahead on their own, we might be leaving behind our Guards leaderless. But P. and N. are now certain our soldiers in dungarees and cloth caps are as good fighting men as all the Provisional government's troops in greatcoats and peaked hats.

By 9:30 A.M. MilOrg's signal has raised seven regiments to fall in behind the First Machine-Gunners. Some 12,000 Red Guards split into two great wings, one marching south from the Vyborg side over Liteiny bridge, another marching east from Basil Island across the Lesser Neva bridge, into central Petersburg. The second wave of a further 15,000 from Narva, mainly women and children, but strengthened by the night shift from the Putilov Works, slogging direct to the Tauride.

Since first light, Smilga has been out with his armored cars, posting one or two at every intersection along yesterday's route. Doubling them at the Troitsky and Liteiny bridges. Making a particular concentration where shots were fired yesterday into the procession. Most of his motorized cavalry sound rather more fearsome than they look. We have only a handful of the Russian-designed, French-built, bulletproof battering rams on four wheels, the crew glimpsed only through slits in the sheet metal, that were brought to such a high development by the Germans. The bulk of Smilga's flying limousines have reinforced paneling and heavy-duty tires, but normal windows and a sporty, even elegant look. Their fighting power lies less in being well protected than in packing such an offensive, speedy punch. The running boards are wide, and long enough to carry a pair of riflemen either side, lolling along the mudguards. Two more stand up and hang on to the rear doors. Up to five more can crouch inside with the driver. The rapid fire of eleven rifles, with attendant bayonets, bombs and sidearms, can be summoned to any point at up to fifty miles per hour!

P. and N. see today's massing of forces as our final warning to the Soviet, a dress rehearsal with almost all the risks of the real thing. If this should turn into the actual insurrection—which is not *my* plan—MilOrg are determined that every last unit of fighting energy at our disposal will be made to count. But why is it not my plan? Because there is *still* too much weight against us: too many regiments in Peter still neutral: some at the front still hostile: too many workers still convinced that the SRs and Menshies will see them through capitalism to socialism by peaceful agreement: quite a few among the aristocracy of labor who regard us as the enemy of their way of life, perhaps even as German agents. What are the forecasts of my marshals? P. and N. see June 18 on a larger scale, much less goodhumored, but with no shooting by either side. Smilga thinks there is an even chance of an armed clash. While Semashko, who keeps out of my way so that he can always say he never heard my orders, is convinced that yesterday's casualties were caused by Kerensky's phantom sharpshooters getting their eye in with a little target practice. He *knows* there will be stronger attacks on us today, swears that more of their blood will run in the gutters than ours. In pursuit of this, he has mounted some of his machine guns on the backs of lorries, muzzles pointing upward from sloping platforms. Not everyone can understand why.

"You expecting to be attacked by Zeppelins then?" boomed Gusev as Semashko sailed past in a cloud of diesel smoke just after I arrived. But the mad triggerman kept at a distance, and only waved.

11 A.M. Telephone call from our other mad young gunslinger, Raskolnikov. He is at the Kronstadt pier, off Nikolai quay on Basil Island, and reports that his fleet of cutters has just discharged 10,000 sailors. Another fleet has landed a further 10,000 at the Angliskaya Quay on the other side of the Greater Neva river. The first lot are marching here. The second are joining the Putilovites along the Nevsky to the Tauride. "We've all brought our pencils," he adds. Your what? "Ask Joseph Vissarionovich."

Gusev, overhearing, bursts into guffaws. "That's Stalin's doing," he said. "He took Raskolnikov's last telephone call. You know how both think their conversations are being tapped all the time? So they say 'Little Kerenskies have Big Ears' and talk in code? Well, they do. Only it gets a bit mixed up sometimes because they have to make up codes as they go along. This time Raskolnikov kept asking: 'Should we come *fully dressed*?' and Stalin kept answering 'What do I care?' Then he got the point, and he said 'I will be bringing my pencils.' Raskolnikov asked 'Your what?' just like you did. And Stalin said, 'We writers always bring our pencils. They're our *weapons*.' And he rang off with Raskolnikov still repeating: 'Pencils? Oh, pen-cils! I see!' So I suppose we'll have to put up with 20,000 matelots in town waving 20,000 pre-1905 muskets they can just aim well enough to blow off their own big toes?"

"Yes," I said. "What would Marshal Suvorov have done?"

Noon. I've been on the telephone to Our Comrade at the Front, and also, rather more circumspectly, to certain of Our Friends in Stockholm. They tell me the same news, news nobody will see in the newspapers yet, not even in *Pravda*. This is: Kerensky's offensive has smashed like the last wave of the incoming tide on the solid breakwater of the German defenses. Now it is ebbing away. It had been launched (for purely political reasons) on June 18 while we made our last triumphal parade through the city. The report of Kerensky's first successes published the day afterward did a lot to rob our achievement of its propaganda impact. For the last fortnight, whenever the war has been allowed to reach the front pages, it has been in terms of advances, prisoners captured, gains being consolidated. Now, Kerensky's bluff has been called at the cost of some 80,000 of our soldiers killed and wounded. Should the Germans attack today, wipe out our retreating Russian rear guard, and mount a direct threat to Peter—then, this might be the change in the climate I have been waiting for. Several things would then become clear: the government's strategy cannot hold back the enemy; the government-plus-the-Soviet cannot command the confidence and loyalty of soldiers or workers. Then . . . this might be our opportunity. But so far the German line has not moved. No doubt, this too is a political decision. They are waiting for something. We are waiting for something. What is it? Can it be the same thing? Our Friends should be able to let me know soon. Meanwhile, any move at home must be kept reined back under continuous control.

1 P.M. The surrounds of Kshesinskaya's Mansion, the depths of Alexander Park, back as far as the Zoological Gardens, are pebbled with heads. (Whoever it was who first thought of "sea of faces"—was it that Scotlander Walter Scott?—coined a cliché which never wears faint. A crowd *is* a sea, with its spume, its white-caps, its whirlpools, its currents, its heavings and tossings.) Even in my muffled cubbyhole at the back of the house, I can hear the dull boom of 20,000 mutters and grumbles. I set to work to keep our incident diary up to date, when I hear a click of heels, a jingle of metal—it is Raskolnikov saluting me. I shake hands and offer a seat on the bed. But he keeps standing.

"Ilyich, *Starik*, boss! You must talk to my sailors. They think the Revolution is in danger. Only the sight of you will convince them the Bolsheviks have not been squashed, scattered, arrested, shot."

How much can he understand of what teeters in the balance with every decision? Does he think I am the hero in the folktale who only has to unleash the power he did not know he possessed in order to defeat all his enemies and provide a happy ending?

I told him that only by *not* appearing, *not* speaking, could I establish my independence. "I am opposed to armed presences on our streets *now*. To any actions resembling an uprising, by accident or design *now*. I never wanted a demonstration of any kind *today*. I give it my qualified support only to avoid a worse alternative." He was white and beginning to tremble.

"Please," he begged, gripping my arm over the chess table. "Just tell them *that*! Otherwise, listen!"

And there was a noise of stamping boots that made the beads on the hangings shake and dance.

"LEN . . . . . *nin*! LEN . . . . *nin*! LEN . . . *nin*! LEN . . *nin*! LEN . *nin*! LENIN! *L'n'nL'n'nL'n'n*!" shouted the sailors in chorus, starting slow and gradually speeding up, like supporters at an athletics competition cheering on their champion. As I came out on the balcony, they had just reached the point where they unload the vowels and the name turns into continuous drum roll, as if cargoes of steel teeth were clacking like castanets. It escalated to the famous Kronstadt "lion's roar" as they recognized me.

I felt uneasy, and rather tetchy. I always do when I see great ranks of independent individuals welded into the trained beast of a thousand faces, all of them the same. Many of the comrades find this a welcome intoxication, a heady reassurance that they are right. I do not like being elevated by this or any drug. Indeed, the proposition that an idea is more likely to be true because it attacts many rather than few is as repellent as it is ridiculous. Kerensky is greeted by the same wave of ecstatic dedication. So once was the Tsar. So now am I. But this is not why I am right, and they are wrong. Trotsky described the feeling all too vividly when he told me once that the soldiers and workers seemed to be hanging on his lips "as on the nipples of revolution." That is it, *exactly*. That is also why it sends through me a shiver of revulsion. And, though I know it is bad platform technique, why I cannot help cutting in, starting my speech long before their noise has tapered away.

1:30 P.M. For once, I do not regret a poor speech. I told them that I had been ill (which was true) and my hoarse voice made that sound more convincing. I called them, the sailors anyway, "the pride and beauty of the Revolution." And I meant it. I welcomed them on behalf of the Petersburg proletariat. Then, in the flattest tones I could reproduce I assured them of my confidence that our Bolshevik slogan—"All Power to the Soviets *Everywhere!*"—would soon flutter from the heights, "despite the zigzags of history." Very soon, they would be called upon to suppress the coming counter-revolution. But for the moment what is required is "firmness, stead-fastness and vigilance." I sensed that none of my listeners, sailors, soldiers or workers, could disagree or fault my advice. There was nothing there to loose the Red Cock.

I was glad to note the cheers were barely perfunctory. Within minutes, the tide had licked round every nook and cranny within my view, sucked out the great rolling mass of demonstrators, and started pouring them across the Neva. Bobbing at their head, rather comically identifiable by the large "B" on its roof, rode an armored limousine containing Podvoisky and Nevsky, the joint commanders of the enterprise. I returned to my timetable, determined to carry on recording the history of these days, until the time comes to take my own small, battered florist's van, chosen for its banal familiarity, to the evening Bolshevik CenCom session at the Tauride.

Raskolnikov has left a note. Perhaps he is more of a profes-sional revolutionary, less of a stagey amateur, than I realized? About the Baltic Fleet. Interesting scale operates here: the bigger the ship, the more likely it is to declare for us. Battle cruisers, heavy destroyers, supply barges, all had promised to sail upriver today and browbeat the Winter Palace—what a sight that would have been! Unfortunately, in the early hours, an unexpectedly decisive Navy minister (NB. *Must find his name and neutralize him next time*) turned up at the Admiralty. He sent a signal instructing all submarines and minelayers to rendezvous in the Sea Channel and sink any vessels trying to get through. Small ships being by nature reactionary, they obeyed. Just the news of the blockade frightened off our water-barge supporters. I don't believe in omens, but if I did, I would recognize this as one. Likewise, the neutrality of many once actively militant regiments. Also—query from the roaming Smilga—what are three companies of Cossacks doing "grooming their horses" in the Square in front of the Winter Pal-ace? Why have the non-Soviet ministers in the ProvGov—Smilga again—deserted the Mariansky Palace and occupied offices inside the Victory Arch, fifty yards from the Cossacks? Of course, he is telling me, not asking me.

My toboggan has started down the slide. Within limits, I can steer around obstacles I know about. But I cannot stop before the end of the run without wrecking the toboggan. Still, such imaginings are saboteurs. What matters is the *facts*! How many do we have?

Between 3 and 4 P.M. Reports of deliberate, concerted attack on our marchers. Along Sadovaya, between the Apraxin Palace and the Imperial Bank, a gap had grown in the procession of Putilov families. As the next segment caught up here, a string of bullets sliced along the front ranks at ankle-length "like a giant skipping rope." As the wounded scrabbled about on hands and knees, unable to stand, those behind scattered outward "as though blown by a bomb," sheltering either behind the shrubs of the Bank forecourt, or under the mock-battlements of the Palace walls. One undercover Bolshevik reporter on the telephone to us from the *Vremya Novoye* offices across the road just kept repeating the strings of words: "Dog and fox, you'd think they were playing that game, you know, dog-and-fox-among-the-sheep, they're on all fours, like dog-and-fox, you know, among-the-sheep, but they won't stop screaming and shouting." I could hardly bear to listen, but worse, in a way, was to come about fifteen minutes later. This had been the demo with the smallest number of armed men, mainly factory hands, a few of whom had bought or borrowed a fifth-hand gun from a deserting peasant-soldier. None of them had been given the combat training of the sailors, the soldiers or the Red Guards. According to a MilOrg steward who rang in soon after, their instant reaction was to turn the intersection into a slaughterhouse. "They didn't have any identifying badges or armbands, you see, let alone uniforms. So they split into three groups firing at each other. As the bodies piled up, they got more enraged, and more foolhardy. They were blazing away with rifles at twenty paces. They wouldn't have stopped for a naked Venus. So I wrapped a red flag round me and looked round for someone they'd all recognize. I found a fellow, a twenty-stone pudding, must have been the factory blacksmith. I put my Browning barrel so far into his ear I thought it'd come out of his mouth. And I marched him to a point in the middle of the triangle. 'Comrades! Here's the assassin!' I shouted. And it was only when they all shouted back 'He's one of us,' they realized they were all on the same side."

That's what I mean by constructive heroism, rational courage—worth a dozen drummer boys holding aloft the colors or ensigns galloping straight into the enemy artillery. That man deserves to have his name on our revolutionary roll of honor. Which reminds me (a) I forgot to ask his name, and (b) I must make certain when we do come to the decisive struggle as many of our people as can must wear the same sash, buttonhole or the like.

Gusev, MilOrg anchor here, claims to know every one of the likely lads among his 27,000 members by name or sight. He promises he will find out who the hero of Apraxin Incident was. He has already dispatched six of our makeshift ambulances to the spot.

4:30 P.M. Since the February Revolution, many homes of the rich, and especially the aristocracy, have been commandeered by organized gangs, either with official approval or without. Once they settle in, only rarely (as with the Anarchists in Durnovo) do the authorities attempt to evict. Indeed, since the original inhabitants of the palaces used to spread themselves thinly, one or two to a wing, and the squatters now pack themselves at least six to a room, you could claim that under "democracy" a hundred times as many people lived in palaces as under the Tsar.

Not all of these are radicals or Anarchists, or even the homeless poor. A few places have been taken over by remnants of the police, ex-government spies and informers, even chapters of the Black Hundreds. Most witnesses placed the first shots as coming from the Apraxin Palace. I hint to Gusev that its neighborhood might be worth investigating as I put the clash on the record. But he has already sent a motorbike off to find some of Smilga's armored cars and guide them there. And so that looks as if that might be it.

4:45 P.M. A flood of messages from our stewards, Red Guard "centurions," Soviet CenExCom people, non-com Bolsheviks in the Army and Navy, workers' delegates, diplomats, foreign businessmen, newspaperman from all kinds of papers, even members of the public. Nine out of ten of them demand to know what the hell we think we are doing. Before any of us here can answer more than a few words, they carry on to denounce us as terrorists, vandals, murderers, foreign agents, Freemasons, Jews, criminals and armed insurgents. They refuse to believe that the CenCom of the Bolsheviks is already at the Tauride, and not at Kshesinska's. I've given up saying "Lenin" when challenged to give my name. The result is usually an alarmed *"Slava bogu! God save us!"* as they disconnect this direct line to Hades. I have to keep on saying: "We may know less than you do. Tell us what has happened *where you are."*

Now enough has got through for us to understand that the earlier ambush on Sadovaya was not just an impromptu amateur trap. It begins to look like a planned diversion of our forces while the main raid on our strongest units was planned where it could strike and destroy as many of our different allies as possible. This second blow has to have behind it the mailed fist of the State. If I read Kerensky right, this is only the *casus belli*, the frontier dispute which will escalate into a border war. It is for this that his general staff has long been preparing its *blitzkrieg* strike, like that Schlieffen "Hammer-Blow" upon which Ludendorff and Hindenburg (wrongly, as it turned out) relied to smash through the Franco-British Western Front. While the capital is reeling with false reports of the Red Uprising, K. will . . . what? Bring regiments back from our Front? Persuade the neutral regiments in barracks here out of their apathy? Pursue a hunt to the kill against the Party? Yes, of course. But what particular poisoned bait will he lay out for them to swallow?

Meanwhile, at least, so far as I can interpret the reports, the maneuver is the one that I anticipated. After communing, one by one, then section by section, with my Men of Confidence on the MilOrg, I suggested almost exactly the battle plan that is being followed by the enemy. And so, though we have suffered losses, our countermeasure will limit them to a minimum. Soon the others will appreciate why Semashko arranged his machine guns at that odd angle.

The second attack began on the Liteiny between Pantelei-monskaya and the nearest turnoff for the Tauride, Furshtadskaya. It was no matter of a few pistol shots snapped into a walking, centipede mass as it had been on July 3. This fusillade was aimed, timed and fired with robotic efficiency. Range, direction, duration, intensity seemed as mathematically calculated as the sights on the heavy, hydraulically operated guns of the *Aurora*. Nevsky and Pod-voisky were on the spot (only because their armored car had broken down) and both soon found evidence that the operation had been planned days in advance, with fire-ports and loopholes constructed in key positions, seats, or benches even, provided for the snipers. All the ambushing force was—as my defense-posture had anticipated—up high.

On Sadovaya, the marchers had been raked at ankle level. They fell as if scythed, almost depeditated. Some did have their feet chopped off. It was mutilation by numbers, but few had fatal wounds. Most of those killed were shot down later, in the chaos, by their own side.

On Liteiny, P. and N. report, the marchers had been raked from in front and above. The weapons were lined along the roofs, bunched along the top floors of every flanking building on the four exits from the intersection. Our people fell *decapitated* here.

Their heads holed, split, even exploded, from dumdum bullets. P. and N. trapped below at their running-board level, had a child's-eye view of a crowd being guillotined. There were children not far off among the forest of legs. They saw one child look up, his face a blank of horror, as the two trunks which held his hands slid faceless down, bowed low to the ground, and pumped blood over his sandals. "It was pissing lead on our reinforced tin roof," said Nevsky. There was nothing the pair could do till it stopped. Except watch the dying around them outside.

Within one minute—P. and N. agree they counted 120 strokes of a hurried twice-a-second church bell—the crossing was clear of every person who could move. The dead were left, "like piles of clothes on the beach," said Podvoisky. A few new orphans and widows tried to stay with their loved ones, despite the pelting bullets, but were dragged into the shelter of doorways by friends. There were not many wounded, the aim had been so deadly efficient. And almost all of those refused the first aid offered by soldiers from the march. Instead, they urged them to counterattack their assailants and blow their heads off.

P. and N. leaped out of their car as soon as the downpour halted, and took charge of the operation the way we had agreed. The soldiers, Red Guards and workers from Narva and Basil were, for once, not shooting each other. But they were not inflicting much damage on the assassins either. From down below, all a man with a rifle could do was blaze away at a rooftop. All the marksmen on top needed to do was keep their heads safely below the parapets. Nevsky rounded up as many of the bowler-hatted ones as he could and set them welding the armed demonstrators into raiding parties. He pointed out that trying to hit back at an already entrenched enemy, familiar with the terrain, was futile. What must be done was to outflank and disturb them. The best way was to break down the street doors, charge up the stairs to the attics and roofs and flush the intruders from house to house. In order to prevent them from escaping on the way, he timed the onslaughts to begin all along the block simultaneously.

Meanwhile Podvoisky had contacted a convoy of Machine-Gun Regiment lorries. Their raked muzzles were already angled, by coincidence, to intersect with the tops of the Liteiny mansions at a distance that just happened to equal the width of the boulevard.

"It was better than a good day's ratting," crowed Nevsky over the telephone. "We sent our ferrets up the burrows and we moved in on the snipers from every side. They rushed to the fronts of the houses and started to clamber over the parapets. They tried to climb down by the balconies. You could see that for a moment they thought they'd made it. Then as they were dangling there, feeling around with their feet, Semashko's boys started hosing them from below. Beautiful!"

They were grabbing the telephone from each other.

"You should have been there, Ilyich," shouted Podvoisky. "Semashko said it was like throwing mud balls at washing on the line."

I reminded them how vital it was that we should emerge from these incidents seeming to be what we in fact are—*the injured party.* The ordinary citizen draws a strong, if often irrational, line between what is done out of doors and indoors. I hoped that our people in strangers' homes—the Liteiny is mostly old town-houses with a "good address" sectioned into warrens of high-ceiling broom cupboards—were not manhandling the occupants. That would be just the sort of Bolshevik atrocity the press would be delighted for once not to have to invent.

I forget that P. and N., and most of their fellow "marshals," are marvelous agitators, street leaders, organizers of demos, strikes and now siege warfare, but not politicians.

There was a silence, and now I could sense them pushing the telephone at each other and making window-washing movements of their hands.

"Well," said Podvoisky after a pause. "I told them not to bother with anybody who had nothing to do with guns. Who didn't obstruct us or warn the ones we were after. But you realize a lot of our people had just seen friends and workmates with skulls bonked like breakfast eggs. Some of them were hungry, starving for revenge. No rape or anything dirty like that. But an occasional bourgeois loudmouth held out of the window and then, somehow, let drop . . ."

And what was happening now?

"Well," P. went on, rather more cheerfully. "Much the same all the way along the Liteiny into the Nevsky and round the corner. Chasing them up to the roof, then Semashko's gunners or Smilga's twelve-piece band blasting them as they pop up. Of course, a lot more got away along there. The rest of the march that kept arriving rather blocked the way for our cars and lorries. The buildings are a lot more complicated, too. You know, shops . . . and so on. Look, you'd better come across in your little van. I think we've seen the end of the shooting."

5:30 P.M. As we follow the route taken by the marchers from our HQ to the Tauride in my little disguised van—Gusev at the wheel—I find myself overwhelmed by the continuing size and persistence of the marchers. Clearly, it was much more than a demo. But how much less than an insurrection? Time and again, opponents demand to know why we seem so confident ("sickeningly smug!" Tsetse howled at me) that we are the chosen ones of the proletariat, history's favorites, picked out to lead the world in the first Marxist revolution. It is not much use saying, like a child—"because I know so." And I can usually rattle off a few lengths of statistic from the bolts I keep stored at the back of my brain. Such as—Party membership: January 5,000. February 24,000. April 100,000. End of June (in Peter alone) 32,000. Delegates enrolled already for the projected Sixth Congress to be held at the end of the month represent 177,000.

These are all facts as understood by historians, political analysts, policemen and journalists and can be counted on to fell most skeptics. But they are no substitute for seeing, hearing, smelling, being splashed by and crushed against, actual flesh-and-blood workers and soldiers parading under your banners. At the very least, 150,000 citizens in arms are voting with their feet today in front of us. What other evidence does anybody need? What other do *we* need? Perhaps this *could* be the time . . .

Even Gusev, overflowing like dough across both front seats, is amazed both at the turnout and at the marchers' refusal to be dashed or diverted by the earlier attacks. I think he would like me to climb on the roof and supply them with a mobile harangue. I keep my dark glasses on and absorb as much data as I can to provide a running inventory of the day's events. If we do not wish to be reduced to a walking pace, embedded in the slowly undulating mass, we have to make detours down side streets.

After crossing Troitsky bridge, the turf-green Neva beginning to be pitted and pocked with what we used to call "fish-mouths" as sharp rain fell from a sunny sky, we left the crowds. To our right, along Millionaya, we drove sedately into Palace Square so that I could snatch a peek at the Cossacks bivouacked there.

I entered in my dossier the name of each *voisko*, or "host," among them, Gusev craning to see what I was writing over his own sandbag forearms. He wanted to know how on earth I could separate them.

"I thought you were the military expert," I said. "Describe to me what they are wearing."

"Well, they've got baggy trousers, kneeboots, the usual dusty-shit greatcoat over regulation tunic. Could be any cavalry. Wait a minute. Yes, forage caps. Does that help?"

"What helps is what you didn't say. No spurs. And everywhere

carrying the flail whip, the *nagaika*. That means Cossack immediately. Forage caps—any colored bands? What about shoulder
straps, trouser stripes, belts?"

"Ah, caps. Red bands, or could be scarlet."

"That means Don or Siberian hosts."

"I see. Blue shoulder strap with red piping. Red stripe on
trousers. Light blue belt."

"Then definitely Don. Siberians are all scarlet—cap, shoulder
flash, trouser and belt. Notice anything more about hats?"

"Of course, one in three wears a fur *papakha* instead. So what
does that signify?"

"Well, if the hat has a crimson top, he's a Kuban. He should
also have on a felt Tatar cloak, the *burka,* and a kind of open
frockcoat, black. The same goes for the Terek Cossack, except his
hat crown's blue. I forget the color of the belts. Now we know—
Dons, Kubans, Tereks. We can soon find out how their sympathies
lie. And we also know they are not Cossacks of the old Emperor's
Guard."

Gusev breathed a pained sigh, something I notice he often
does when we have a talk like this.

"All right," he said. "How do we know that?"

"That's a bit tricky. Though absence of spurs on a cavalryman
is an infallible sign that he must be a Cossack, if he does wear
spurs and is a Don Cossack, then he is, rather was, in the Emperor's
Guards. Of course, it's true he could be also a Kuban or a Terek
in the *konvoi,* the imperial escort regiment of what was once the
New Guards."

By now we were out of the immense, man-dwarfing Square
and turning into Nevsky Prospect. No marchers here—they only
join from left and right further on where Sadovaya crosses it. The
avenue does not look much different from how I remember it on
my first visit in '91. No, '90.

Regardless of all those tedious sectarians, paid agitators, disguised Jews, outside extremists, common criminals, German agents
and drunken roughs shambling about in another part of the city
forest, guns in hand, these bourgeois Peterians were carrying on
in obedience to their favorite motto—"Idleness as Usual." Of course,
shopgirls, waiters, droshky drivers and so on are working, but then
one would only notice that sort if they stopped working, wouldn't
one?

Smart Peter-dwellers had just been nagged by the rain into
the coffee houses, bars, restaurants and shops along what is our
capital's Bond Street or Champs Elysées. Not that there ought to

be much to drink, eat or buy anymore behind those glassy fronts which line the pavements like a pair of mile-long conservatories. Not much anyway, that is, in the mirrored front rooms and palmy lounges which are open to casual visitors.

Nevertheless, even today, society folks, or those who aspire to be confused with them, are consulting their watches to decide what ritual of their crowded day would now be appropriate. Whether to sip that pale, strawy tea only Gusev ever orders by the mugful, shouting out after the first gulp, "Orderly, this horse is unfit for active duty!"; crack a preprandial bottle of parsnip wine or sultana brandy; tackle the "special" (and sole) official meal of every day— an anemic *borshcht* followed by a few old rissoles Gusev invariably bespeaks as "your delicious goat turds." *Slava bogu*, we aren't eating out today.

A closer look reveals that since my last visit the windows have been provided with recessed wire or chain shutters which can rattle down outside at the first rumor of invasion by alien troublemakers from far-off Basil, Narva or Vyborg. From what I can glimpse from the speeding van (Gusev boasts that downhill he can "do" sixty-five) a typical display seems to be a mysterious *mélange* of wasp-waisted corsets, decorated dog collars, hanks and plaits of hair, and masses of hothouse flowers, many of them orchids.

"Jetsam from a sinking ship, boss." (It was Gusev's turn to instruct me.) "Even the middle class are losing their fat. If their wives and daughters needed waists, they only had to eat what we always ate." (He patted his ripely curved stallion's belly which fleetingly tightened and hardened under his caress to a more ideal proletarian dimension.) "Everything's 'fashion' to them, even revolution. They all want cropped heads, the same shape from bum to tit, like our women comrades. Once they used to get their wigs from the working girls selling their curls. Now countesses and ballerinas can't give it away. Dog collars—that's obvious. With food so short, nobody dare feed dogs. Dogs've gone to those who dare eat 'em. Same with flowers. You'd be amazed how much your nobleman or your merchant'd spend on flowers. It was really big business. They keep on growing, so the smallholders keep on bringing them to town. Why do you think I commandeered a florist's van for Party transport? I knew nobody'd bother ambushing or looting it."

Speaking of looting . . . As we came to the Sadovaya intersection, I understood why Podvoisky's voice on the telephone had faltered a bit when he came to mention the Nevsky shops. It was as if the avenue had been divided into two self-contained blocks, like tanks in an aquarium. As if what happened in one was entirely separate from what might happen in the other, just yards away. Up to Sadovaya, early evening was proceeding as usual. Umbrellas sprung up and shaken down, hats raised, heads inclined, bills presented, money paid, shop bells jangling, figures crossing and recrossing, in the square dance of the human ants.

Beyond, along the stretch to Liteiny Prospect, not only was the whole width of the road still packed with marchers but every single shop on either side had been smashed open and its contents torn out. It was as if a barricade of corn sacks had been savaged and ripped by giant wild roosters. Obviously, there was more in the storerooms and vaults than in the window displays because the paving stones were like palettes. Palettes, daubed white with flour, yellow with semolina, streaked with cosmetics, stained with red and white wines, sparklingly outlined with all sorts of chippings that had been ground into the cracks—beans and buttons, glass and china, sweets and needles, things that looked like pearls and precious stones and things that were pearls and precious stones. Every few paces, the map of an imaginary island appliquéd in that shiny skin of red custard which is always blood.

Round the corner, on Liteiny itself, things were worse. Here what had been attacked were hundreds of houses, each home to several families. To have your doors smashed, your stairs trampled, your windows blinded, your rooms invaded, your privacy exploded is a painful, intimate wound—as revolutionaries know better than almost anybody.

These houses had not been seriously damaged. Bricks and mortar are surprisingly bulletproof. But they looked . . . violated? Not quite. More like humiliated. As if they were a line of old men paraded for inspection, half-dressed, with flies undone, drunk or sleepy. These people would not forgive us. Our dead and wounded were already gone, easily forgotten, or not credited. But this destruction would be visible on this spot for weeks, an illustration of what Peter would be like if Reds were allowed to go on the rampage, defying law and order.

It did not help that the pavements were blocked, four or five times, so far as we could see along the Liteiny, by the corpses of horses. It is amazing how much liquid these four-legged leather bottles can hold—blood and urine had gushed out making quite sizable pools on the road, pools the marchers had to stomp through. They could not detour because of the moving weight of people behind, and to each side. Gusev was more outraged by the number of rifles thrown away in doorways, halls, areas and passages. No matter, as I was able to point out, that they were almost all Russian-made American-designed Berdans (.420 inch with a range up to 3,750 feet) issued in the year I was born and phased out by 1891. He would descend, muster a dozen passing souls, and on the authority of being a Bolshevik, or perhaps just being twice the size of the largest, force them to pick up the guns and sling them over their shoulders.

I had seen enough. I operate best when I am not swayed by smells, sights, noises; sense impressions can overload my brain, as on the day of Father's funeral. I need firsthand experience to be able to decipher and evaluate the flow of information passed on by my agents and adjutants. But I am a quick student—one look is usually enough. From then on, I can often understand what is happening better than those who are in the middle of the action.

I had marked on my pocket map an alternative route to the Tauride which avoided following the marchers all the way. It meant driving on up the Nevsky, turning left on Ligovskaya and jigging round Preobrazhensky Barracks. It was a short step then to slip into the Palace through a back door. The soldiers of this regiment, the most anti-Bolshevik in the city, could be observed in their halls and dormitories, polishing their equipment—so far still passive. I left P. and N. to circulate the town and improvise. I went straight to the Bolshevik office on the ground floor to catch up on the latest reports.

Raskolnikov was first to rush across with his news. I couldn't tell from the screwed-up little-boy expression on his face whether he expected to be praised or blamed. He told me that his sailors had arrived here at the Soviet headquarters in a fume of rage and fear after the attack along Liteiny. The Palace has no guards of its own—well, perhaps a dozen under Colonel Nikitine, deputy head of the supposedly abolished Secret Security Police, the SSP. Many Soviet bosses were certain they were going to be strung up or bayoneted before the night was over. The best they could think to do was to keep on in continuous session and at least look as if they were ruling the country. This was a trifle inconvenient for them because the windows had to be left open on account of the heat and troops kept climbing in and squeezing them along their benches. Those sailors who weren't practically on the knees of the delegates, or breathing down their necks, pressed close in rank upon rank outside. "Like cattle waiting to be fed," said Kamenev. "What on?" asked Zinoviev. "On whom, eh?" Various Menshevik and SR orators had been dispatched to distract them, without much success. Old Tsetse had returned complaining that he could not get a word through for a drunken sailor who kept on chanting: "Take the power when it's handed to you on a plate, you stupid bastard!" Then Chernov went out, the darling of the peasants, and therefore expected to be popular at least with the peasant troops. (Sailors tend to be townees.) He also had an unruly reception. "Search him! He may be armed!" So much so that the Soviet was thrown into uproar when several delegates ran in from outside shouting—"They've kidnapped Victor! The Bolsheviks are strangling Chernov!" Raskolnikov rushed out only to find Chernov, dirty-white as an old handkerchief, already just a scared face inside an armored limo. But Trotsky was on the bonnet in a hurdler's leap and already in mid-harangue—quite a good agitator's trick if you can do it convincingly. (It gives the listeners the illusion that you must have put forward a lot of argument they've missed, enabling you to jump a few stages to a conclusion.)

No one is better known in Kronstadt than Lev Davidovich. He regularly turns up there on the quays to keep his sailors informed. He acts as their spokesman and advocate before the Soviet. He knows the Ekaterinburg Twirl as well as Sverdlov, the effect, at once disarming and bonding, of pressing flesh. Yet, here, he felt a chill as the hand he offered was refused on every side with snarls and growls (he told us later). The noise was worse than a slaughterhouse, and only a few could hear anything he said. Then Raskolnikov plunged into the herd, fighting his way to a boy bugler, and holding him up above the heads like a ventriloquist's dummy until they got back to the car.

"What shall I play?" pleaded the boy. Raskolnikov's face went blank. What did he want the message to be? He looked up to Trotsky for advice. Lev Davidovich's reactions were, as ever, swift as those of a Tatar cutthroat. Instantly he said—"Play what's it called . . . 'Come to the Cookhouse Door!' " *Dumtittydumtumdumtum* sounded. Silence fell for a second. Then the great mass audience shook with waves of applause, which spread wider and wider as more and more got the joke.

Trotsky did not pause. As the cheering rattled to a standstill, he could be heard saying: ". . . and so, comrades, friends and fellow workers, that is why I am sure you all will agree with the logic of our case, the Bolshevik case, and here Vladimir Ilyich and I have always been on the same side. Let's take the vote then. Raise your hand anyone who believes it makes sense to damage our cause by cheap, stupid acts of violence? All right, let's see who is in favor of lynching, beating, torture, murder. Where are you?"

Nobody offered himself. The mood had been broken, for the

moment. Those who could kill, had perhaps killed or would do so later, could not bring themselves to be seen taking a democratic decision to kill.

"Citizen Chernov. You are free!"

Chernov squirmed out and bolted back into the Tauride.

"He didn't even say 'Thank you,'" complained Raskolnikov.

"If those fools inside there had not raised such a babyish hullaballoo," said Trotsky, "I'd simply have got into the car and driven him off."

6:30 P.M. Soviet leaders like Tsetse, various noncommitteds like Sukhanov, keep asking Raskolnikov why he doesn't simply lead his flaming Kronstadters back to their base since there is nothing here for them to do, no revolution to defend, no counterrevolution to suppress. He does not know what to answer for the very good reason that he does not know what to answer. My instructions (through P. and N.) were for him to wait for further instructions once he reached the Tauride. Now, it is becoming rather embarrassing to have them packing the small Potemkin Square, getting on everybody's nerves including their own, and nursing a revenge they are unlikely to be able to satisfy—for a while, anyway. Raskolnikov complained that the two leaders he had consulted (Kamonev and Zinoviev) gave contradictory orders. When they were each consulted again, and told what the other had said, then each said the opposite of what he'd said before. So the Kronstadters insisted on him coming to me.

There seemed no alternative in my mind. So I put to as many of the CenCom, and the ExCom of MilOrg, as could be found, the proposition that the sailors leave the Tauride and official Peter. They retire north across the Neva to spend the night, either in the basement of Kshesinskaya's, or in some of the empty halls on the Peter and Paul island, where the fortress garrison is on our side. That way, they would be no provocation to our enemies. Yet they would be still available if we needed them. It was agreed.

July was turning out to be an unlucky month for the boys in blue from Kronstadt. They had been attacked on the march by well-entrenched government sharpshooters, losing tens of comrades, many of them veterans of the bloody sea battles of the Russo-Japanese war. They had been prevented (on my orders) from taking their revenge on every posh apartment dweller whose windows or roof had been used for the ambush, and been allowed to execute only those caught red-handed. They had been deflected at the Tauride by the semi-Bolshevized Trotsky when trying to find a scapegoat among the Soviet leaders. They would be trailing back to a night on a bare floor, at best a half share in some other conscript's meager rations, while under threat of being disarmed. Now, instead of a glorious onslaught on the capitalist lackeys, victory and the fruits of battle—acclamation . . . drink . . . women . . . a place in history . . . what? Worse was to come. For them and for us.

These last two days have been an unfortunate combination of events, a tragi-comedy of errors. I know, as a Marxist, that accidents of timing, peculiarities of climate or weather, coincidences of place, personal quirks, individual failings, even the achievements of great heroes or great villains, cannot finally do more than *appear* to change the course of history. What must be, will be. Nevertheless, when you are there, when you have to observe what a difference can be made by going down the wrong street at the wrong minute, these near-misses can be painful to endure. After all, the next thing to a close shave is having your throat cut. Everyone feels this, the leader more than any. The difference is—the leader must never show it. However, I could not help feeling for our poor Kronstadters.

7 P.M. No sooner had they left, than there stormed into the Palace the second wave of armed marchers from Putilov. They had twice been fired on by snipers who showed every sign of having set up their traps with official collusion, supplied with the latest weapons and ammunition, also well disciplined and trained. Indeed, some of those captured had confessed to being briefed and controlled from the Ministry of Defense. (It's true they were hanging by their toes from top-floor windows at the time, not a position that makes for extreme devotion to literal accuracy.)

The workers who had been savaged by hidden marksmen today near the Apraxin Palace on Sadovaya also arrived at the Tauride, carrying their dead and wounded. Then, they found, in the nearby gardens, dozens of casualties (the corpses had already gone) from yesterday's attack by the Fontanka Canal. The anger which had been seething along the march, and led to occasional wild and pointless beatings of passing pedestrians or gunning of spectators on balconies or roofs, was now boiling over in Potemkin Square. Many in the crowd heard for the first time of any unprovoked violence against the people. And when they learned that it had occurred *twice,* their wrath began to turn against the SRs and the Meks in the Soviet whom they had once regarded as their spokesmen and protectors.

About fifty of them, wild-eyed and hoarse-voiced, smeared with blood and dust, hair sprouting in greasy spikes, smelling of

vodka, sweat, rain and cordite, forced their way into the hall where
the CenExCom of the Soviet was still meeting. A few delegates,
according to Zinoviev, started in terror and went pale as if faced
with demons from Hell. Others squeaked and shouted: "Bolsheviks! Send for the guards!" Only there *were* no guards, just Colonel
Nikitine and his dozen token janissaries.

One of the Putilovites leaped onto the platform, pushing in
front of the speaker. He wore a peaked cap, a short blue blouse
without a belt, and brandished a rifle in a sculptured hand. He
was juddering with fury and excitement. "A classical sansculotte!"
cried out Sukhanov, almost as worked up, scribbling in his notebook. Gregory rushed into our Ops Room and dragged me to the
door. "Listen to this, Ilyich," he cried. "The proletariat are leading
themselves. They don't need us. Perhaps they'll start without us."
He was alight with hope.

Certainly, this sansculotte looked different from the rest—like
the sort of young hero that girls sketch at boarding schools or
convent colleges before they have an opportunity to scrutinize a
genuine male model. He was elegantly thin, blue-eyed and blond-
haired, fine features with rather too many squiggles in them. He
was speaking in almost as beautiful a tenor as Gregory with what
sounded like a Volga accent, possibly even Simbirsk, though his
words were often incoherent. As I eavesdropped through the crack,
I heard him say: "Comrades, how long must the ordinary man put
up with being betrayed? You're all here debating and making deals
with the bourgeoisie and the landlords. Do you think we don't
know? This is treachery. Well, just get into your heads *we are not
going to allow it*! All together, we've brought thirty thousand of us
here from Putilov. We're going to have our way. We're going to
hang on to our rifles. Your Kerenskys and your Tseretellis don't
fool us."

I was cheered by his interruption, especially that last bit. But
how would he survive the reaction of the Soviet leaders behind
him, the grim, set, Easter-island faces of the once master manip-
ulators, crowd-pleasers and democratic demagogues, under whose
noses he brandished his rifle? They tried to look like broad-minded
headmasters gratified by the slightly daring, and naughty, behavior
of an overexcited head boy. But the opinions he uttered were
deeply unpalatable to the Congress, particularly with a gun in
hand. Someone on the governing body had to stop or distract him.

It was Chkheidze, longtime Menshevik leader in the last two
Dumas, in a flash of Georgian cunning, who silenced the gate-
crasher. He leaned over gracefully from above, and, as if passing

on some personal message, crushed into the worker's hand a piece of paper. "Here, comrade, please take this," Chkheidze murmured, almost purring with friendliness. "It tells you *exactly* what to do. Read it and tell your friends. And now we really must get on with our business, you know. Thank you, so much."

The young fellow, flattered and baffled, was then quietly eased down into the body of the hall. When he looked at what he had been given, he saw that it was a printed leaflet, issued yesterday by the Soviet CenExCom, telling armed workers on the streets to go home, otherwise they might cause problems for those who were trying peacefully to extend and defend our Revolution. He read it with difficulty, repeating it to his friends, obviously finding little help there, or relevance, to the feelings he had just expressed with such authentic fury. But his moment had passed. As he and his companions pushed out and melted into the crowd, more thumped on the doors and squeezed through the windows.

It is a strange experience to observe history being made at such close quarters. Perhaps you have to withdraw from this spot at this time through one dimension or another to see the pattern. Rise above, by standing on a neighboring hill, floating in an observation balloon, or by looking back after a month, after a year. Clearly, it is not always possible to make sense of what people are doing since what people are doing does not actually make sense anyway, even to them. Could a comparison be that between the microcosm and the macrocosm in modern physics? On the scale of atomic particles, the impossible is happening in the movement of a million, million tiny solar systems. What we do to each other here has no meaning on that level. Yet back again, on our scale, these fuzzy multiplications of the Milky Way manage to produce a solid world—tables you can eat at, chairs you can sit on, women you can caress, tyrants who can torture you, theory and practice that can intermingle.

At 9:30, two almost simultaneous occurrences. A sailor is a sailor, a Red Guard a Red Guard. They need only be themselves. I look for those who carry the votes, the support, the guns, the spanners of hundreds, perhaps thousands of their comrades. It is perhaps a flaw in my approach to revolution. When I see a demonstrator, I see a single person. When I see a "delegate," I see multiplication at work, arithmetical progression even. I see *the people*. So I went out at this time to welcome a deputation of some ninety workers who represented the men of fifty-four Petersburg factories. Here is concentrated power, I told myself. *This* is what moves mountains. I heard them (by invitation) address the Soviet

CenExCom, and everything they said reflected the impact of our concentrated propaganda. The five who spoke used exactly the slogans I would have suggested for them. My notes read—"We demand that power pass to the Soviet. . . . We trust the Soviet but not those the Soviet trusts. . . . We demand the immediate confiscation of all land, immediate workers' control of industry. . . . We are not prepared to wait for a Constituent Assembly." Can there be any doubt that we are winning over the proletariat of Peter?

Meanwhile, at this same moment, another body of our supporters had arrived outside. These were the 176th Reserve Regiment from Tsarskoe Selo, once the summer palace residence of the Romanovs, just a short train ride to the south of Peter. Rather underemployed, surrounded by evidence of the Tsar's colossal self-indulgence, they had been entered on our books as one of the most Bolshevik units in the neighborhood. And they had confirmed this by arranging themselves a visit to the capital solely to help us, and any others who were determined to preserve the Revolution against its enemies. However, when they appeared, they would find no socialist authority to rally round. But they kept together and ordered their officers to find them the workers' leaders. It so happened that instead of me, or someone they had even more chance of recognizing (Sverdlov, Kamenev, Trotsky, Zinoviev) they came across a Menshevik. He took advantage of their ignorance (and who could blame them?) of who was who and what was going on and instead recruited them to guard the debating chamber of the Soviet, and its CenExCom.

As it happened, they did nothing, either way, for any side. They patrolled for a bit as sentries, just as they would have done at Tsarskoe Selo. After about half an hour, most of them drifted away toward the town, the bars and dance halls of the red-light district. By the time we had identified them, this seemed the best course. Is this an episode any historical novelist would feel the need to invent? The leaders of the undefended anti-Bolshevik Soviets employing a pro-Bolshevik regiment to support their authority, although that pro-Bolshevik regiment had just traveled up to town to support the Bolsheviks in overturning that anti-Bolshevik authority?

Will future historians even ever get all these crisscross trails in the sand in the proper order of time, place, people and policy?

Like crowds at a sports ground or a racecourse, each group which pushes forward has its own favorite for whom it shouts. Now, instead of Chernov, they were calling "Tseretelli! Tseretelli! He's the one we want!" I don't know the whereabouts of the tall, elegant Georgian who always speaks at a forty-five-degree angle to his listeners, a blue wormy vein jumping in his temple. This time he certainly took care not to make himself available. This gave the crowd something to complain about. From being his supporters, calling for him so that they could express their trust and admiration when he appeared, they now became his critics, demanding he show himself to be cross-examined and questioned. "Tseretelli! Give us Tseretelli!" they began to chant, stamping their feet, tens of thousands of them, in a way that could frighten, exhilarate or paralyze anyone hearing it, but never be forgotten.

Going back to our Ops Room I caught sight of Nikitine in a cubbyhole on the telephone. He was some distance off, his face haloed in the brown glaze of an oil lamp with bronze reflectors. But he was shouting with such vehemence that although I could not hear what he said, I could read some of his lip movements. "Cossacks! Must have Cossacks!"

I turned to Zinoviev who was up on an inside plinth, taking the place of some looted classical goddess, staring out and down at the bellowing and billowing masses, "vaccinating himself with the mood of his audience," as Trotsky once put it.

"Gregory," I ordered. "Go out on the balcony. *You* are what they need." He gave a delighted salute, and trotted up the great staircase as fast as his short, stocky legs would carry him. A diminutive, comic, but powerful, figure, he is like a giant made out of soft clay that the potter had given a sudden slap from above before baking in the oven. He must have waited a while, for the chanting and stamping went on and on. Eventually it stopped. There was a silence, a faint titter, then Z.'s almost falsetto fluting: "You asked for Tseretelli! Instead you got me! That's how things are these days."

The contrast between the two, as extreme as that between a pair of circus clowns, appealed to the crowd's sense of humor—I could just imagine his face, as I have seen it so often in exile when he joked me out of a mood of reproof. He would be rolling his eyes, massaging his jaw with a heavy hand, and pretending to hide a spreading smile. There were rolling tides of laughter. His listeners were off-balance, temporarily forgetting what their complaints had been. As I went back into the Ops Room, I was confident he was well on the way to kneading them to dough.

By the time the Cossacks got here, so I had anticipated this morning, the sailors would be halfway to their various lodgings in old Peter, while the last of the Putilovites would be winding south to the Narva gate and their suburban tenements. The government would be deprived of retrospective justification for their earlier attacks on both sections of the march. The only excuse for bloodshed was an attempted uprising by the Bolsheviks. The Soviets would be forced to admit how pathetic were their panics and calls for help from "loyal" troops. All that would remain, by this evening, would be an empty square and deserted gardens; a committee still with many members talking away ignored by the rest, like penitents at an altar: a light topping of litter; and a platoon or so of drunken workmen and servicemen, asleep with their arms round their guns, to commemorate two days of Red Terror.

I'm afraid I was just a little bit out in my calculations.

7:30 P.M. Podvoisky telephoned from the Troitsky bridge. He and Nevsky had secured this with a small detachment of Red Guards to make sure the Kronstadt sailors crossed safely to their billets in Peter & Paul. Most of them had given up anyway, taking their cutters directly back to their island barracks. It was unfortunate that only a few thousand of the most determined and intransigent were trailing by when the Cossacks rode into them.

If the cavalry had taken the shortest route to the Tauride (as I had expected) they could have cut across through any of half a dozen wide streets, or even up the great avenue of the Nevsky Prospect. And even if they *had* chosen to gallop along the Neva embankment, as they did, a delay of only ten minutes would have found them passing by Troitsky bridge without a sailor in sight. Instead, ill-informed about what was happening at the Tauride, relying on Nikitine's alarm summons to deal with "Big Trouble," they not unnaturally assumed that this great, thick snake of dreaded Kronstadters, guns aloft, surly and slow to disperse, must be the colonel's problem.

"There was no challenge, no attempt to let us move away," spat Podvoisky. "They charged straight ahead. The first four lines had lances mounted. They speared our front ranks like fish in a barrel. Striking them in the middle. Hoisting them up and throwing them over their shoulders. *Laughing* all the time. Then the next four had sabers out, cutting and slashing at the remnants the others had missed. Vladimir and I emptied our revolvers into them at six feet range. But I don't think we hit a horse. It was all over so fast."

But now, at last, it became our turn for some good fortune. The Cossacks did not find their next opponents so unprepared. But I must try to keep to the chronology. Back at the Tauride Palace, I was entering in my dossier the details given me over the telephone. It was a sad story, but still I was determined not to be too depressed. Gregory's speech to the Putilovites had been as successful as usual. Now he was sitting with one leg over the balustrade, swapping jests and anecdotes as they packed their belongings for the long trek back. Soon, they would be gone. And if I still remember the weather science Father had taught us (for some reason the Tauride is full of alcoves with miniature meteorological stations), I estimate the afternoon's spitting rain will become tonight's deluge. This should really clear the streets. The action was over.

Colonel Nikitine did not share my opinion. I could tell from the way he paced up and down along Shpalernaya Street outside the north door of the Tauride looking west and consulting his great golden gob of a watch just like Father's. This was the way his Cossacks would come, I now realized. By my timing, they would still be too late.

8 P.M. The colonel and I both jumped. On a wet wind along the Neva, came the noise of heavy, repeated firing, not machine guns, I thought, but massed rifles, backed by hand grenades and mortars. So it couldn't be Semashko's boys. Nor the sailors. Nor the Putilovites and Red Guards who were still around, but just leaving. At that moment, it was a piece of a jigsaw puzzle left over when it had all just fitted in place! Some other small army that ought not to exist had entered the battle. Nothing makes more for chaos, the multiplication of wrong decisions and fatal choices, than prolonged lack of trustworthy information.

Was it only sixteen hours since I awoke to the scratching on the shutters? Sixteen hours of puffy faces talking; of dead horses draining in the gutter; of glasses clinking and teacups rattling in the cafés and bars of the lower Nevsky Prospect; of shops smashed open and ripped apart along the upper Nevsky like children's bearbanks; of soldiers, sailors, workers, Red Guards, families marching, marching, marching as if on the treadmill, as if in a nightmare; of the hot disc of the telephone flattening and braising the ear while pouring into it a demon's confession of pain, murder, fear, despair, revenge, bloodshed—all of which turned out to be true.

This is my protection, my secular cross, my necklace of garlic. I have been able to keep in touch with reality through the eyes, ears and mouths which report for, and to, me. No one else in Peter has any such network. But now I encounter an unexplained event I too find that the mind so hates vacancy and uncertainty, it will invent anything to fill the gap.

Nikitine and most of the Soviet leaders are so confident that this is it at last—Bolshevik Seizure of Power—that they almost convince me! Kamenev and Zinoviev are certain we are about to win and take the air of the victor with the SRs and Meks. They, in their turn, now see no need to conceal their utter hatred of Bolshevism. It won't last long, this *putsch*, they point out. Because Nikitine has sent for the Cossacks. . . . Tseretelli has asked Kerensky for troops from the Front. . . . The neutral regiments in Peter are about to intervene actively on behalf of government and Soviet. All sides (except Colonel Nikitine) look to me to see what I believe. I keep my own counsel.

8:30 P.M. The last few thousand of the Putilovites (compared to the earlier masses they seem like a handful) are singing songs, chatting in small groups. This is also a social occasion. Lots of activists have not seen each other for years: not since they were together on trial, in prison, in exile, in hospital, in the street fighting, spouting on the corner, in the underground. Then we all hear at the same time what every Russian registers with a leap of the heart or a slide of the bowel—the hoofbeats of massed horses. The Cossacks are coming!

Certainly, some *things* come lolloping along Shpalernaya out of the darkness and straight past the Tauride. These are Cossack horses all right. But there are no riders on their backs, clinching evidence of a Cossack defeat, or at least setback. Somewhere along the Neva, after stabbing and slicing our sailors, the Tsar's executioners on horseback had clashed with alert soldiers (presumably on our side) who gave them the mauling their history deserves.

This false alarm (Nikitine is green) has finally decided almost everybody to get out of the Tauride. Typical of the mistakes of this night, at the first clip-clop of hooves a lot of people leaped for their guns. Half a dozen went off. Then even more leaped for their guns; a dozen went off. In three minutes about ten citizens were wounded. When the skies opened, and the rain fell in improbable, slow, giant teardrops, the moral seemed clear.

9 P.M. My predictions, based on an analysis of what was known at dawn this morning, have not been so *very* far out. We have managed to keep the day's demonstration under control. Along the way, we have had setbacks and victories. We have learned (painfully) some more lessons on how to run a revolution without putting all to risk too soon.

But this strange, educational, day was not quite over. The CenExCom of the Soviet, its heart beating at all the ebbs and flows that turned out not to be ebbs and flows—the Bolshevik gunfire that never came nearer, the Cossack hoofbeats that came and went—settled down to a leisurely attempt to make sense of what didn't happen.

B.-B., who had been taking my calls, brought me up to date with the riderless horses mystery. Good old Gusev, whom we'd all rather forgotten, assuming if anything that he was guarding our HQ (which, come to think of it, was what I had told him to do), had grown bored. His interpretation of the day's program featured (on no evidence I know) a counterrevolutionary punitive expedition by Cossacks into the workers' stronghold of Vyborg. The sailors, the machine gunners, the armored cars, the Red Guards, the Putilovites—all seemed booked. Anyway, they were under other commands. So he found a rebellious, pugnacious regiment none of us had heard much about—the First Reserves. He persuaded them to set up barricades at the south end of the Liteiny bridge and wait until the hated cavalry of their oppressors arrived. It wasn't easy. They wanted to plunge in and take part in the battles of the Nevsky and the Liteiny about which rumors reached them. But Gusev persuaded them it was too late. Then they wanted instead to take their revenge on those behind the attacks—either the Soviet leaders in the Tauride or the government ministers holed up in the Victory Arch in Palace Square. Gusev persuaded them that these were being dealt with. The hardest task was toward the end of the evening when the Red Guards and the machine gunners, who came from Vyborg, passed through the barricades on their way home, explaining that Trotsky and Zinoviev both had made speeches calling on all Bolshevik supporters to disband and disperse. B.-B. asked Gusev how he got round that.

"I just said . . . Do you want to kill some Cossacks or not? Now's your chance. Otherwise don't blame me if your wives get murdered, and you get raped, in your beds."

They were still arguing when round the bend, lolling in their saddles and grinning away like, in Gusev's words, "a load of fucking ponces at a picnic," came the clattering, multicolored horde. Gusev had barricaded the embankment in classic style—his soldiers in a hollow ellipse behind, three deep, one row lying flat, the next kneeling, the last straight and formal as a firing squad at an execution. And that seems to have been what it was—the gunning down of a target, bunched together for easy aiming, unable to swerve aside, charging too fast to slow or stop, a target getting larger every second, impossible to miss.

The Cossacks had no chance to use the lances which they had ported and secured in their holsters, nor to draw their sabers. One or two made an attempt to unsling their carbines, but the worst the majority could do was lash out with their whips. All their energy was concentrated on steering their horses toward an escape: some jumping the rails into the Neva on the left, others wheeling into the side streets or bolting for the wide Liteiny Prospect on the right. The mass went ahead into the thick hedge of rifles that were shooting now up their nostrils, and into their horses' bellies. About a tenth of the three Cossack companies were blasted out of their saddles in about two minutes, their mounts careering on along the Shpalernaya and past the Tauride.

I instructed Gusev to get his soldiers out of the area and back into the safety and anonymity of Vyborg as soon as possible. He should have done so immediately—what was delaying them? B.-B. explained—"The men insist on relieving the Cossacks of a few souvenirs. They've got a lot of scores to pay off from the old days. Mainly they're taking the *nagaika*, he says, though a few are stripping the medals off the dead. Also Gusev feels he owes it to military honor to leave the wounded comfortable. So he's bandaged them as well as he can and left them sitting up along the river-wall. With their legs out, and their caps in their laps, he says they look like a row of crippled ex-service beggars."

10 P.M. What I'd now begun to think of as the July Days, more like weeks already, were almost over. Surely? There seemed to be no one left, on our side anyway, to march away or march back, to be ambushed or to lie in wait, to shoot or be shot at. I left the Ops Room and strolled over to the tall, columned windows, most of them now broken, to smell the night air and listen to the hissing curtains of rain. What I heard was the steady tread of military feet, soldiers, lots of soldiers, guards probably, moving under orders at a brisk, disciplined pace.

I had no idea who they could be. I shouted for B.-B., for Trotsky, Zinoviev, Kamenev, any of the others still around. We stood together by the great doors into the courtyard, waiting to greet whatever it was. *"Du calme, du calme,"* whispered Lev Davidovich under his breath.

For the umpteenth time in the last forty-eight hours, our lack of nervousness or worry worried and unnerved our opponents. I could hear one muttering, "Bolshevik troops, this is the insurrection at last."

Round the corner wheeled the head of a column of the Izmailovsky Guards—I recognized their shoulder flashes—led by a couple of officers, lieutenants, on muscular, curvetting horses. The men were swarthy, small, sullen peasants, just the material for a revolutionary patrol. But not this time. This parade of belted sausages, winking buttons, shining boots, could only be staged to back up the powers that be. I'd forgotten this was how soldiers used to

look and move as they executed the drill movements to the shrill
shouts of their NCOs, turning left and right on stamped heels,
advancing and retiring in small blocks, or long files, until the flowing column filled the space in front of the Palace. The two officers
reined up facing the balcony where the Soviet leaders were observing these maneuvers as if they could not believe their eyes.
They had rubbed and rubbed the magic lamp (that is, summoned
up any regiment that was willing to appear in their support) almost
as a matter of form. And lo and behold! The genie had twirled
up from a crack in the ground and was now at their service. "This
is the regiment that arrested me and our Soviet in '05," observed
Trotsky, whistling through his teeth. "Now it has come to protect
their Soviet. How the whirligig of time brings in its revenges." The
tune he was whistling was "The Marseillaise."

Out from behind us poured the Soviet delegates, applauding
the officers (not the men). Authority was once more in control.
The delegates began to sing "The Marseillaise." Clearly there was
some association of ideas here. As their voices mounted, they began
to enjoy themselves. Martov, who had been in the front, turned
round, and pushed his way back past us. He looked me in the eye,
the first time we had made even such contact for months. He flicked
his head toward the now purple-faced, swollen-necked choir. (*Aux
armes, Citoyens!*)

"A classic sign of counterrevolution," he snapped and walked
off into the night.

It wasn't the only one. . . . For now the government made the
move I had been long expecting, and to some extent dreading.
Though since it was inevitable, it did not catch me off-balance.

10:30 P.M. B.-B. had gone back earlier to his flat, about a mile
away, near the Nikolai station. He too had been stretched throughout a long day and was ready to collapse. Just as he was drifting
off, he was disturbed by a telephone call. The speaker would not
give his name but B.-B. recognized the voice—it was Nikolai Kransky, a Bolshevik sympathizer and well-known radical advocate, now
assistant to capitalist Minister Pereverzev, head of the Justice Department. Kransky could not speak long—other, unauthorized,
listeners might also know that voice—but the message was clear.
The government had assembled a mass of documents "proving"
that Lenin had been in contact, through intermediaries, with the
Germans. These would be the basis for my arrest, along with some
of my associates, and our trial on a charge of espionage.

B.-B. telephoned this on to me at once at the Tauride, urging
me to adopt some disguise and catch the first train back to Mus-

tiamiaki, from there possibly slip into exile for a while. I told him since I was determined to be here for the Revolution, it seemed rather unsporting to duck the counterrevolution. I assured him my plans were well laid. Also (though I didn't say this) since I was about to dismiss such charges as forgeries, slanders and provocations, too ludicrous really to be taken seriously, it would not look so good if I fled at the first rumor of a warrant, like a defaulting bookkeeper.

Midnight. Some of this story must already be circulating in the Tauride, from the side-glances and sudden dropped voices of the delegates as I pass. The Izmailovsky lieutenant was still making a long, passionate, but vague and rambling, speech about his devotion to democracy, the people, the peasants, the workers, the Soviet and the workers' peasants' people's democratic Soviet. Meanwhile his peasant soldiers stood rigidly at ease, beyond the sound of his voice, in the rain. Their presence appeared to give the Soviet delegates even more confidence and security. Several made a point of telling each other in raised voices, as they passed our Ops Room, that many many more loyal defenders of dual power, government and Soviet, were on their way.

Would they have believed that under their noses—an irony that gave me a little jolt of pleasure—I was still struggling to persuade my own loyal fighting force *not* to take to the barricades? Several MilOrg leaders felt so much blood had been spilled in the last two days, so much anger and indignation had been aroused, so many waverers politicized, that we must press ahead. Podvoisky and Nevsky were not there, nor Raskolnikov nor Semashko. Gusev was the main spokesman, though he claimed backing from the others. I think he had not quite recovered from discovering that he had commanded a whole new regiment nobody knew anything about, the First Reserves, and that he was the only one of our commanders to take the offensive and not lose a man. ("Beg to report. Two black eyes, three broken ribs, one concussion, one dislocated knee, result of stampeding horses, COM-*rade*," he shouted, clicking his heels.)

There was quite an audience for his little briefing, so I thought I'd better make sure the point was unmistakable. This was a *political* decision, not a military one. Nevertheless, to maintain my authority in both fields, I hoped to demonstrate that, even if it were a question of how best to seize and hold Peter, my way was the correct way. As ever, I opened on the attack and on my opponent's (as he thinks) strong point.

I congratulated him on the victory at Liteiny bridge, passing on the thanks and praise from the Kronstadt sailors when told the news of the trouncing of their attackers. But I suggested all of us present would be grateful for some elucidation of detail. How did he know the Cossacks were in action since he had not heard of the clash with the Kronstadters at the previous bridge, the Troitsky? On his own testimony, they had slung their carbines, holstered their lances and sabers. Might they not have been on some peaceful mission? And was not his unprovoked, sudden onslaught just the sort of unauthorized, impromptu violence we had all agreed was *strictly forbidden*?

Gusev adjusted his belly, and pretended to be amazed at such a thought. "They were Cossacks, boss. We'd both seen them earlier in Palace Square taking no account of our demo. Suddenly, they're hell for leather pelting toward the Tauride. What was I to think? Anyway, what's a few murdering bastards of Cossacks, more or less? We're going to have to wipe them out after we take power. Am I right, comrades?"

The comrades showed such enthusiasm in answering "yes" that I skipped on to the next hole in his position. I congratulated him again, this time on coming up with a regiment nobody knew about, what's more, one firmly on our side. I didn't want any more appeals to the floor, so I hurried along. Well done! But *why* had we not known about it? What sort of files were we keeping on the units around the capital if we could overlook such a sizable body of armed men? Had we possibly overlooked an equal number who might be hostile to us?

Had he noticed that, except among the Putilov contingent, soldiers far outnumbered the workers? That, except for the Kronstadt contingent, the sailors were extremely scarce with the rest of the Fleet barely represented at all? That we had started the day with a minority even among the garrison troops in Peter, and we had ended it with the majority moving from nonintervention to active support of Soviet and government?

(As I spoke, there was a tramp of feet. Another regiment, the Preobrazhensky, began to file into the Square in parade-ground order, from its barracks next door, the Izmailovsky doing a double-shuffle to make room for them. Their commander also climbed onto the rostrum to dedicate his strength to the Soviet. The band struck up "The Marseillaise" once more. Soviet delegates joined in with even greater fervor. I repeated Martov's quip.)

After a pause to allow that to sink in, I instanced another sign of counterrevolution, one that may have been lurking there, ready in waiting since the beginning of the month, just to take advantage of any overconfident, underprepared attempt to seize power, our attempt that never was. If we had tried, *we certainly would have been defeated*! Troops from the Northern Front, much tougher, more seasoned fighters than any available to the authorities here, were even now moving to the capital by train.

Tell me about our own forces. How many of the Kronstadt sailors, beaten more than once already, are willing to set sail again and fight once more? Have you consulted Raskolnikov? Why not? So you don't know whether one of our strongest striking arms is fit for battle? The same goes for the Red Guards of Putilov. Have you checked them? What about your commanders? How did they conduct themselves over the last two days? How many of them are fitted for street warfare? Have you prepared stocks of food, not just for fighting men, but even more importantly for the workers and their families who will back us, help us, hide us? The servicemen on our side were quite well armed, but many civilians had weapons that were obsolete, or none at all. Where are our armories? What plans have you made for retreat if we fail? Have you arranged for the seizure and immobilization of the drawbridges over the Neva? Have special units been instructed on how and when to take over stations, telephone exchanges, banks, strategic points?

Gusev could only stutter on about the plans revised by Podvoisky and Nevsky at my request at the time of the June demonstrations. I do not let him off the hook. I dare not. He is one of my most loyal, determined and courageous aides, and our association goes back almost to the turn of the century. There is no one I would rather have by my side on the day of the Revolution. He is a born fighter. But the day before and the day after, he could be a handicap. He sees everything, (as to a large extent do Podvoisky, Nevsky, Semashko and others among my Men of Confidence) in purely military terms. By neutralizing, atomizing almost, poor old fat-gutted Gusev, I aim to show all present that killing Cossacks, frightening the Soviet, outraging what the workers call the *burghu*, is not enough.

A far more damaging blow is the government claim that it has proof a certain Vladimir Ilyich Lenin has long been in the pay of the Germans, and today has lured the Bolsheviks into launching a *coup d'état* timed to coincide with the enemy's July offensive.

The meeting shook, then blenched, as if from a near-miss by a howitzer shell. But immediately afterward, they were nearly all chuckling.

Who is going to believe such rubbish? The gutter press had

said that, and worse, time and again! Show me workers and peasants, in or out of uniform, who can be convinced that our party and theirs could be led by such a traitor. So where is this Hun offensive? Our comrades at the front may not be advancing anymore. But they are holding their ground like true sons of the soil. And so on and so on.

It seems a pity that all history's lessons have to be learned after, rather than before, that painful error which it is the lesson's purpose to teach us to avoid. Few people examine the evidence in a period of counterrevolution, above all a time when what you believe is what you want to believe. For the bourgeoisie, an external enemy (Germany) has put them in risk to an internal enemy (the Bolsheviks). Therefore the two must be in collusion, possibly identical. When this is repeated often enough, it starts to become an article of faith for the little bourgeois, the lower middles, the lumpen proles, the ignorant, unsatisfied and frightened of all classes. Russians are taught to see life as a battle between single figures, archetypal personalities, riders in the sky. So it is easy for them to visualize a divide across which battle is joined between (on their Right), the Good Side embodied in the Tsar—Christ—Your Local Lord—the Church—the Slav General, and on the other, the Bad (or Left) Side, the Terrorist—Satan—the Jew—the Worker—the Outside Agitator—the German/Japanese agent. There is no doubt which we are. But I am drifting off into one of my lectures . . .

I tell them—these documents are not forgeries in the usual sense but genuine originals cleverly adapted and doctored to fit a false context and serve an ulterior motive. The experts employed are better even than the best that only money could buy. They are ideological opponents fueled by vanity, rivalry and a long vendetta against me and the Bolsheviks. An infamous pair, working in harness for the first time. The French spy, a former assistant editor of *Pravda*, sometime Party deputy in the Duma, Alexinsky. And the right-wing SR smeller-out of police spies, the champion trapper of double agents, of course, I mean Burtsev. Two of the supreme sleight-of-hand operators of our century.

Don't tell me such a blatant trap can never be sprung these days. Even now, as we talk, it is working. Ask yourselves—why are the nonpartisan regiments rallying here behind the lackeys of the bourgeoisie just a few feet from us? I can tell you. Because they have just been shown the "evidence," tonight, by their officers. They have heard it authenticated by a few right-wing Soviet spokesmen. They are being urged to act on it by pro-government propagandists of every political shade.

Kerensky is on his way back from the Front with more "loyal" troops. What is the first thing he will do when the case against me is published? Order the arrest of the German agent, Lenin, and his Central Committee. This will be taken as a signal to all the dark forces of reaction to flood out from the woodwork and attack our people on the street, in their homes, at work—anywhere they are not protected. This is the moment the enemies of the Revolution have been waiting for. If we had staged our bid for power a few hours ago, we would already have found ourselves being put down, like unwanted animals, by superior power.

The forgeries by then would have taken on the absolute radiance of truth. And one more thing. I spoke to our Man at the Front five minutes ago. I had a hard job getting through, since he is fifty miles nearer to Peter than when I last telephoned him. The German counterattack has not only started—it is racing forward with exceptional speed and efficiency. Yet another piece of their "evidence" that our insurrection was timed to aid the Germans and the Germans' advance was timed to aid the Bolsheviks.

So, *chto delat?* What's to be done, comrades? First, we must try to minimize the damage that will be inflicted upon us. For myself, I am, of course, willing, eager even, to appear before any democratic court, and a jury of free citizens, to clear my name. But if supposedly incriminating correspondence, testimony of involvement with people I have never even met, assumptions of guilt by commentators and columnists, are plastered across the front pages day after day, then a fair trial will be impossible. We shall have another Dreyfus Affair. So can I suggest that an approach be made to the CenExCom of the Soviet here asking all comrades from the Broad Left in the print, or on the editorial teams, to block the publication of such allegations, while the case is *sub judice?*

Second, we must defend our own soldiers, sailors, Red Guards, armed workers. If we agree to them all staying away from the city center, not appearing on the streets wherever they remain under our control—Kshesinskaya's, Peter & Paul, Kronstadt, the Red tenements of Putilov and old Vyborg—then we must have a guarantee from the government and the Soviet that they will not be disarmed by force, one by one. We must also insist that, so long as we too renounce force, we shall be protected from attacks by mobs of any type, in or out of uniform. Third, if these two insurance policies fail, then we must all be prepared to fight and survive on both levels, in the underground as well as in public, as we did in the old days.

Finally, I propose we all disperse and reestablish contact with our sections, explaining to them what we are thinking and doing, warning them that this may be the worst yet, the worst ever. It all depends on how we hold ourselves over, at most, the next three months whether we shall win or lose. If we win, we will have made a new kind of history, chalked up an immortal victory beyond any in the annals of war—what are they, Sergei? (I called to Gusev). Thermopylae, Philippi, Lepanto, Agincourt, Borodino? But if we lose . . . then we will not get a second chance in our lifetime.

JULY 5	PETERSBURG	1917

These two July days have been written up in odd moments at Kshesinskaya's and finished off in a corner of the Ops Room at the Tauride. They fill one medium exercise book, enough for a long short story or a slight novelette. I put both under the same heading. For July 3 in Peter, though only reported to me at second hand, and July 4, though mainly my own experiences plus some I was told, were one incident that stretched on until the early hours of July 5. But what happened today, July 5 itself, when several severe blows rattled our whole Party, deserves an entry on its own. After the dampening down of Gusev, and the warning to all ExCom and MilOrg people, already recorded, I was not as serene as I hope I appeared. As I strolled out this early morning into the square, on the way to pick up Gusev and Zinoviev, and the van, Trotsky fell into step beside me. Like Gusev (I don't know why) Lev Davidovich is another with an amateur's obsession with soldiering. He held my elbow to detain me with the unmistakable delicate finger grip of his, like a safecracker's.

"Have you heard the Guardsmen's drill shanties?" he whispered.

The Ismailsky and Preobrazhensky had been joined by a couple of others—I couldn't quite see their colors since the Palace lights were now dimmed—and they were marching and counter-marching through the rain, a traditional kind of living geometry, singing some schoolyard rhyme. Though not perhaps the rhyme invented by schoolkids you'd care to meet on a night like this.

> One, two, three, four.
> Fuck the Jewess against the door.
> Three, four, five, six.
> Up the arse of the Bolsheviks.

Five, six, seven, eight.
How long will Christ wait?
Seven, eight, nine, ten.
Till the Little Father's back again.
One, two, three, four.
Nail the peacenik to the door.
Three, four, five, six.
All the Reds have Jewboy dicks.
Five, six, seven, eight.
Bleeding hearts menstruate.
Seven, eight, nine, ten.
Make way for the *men.*

I retrieved my elbow. I'd always heard how fastidious Lev Davidovich was. One of his objections to joining our Party had been that he found it hard to believe we could have on our CenCom someone who told such filthy jokes as Stalin did. What was the point of listening to this stuff—did anyone doubt that peasants in uniform are still peasants? Anti-Semitic, reactionary, superstitious, violent, woman-hating, obscene?

Trotsky curled his lip. "As a Jew, I sometimes think that could be a description of most Christians. No, I just wanted to see how *you* reacted. If we don't get these creatures on our side, we will never win. Don't tell me they think up this stuff for themselves. How many would ever use the word 'menstruate'? Reaction is much better organized, perhaps, than you think, Ilyich."

"All the better. If they made it up themselves, we might have a problem. Look! If people do not want a revolution, no party can force them into it. In three months, life, reality, history, the world, whatever you call it, will have taught them a different tune. Believe me."

We shook hands. I seemed to have cheered him up. His trouble is he always thinks that he is separate, different from the rest. He has never recovered from being chased home from school in Odessa by roughs shouting—"Who Killed Christ?" Still, as I find so often in life, by encouraging him I had started trains of thought that discourage me. As I waited for Gusev in the van to take Gregory and me to the *Pravda* office, I couldn't help tuning in to the next verse from the ghastly little *smerdi.* Quite sophisticated in their way—now they were reversing the count.

Four, three, two, one.
I fuck with my gun.

> Six, five, four, three.
> Hang a striker from a tree.
> Eight, seven, six, five.
> Not a Jew-boy left alive.
> Ten, nine, eight, seven.
> Every Ivan goes to Heaven.

I knew I was going to stay awake worrying how to get people like that to follow us. Thank . . . whoever, for good old Gusev.

"What does that Bronstein know?" he demanded, picking up his belly and hurling himself into the van after it. "Let me tell you, about swaddies. Throughout history the generals have always discovered—never trust what a soldier says. It's what he *does* that matters. Those drill ditties are sung to please the officers they've got now. Different officers, different songs. Now when they're on their own, with just the sergeants, here's what they sing . . . And his bass filled the van.

> One, two, three, four.
> Fuck a Countess against the door.
> Three, four, five, six.
> Chop off the end of the officers' dicks.
> Five, six, seven, eight.
> Where's the food the rich folk ate?
> Seven, eight, nine, ten.
> Very soon, we'll be home again.

"See what I mean? You give them that speech about Bread, Peace, and Land, and I bet I'll have them doing the 'Internationale' like Chaliapin. . . . Five'll get you fifty in gaspers."

As he drove, Sergei Ivanovich talked in a way I'd never heard him do before. What I'd said to him about Trotsky's experience as a boy somehow sparked him off.

"Anti-Semites," he said. "They're no good, you see. Because they never look at real things and proper people. They're so obsessed with Jews, they can't tell their ass from a hole in the ground. You know how really Jewish Jews think anybody who is really marvelous must have been a Jew? Well, your Black Hundred Jew-hater thinks everybody who is really *horrible* must be a Jew. Now you taught me, Ilyich, it's no use believing something because you like the idea of believing it. Truth is what counts, even when it hurts. In fact, you said once, 'You can usually tell it's the truth *because* it hurts.' Right! But let me tell a tale.

"It was in the March Days, in Peter, before you came back. Everybody was on street corners spouting then. I was on my soap-box, actually a beer crate. I never saw a soapbox. And this ratty lot of Black Hundred types gathered round me.

"The rattiest one asked me: 'What are you, then?'

"I said: 'Comrade, I am a Bolshevik.'

" 'Don't call me comrade,' he said.

" 'Very well. I will rephrase my answer. Shit-head, I am a Bolshevik . . .'

"His friends all laughed like hyenas and he was very, *very* ratty. But I was a Greek god in those days. Well, Bacchus was a Greek god, wasn't he? Anyway, he didn't dare take a swing.

" 'Oh, a Bolshy, are you? And a Jew I suppose.'

"Well, boss, I'm as much a Jew as a Chinaman. But you're an agitator, you're an agitator. So I said: 'And what if I am, comrade shit-head?'

"He thought he'd got me now. 'If you are a dirty Jew, and I see you are, you dirty Jewish Bolshy, then you killed Christ.'

"Well, I reached out, and I don't know if it is a record in weightlifting circles for an outstretched arm, but I hoisted up all eight stone of the little bugger by the hair and I told him . . . 'I don't know if your Jewish Christ ever existed. I don't know if what your Jewish apostles tell us about him is true. But if he did, and if it is, this Jew was a rebel against a colonial oppressor, the Roman Emperor who was worse than the Tsar. Until one day, he gave up preaching against the occupying power. He stopped saying, sell your cloak and buy a sword, and he became a collaborator. The Romans killed him just the same. But if they hadn't and if I'd been there, I'd have killed your Jew Christ with my own hands.'

"Well, boss, you've got to remember these Black Hundreds are as poor and ignorant as anybody in Russia. Nobody has ever told them the truth, about anything. They are exploited and they hate their exploiters. Which is good except that the only exploiters they see to hate are Jews. Didn't Bebel call anti-Semitism 'the Bolshevism of fools'? They've got to learn to hate the other moneylenders, landlords and capitalists *as well*."

I really ought to take back that earlier stricture. Gusev *is* a politician after all as well as a fighter. I slapped his hambone forearm.

"Eight stone from the horizontal, eh?" I said. "I'll try it on Radek."

As we drove along the Liteiny in the van, our road ahead cleared by an armored limousine as clustered with sailors as a branch of buddleia with butterflies, we saw a stream of expensive carriages trotting toward us in the other direction. It seemed to me that the curtains were mostly drawn closed, with only an occasional mousy nose or an owly eye peeping out, while each coachman up above adopted the clenched, concentrated expression of someone on a mission of life or death. I thought we had hit some long-held-up funeral cortege, though no one was in mourning, or perhaps some disreputable, semi-legal marriage procession. Certainly, there was a fugitive, furtive air about this one-way traffic. Most of the luggage, and there was plenty of it, showed signs of having been loaded up in a hurry, bits of clothing protruding from half-closed lids, bags and sacks and parcels lashed on as if by an afterthought.

Our bodyguard of Kronstadters stood up on their running boards or mudguards, laughing, jeering and making vulgar gestures, as they passed each carriage. Gusev also began to guffaw when we got abreast.

"What's so funny?"

"Sorry, boss," replied G. "It's the what-you-call-its, the burhjuves making a run for it. They've grabbed the family silver and the railway bonds and they're catching the next train out of the Finland station. *They think we've seized power!*"

They didn't know what we knew. I must say it *was* quite funny in its way. Of course, Gregory couldn't resist topping it. His head thrust through the porthole thing separating the driving cabin from the cargo hold—he looked like the Aunt Sally (Uncle Solly?) target at the fairground.

"What did you say B.-B.'s address was at Nievola? I think it's my turn now for a month in the country."

At the *Pravda* presses on Moika Street, I saw through its setting and layout the CenCom statement congratulating the Party and proletariat, our servicemen and our Red Guards, on a magnificent display of strength and confidence, recommending them all to conserve that strength and retain that confidence until we called upon them. I then sat down to outline a few articles for future editions, sketching in the headings: "Another Dreyfus case?" "Scandal, slander and sensationalism!" "What is state power and what is counterrevolution?" I'd gone beyond exhaustion. I would have written the pieces too if Gusev had not come in with some really good news that had just arrived on the office Hughes telegraph. This was a formal request to all editors from Chkheidze, as chairman of the Soviet CenExCom, and Tseretelli, as a CenExCom member and also a government minister. It suggested in the interests of truth, revolutionary honor, and natural justice that they refrain from featuring any of George Alexinsky's libels. As we watched the machine, it tapped out one acknowledgment and agreement after another. I checked with the list of Peter papers I carry in my wallet. So far as I could make out, not a single one would be printing that story in today's editions, due on the street within a couple of hours.

I decided to celebrate by walking back to the flat with Gregory instead of sitting cramped at a desk. Dawn was breaking, gilding the domes and crosses of Peter with heavenly alchemy (Shakespeare?) The air was like cream. The light was that clear varnish over a picture of the city that would make anyone feel born to be a painter.

Ahead of us was a convoy of lorries, open backs, packed with what Russian soldiers call "Junkers" (cadets training to be officers). Their faces were shiny as headlamps. They waved batons, fencing foils and the occasional pistol, elated at any chance to attack the lower classes. Zinoviev and I slipped into the first street leading off to the Embankment. Perhaps, we moved too hastily. Something about us attracted their attention. The first lorry began to slow down and the cadet in charge, resplendent in gold braid like a mess of scrambled egg, shouted something at us while firing in the air.

"Keep walking!" I muttered to Gregory. "Stagger a bit. The Russians love a drunk."

He was already staggering. Now he began shaking his head like a wet dog. "No, no, no, no, no!"

It was not a time to argue so I held on to his arm and shook too. Only then did I see what he had seen. Ahead of us, in this new street, was another armed troop of our enemies, the Moscow Regiment—I recognized them from the full-dress ceremonial banners they were flaunting.

When the two came close enough, somebody would recognize one or both of us. As a pair, we had frequently of late been caricatured in the sensational press. Small changes in appearance can confuse even trained detectives—swapping hats, say, the removal of an overcoat, the adoption of a limp—but none of these work while you are actually being observed by a hundred pairs of eyes.

Here was an opportunity to test a trick taught me by Kamo, our Party bank-robber and a great escapologist. It was based on the assumption that almost anybody can be discouraged from staring at you if you do something they will find sufficiently anti-social and unattractive. Sometimes picking your nose can be enough.

This emergency called for stronger measures. "Do what I do!" I ordered Gregory, and I began to piss into the doorway of the nearest house. He breathed a long, passionate sigh.

"I was pissing myself already," he said.

We stood together, regarding the door with happy smiles, while our crystalline barley-sugar rods of urine sparkled and foamed on the bottom step. The cadet-major stopped about ten feet away. He cleared his throat. The white-fringed head of our brown stream ran between our boots into the gutter and had almost reached him. This was too much. He put his pistol back in his holster. He turned away, waving his platoon to drive on.

At the Elizarovs' flat on Shirokaya, having dropped off Zinoviev at his safe-place, I went straight to bed, and to sleep. It was 5:30 A.M.

Instantly I was awoken. It was 7:30 A.M.

"Quick, Ilyich, you've got to be out of here at once!" Sverdlov's whisper is like anyone else's bellow. I dressed at the speed of a stage acrobat. My cane in one hand, my escape bag in the other, I was ready to leave even before my watch showed 7:38. Only then did I think to ask—why?

As we walked the almost empty streets together in swapped overcoats, July mists from the Neva, like breath on a mirror, presaging a blinding hot day, Yakov brought me up to date.

(Up to date? I'd only been out of circulation for two hours. But then an hour is a long time in our kind of politics.)

It's easy to forget how small a place Peter can be. Half an hour after Zinoviev and I had left the *Pravda* offices, they were stormed by a "Junker" raiding party, out on a spree. Taking our handful of Red Guard sentries by surprise (sloppy security there), they shot down those outside, stabbed or bludgeoned those within. Our lovely new presses and composing machines were smashed to pieces, then thrown out of the windows. All our stocks of newsprint, plus the entire run of today's edition, were set on fire and left to burn in the streets. The pillar of smoke and the big white cross daubed over our wrecked double-doors, remain as a warning to the whole city. The hard left are going to be given a good hiding—and no decent law-abiding citizen need fear he will be reproached for joining in.

Even more daunting, the voluntary embargo on the Alexinsky/Burtsev lies has been breached—twice. First in the gutter sheet, *The Living Eye* (*Zhivoye Glaz*) a semi-pornographic satirical dog's breakfast of fantasies, libels and jokes, always dismissed as having a tiny circulation, yet always found under the blotter on the desk of the top person, and nearly always believed by him except when it writes about *him*. Whatever appears here, if it suits their editorial interests, will reappear tomorrow in every metropolitan daily. And just to make certain that the mercenary mob, the Black Hundreds, the pensioned-off police marks, the underworld of crooks and madmen, are also alerted, Alexinsky has printed most of the allegations himself in a leaflet that an army of beggars is even now hawking on the streets.

I sat down on a bench, and shook my head to clear the black cloud that was beginning to obscure whole sections of my brain the way the London fog used to blot out whole parishes of the city. For every move, there must be a countermove, until the game is over. Our game has just begun. "All right, Yakov," I said. "Here's what we do. Somebody, Joseph Vissarionovich perhaps, must go to old Tsetse and tell him we'll negotiate a withdrawal of forces, peacefully and in an orderly fashion. From Peter & Paul, or wherever. From Kshesinskaya even. We are twice as weak as we were yesterday. Tomorrow they will be ten times as strong. We want no provocations, no excuses for them to stage another *Pravda* bashing. . . . Then . . ."

"Already," Sverdlov interrupted. His favorite word. Usually it means that he has anticipated your suggestion and carried it out successfully. Here, unfortunately, it meant he had anticipated my plans but they hadn't worked.

"Stalin went to Tseretelli. His own idea, would you believe? He learns slow but he learns, that one. It was rather embarrassing. Joe said—'Don't worry, if you want to come to our HQ even, there will be no bloodshed.' Tsetse laughed. 'There will be no bloodshed,' he said, 'because we outnumber you. You will lay down your arms and leave quietly when we tell you. Otherwise we will wipe you out.' Joe's face was purple as a strangled turkey when he told me. And that was an hour afterward. If he hadn't been more afraid of you than of the Soviet and the government combined, I think he'd have killed Tsetse on the spot."

I could feel my face flood with heavy, angry blood that I dispersed only with an effort of will. You cannot make correct decisions when choked with emotion.

"All right," I said. "Let's think. So we'll go to Kshesinskaya's now. Raskolnikov has turned the place into a fortress. Machine-guns and mortars linked in a web of overlapping circles of fire. A rabbit couldn't get within sight of the walls without being stuffed with lead from three sides. We'll *make* them wait. At least until we've disposed of the files."

"Already!" he sighed. "The Moscow Regiment, tarted up for a Tsar's birthday, was there before us. Unless we wanted a full-scale civil war, with our people scattered, Podvoisky and me had to push through and let them in. Raskolnikov was fit to be put in a straitjacket, but finally gave way and marched off his gallant five hundred. We delayed long enough for Podvoisky to destroy the most compromising documents, but I'm afraid we couldn't get rid of them all. Still, what you need, names, addresses, aliases, contacts, I've kept up here." He tapped his black leather *shapka*.

"So they've got some of our secret papers, only we don't know which ones? That's marvelous. That's the worst of all worlds. It makes it almost impossible for me to read their minds and foresee their plans against us."

Yakov smiled, that sweet, ancient, wise Jewish smile, creasing that white, knightly profile of milky skin and raven hair. It is a look he shares with Lev Davidovich, like a statue moving, which most of us find irresistible. Though to a few, Stalin for one, it is strangely abominable.

"Let's face it, chief. We *have* no secrets. So they'll find one of the score of copies you had made of key targets to be seized. It won't tell them anything they don't know before. If the authorities could suppress us by knowing what we decided at CenCom meetings, we'd have been flattened long ago. After all, they had Malinovsky and other police spies as our MPs, as our editors, on our CenCom, probably all four. Alexinsky has always been in the pay of the French government. Yet here we are. Next time we'll topple them, eh, boss?"

Sverdlov was right. Here was another comrade I had too often underrated. I had only one last protest, and I knew the answer . . . already.

"What about that famous safe in the ballerina's bathroom that will blow up if anyone touches it who does not know the correct approach? Has that been exploded? What can be in it, by your argument, that justifies all these defenses?"

"The answer, Old Man, is that it won't blow up whatever anybody does. The explosive is all fake. I reckon they'll need to get a sapper from the front to certify it won't go off and until then they'll have some very uneasy moments. As to what's in it, I thought you knew. A copy of Marx's *Das Kapital*, first Russian edition, 1872. You know, the one the censor allowed in because he said it was so dull it would never create any revolutionaries."

"But what must be done, if you'll excuse the phrase, is to get you out of that flat double-quick before Colonel Nikitine raids it.

There isn't a warrant for your arrest, yet. But it seems obvious there will be one when Kerensky gets back from the front. Meanwhile, just over the last couple of hours, the White Terror has begun. The Cossacks are out on their horses, hungry for revenge. The Junker cadets are out in their transit trucks looking for Bolshevik strongpoints to demolish.

"Gangs of 'honest toilers,' " hired by the day, outraged to find Lenin's German spies still at liberty, are everywhere. Their job is to beat up lefties. Thrash known activists within an inch of their lives. At least one of our lads has been killed. Poor old Voinov. Strung up in broad daylight and left dangling from a lamppost. Know what his crime was? Passing round our two-page newssheet, *Truth Bulletin* (*Listok Pravdy*). All it had in it was our Order of the Day. 'The demo is over, everyone go home peacefully.' They didn't bother to read. It was enough that your signature was on it. If they catch you, your life won't be worth a bean."

He studied me like a tailor. Or an undertaker. "You're even more of an eyesore in my coat than you are in your own. I suppose it's because mine is made to measure. And yours doesn't seem to be made to fit anybody."

So we swapped back. I felt much more comfortable, certainly much safer, in my old ulster bought from a market stall in Leather Lane, Holborn. It fits me because it fits everybody. The spirit of democracy applied to haberdashery. With the collar up, my cap pulled down, I can fade into a city wall, if it's grubby enough, anywhere in the world.

Yakov now, his sole vanity is dressing to catch the eye. Those black leathery costumes, part deep-sea diver, part bareknuckle prizefighter—they'd hit you in the eye at a Parisian *bal masqué*, or a Venetian carnival. Here in Peter, he's every Smolny schoolgirl's idea of a Bolshevik assassin.

We linked arms and set off to find me a new home for the night.

JULY 6   PETERSBURG   1917

The place Yakov has recommended, at least as an overnight bolthole, turns out to be the flat of Marya Sulimova on the Karpovka Embankment. It is on the sixth floor and because the canal curves away below us we can see any group approaching us for more than a mile either way. I spent most of yesterday writing by the window ("Calumnies and Facts," "The Abominable Lies of the Reactionary Press," "A Russian Dreyfus Case") in between staring at the slatey waters wrinkling in the fitful summer breeze.

It was only when I had finished the articles and carefully wrapped them up in old newspapers for collection by one of our runners, that I realized the canal was not empty. And had not been empty since I started. There was a very old man there, but swaddled in neat and clean rags, poling a punt backward and forward with impressively youthful energy.

I leaned forward for a closer look, taking care to keep in the shadow. Was it my imagination? I scratched my head. After the sort of delay it takes for a shout to cross an Alpine valley and echo back, he scratched his head. There could be no mistake. I stepped back in alarm. I took my Browning from the bag at my feet and this time, gun in hand, peeped out of the other side of the window. After another delay of the same treble beat, he scratched his head again and pointed to an object in the bottom of the boat, invisible to anyone on lower floors. It was a semi-automatic Luger, at a guess. He put his thumb to his mouth. Should *I* copy *him* this time? I noticed I already had the knuckle of my thumb between my teeth.

Just then I heard the agreed knock on the door and opened it to Sverdlov. He was jumpy and a bit irritable.

"My Red Guard down below says you have been sitting in the window frame all day like a nob having his picture painted. He says he would have recognized you anytime. He also doesn't think it's a good idea to make signals from there."

My reply was not exactly characterized by comradely good temper or even normal human politeness. We are all under pressure. I insisted Yakov get rid of my protector, pointing out that to have an able-bodied ancient so obviously doing nothing but keeping lookout was equivalent to flying a red balloon from the roof reading "suspect hiding here."

He agreed.

"You above all, chief, are in deadly danger. General Polovtsev, district commander, has been given the blessing of the SovExCom, and the government, to disarm the workers and the rebel regiments. We've lost all our meeting halls, arms dumps, and local committee rooms. Now they are drawing up lists of safe houses to raid, the addresses of anyone who ever had any connection with any of us. That's just the official campaign. Five hundred officers have sworn to hunt you down personally in their off-duty hours. Almost all the old CID are rallying to the Ministry of the Interior by the minute as volunteer Lenin-hounds. They've even brought out Tref, the wonder dog, the most decorated animal in Russia, to lead the chase. And I'm sorry to say a lot of the workers are being misled by the 'German gold' stories as well. It's no good trying to blind them with the real facts. 'Lenin the Spy' explains a lot of things for the moment. I've even had Bolsheviks from the army and the factory saying to me today about that train behind the lines, 'Why was it him? Why was it *only* him?' "

I made a few alterations to the articles to meet these points. When Sulimova got back, she would typewrite them for me, then hand them over to the messenger who arrived along with Nadya. My wife was also full of news of the ProvGov–SovExCom onslaught on the Bolsheviks.

"You were well advised by Yakov to leave the steamboat flat," she said, laughing with surprising gaiety.

"After you'd gone, Marya began to get the rooms neat and tidy. When I asked her why she was plumping the place up, she said 'For the unwelcome guests, of course!' And so we sat about, hardly daring to crease a cushion, or drop a fingernail of ash, until quite late in the evening. Marya laid out all the books and opened up all the files, as if we were soldiers expecting a kit inspection.

"I thought how often you'd complained about the mess in our houses. 'Volodya would be pleased,' I said. 'But do the police or the soldiers care?'

" 'Well,' she said. 'They love it if it looks like a pigsty. They like to think we must be the scum of the earth. So I always show my passport describing me as an hereditary noblewoman. I try to give them the impression they're visiting people of taste and culture like their boss's family or their colonel's wife. They don't like to be thought *ni-kulturney* so they hesitate before forcing anything that might break and they can miss things in plain sight.'

"Not that, as you know, we had left anything there to hide. Marya was a bit behind the times with her idea that we could keep them in their place by being ladylike. It wasn't until quite late— you know how quiet and backwaterish it is on Shirokaya—that we heard a lorry parking outside the door, the engine roaring, rough voices questioning the janitor, then the bell ringing and fists knocking and shouts of 'Open up, you red bastards!'

"Marya opened up so quickly that they all fell in, like schoolboys larking about. Even she was a bit taken aback, they looked such a fierce lot—awful boily officer-cadets, with bad breath and greased hair, and great, coarse soldiers, twice their size, and obviously half expecting to be ambushed by dynamiters.

"Your sister flourished her passport and remarked to the nicest-looking officer-trainee—'We, my sister-in-law Lady Nadya and I, have been used to such outrages, such night raids, by the now happily abolished tsarist secret police. But, as democratic revolutionaries, in the revolutionary democracy of free Russia, we protest against such illegality.'

" 'Fuck you, you Communist hag!' remarked the nicest-looking officer-trainee, spokesman for the authorities in what you, Volodya, a few months ago called 'the freest country in the history of the world.' "

She was enjoying herself, experiencing that surge of carbonation along the veins that always follows a dive through danger. Yakov and I poured each other a small vodka, a large one for the messenger, and settled back to hear more.

"Nobody produced a search warrant. The first lot just blundered about turning everything over, willy-nilly, like half-grown youngsters playing a game too childish for them. Then a second lot came in. They were clearly remnants of the old Okhrana, led by Colonel Nikitine. I recognized him from that photograph you had printed and pinned up at all our committee rooms. Did you know they have all been seized? Handed over to the Black Hundreds? Yes. Well, he went straight to your room, Ilyich, as if he were following a map, and started sorting through the papers Marya had left out. She was right about that bit. He clearly didn't like looking for secrets somewhere where nobody had bothered to hide them.

"We were not allowed, at first anyway, into your room. So we had to sit and watch the troops looking for somewhere a man (you, Volodya) might be hiding. They searched and prodded under the beds, behind the curtains, in the cupboards, places even young Gora could not have curled up in. They made us produce all our keys. When we opened the cases and trunks, they threw everything out and then stabbed the depths with their bayonets. The depths were rather shallow, and a child could have seen none of them could hold a man. But whenever either of us relocked something, they became angry and insisted we open up again in case Lenin had slipped in when they weren't looking. This happened over and over again, as each new couple of soldiers caught one of us turning the key. The 'German spy' was all they could think of. There must be a reward, I suppose.

"Meanwhile the colonel had gone through every book, every piece of paper, in what looked like a very scientific, ordered examination and he left soon afterward with an armload of documents. Once he had gone the others did not quite know what to do, tending to revert to type as Marya had expected. Two soldiers sat at a table and browsed through the letters Ilyich had received from soldiers at the front. They started reading them aloud in mocking voices, bad imitations of a posh drawl, accompanied by jeering comments all round. But then they began to get involved. Here were soldiers, just like themselves, only under fire at the front. They were writing to this German spy and actually *thanking* him for showing them the way to end this horrible war. I'd read them all, of course. I'd answered many, forging your name. So I was not surprised when they began to ask each other how it was possible that their fellows in the trenches could be on such pally terms with a traitor.

"In the other room, one of the cadets kept asking me over and over again, where had you lived before? How did you earn your living? If you were an author, where were your books? This last was the easiest. 'Here you are,' I said. 'Would you like to read them? Take them with you.'

"He seemed very pleased until he saw his fellow cadets looking at him. And he handed them back.

"Just as they were leaving, Anna's Mark turned up and there was a dispute as to whether or not he was Lenin. Afraid to be accused of underenthusiasm rather than overzealousness, they decided to take him to the station. I was cross-questioned about where Lenin was if this wasn't him, and Marya shocked them all to silence by pointing out icily that even under the tyrannical tsarist laws a wife could not be forced to betray her husband. One was so taken aback that he let slip that the authorities knew you had stayed with B.-B.—in Finland. They were just about to leave us all as we were when Vera Ilyovna peeped through the door, saw all the intruders, threw her apron over her head, and began wailing like a Tatar, before trying to run away. Such guilty behavior all the soldiers understood. So they arrested me, Mark and Vera. I kept trying to explain that the poor girl was a servant, and not a very bright one at that. I must say she proved even dumber than I thought possible, totally unable to give the name of her employer. The word 'Lenin' particularly foxed her. She thought it meant some kind of bandit, outlaw, demon from a fable and kept shouting that her priest had specially warned her never to have dealings with what she called 'Olenins.' In the end, they took us all away. Only to find when they got us there that Colonel Nikitine denounced them all as *Dummkopfs* and sent us home. How was your day?"

I went to bed early, soon after Sulimova had arrived and typed the articles. Sverdlov, Nadya, and the messenger then left together, their old bundles of newspapers looking the last thing anyone would want to steal. It is best that we should all remain as scattered as possible. Nadya will be safer with my Anna and her Mark than with me.

This morning I asked my hostess whether General Polovtsev's men had managed to carry off the papers of the MilOrg intact. "Yes, but don't worry," she said. "There's nothing there to incriminate anyone. It's all plans for a hypothetical future. Your name's not mentioned. Ever."

It's amazing how even clever people find it hard to adapt their minds to the logic of clandestinity. What about her name, I asked? Oh, yes, *her* name was on everything. She was the MilOrg secretary, after all. And her address? Well, naturally, yes, that was on file with the Interior Ministry, like everybody's. "Then, my dear Marya Ivanovna, you see, they will come looking for you, and they will find me. If they find you, it will mean an interrogation, perhaps a few days inside. If they find me, I'll be topped. So I'll take my cane and my carpet bag and I'll be off."

The same thought had occurred to Zinoviev who arrived shortly after. He was very panicky, sweating and bulging, begging me to tell him, like a child, that our story would have a happy ending, that we'd get out of Peter alive, that the Revolution would come soon and end all our troubles. What he needed was his Yiddisher Momma, but then all Mommas are Yiddisher Mommas and they all say the same—"Eat!" I had noted in my brief turnover of Marya Ivanovna's flat yesterday (a routine precaution) that she had on a slate shelf in her pantry what looked to be the rewards of a visit to the country—a dozen big brown eggs, a bowl of thick cream, a block of country butter with pearls of water clinging to its cheesy surface.

Perfect greed driveth out fear. Twenty minutes later, Gregory was chin-deep in scrambled eggs, rallying me for my pessimism and caution. This mood lasted through our farewells and thanks to Sulimova, the walk along the riverbank as far as the Grenardsky bridge, where he had arranged to meet our next host, Kayurov. This was our exit into the Vyborg side, into probably the only district of Peter where we could feel reasonably protected by our comrades, the militant workers. But as we approached the rendezvous, Z. indicating K., a lonely figure with a fishing line looped over the edge of the bank, the Moscow regiment rounded the bend of the boulevard, marching toward us. We could both hardly help recalling the wrecking of *Pravda,* the occupation of Kshesinskaya's, our escape by that embarrassing subterfuge. Ahead of us, Kayurov sat down on the wall and put a newspaper (*Rech*, by the look of it) over his face. I trudged on, as much inside my clothes as a pupa inside its chrysalis, eyes fixed on a crawling caterpillar just ahead of my toe-caps. When I looked up, Zinoviev had vanished, a piece of tissue paper blown on the breeze.

Once the soldiers had also crunched by, probably on another punitive expedition, K. rose and led me to his house on the far side of the Balshaya Nevka. His family could not have been more welcoming, more sympathetic, a real salt of the earth group, father, mother, and rosy-cheeked son. Still, after a while, there was something in the air. Something physical, something medical perhaps, something dangerous certainly, that I could not quite sniff out. Perhaps (I thought at the time) I am like some of the real old combatants-in-arms we used to know in Switzerland whose sense of smell had been (literally) distorted by police blows to the head. For the rest of their lives, the messages they got from their noses were usually revolting and weird. One or two were so distressed they killed themselves.

This smell was real all right. But what was it? I had almost had it when my attention was distracted, around midday, by the arrival at the tenement's ground-floor entrance of a brand-new chauffeur-driven Renault, complete with government permit on the windscreen. Kayurov explained that we were due at a meeting of the Executive Commission (otherwise the hard-core handful of professional revolutionaries) of the city party. This was held at the Russian-run, French-owned Renault factory, where the watch-man's lodge is the official meeting place of its trade-union committee. The driver never even glanced at me. While I was there about a score of motorcar men hunkered down with backs to the walls pretending to be relaxing over an open-air game of cards between shifts, and acted as bodyguards.

Inside, I found not just those half-dozen activists I had expected but around fifty or more delegates from our groups all over Vyborg, notably a solid phalanx from the huge Metallist works which employs almost as many as the Putilov at Narva. These latter particularly were in combative mood over the "Lenin is a Spy" stories which lead the front page of every daily paper in Peter this morning. Their solution is for me, Zinoviev, Kamenev, Trotsky, Stalin and the rest of the CenCom, the entire executive of the MilOrg, the CenComs of the Peter party and of all our local branches in factories and barracks—some 200 people—to surrender to the Minister of Justice. We should march there, and *demand* to be tried for treason. The slogan they have supplied is quite good—"100,000 Bolshevik Proletarians Cannot Be German Agents"!

Odd that the most hostile audiences I have ever faced have always been made up of people from my own side—but then that is revolutionary politics! When I opened my reply by saying, "Thank you, comrades, but for the moment I must decline your kind invitation . . ." I thought I was going to need my bodyguard. And had some doubts that I could trust them either, once they'd heard what I had said.

However, I remained unmoved. The opening of a difficult speech is always the time for intransigence. Toward the end, it can never hurt to make a few compromises, possibly already decided upon, but thrown in as if in response to the power of the arguments heard and the strength of feeling exhibited.

I told them that the decision was a *political* one to be made by the CenCom *alone*, on the basis of reasoned, informed judgment of all the facts. We would not be moved by mass meetings, or even secret ballots, fueled by pride and hurt feelings. There was no way that we could or would give up that right and that duty. I *had* offered myself to the SovExCom, agreeing to appear and submit to an examination of my finances, my policies, my possible motives. Kamenev had negotiated on my behalf, suggesting to our Menshevik and SR fellow revolutionary democrats that, during the investigation, I could be available in some agreed place, such as the Peter & Paul Fortress, where several former tsarist ministers remain comfortably and safely lodged. But (I went on) we had been instructed that we had no right to make conditions. State prisoners would be imprisoned wherever it suited the authorities. Kamenev then pointed out that in the Kresty, for example, prisoners, even on remand before trial, were kept in solitary confinement, exposed to beatings, to starvation, often to torture, by the Junkers who had taken over running the place for their amusement. No leader of a legal, recognized socialist party could be subjected to such dangers and indignities. "So be it," was Tsetse's official answer to Kamenev. "Leave Lenin's address at the desk as you go out."

"Do you think I would be here today," I challenged, "if Lev Borisovich *had* left my address? Isn't it clear that it is thanks to the solicitous care lavished on me by the Kerensky government that I am living on the run? The revolutionary has only one friend. Fortunately, your name is legion. You, my brothers, the workers, are hiding me."

This stirred them quite a bit. They were listening to someone

like them, battered by life, looking older than his years, balding,
wrinkled, wearing clothes unworthy of a stage tramp, who'd given
up not just luxuries and comforts, but most necessities, for their
cause. So I took them on the tide, and told the story of my yesterday. The raid on my sister's flat, the arrest of my wife. The
presses of *Pravda* ruined half an hour after I left. The head on
encounter with the Moscow regiment and the Junkers in the street.
Even the piss in the doorway. They were roaring, on their feet,
on my side. The excremental anecdote never fails with most workers of every nationality, and any Germans.

I reminded them how lucky they were to be domiciled, where
I was just a roving lodger, in the independent Bolshevik Republic
of Vyborg. Across the bridges, "White Terror" is not a figure of
speech anymore. Those class collaborators and social climbers of
the now dying Soviet, the Mensheviks and Social Revolutionaries,
are backing the bourgeois government in its every attack on the
people. "Dual Power" is simply a rubber stamp for each autocratic
act of state terrorism—for the lynching of left-wing militants; for
the arrest of their leaders; for the campaign of slander; for the
return of the death penalty for military disobedience, on the home
front as well as in the line; for the active continuation of the war;
for the refusal to share out the land; for rationing by the purse,
not the person; for the continuation of gigantic profits out of
armaments. The counterrevolutionary dictatorship hovers near,
waiting to take over, wearing its double mask. On the one side,
the patriotic savior, the demagogue, the reformed socialist; on the
other the baseborn Cossack general, the blunt speaker, the non-
party universal uncle.

"We must be alert to smash the new Bonaparte in whatever
disguise—Field Marshal Kerensky or Kornilov the Dragon-Slayer."

At last I had hoisted them to their feet, like a sturgeon hooked
deep at the end of its play. It was time to go, despite more questions
about the slanders in the press. *What should they say?* I distributed
a variety of advice and information as I lowered my shoulders and
charged for the door.

"It's up to you. You don't always need arguments. Do you
look for evidence to disprove it when someone says your mother's
a whore? Or do you knock his teeth out? Which answer do you
think he finds most convincing? Who is this Lieutenant Ermolenko,
sent back to spy on us, after being recruited in his German prison
camp? Does it seem likely his Berlin controllers would have trusted
this raw recruit with their biggest secret, the name of the top agent,
Lenin? Ermolenko's said to be a double agent. What that means

is that he is employed either (a) by the German Kaiser to spy on Russian capitalists, or (b) by Russian capitalists to spy on the German Kaiser or both. But either way, he's not an agent for *us*, for Russian *workers* or for German *workers*. Either way, he is working for *our* enemy. Would you trust a word he says? When have I ever shown any leanings toward the Hun or his henchmen? I refused to see Parvus, ex-Russian revolutionary turned German patriot, millionaire smuggler of rubber goods and sanitary towels, Wilhelmstrasse hireling. When I passed through Denmark, I denounced him the moment the war began as "the renegade who licks the boots of Hindenburg." As for Ganetsky and Kozlovsky, Bolsheviks in Scandinavia, from whom I am supposed to have received millions of German gold. They are not even Bolsheviks or Russians, but Polish Social Democrats. They have never given me money either for myself or for the party. . . . Read the articles in *Listok Pravdy*. We've got a few here. I'll be writing at greater length in Gorky's *Novaya Zhizn* soon. . . . But you don't need any more facts. Comrades, you know what you know. We Bolsheviks are against *all* capitalists, *all* exploiters, *all* warmongers, *all* monarchs, *all* the time, and *everywhere*."

It was in the limousine going back to Kayurov's that I remembered what those smells were—bitter almonds, rotten peach, acrid metal, burned wood, an unmistakable combination.

"How long has your boy been making bombs?" I asked.

It turns out that this young rebel is part of an anarchist group preparing for the eventual overthrow of such as his father and me, once our cause is victorious and we have become tyrants and reactionaries in our turn. They call themselves the "Herzen Gang," like American outlaws. I know the passage that must have inspired them and recited it from memory. "Then once again a cry of denial will break from the titanic chest of the revolutionary minority, and again a mortal struggle will begin, in which socialism will play the role of contemporary conservatism and will be overwhelmed in the subsequent revolution, as yet unknown to us." It seems a curious waste of energy, verging on mental unbalance, when you think of how much we need young people in our movement. I gave Kayurov a reference to Marx his son might think worth looking up. A speech he made after the failure of 1848, the same event which provoked Herzen's essay. Marx ends—"From now on, the workers' battle cry must be, The Permanent Revolution!"

I also instructed him it was a grave breach of security, not to mention a high domestic risk, keeping such materials at home and that I would have to leave now. He seemed a bit cast down but I think he understood. (NB. Must remember to mention the incident to Yakov and have it filed away in his multi-leaved cranium. When the Revolution does come, and we take power, young Kayurov and his Gang may be better off for a little spell of reeducation.)

I am not the only one with a nose for bomb-maker's chemicals. What about the wonder dog, Tref?

I had the Renault drop me off not too far from my next stopover. Fortunately I had got Yakov to write me out his list of possible places for just such an emergency flit. I had memorized them before burning it. Poletayev, corner of Bolshaya Bolotnaya and Mytninkskaya streets. I am glad too I have made a point of keeping my escape bag with me wherever I go. I must be completely portable at a moment's notice. I have to accept I may be a fugitive for some time.

I remember Poletayev well. Tall and yet stubby, with little feet but no legs, little hands with no arms. Undressed, he must look like a large thumb with tiny warts. He was one of our men in the Duma as far back as '08. A bachelor, almost a hermit, encountered only in corridors and committee rooms, on street corners and at factory gates. In those days, I remember Gusev used to complain, Poletayev would never admit where he lived to anybody. An ideal host for one night, a perfect break in the trail. "I don't know what his system is," Gusev had reported. "You knock on his door. No one answers. You go away. Half an hour later, he turns up saying he understands you want to see him."

Would his system still work? I had arrived unannounced and nobody answered my knock. I couldn't hang around for more than minutes on the doorstep, the most exposed place in a workers' district. Here the whole street keeps a friendly eye on unexpected visitors. Within minutes, he was standing behind me. "Hello, Ilyich. I understand you are looking for me."

It was my ideal place if I had been a bachelor. Everything in one room. Everything in its place. Nothing existing without a reason. Spotless too. If a cockroach broke in, it would be detected within seconds. A chessboard with only three pieces on either side. The end game, my favorite. If I get that far, I always win. I grow bored with the early stages. He sat down at the board. "Your move," he said. He won. "I've been thinking about it all day," he said generously. I had to have some revenge.

"Very good system," I said. "Your security routine. You rent a room across the road as well. Sit near the window, behind the curtains. You come to this room only late at night. So it's possible to be always out, yet always at home. Brilliant!"

I had to go out in the evening to a meeting of our CenCom at Fofanova's. Marvelous woman, epitome of the best in secretaries anywhere in the world. Her millionaire publisher boss cannot expect better. Yet a true comrade, an equal, an intellectual, an activist, an expert in unarmed combat, with none of that night-nurse manner many secretaries have. As if, before they leave, they'd like to change your nappies and give you your bottle.

But I just want to round off on Poletayev. I followed the same pattern on my return, knocking and waiting. He was there again in minutes. This time, however, he took me across the road to the opposite corner and unlocked a door of a room there. It was exactly like the first, even to the chess game, except that the bed had been turned down for me. "A little extra precaution," he murmured. "The system in reverse."

JULY 7   PETERSBURG   1917

Last night, a dozen or so of us, all CenCom members, met at Fofanova's. Marguerite Vasilyevna has a rambling, fifth-floor flat, cluttered with shiny, scuffed furniture, mostly junk antiques, in an old, Paris-style red-brick block at the heart of Vyborg, almost the end of the Bolshoi Sampsonievsky Prospect. This is another sort of place I'd have liked to have lived but with wife or lover, perhaps a couple of children, if only I had been some other, not so very different person, instead of a professional revolutionary.

Kerensky has just steamed back from the front in a lather over "the July Days." According to our informants, he has dismissed the justice minister because by releasing the dossier about Lenin-the-Spy *before* arresting me, Pereverzev has (a) given me, and the Party, a chance to go underground; (b) frightened off Ganetsky/Fürstenberg who was just about to cross the frontier, and fall into a trap, carrying incriminating documents. It seems Kerensky had telegraphed instructions to pick me up and lock me away on the first day of the street disorders, i.e., *when I was still in Finland*! The CenExCom of the Soviet, showing a bit of backbone for once, protested that there was too little evidence, and has kept on protesting even though this latest downpour of slander. However, just before we all assembled at Fofanova's, the Soviet have been addressed by Kerensky and changed their minds. What was new? He had read aloud a telegram from the front finally admitting a massive breakthrough by the Germans, and this was enough. Arrest

Lenin! (And Kamenev and Zinoviev.) Charge them with treacherously assisting the enemy in time of war—a capital offense.

Meanwhile, in a couple of hours he has created a new offense, also deemed treason, though attracting only life imprisonment. This is inciting any military personnel anywhere to disobey any laws, or any orders, by the authorities. And for this crime he is issuing warrants for Raskolnikov, Semashko, Trotsky, Lunacharsky and Kollontai. (This morning's papers confirm that Lev Borisovich, Gregory and I have two days to surrender, after which we will be classified as outlaws with a price of 5,000 rubles on each of our heads. No doubt the action against the others will follow soon.)

The question to be discussed was: How many of us, if any and if not all, should offer ourselves for trial? I reported on the feelings of the Vyborg activists I had met at the Renault gatehouse. I hoped, I said, that I had got across to them that this could not be a simple choice between red heroics and blue funk. They should understand (we all should understand) that the decision would be made, without emotion, simply on the basis of what was best for the Party, what would most aid the cause of the Revolution. To lock ourselves, the entire leadership, behind bars, would be to offer the counterrevolution a chance it could hardly fail to take. Nevertheless, I felt obliged to report that, on my sampling, the majority of workers, having been denied a real fight in the streets, now long for at least a real fight in the courts.

Despite general agreement on this impersonal approach to the question, almost every single individual insisted *he* should stand trial while urging that the rest go into hiding and keep the organization in working order—even Gregory. (Though he followed a typically Zinovievian course, shouting, very loudly, his determination to be a martyr while, very quietly, soliciting his neighbors to prevent such self-indulgence and unite in demanding he be preserved for the future, by going into exile if necessary.) No decision could be arrived at which covered every one of us. Some had been mentioned, even in rumor, on any government list of wanted persons, much to their chagrin. There seemed little point in counting their votes, which veered from one extreme to the other, according to the games played by their imaginations. Finally, as curfew time approached, we arrived at a compromise. Gregory, Lev Borisovich and I agreed that for the next few days we would avoid capture until we had seen what Kerensky would do next. We could decide whether the Soviets were remaining passive with "dual power" no longer operating. Then, whether tracked down or not, we would present ourselves to the courts.

Tonight, Gregory and I are staying in an entirely different part of Peter, the Rozhdestvenskaya. It is roughly the area south of Smolny and the Tauride, quite close to Bonch-Bruevich's, an upper-working-class precinct on the fringe of official Petersburg. To get there from Fofanova's is a long tram ride down the Sampsonievsky, over the Neva by the Liteiny bridge, and through some of the places where the fighting had been at its fiercest only a couple of days ago.

We should be safe enough here for a few days. The flat is in a building which forms a kind of peninsula into a square so it has several exits. Our hosts, the Alliluyevs, have just moved in. So nosy police, and even nosier neighbors, have not yet formed an estimate of who, and how many, are sharing the rooms. Gregory tells me that Joseph Vissarionovich is said to be courting one of the daughters of the house. Stalin in love! That should be a sight to see.

JULY 10　　　　PETERSBURG　　　　1917

Tonight will be our third night here at the Alliluyevs. Tomorrow, we move on again. It has been a good time for us, personally, in this home of skilled, intelligent worker-supporters. Husband Sergei is away all day, sometimes part of the night, at Peter's central power station—a key position when we finally pull the electric switch! His wife, Olga Yevgenyevna, is also away all days, sometimes nights, at the Marie Hospital on Liteiny. Their small children are spending the summer with grandparents in the country. The two growing daughters, Anna and Nadya, one a secretary at the Tauride, the other a high-school pupil, do not cross our paths much. Though their giggles often provide a kind of counterpoint fugue with the bubbles in the plumbing.

When the place is empty, it is *empty*. Nobody but us for hours on end. Gregory and I have been able to scribble away as if on a conveyor belt (new Yankee contrivance for speeding up production without workers noticing) in a propaganda factory. His workbench is a small back room (once a nursery) overlooking a courtyard, while mine is up among the rafters in a homemade windowless attic.

Originally, it was the other way round, out of deference to my seniority. But Gregory kept complaining that he felt he was in his coffin. I got distracted watching the tenants way down below coming out to get tap water, empty slops, dry clothes, chop sticks, or just brown themselves on a kitchen chair in the sun. I kept wondering where they worked, how much they were paid, what they thought about the war.

Since I feel comfortable all boxed in, indeed the more cribbed the space the better, and Gregory perched high there makes as good a sentry as a goose, we changed over.

We've also had quite a few visitors. My Nadya has been round often, proving herself a really lively, perceptive reporter of the world outside our walls, somewhat (I must admit) to my surprise. She tells us there have been more raids on the steamboat flat. Annushka, the maid, has turned perfect holy-fool, driving the investigators into fits of frustrated fury (much as she did me). How could anyone be so sincerely ignorant of almost anything, and everything, that exists? It *must* be a cover, a false personality.

"I am the village blockhead" she used to announce, as if it were an official position. N. tried hard, as no doubt did Annushka, over reading and writing. But she has so far resisted learning even the letter "A" needed to make her mark.

When the police came again, she was shown Anna's husband, Mark, the flat owner, now her employer, but she proved unable to pronounce his name or describe who he was. Assured, with typical CID cunning, that it was known Lenin was on the premises, the only question being where, she led them to the oven. "He may be sitting in there," she suggested.

Through mishearing and mistaking the questions on her first interrogation she has rooted in her mind the conviction that here in the city breed dangerous, protean demons, able to take any shape, known as "Olenins." So her every sighting of an Olenin starts informers sniffing around and sucks in the Lenin-hunters. It has become quite a regular entertainment on Shirokaya Street for the neighbors.

When Nadya came here on the eighth, Gregory and I plus Lev Borisovich (Kamenev) had more or less decided to go underground. There seemed very good reasons. To survive, the Party needs to develop two roots, two wings: one legal, public, propagandist, civilian, working through the Soviets and other open bodies—the other illegal, secret, agitational, armed, working through any cover we can get from Freemasons and Black Hundreds to Anarchists and criminals. We are an instrument of nature, multi-adaptable, polymorphous, surviving by heredity and environment through flood and drought, driven by that eternal force "so careful of the type, so careless of the single life" (Duke Tennyson). We must operate on the basis that, whatever the enemy wants most, we want least. We three top their list for capture, and therefore should top our own list for escape. We are also well chosen, like cuttings in a garden, to renew all the Party's various strands, strengths and qualities, another time in another place. The charge against us is the most grave, most damaging, most severely punishable, most highly publicized. Gregory and I, in particular, are most personally hated, pursued, reviled in the press, in reported gossip in factories and barracks. We are most likely to be wiped out trying to escape, resisting arrest, by mistake in the dark, through suicide, or heart failure on the operating table. We must expect the worst at the hands of irate patriots, identity unknown, who unfortunately went too far. Even if we stay alive through arrest, imprisonment, transport between jail and courtroom, there is no possibility of a fair trial, even by the standards of the bourgeois democracy. This is the argument made by sister Manyasha, supported with passionate nodding by Nadya, backed even by many of those who are offering themselves for trial.

.   And yet, it does go against the grain to run away. If the charges against me are so laughable, why not let them be laughed out of court? Why not take this opportunity of the best rostrum, the most elevated beer crate, the loudest megaphone in the nation to spread the Bolshevik message? The Party has seemed to be on the defensive ever since April. In June, again in July, we continued dampening down the ardor of the masses, sending our fighters home, unbaptized by fire. Now that the forces of the capitalist government, in coalition with those "socialist" careerists, are beating up, shouting down, silencing and disappearing everyone to their Left, should our leaders go into hiding as well? Why not stay and play the Tribune of the People from the dock as Lev Davidovich did so electrifyingly in '06?

Rarely have I been faced with a decision that left me so divided. On July 7, I wrote to the CenExCom of the Soviet offering to put myself into their custody and asking where to do it. July 8, I inclined to the opposite. July 9, I alternated all day as more and more news of the campaign against us came in to our safe house. First, it was bad. The government was setting up a commission to investigate the evidence available against Semashko, Raskolnikov, Kollontai and Lunacharsky (curiously enough, no mention of Trotsky) on a charge of organizing armed rebellion—warrants to be issued immediately; and also against me, Zinoviev (no mention of Kamenev), Parvus and Haniecki/Ganetsky/Fürstenberg—warrants already sworn.

This was an odd indictment. Not just the absence of two key

names, and the inclusion of two non-Russians (Haniecki, etc. is, always has been, a Pole; Parvus, a naturalized German) who by definition cannot be accused of treason. These open hearings will reheat, and reserve, every stale lie about us while we, if "locked up," will be denied opportunities of cross-examination and rebuttal. It will be in effect a trial of us, in our absence, which will render the actual trial, with us in the dock, a *fait accompli*.

The next installment was better, possibly very good. The chairman of the inquiry, future prosecutor at the trial, is to be Nikolai Karinsky. I could not for the moment recall where I had heard the name before, but Gregory shook with laughter. "Don't you remember?" he sobbed. "O clever Kerensky! Nikolai is the deputy minister of justice. No? Still doesn't click? He's *nash*—one of ours. He rang B.-B. to warn us the Ministry was faking the German spy thing against you!"

The final chapter of the day's story was the worst of all, perhaps. Certainly for me. This is the only time I can recall, since I became a full-time revolutionary, that I made a political decision for other than political reasons. That I fed my own individual emotional variables into an historical equation. That I risked altering the future for personal gratification.

My only excuse is the shock. I thought I had anticipated, and steeled myself against, any filth the enemy could throw. But I was totally unprepared for Chairman Karinsky's announcement, late this afternoon, but in time to make the headlines in the evening papers, that he would also be investigating another charge against Lenin, based on papers newly unearthed in the Okhrana files. This was that since 1900 I had been a paid agent in the RSDLP of the tsarist secret police.

Nadya later told me that my face turned to lead. Gregory said the color of putty, or, he told a lie, that offal of old horses you give to prize hunting dogs. Marya thought I was having a heart attack. As for me, I felt as if my feet had been set in a block of instantly hardened concrete and I had been dropped off the end of a pier.

"I will go to Karinsky now," I heard myself shouting. "I will demand to be heard. I will insist on the right to see all the documents, confront all the witnesses, have my defense read into the record. We must release my decision to the press. In case they do not print it, spread the message through our networks, on streets and in factories, by leaflets, street-corner speakers, word of mouth, the whole machinery."

I sent Nadya to collect Lev Borisovich (Kamenev) who was in

the same building, three floors down. "Ask for Ivan Ivanovich Ivanov." But just before she left, I saw me mirrored in her eyes, a large, bald, cratered moon-face puckered by pain, dwindling to a spindly beansprout body. I stopped her by the door. Soon the place would be full of shouting, sweating comrades and privacy impossible.

"Let us say good-bye," I said, embracing her. "We may not see each other again."

I felt a glow of self-sacrifice, of what I suppose is religious abasement, a sweet lump in the throat, a pretty tear in the eye. It was revolting. Then I knew I would be making a foolish mistake. I also knew I was not going to make it. Gregory was hovering by my shoulder, much like putty himself. "Are you with me?" I whispered above the noise of more visitors at the door being admitted by Marya. "Well . . . if you are sure . . . after all . . . yes, then yes," he replied, eyes rolling. "You're a bigger fool than I took you for," I said, grinning at his shiftiness. "Stick with me. Keep your mouth shut. And you'll be out in the country before you know it."

My reaction to Karinsky's charge, or rather report of an allegation that could lead to a charge, had been instinctive. Which is not to say that it was right. It is the one noninstinctive lemming in a thousand that stays at home which carries on the species. The accusation of acting as a German agent, even of accepting German money and assistance, did not bother me. Nor would it any mature, dedicated revolutionary. No doubt some of the money coming through Stockholm is German. I took it when it was Japanese. To overthrow the most tyrannical state outside the Orient, ruling over a sixth of the world, is an operation that requires a constant flow of cash. Just our newspapers, all forty of them, with a print run of a million and a half a week, require a huge subsidy. Everyone who knows me, or of me, accepts that I do not care where the cash comes from—from capitalist inheritance, from smugglers' profits, from bank robberies, from forged notes, from the German secret service.

Those who supply it may think, as those who discover who is supplying it may also think, that this makes me a pawn of my financiers. That I take orders. That I serve their ends, rather than my own. But they are wrong. I know, even when the sums spiral up into millions of pounds, tens of millions of gold marks, hundred of millions of rubles, that I am following my own path. Ludendorff may fancy he has bought a weapon to destroy his enemy, the Russian government. And we will do so for him. But then we will destroy the German government, and the French government, and so on, among Allies and Central Powers alike, for ourselves. *We are Revolution.* We are too hot for anyone to own, or handle, without getting burned.

I do not allow our financial dealings to be known by anyone who has no need to know. My conscience is clear. When challenged about various supposedly tainted sources of our money, I can lie, if need be, with a confident, contemptuous smile.

But to be accused of being an agent, like Malinovsky, like too many once seemingly trusty, noble, brave comrades whose names are surfacing in the Interior Ministry archives, is to stand suspected of the vilest crime in my calendar. Why then, when the accusation is made, does my body react as if I were guilty? Why do I have that haunted feeling that otherwise comes only in dreams—when I am certain that everyone will refuse to believe my denials, even when the truth is on my side, and lies clear for all to behold?

By now the flat is bursting with leading members of the MilOrg and the Party. I am looking and feeling better. Gregory has almost become a heroic statue of himself. Almost everyone who button-holes us insists that we cannot possibly be permitted to commit the crime of romantic adventurism and fly into the government web. The latest accusation—police spy as well as German spy—has begun to make many among the workers and soldiers who doubted me think again. (Perhaps that was Karinsky's intention? He's not a friend of the devious B.-B. for nothing.)

Marya puts forward the argument that this latest slander demonstrates that the courts are not even interested in *pretending* to find the truth. Kerensky's aim is to work up the mobs, seed them with *agents provocateurs,* then somehow or other let the lynchers get hold of me between prison and court. After that, it won't matter if I'm cleared later, rehabilitated, and have a street named after me. It's a good speech, and wins an almost unanimous resolution instructing us both to get out of Peter tomorrow. "*And that is an order,*" says Sverdlov. "You must put the Party before your foibles about honor and reputation," adds Kamenev. "You've convinced me," I reply. "I'll see if I can possibly persuade Gregory to come too."

When the comrades have gone, G. and I lay out the spread of foods they had brought along as a kind of last breakfast for the condemned men. We turn them into a farewell supper for the two Alliluyevs, Sergei and Olga—we've hardly seen Nadezhda or Anna for more than a moment.

This is the time of the day I like best here. We always try to prepare hosts even if neither of us is much good at it. Now this is very superior stuff, and we can see they are enjoying it. I like to hear them talk. Sergei tells us about the power plant workers, the aristocracy of labor, well paid and well treated, since both they and their bosses realize they can close down much of the city and its industry within seconds. They have tended to be very middle of the road, many of them supporting the Kadets or the right-wing SRs. But lately, he says, they have been making the jump to Bolshevism. Not because of speeches, or leaflets, or Party newspapers; they're a cut above those. Certainly, not through action on the streets, or class war at work. They even have a nonstrike agreement! What has convinced a growing number, Sergei says, is the Marxist study-circle. They are being revolutionized by reading philosophy, politics and economics! It sounds too good to be true to me. Theory never takes hold, even as theory, until it has been tested in action. At least, that's the theory—ha! Still, we are not expecting much action from the power workers until the moment comes. Just pulling a few levers, flicking a few switches. I've learned enough from Sergei to do it myself, if necessary.

Olga also has interesting tales to tell. Her hospital is within yards of the Liteiny intersection where the snipers on the roofs opened up on our marchers led by Podvoisky and Nevsky last week. She confirms that it must have been officially arranged. Extra nurses and doctors called in, beds freed, operating theaters made ready, according to a timetable. The hospital staff were directed there, not for the democratic demonstrators, the factory workers with their wives and children. These were refused even first aid. The hospital was waiting for casualties among its own assassin bands, and my heart gave a leap as she assured me there were many more of these killed and wounded than had been expected. Olga is just a ward maid. But she led her fellow domestics out into the Liteiny Prospect to treat, at least with bandages and a glass of tea, those who had been attacked. Her estimate, gathered with the help of friends in other hospitals, is that at least five hundred must have been killed or seriously wounded in the three days. "There were more taken away by the Bolshevik ambulances. But our Putilov people would not give up a single body to anyone. They humped them all the long way home to Narva."

JULY 11   PETERSBURG   1917

Last night, our farewell meal over, our last chat finished, I was becoming impatient to start our moonlight flit from flat and city.

I studied the map of the northern and western suburbs and country districts that Sergei had bought at my request. We did not know
our exact destination yet—Stalin, Sergei's old pal since Tiflis days
of '04, was consulting our Party experts on going to earth. But it
was clear to me that it must be somewhere between Peter and the
Finnish border.

Here again occurred one of those misunderstandings common
between professional and amateur conspirators. Sergei was growing rather irritated with the way I was reciting aloud lists of streets,
intersections and prominent landmarks, committing them to
memory.

He protested he had been born in Vyborg district, walked
every inch, remembered every corner. I had to point out that my
precaution was only common sense. True, *he* might never get lost.
But what if we became separated, and the other two of us had to
find our way to the rendezvous on our own? We could hardly ask
a gendarme.

Just before midnight Joseph Vissarionovich arrived squiring
a young Anna and an even younger Nadya. "A sly kulak on the
way to the state fair with a prize gosling tucked under each arm,"
joked Gregory, getting a not very comradely grimace in reply. Both
Sergei and Olga have consulted me separately over their worries
about Stalin seeming to woo both their daughters. They admire
"Koba" very much as a long-serving comrade, also consider him
one of their closest friends. But *their* closest friends. He is nineteen
years older than Anna, twenty-one years older than Nadya. Both
are lively, intelligent, daring creatures, reared on Bolshevism, but
still, within, tender and fragile. "It is almost as if he had some kind
of power over them," mutters Olga, not quite meeting my skeptic's
eyes.

Normally I take little notice of intimate relations between Party
members unless they present a security risk. Now I saw this threesome assembled, there did seem something perverse, if not perverted, about it.

Stalin is not generally accepted among Party leaders as more
than a second-rank Bolshevik, a four-plus. "Our most outstanding
mediocrity," Trotsky calls him. I find him an ideal *apparatchik*,
regimental sergeant-major, senior foreman, clerk of works—the
activist who gets things done, but who does not necessarily know
what's to be done. Last night, for the first time, I wondered if I
had misunderstood him. He is not on the government arrest-list,
so he is not likely to spend the next few months of counterrevolution either in prison or in hiding. Could it be that he sees a Party

left leaderless as an opportunity to advance himself? Surely not!

But then I had never before seen him, as he was in the Alliluyevs' flat, radiating this almost embarrassing virility. Gregory's description, intended of course to sting, was quite accurate in its way but as usual superficial. As J.V. stood there, with the stooped shoulders of a weight lifter, yellow-eyed, face pockmarked as an archery target, hair fanned out like a house-painter's brush, a comedian's stick-on moustache, I received some vivid conflicting impressions. A shabby, man-eating tiger in a traveling circus . . . a faintly down-at-heel card sharp in a big-city poker tournament. Always glossed with a patina of the slightly imperfect, distinctly dangerous when foiled.

The girls, winking and blinking starry eyes, intoxicated as you can only be when you have drunk nothing, flanked him like supporting emblems on a public monument. "Hello, old 'un!" they said to me, almost in unison. Stalin explained that the CenCom's subcommittee of specialists had recommended that Gregory and I lie low in "nearby emigration" at Razliv, an overspill workers' town grown up to service the great arsenal at Sestoretsk, handy for the Finnish border.

"I know it!" I said, rather to everyone's surprise. I reminded Gregory that its railway station was Byelo-Ostrov, the first stop we had made in Russia when we returned after the February Revolution. "Of course," he said. "The arsenal workers carried you shoulder high. Then you caught up with the latest editions of *Pravda* and complained about what a mess Joseph Vissarionovich and Lev Borisovich were making of the job."

Everybody laughed, except J.V. One of the girls turned to him. "But you were there yourself, Uncle Joe, weren't you? You've often told us how you were the first to greet Ilyich on Russian soil. Did the old one give you a telling-off then? You never said *that*. What a laugh!"

Stalin's lips became outlined with a faint blue, standing out as if painted with stage makeup. He started inhaling in quick, shallow breaths. I don't know whether the others noticed these tiny changes (Stalin is not someone you stare at too directly unless you want a blazing row) but I had been alerted enough by my discussions with Sergei and Olga to observe him in a way I would otherwise have not attempted. So I jumped in, and took over.

"Never mind about our destination," I said. "How are we going to get there? What are things like at the Finland station? If that is too risky, how far must we travel through the suburbs until we get to a station that won't be watched? The nights are still light. Should we be in disguise? Or will we be all right driving across town in a droshky? Why are we wasting our time?"

J.V. said the Finland station was a hornets' nest of police, uniformed and plain-clothed, spies and informers of various degrees of professionalism, the hosts of bourgeoisiedom flooding back from their country bowers to celebrate the last rites over Bolshevism, the usual drunken officers obsessed with rounding up shirkers and traitors. After much debate, the escape subcommittee had decided that Gregory and I should not try to pick up any train going due north through the Vyborg district. Instead, we should leave separately and follow the branch line through Old Peter to the Primorsky halt, in the suburb of Novaya Dervnya, about six miles to our northwest. It gets to ByeloOstrov in the end, though by a roundabout, less popular route.

The subcom have also decreed our safest method of transport will be on foot. Taxis are often stopped by Cossack patrols. The trams have become the happy hunting ground for detectives out to earn promotion. And, yes, the less we resemble the posters of Lenin and Zinoviev, now on every hoarding, the better.

It was the girls who insisted they should be the ones to transform my appearance. And since this necessarily involved the use of a razor, I trusted their skillful paws more than the shaky claws of my nearer contemporaries. We took over the tiny family bathroom. I sat on the closet. Young Nadya stood in the bath. Anna half-perched on the basin.

They began lathering, snipping, scraping and gossiping away as though they had spent their lives being lady-barbers. Not unexpectedly, their chat often turned to Joseph Vissarionovich Djugashvili, Stalin, their "Uncle Joe." He seems to have dropped "Koba."

How he had been diligently pressing everyone to agree that we two must move out into the country because he was so eager to move into Gregory's room. How their parents are not so keen.

How Sergei and Olga were delighted (honored!) to hide us two in an emergency. But did not look forward to a permanent paying guest, even good old Joe. It meant them sleeping on the floor of the dining room. How J.V. was widely thought to be sour, grumpy, crude, rather frightening, like a bear with a sore head, but how he wasn't like that at all. How is he? Well, before we came, he was a regular visitor. To allow Mother and Papa to rest, and have an early night, he will often get together with the girls in the bedroom they share. How, once in there, he becomes an entirely different person, well worth staying up for. How be brings them some tidbit, a piece of fruit, a hunk of cheese, a slice of sausage. How he tells them anecdotes of his Siberian exile, and the way he got on Sverdlov's nerves. How he mimicks Yakov, also Gregory, and Lev Davidovich, and Radek, but apparently never me. "He hero-worships you, Ilyich. He says it's an amazing thing but in the end the Old Man is always right." How he takes down the family volume of Chekhov's short stories and reads aloud, acting all the parts. How his favorites are "Chameleon" and "Dushechka"—he knows the second almost by heart. How he also loves Pushkin and Gorky and reads from them too. He is the most charming, interesting, older man they have ever met. And what does he receive in return? Oh, well, he's lonely. He seems rather withdrawn, and uneasy, with most women. And who knows? (Giggles and blushes.) Anna is certain he is a little smitten with Nadya but Nadya thinks she is far too young and he is really interested in Anna.

By now, my grooming is over. But the girls hide the mirror behind their backs and refuse to let me see how I have been altered until I answer a question: Was Joseph Vissarionovich there to meet me when I crossed the frontier at Byelo-Ostrov or not?

Myth-making, legend-building, the cult of the revolutionary *übermensch,* the emphasis on the individual exploit, this journalist's view of history, or even worse, these fiction writer's falsehoods, are alien to me. I leave such stuff to the SRs. On the one hand, I am prepared to overlook some such novelettish heroics, remembering that J.V. is after all entertaining two pretty, young Red maidens at the end of an exhausting and dangerous day. On the other, he is not exactly Tolstoy's Levin or Pierre, having already married and buried one wife while his listeners were still in kindergarten. Either way, I will not tell lies to enable even the best of comrades to unravel their sexual crocheting.

So I said carefully: "I did not see him myself. You must ask Gregory. He kept a log of our journey. Now, let me see what has happened to the Old Man who is always right."

I looked and instead of a reflection, there was a framed portrait of another person. He might have been an ancestor, since some details remained faintly familiar. Those Tatar eyes that I glimpse only occasionally (since I am not much of a frequenter of looking-glasses) in shop windows, on the surface of a pool, stretched out across the rounded back of a motorcar, now float behind a stranger's mask.

Those cheeks, that chin, the jaw—if they are mine—seem to have been eaten away by the whiskers that once were sewn across them. The entire balance of the face has altered. What was there before could not be categorized as particularly striking, noble, dignified, memorable. It was nearer plain, ordinary, businesslike, mundane. Yet I think it was also honest, direct, disciplined, *serious*. Now it is boyish (an adjective, among fictionalists, usually used, I note, only of girls), mischievous, comical and, I'm sorry to say, hopelessly *silly*. Still, as the whole point of the exercise is not to resemble myself, I am glad. The girls then put on me their father's second-worst old, rusty brown coat, pulling down over my even balder pate a yokel's gray cap, and propelled me into the next room.

I could see it was a success. All four of them around the table reacted without thinking to the appearance of this stranger, fatuously grinning, from another room of the flat. Stalin and Sergei came forward, half-welcoming, half-challenging. Gregory and Olga shrank back, half-scared, half-shy. Only a few seconds, yet they already knew.

"Konstantin Petrovich Ivanov, Finnish agricultural worker, at your service, gentlemen," I said. Even then, and for the rest of the evening, they would be talking normally to me and then their eyes would become uneasy like people obliged, in some epidemic or disaster, to undress and make conversation with those they hardly know.

Our six-mile walk, which took us more than two hours, was uneventful. Sergei and Joseph, hands on guns in their pockets, took turns at going ahead and behind me. It was agreed that if I were threatened by exposure, I should take to my heels while S. and J.V. stayed behind, shooting, to cover my escape. As the milky radiance darkened to an inky purple, we trudged along, meeting almost no one. Then, at the same time, Sergei and I exclaimed, "This is the place!"

We'd been told to look out for a dark copse of trees just before the Stroganov bridge crosses the Malaya Nevka and you couldn't get much darker than this. We could just about see each other's faces, if you knew where to look, faintly glimmering.

"Good work," I said. "He knows his precautions, this Comrade Whatshisname . . ."

"Yemelyanov," said Yemelyanov.

He had been sitting at the base of a tree, head bent forward over his chest, hands up the opposite sleeves, Chinese-style, so that no pale flesh would catch anyone's eyes. Now he came forward, a white oval attended by two small rectangles, one of which shook my hand.

After I had said good-bye to Sergei and Joseph, Nikolai Yemelyanov advised that we should catch the train without risking being seen in the station. Instead, we cut across the railway tracks. At one point, a long goods train barred our way. Yemelyanov ducked low beneath its struts and around its wheels with the nimbleness of a cat in a china shop.

He looked back a little anxiously. But we were both relieved to find that, despite a sedentary life, my exercises and my Finnish holiday had kept me as agile as my guide.

Y. steered me away from the tiny, lighted waiting room. We waited on the far side of an unused signal box where we would keep an eye on the 2:30 A.M. train without being seen. Soon it began to get up steam and we slipped out and climbed aboard the front platform of the last coach. I remained out there in the cool dark while Y. went through each carriage, compartment by compartment, sizing up our fellow travelers.

"It's fine," he said. "They all look like you, *starik*. Finnish peasants, that is. Let's take a seat."

I declined. I decided I would be safer on the steps, with my feet over the side, ready to leap off if there was any danger of being examined and identified. I suggested Y. stand with his back to me, in the corridor, to block the view.

He objected that I might let go accidentally.

"Don't worry," I said. "I've spent a quarter of a century learning how to hold on."

About ten miles from Byelo-Ostrov, at a small sub-station, half a dozen tipsy officers, in crumpled white jackets and with hats askew, came shouting out of the rail-side snackbar. They clambered into the next coach.

Nikolai lay down across its exit, like a flat-out drunk, blocking as much of the door as he could. The officers got out their bottles and cards, started up rounds of dirty songs, occasionally breaking off to curse this German-Jewish plotter Lenin.

One of them came back after a while and stood astride Nikolai sniffing the air and belching. He noticed me. With that pointless, persistence common among boozers, he began trying to look at my face. All I could do was to seem drunk as well. When he peered over my left shoulder, I swayed low to the right. When he moved round to the right, I swayed even lower to the left. I tried to keep in time to the beat of the wheels.

The train was going slowly, its furnace low on a wartime diet of softwood and sacks of rubbish. But it seemed to me almost coasting to a stop as I stared at the ground lazily unrolling between my toes. Then, just as impulsively as he had grown interested, he became bored with me and went back to his compartment.

"Another ten seconds," said Nikolai, "and I'd have skewered him up the ass with my knife."

JULY 12   RAZLIV   1917

Razliv is a strung-out village of fairly new-built houses, all holding back from what is little more than a track, protected against casual observation by dense-packed lilac bushes, rows upon rows of birches. The home of Nikolai and his wife, Nadezhda, is at the furthest end, backing on to open country. It has not been selected by Escacom without much forethought.

The Yemelyanovs are said to have been Party members since the early 1900s. So they are old hands at underground work. Even though Nikolai now has a permanent job at the arsenal as a skilled fitter and turner and Nadezha seven sons to look after. Stalin had not briefed me about their family, ranging from two and a half to seventeen. For a moment, I feared that a secret shared by so many, and of such tender ages, could hardly remain very secure. I must have shown something of this in my expression this morning over our late breakfast. For Nikolai began to laugh when I murmured that I had not expected to share my hiding place with so many others. "As you well know, Ilyich, children comprise the only wealth the Russian worker or the Russian peasant can amass."

It soon became obvious the Yemelyanov boys, like the Alliluyev girls, have been fed all their young lives on the milk of Bolshevism. When the grown-ups finished eating, they crowded round me with questions. Tell us about the "sealed" train, the July Days, your life in London and Paris, your boyhood on the Volga, and, of course, that red-letter day you will remember as well as our papa has always done—October 19, 1906! I turned to Nikolai, hoping for a hint. But his great, cheesy, moon face was as eager and agog as those of his team of boys.

I rarely allow a useful fact to escape my mind-cage, especially if it is in figures. But none of the great dates of '06 seemed to be in October—indeed, how many unforgettable days were there in '06? When this happens I often find it a useful mnemonic to trap the memory in a corner, force it to jump in the deep end so to speak. So I said: "Of course. October 19, '06! Neither Nikolai or I will fail to recall October 19, '06. Why, October 19, '06 is the day when . . . it seems like yesterday . . . October 19, '06? You did say October 19, '06, did you not?" I paused, gazed at the ceiling with

a half-smile, like a conjurer pretending reluctance about performing his favorite trick. "Yes! Yes! Yes!" they chanted, as if this were
a familiar holiday ritual.

"So . . ." I announced, and even while I slowly repeated the
date again, with the most convincing confidence, I remained blank
about its significance until the final digit. "October 19, '06 was . . .
the day I first met comrade Nikolai Nikolaevich Yemelyanov. It
was in Café Stroganov on Bolshoi Sampsonievsky Street. He was
bringing me shorthand reports of Lev Davidovich's speech from
the dock. I was editing them at the table for publication in the
Party daily."

There was a lovely uproar around me of applause, excitement
and perhaps just a trace of relief. Tears stood in Nikolai's ox eyes.
So *that* was why he had been somewhat stiff and uneasy with me
on our train ride and our walk here from the station under the
stars.

He thought I'd forgotten him—quite rightly, and after all
understandably. Unlike Sverdlov or Burtsev, I've never had to
cultivate the reputation of the Party boss who keeps inside his head
a file card on almost everybody; photograph, full-face and profile;
all recognized cover-names; time in prison and exile; last known
address; any question marks. What I command my brain cells to
register and hold are the movements of things and people in the
mass, over long periods, across great spaces. My aim is to attempt,
as far as is humanly possible, to reach an objective, scientific truth.
How often had Nadya and Inessa laughed at my insistence on
checking, double-checking, even reduplicating the arithmetic of
printed statistics in reference works? But a casual encounter eleven
years ago, not even embossed on the meninges by shared danger?
Nikolai is lucky I could force such a ragged fragment to the surface.

I thought of Stalin also lining the walls of his burrow with
such tiny trophies. At least Yemelyanov's anecdote, though trivial,
is true. He is not aspiring to more than a silent walk-on part. Stalin
is indicating by his presence that he is a prominent member of the
leadership, backing me from the beginning in my campaign to
over-run the bourgeois "revolution" and gallop ahead with our
socialist Revolution. While the truth is, J.V. is the arch-temporizer.
Instead of coming to support me at the frontier, he remained
behind still in favor of the war, still backing the provisional government under Prince Lvov, still behaving like a bloodless Menshevik with cold feet and acute anemia.

I felt, almost as if I were pressing the plunger of a syringe, a
spurt of bile. For a moment, I allowed myself the luxury of imag-

ining that I might be envious of him. Then for another moment, the fantasy of hating him. It passed, this twinge of emotional indigestion. There is work to be done, real things lie to hand. At last thought. How many of the Alliluyevs know that Gregory and I learned from the files in Sverdlov's head, unchallengeable from his own firsthand observation? That Stalin has not only been wived and widowed, but also took himself an "exile-bride," a Siberian peasant woman, half-mistress, half-serf, by whom he has a child, now abandoned? It is not something I can bring myself to consider discussing. Gregory, though, one can be almost sure, will leave news of it with *someone* in Rozhdestvenskaya. The odds are that one will be Olga. He will whisper it as he kisses her hand.

Nevertheless, when bear-hunting in the taiga, I'd rather have Stalin's bastard as my loader behind me than all Zinoviev's cousins as hunters in front. And surrounded by the Yemelyanovs, including the two-and-a-half-year-old, I felt inside a fortified city. Looking at the glowing hot-potato faces in the ring, I raised the glass Nikolai pressed in my hand as I spooned down the last spoonful of *kasha* and cream.

"May we all never forget July 12, 1917!"

JULY 13   RAZLIV   1917

A sleepy Gregory at late breakfast with the ten of us. He arrived in the early hours, traveling by the same route on the same train, guided by the elder Yemelyanov boy, Slava. Latest news—Raskolnikov, Semashko, Lunacharsky, Kollontai, Kamenev arrested and held under Kerensky's martial law without charge, or expectation of early trial. So much for our plan of using the courts as a platform! We can hope that Bolshevik leaders, protected by our very notoriety, our long years of struggle, internal and external exile, imprisonment and flight once shared with our newest oppressors, the Mensheviks and SRs, remain for the moment safe from enemies, inside and outside the jail. Not so the middle ranks of Party management—the ones who never get their names into the papers—dragged from their beds or seized at work and beaten all the way to the police cells where they are left locked in with their torturers. Not so the proletariat of our proletarian party, the anonymous carthorses whose names even the Okhrana do not bother to register, killed or maimed on the spot, leaflets under their arms, paintbrushes in hand, agitating for *us*.

Gregory has a particularly horrible tale to tell. Yesterday, both the Alliluyevs, G. and Joseph Vissarionovich, plus the two girls, all happened to be home at the same time. Around noon, they heard shouts, barked orders, clacking hooves below and could just see, by squinting out of the corner of the window, the bobbing backsides of Cossack horses and the finish of a wall slogan still dribbling wet: AND LAND.

Then they caught the sound of a man's voice, gone high and shrill, crying "No! No! No!," obviously begging for mercy. Another deeper, angry and cursing followed by an agonized scream as clear and clean as a train whistle.

Our rules are fairly strict in such situations—avoid sacrificing the larger for the smaller, the future for the instant, the plan for the individual. What the group should not do is interfere, risk blowing a safe house, endanger two party leaders, two party workers so far unidentified by the police, two vulnerable youngsters. But what our policy *is,* and what we *do* in emergency, are two separate things. Only the moment supplies the justification. I asked Gregory what they did.

"What did *I* do, you mean?" he asked. "I was all for going to the roof to see exactly what was happening. But I was too busy with Sergei, holding Stalin back. He wrenched up a floorboard with his one good hand, chopping away as if it were an ax, scattering splinters everywhere, and dragged out a huge Luger automatic. He wanted to go down and kill the Cossacks. While we calmed him, Olga insisted on going, putting on her full-dress nursing auxiliary uniform. She said the officer saluted and apologized but still looked awfully pleased with himself. In the gutter, she said, was a worker's body, two sides of meat almost cloven from crown to groin, apparently by one butcher's stroke of a saber. Even after all the casualties of battles and riots she's seen in her hospital, she'd never known a blow like that. She could still not believe it possible."

We were all a bit sickened by that story, one that must be repeating itself all over the country. It strengthens me in my determination to stay free and be able to devote my energy to tuning up the Party machine for the armed insurrection. Every atrocity such as Gregory reported hardens our fighters. The counterrevolution has not reached its peak—the Man on the White Horse, or today the man in the white armored Rolls-Royce, is still just over the horizon. When it is throned at the summit, bloated and sated, believing it has crushed all its surveys, then we will rise up out of the dusty plain like the dragon-seed warriors of Jason the

Argonaut. Our power is like that one the new physics is discovering, the power of the atom which now seems the motive drive of the universe. Anyway—the more they split us, and compress us, the greater will be the explosion.

Stalin does not draw the same conclusion. Gregory says yesterday's incident confirmed J.V.'s view that we are just beginning a long retreat and withdrawal, that nothing can be started until the war ends. Apart from Sverdlov, Stalin and Trotsky are pretty well the only two seasoned revolutionary leaders still free in Peter! At least Lev Davidovich, I would have thought, in his new Bolshevik lion-skin, would have shared my interpretation. But Gregory still tells me he is so insulted at not being rounded up with Kamenev and the rest that he has written a letter to the government pointing out that he is equally responsible with me for our activities in the July Days. He insists on being arrested!

Trotsky deposited the letter before the Soviet ExCom at the Tauride and stormed out. Not a very intelligent maneuver—I can say that all the more sincerely since I myself was almost provoked into an identical gesture—either as practical politics or theatrical propaganda. It springs, I suppose, from that Mephistophelian pride of his.

Not that it evoked much sympathy. After Trotsky had gone, Tsetse moved a resolution accepting his generous offer but regretting that he had not left his address! Much the same jest as he had made to Kamenev about me. How they all must have guffawed once again. When the others were out of earshot, Gregory asked a trifle nervously if I felt safe enough here and didn't think I'd be better off across the border into Finland since it was so near. So I showed him around, pointing out all our advantages. He was especially struck, as I had been, by Nikolai's forethought. Moved to Razliv in '07 when Interior Minister Stolypin's punitive expeditions were at the height, he built this house, anticipating a generation of underground activity. So he gave the place two foundations—a real one below earth level, a dummy one on top —and in between there is a hidden drawer of concrete, stuffed with Party textbooks, arms and ammunition.

I also walked him down the garden, an admirably wild and overgrown obstacle race of rockeries, sunken vegetable beds and climbing frames, shaded to right and left by high, interlocked holly bushes. At the bottom is a large duck pond, filled and drained by a sizable, navigable stream. This runs on into Lake Razliv, and its woods and water meadows, accessible only by boat. It would be difficult to construct a more practical, made-to-measure bolt-hole.

JULY 15   RAZLIV   1917

I have been here four days now (G. three). We spent only the first two nights in the house. Despite being half-hidden from the track, Nikolai thinks there is still a possibility that a strolling summer visitor, or a companionable neighbor, might pass by the front door and spy strangers in one of their rooms. Nobody here ever draws curtains, night or day. To do so would really arouse suspicions. So N. has given out that he is redecorating the place, with all the family at work on the project, to explain why they have moved to a shack in the back garden.

For half a day, I stuck it out down below with the kids. I love children. But not twenty-four hours a day. So I suggested that Z. and I withdraw up the ladder into the hayloft where we constructed ourselves a makeshift office from an old deal table with sawed-off legs I found in the shrubbery and a couple of spare bentwood chairs. We found this suited so well that now we also sleep here among the hay. The only drawback is the July heat, during the afternoons. The two of us would sometimes just sit here under the toasting eaves, staring at each other, blinking the sweat from our eyes, no more able to move than a plum pudding is able to jump from the steamer. Indeed, I still feel I am continuing my interrupted holiday at B.-B.'s and do not bother much to read.

Z. keeps me up in Peter affairs from the papers, each bought and delivered separately by a different Yemelyanov son to avoid attracting the paper-seller's curiosity.

As ever, *Zhivoe Slovo*, which broke the embargo on the German spy story, outdoes the others in the sheer confident effrontery of its fiction. I had never encountered its gossip column before. Certainly I had never expected to be mentioned there. So there were two new experiences for me today as Gregory read aloud to me what I understand is called an "item."

As everyone who had the misfortune to remain in the better districts of the capital during the so-called July Days knows to his cost, the shooting of innocent civilians was organized by Mr. Lenin and his pack of "sealed" Bolsheviks. Some, we are glad to hear, are now behind bars, and no doubt feel at home.

Too many, however, remain at liberty and are free to continue with their plotting—Mr. Lenin being the most notorious.

Is it possible that, despite the various rewards offered, despite the hunts carried out by our splendid young "Junkers" and our noble officers on leave from the front, no one can run this fox to earth?

We offer our help. We have just learned, what was not difficult for someone with an ear to the ground to learn, that Mr. Lenin was around Nevsky only days ago under the alias of Comrade Chaplinsky. Patriotic waiters from a fashionable café-theater we forbear for the moment to name have given us eyewitness accounts of his evenings there.

How he hired a private room for a week and there dined, and more, perhaps, with the Swedish actress Erna Aimusta. Fortunately for her, maybe, she has returned to Stockholm only yesterday and so is beyond what might have been the legitimate resentment of a long-suffering public. What remains are Comrade Chaplinsky-Lenin's outrageous bills—at least five bottles a night of French champagne at 110 rubles a bottle. And this apostle of liberty, equality, fraternity nevertheless undertipped the servants while abusing them as "lackeys."

Who doubts that he will soon be on his way to Berlin, most probably in a U-boat?

How pleasant it is to doze, almost in a coma from warmth and lassitude, while Gregory drones on such nonsense. The more serious reports he abstracts and concentrates, filing in separate piles for my later attention. I feel totally protected up in this badger sett, behind its two rows of walled barricades. Now even more so, when I have added a third. Except when being used by one of us answering a call of nature, the ladder is hidden with us and instructions are that *no one* is permitted to know we are there until we have heard their voices and identified them.

JULY 16   RAZLIV   1917

There are times when I wish the Anarchists would just get out of our way. Of course, they make a point of not joining anybody's side, even their own. But I would say in the historic task of creating the Russian Revolution they have been more often an obstacle than a help. Not a silent, immobile obstacle, like a rock in the stream you can learn to steer round, but one that moves at high speed, in every direction, bellowing at the top of its voice.

They have not been much use to us in the July Days. They started the whole thing off seeking revenge for the Villa Durnovo in collaboration with some of our Bolshevik soldiery still smarting from the failure to boost the June demonstrations into an insurrection. At that time, there was something of a split between our leadership and our rank and file, and Anarchist militancy seemed very attractive. The atmosphere was not helped by some of our orators who became tipsy on their own rhetoric, viz: Zinoviev who stirred up the Machine-Gun Regiments to oppose a transfer to the front with the slogan—"Now you have a choice of death in the trenches for interests that are not yours (*right*) or death on the barricades in your own cause (*wrong*)." We wanted to preserve them from the trenches. But, in July, all they would have got at the barricades would have been equally useless death. Street-battles are not an end in themselves, only a means to power. Unless they lead to power, they are as wasteful as the Charge of the Light Brigade.

The truth is that Anarchists are disturbed people, like overactive children who cannot sit still. They must be on the move, doing something, anything. What that is hardly matters. In the July Days, having lit the fuse, they were determined there should be a big bang. It could have worked, their attempt to kidnap Kerensky and take over power. But I could have forecast they'd miss him by being twenty minutes late. All they did was frighten a lot of people for a little while without achieving a single gain for the cause.

They are best restricted to talking. I must admit they are very good at that. Almost the only people whose speeches read as well as they sound. One of our undercover members in Voline's section has sent me a copy of an address he made illegally a week ago to a group of shipyard workers. It is so good I want to have it printed in one of our papers. I particularly like this bit:

In the name of the Revolution, the death penalty and military courts have been brought back into an army broken, tortured and exhausted after three years of war.

In the name of the Revolution, the vote of the Constituent Assembly will be removed from soldiers whom their officers suspect. In the name of the Revolution, the best revolutionaries, the heads of the revolutionary working class, are being arrested, while Gurko, Vyrubova and other tsarist servants and creatures of Rasputin are being released. In the name of the Revolution, the working-class newspapers, the working-class printing presses, lovingly built up by so many small subscriptions collected by the poor from the poor, are being closed down.

In the name of the Revolution, the calling of the Constituent Assembly is being postponed, and instead an assembly of dead souls has been summoned to Moscow, there to be revived by ministerial appeals for sacrifices.

In the name of the Revolution, the secret police have come to life again, the individual's liberties have been suppressed, and the old atrocities of the police chiefs will be started again.

In the name of the Revolution, the Imperial Laws have come back into force, and the gains of the great Russian Revolution are to be abolished.

In the name of the Revolution, the gates have been opened to the most hideous counterrevolution.

I wish I could train our agitators to spout impromptu like that— and every word true enough for me to stake my life on it.

JULY 18   RAZLIV   1917

Our host, clearly an underground plotter of some resource, has prepared a further retreat in advance. First, he had confided to his neighbors and his friends at the arsenal that later in the year he planned to keep a cow on the far side of the lake. Then, before our arrival, he knocked together a rough shack on the swampy meadows he leased there, explaining that it was to house seasonal farmhands who would cross over from Finland to cut and stack the long grass. We were to impersonate these laborers if we were spotted in this isolated spot—an unlikely happening, Nikolai assured us, since it was virtually unreachable, except by boat.

Around dusk this evening Nikolai's turnip-head and cutout teeth bobbed through the trapdoor.

"*Slava bogu!*" he cried, "It's hot up here, comrades. Sorry to say, though, it's going to get even hotter down below and outside. There have been rumors for ages that you are working in disguise in the rolling mills at Sestoretsk. It seems Kerensky has decided there may be something in it. He's sent a punitive detachment to surround the district and sweep it for you. The commander is Captain Gvozdev, a dangerous bugger, born and bred here. I remember him well. As a lad he was known as 'the British Breakfast,' because his ears were like two great slices of smoked pig, what d'y'call it? *Bacon!* Young Volodya says this afternoon he saw three armored cars, mounted with machine guns, by the village post office. And Dmitri reports sighting Cossacks beating across the brushwood on the hills through his field glasses. They've been asking the postmaster about who lives where, cross-checking names and addresses of wanted politicals. I'm probably all right. He and I have an arrangement going about getting stuff backward and forward over the frontier. But if they start a house-to-house search . . . we must get you into deep country tonight."

We left as soon as it was dark. Or as soon after dark as Gregory had been really well fed on at least a dozen *blinis* and sour cream by an indulgent Nadezhda. He insisted. He said we might never get to eat like humans again until we took power, and knowing my ascetic habits probably not even then. As we steadied the rocking rowboat, the three of us darkly hatted, caped and gloves, only Gregory's greasy chin glistened under a fitful moon. Nikolai paddled us over the pond, down the winding, keel-scraping stream and out into the expanse of Lake Razliv which seemed to curve round us like the bottom of a bowl.

"You see, the columnist of *Living Word* was right," hissed Gregory. "You are fleeing the law by water."

JULY 25   RAZLIV   1917

We are now fairly well established here. By day, I work, writing the most practical work of theory I have ever attempted, "State and Revolution." In moments of rest from this, I turn to pamphlets and letters. The place I have found I call my "green study." It is an open-air office where a fat tree stump makes a desk, at which I kneel or squat, and latticed branches overhead permit a cool, seabed light while keeping out the full glare of the sun. By night, things are not so good. It is hard to believe that only a week ago above the bustling kitchen-dormitory packed with Yemelyanov children, it was often—usually even—too hot to sleep at night or stop dozing by day. Here, as the sun goes down, the damp rolls in from the mist-striped lake, and chilly gases reach up from the marshy turf. When he called this straw igloo a shack—I have to say it—Nikolai was guilty of positively gutter-press exaggeration. Beside this scarecrow sentry-box, a hovel would stand out like the Winter Palace. It is hardly more than a beehive dome tacked on to a rectangle of thatch, about the size of a single bed, all supported by half a dozen wobbly poles. Instead of walls and floor, there are roughly packed bales of old grass which alternate bumps and chinks

in exactly the places you least want them. And the smell! Whoever
started the romantic nonsense about the scent of new-mown hay
never spent night after night basting and impregnating each inch
of flesh with it like a shoulder of lamb steeped in garlic.

Nikolai has provided us with a blanket worn almost to trans-
parency in spots. Every time we lie down, Gregory and I insist on
giving the other the largest share of whatever warmth it affords.
Each of us recites the praises of his own particular overcoat. G.'s
actor-manager style, silk-lined under heavy broadcloth, with an
astrakhan collar so deep and thick that sometimes when I watch
him staggering toward me, half-bent under its weight, I am reminded of some Israelite prophet carrying the fattest black sheep
of the flock uphill for sacrifice on the mountaintop. My own is less
showy but rather more geared to the needs of the rough-liver.

It is not the one I bought in Leather Lane, fortunately. It was,
much to my surprise, a present from Stalin. At first, I thought this
fufaika more suitable for Siberia—about as much shape as a blanket
roll, oiled waterproof cotton outside, heavy tweed inside, and stitched
all over into handkerchief-size squares stuffed with raw wool. Only
now do I realize that when darkness comes to the shores of Lake
Razliv, you *are* in Siberia.

This ritual over, we turn our backs and subside into sleep.
Later, like old married couples grown selfish and petty by the long
rubbings of domestic intimacy, we use the excuse of semi-con-
sciousness to start stealing the blanket back, tug by tug. Around 3
A.M., "the witching hour" (*Hamlet*)—but not because then grave-
yards yawn, rather because now secret police drag you from bed
—Gregory sits up and shouts: "Jehovah, Lord God of hosts, this
is a *tomb!*" Then we slide together, interleaving blanket, coats, arms
and legs, so close I feel his heart banging exactly in time against
mine. I never understood before that, however ill-matched their
pulses are separately, once any two people share the proximity of
the *letto matrimoniale* the ballads sing true—two hearts do beat as
one.

Gregory is the caricature prototype of twentieth-century man,
designed to fit as snugly in a city as a yolk in an egg. When he is
exposed to more than 10 percent of the sky, he grows panicky and
has to put on a homburg and lie down. "*La grande horizontale* of
Bolshevism" Trotsky called him. Only Zinoviev could have sworn,
sincerely and with a sob in his voice, as he did once during the
witch-hunt days of late '05—"I'd rather die on my sofa than live
on my knees!" Yet even he, as the venison bubbles in the black
bomb of a stewpot, a chill breeze warms itself and us fanning the

orange-tipped tinder to white gold, the first and last vodka of the day lights a flaming canal down to the pit of the stomach, and the black granite sky sparkles as if sugared, will murmur: "This is the life, Ilyich. *This is Russia!*"

Then we forget all the drawbacks—the most severe being the impossibility of lighting a fire inside our hay-filled shack, a pyre just waiting to be put to the torch. Instead we pretend it is all good for us. We both know that Nikolai would find us some thicker, heavier covering if we asked him. We also know that it would have to be taken from the beds of the children. He and Nadya already sleep uncovered on top of a stove in that overcrowded single room. We know we could have more appetizing food—the piece of meat arrives only once a week to flavor the potato and cabbage stew we keep going for the next seven days. The Yemelyanovs eat better than most of our working people. Something you often find in times of near-famine with those who live half-and-half on the fringe of town and country, getting the best of both. We are both aware that N. is a manual worker, his wife perhaps even more so, and that they must expend far more energy than a pair of middle-aged, sedentary intellectuals. As for the children, well, I have never met a boy who wasn't always hungry, even in a palace. Those *blinis* and sour cream wolfed by Gregory were a generous offering donated by all nine in the household to a Bolshevik hero. For them, a once-a-year treat. None of them, even the smallest, betrayed any hint that this might be a sacrifice. But I had kept note of the household patterns. And I doubt if their piece of meat appeared more than once a month.

We now have regular couriers in and out of Peter, notably the faithful, wily Shotman who will go twenty-five miles in the wrong direction on either side of Razliv to throw off shadows, aware that Kerensky's secret police are watching everyone who might lead to me. He brings news of offers of all kinds of furnishings, internal as well as external, for belly and back, not just from my Nadya and Gregory's Zina, but from masses of party workers and supporters, some of whom seem to suppose that we are literally underground, like foxes.

He also brings news of endless bread queues where the weaker often faint, lapse into a coma and die from starvation in the line while the stronger carry on for another three or four hours to find not even a crust left when they reach the window. He tells of thousands without enough clothes to come out decently into the streets, even in this torrid summer weather, leading to the frequent sight of sweating women wrapped in curtains, quilts and tablecloths, of men overcoated for winter above the knees though naked below and inside. Bare heads are invariable, bare feet common. Nobody goes down back alleys or dark streets anymore except in company. Even then, they can be surrounded and robbed *en masse* by larger groups who strip them entirely, not just of money, valuables, jewelry, but of each item of clothing, of every single thing—underwear, socks, spectacles, false teeth, toupees. It is like a capital city after some terrible plague, some nationwide earthquake. Mankind, a universal wolf, preys on itself.

This inferno of calamity is not produced by accident, nor is it beyond rational human control. It is a perfectly understandable result of the sharpening of the class war by the enemy. As the forces of Revolution gather, strengthen and concentrate, Marx warned us, so do those of reaction. The bourgeoisie have now spread wide the myth that in the July Days we Bolsheviks tried by violence to take over the government but were defeated by noble forces loyal to the authorities. These are now teaching the people the lesson to be drawn from this. Every attempt to introduce socialism is against nature, human and divine, and leads on to chaos, hunger, despair, death, disaster. They cry: *Si monumentum Leninum requiris, circumspice.*

AUGUST 9   UDELNAYA   1917

Around this midnight, I began to lose some trust in the conspiratorial talents of my colleagues. If this is the best they can do with such a simple task, I thought, then I do tremble for the success of the Revolution.

Admittedly, I had just waded across a stream which must have risen in the Arctic and was not on our planned route, soaking myself up to the armpits. Though excruciating at the time, bringing on head pains like stabbing ice splinters, this turned out to have one advantage. The oozing boots, the clinging trousers, the layers of damp between clothes and the skin, proved a useful protection against the next hazard, also not on the itinerary. Without such uniforms, I doubt whether any one of us could have survived crossing a burning wood, then field after field of smoldering peat. With each step, it was puffing out an acrid smoke which stretched ankle-deep for as far as the eye could see on a moonless night. Every now and then, our range of vision would increase for half a minute as a bush that had been invisibly roasting flared into a ferny fan of scarlet fishbones.

I knew our general eastern direction was right since I was the one taking bearings by the stars. Without a map, we could not be more precise. Yemelyanov had refused to bring, or even consult, one before we left, protesting like all these theoretical escapologists that he had been born and grown up here. And in this strange Dantesque landscape, I suppose even someone who lived on the exact spot might be forgiven for becoming disoriented. Nevertheless, I did not forgive him. I pursued him with criticisms, and occasional curses, so that his only respite came when the ground sloped and we all descended, step by step, into a stifling sea of fog which often closed over our heads.

I was glad I had not forgiven so easily when finally we emerged, just after midnight, dry again, smelling faintly kippered, into scrubland. For we lay on our bellies in silence, staring across an embankment at a huddle of ill-lit shacks, for so long that I feared Yemelyanov must have fallen asleep. "All right," I said testily. "Who's going ahead first?"

There was another, shorter silence. Then Yemelyanov whispered: "It's the wrong station. It's Dibuny. The most heavily guarded stop on the line."

I swore (quietly). Now tuned in, I realized I could see uniformed figures stamping about, craftily dragging on cigarettes held cupped in hands low down behind their backs—an infallible sign of worker origin. I could hear the clump of grounded rifles, the squeak of leather. The low mutter of the private soldiers contrasted with the loud tenor of the officers, some of whom could be seen moving across the orange screens of the windows, waving cigarettes in holders, raising shot glasses of vodka.

Somehow, I at least had to get to Udelnaya station and catch my train across the Finland frontier. Shotman and Eino Rajha, both Finnish citizens, had done so several times on foot recently. But their papers were rigorously checked, both ways, even the name and number sometimes being telegraphed to the nearest police post. Rajha is a railway foreman and instead has fixed for me to pass over as a locomotive fireman.

In situations like this, a group like ours has to operate as if it were a scouting party under military discipline. There was no way we could advance without risking losses. So I ordered Shotman and Yemelyanov to approach the one-man ticket office from different directions, and as strangers to each other, to test our chances of getting aboard the next Peter train without being detained.

Through my field glasses I watched first one, then the other as they came into view of the guards. Both were challenged, halted, told to approach the platform and then put under arrest. With the help of a close-up of lip movements, and words which floated to us on the breeze, I was able to follow their interrogation.

Shotman, known as "the comrade from Monte Cristo" because of his many escapes from impossible traps, was released in minutes. His papers were in perfect order, indeed almost completely genuine, and covered with so many stamps and overprints from previous examinations that it would be a brave official who challenged them now. He also offered a cover story which was 90 percent convincing. The occasional suspicious deviation only made it more like every genuine explanation for travel in wartime. Moving any distance across country was so difficult, boring, expensive and sometimes dangerous that anyone who had a legal reason understandably combined it with a few mildly illegal errands. What was even more important, Shotman had already searched himself so the "frisk" by two NCOs found nothing that did not fit with what he had claimed. As he saluted the officer in charge, the Peter train arrived and Shotman climbed aboard. Inside, I could see that he had moved to the far window and was determinedly peering through it, displaying no interest, let alone concern, about what might be happening on the station. What a "pro"!

Yemelyanov seemed purposely clumsy and provocative. He scowled at the officer, replied insultingly. he had not thought up a reasonable tale to explain why he was there—he said he owned a small farm not far off and had strolled across (at 1 A.M.?) for a drink at the café-bar. But his papers, also genuine, showed him to be a turner at the armaments factory at Sestoretsk. Two such occupations were not impossible (after all, Yemelyanov had hired a farm to give us deep underground shelter) but they were rare enough to induce further probing. Then a party card (!) was discovered in another name, giving the owner's job as fitter at the Putilov works in Peter. Nikolai said he had picked it up in Razliv! Yemelyanov was questioned about Sestoretsk but gave answers that were almost too convincing. He correctly named every foreman, offering to go back fifteen years through each's predecessors. Asked about the arsenal's doctor he volunteered that he was a "drunken, ill-trained oaf." "He's my uncle!" screamed the interrogator. Nikolai had established that he was a longtime resident. But was he a Bolshevik? What did he think of Kerensky? "Lenin seems a good sort," he replied. So he *was* a Bolshevik. "No, but I hear Lenin's a decent fellow."

As he repeated this, Gregory was groaning in fury and contempt, Eino was chuckling quietly, and I was thinking. The officer lost interest in playing detective. He stuck his revolver into Yemelyanov's belly, forcing him backward until he reached the door of the newly arrived express to the frontier. "If I thought you were one of Lenin's men I'd shoot you now. Get on and don't get off until you reach Finland."

As he spoke, the stopping train to Peter, with Shotman aboard, gradually pulled out of the station. Fortunately, Gregory, Eino and I were also on it, lying flat in the corridor.

It was when I had heard Nikolai Y. mention my name—a mistake even the most naïve Bolshevik was unlikely to make—that I understood what he was up to. He was compensating for having lost us our way by creating a distraction we could use to slip by. Sliding on our bellies across the open patches, scurrying from bush to bush, we had sneaked round to the back and hauled ourselves on board.

Out of sight of Dibuny, we got up, dusted ourselves down and took seats in a dark, third-class compartment. Not a moment too soon. A cheery face, a bespectacled plum pudding, peered round the door and shone a green lantern on us. The conductor turned out to be a friend of Rajha. Eino pumped him about the latest Peter gossip. Gregory slept. I hid my head in hands, pretending to do the same. "Lenin now, you know who I mean?" asked the conductor. "I'm told he's born a Finn like you and me. They also say he's carrying two and a half million rubles."

"What's it for? Where did he get it?"

"That's what I ask everybody, where from, for what?"

From Udelnaya, almost on the outskirts of Peter, Eino guided us to the small, bare flat of another Finnish party member, Emil Kalske. (Before we left the station, I had a search made for Alexei S., whom we had not dared contact on the train, but he was nowhere to be found.) Eino's wife, Lidia Parvianen, slim and blond as a water-sprite, was already at the flat with Emil's wife, Etta.

Lidia is used to admiration, from men and women. She automatically takes the initiative wherever she is. Though a visitor, she already had the samovar steaming and a stew bubbling over a tiny oil heater. As Gregory, her husband and I tucked in, Etta, dark and rotund as a harbor buoy, rolled about shyly in the background. It was only when Lidia and Eino were leaving in the early hours, and Gregory and I were wrapping ourselves in old newspapers on the floor (there was only one bed, itself little more than a double blanket) that Etta brought herself to speak—and then

only into Lidia's ear. It was a question for me and I was almost
asleep before she was persuaded to ask it. "Tell me, Comrade
Lenin, they say, though I don't believe them, but they say and I'd
like to know, is it true that when you, the leader, stay in any Party
house, before you leave, well—you always wash the dishes?" I could
hardly credit such a query. "Naturally," I said. "Of course I wash
up. I often sweep the floor. Don't all men? I mean, all Bolshevik
men? How often have I said that in bourgeois marriage, women
are the proletariat. How could I fight exploitation outside the home
if I did not oppose it in my own and others?" I looked up and I
saw only a ring of laughing faces. It seemed what I'd said was a
tremendous joke. Only Etta looked down with an expression of
pure adoration such I had only ever seen in one other's eyes. . . .
As I sank into great, sweet, devouring waves of sleep, I thought
of Mother.

AUGUST 10   YALKALA   1917

I had gone to sleep in the early hours of yesterday on someone's
floor along with Zinoviev, a couple of badly wrapped parcels in an
awful draft. I was just trying to remember our host's name, yet
another of these wonderful Finns—Kalske, was it? Emil Kalske—
when I was distracted by a rather more threatening conundrum.
Was that someone bending over Gregory and was he carrying a
weapon, a truncheon or the like, in his hand?

"Don't move. I have a gun," I hissed.

"Ilyich? Is it you?"

And the figure struck an old-fashioned tinder box, a spray of
sparks followed by a smoky light, haloing Alexei Shotman. I handed
him a candle, illuminating a dreadful carpetless, almost furni-
tureless kitchen-bedroom, where Gregory snored on among his
wrappings, and Mrs. Kalske (Etta?) breathed, shallow as a cat, in
her corner.

"I couldn't think who you two could be," explained Alexei. "I
never carry arms so I picked the best to hand, the housewife's
saber, the rolling pin. I never saw you on the train."

"We couldn't find you, off the train, at Udelnaya," I replied.

"No, don't tell me. Of course. Your perfectionism in clandestine
operation. That's why you are still alive. And, I don't forget, also
why many of us are. It was not necessary for you to come to our

station. So, as a precaution, you jumped off in the dark, eh? Six miles up the track? And you've walked it here?"

"Four miles. Sorry about Yemelyanov. No map and no timetable. Still, he did give you cover. These country conspirators! I have to depend a lot on them. I wish they'd be less brave and more cunning. I'll be on your next train too, but out of your sight till we're safely there. Then I'm pushing on to Helsinki to fix you another burrow. You won't believe this one—it's the flat of the police chief!"

But I was already sinking once more. Shotman pursed his lips and the light vanished. His yellow, varnished face, a Rembrandt, melted into that of the woman on the thin mat, then Mother, then a pale mask. Was it laughing too? The window was hardening into light when I opened my eyes again. Another strange head, so near as to be out of focus, was hovering.

"Kalske, Emil. Bolshevik. At the Aivaz plant. Didn't mean to disturb you. But Eino was just now telling me who my guests were. I couldn't believe it. Zinoviev. And Lenin. I'd never have recognized you." I was awake now. There was a lot to do. I must finish the pamphlet, "On Slogans," but the poor devil has not got so much as a decent table and chair. Well, I'll write on the floor, I thought.

"I'm glad our disguises work, comrade Emil. What would you say we look like, now? Don't try to be flattering. It's important to get these things right." I sat up and adjusted the wig unobtrusively.

Kalske considered. "Well, Gregory Ivanovich here. It's as if his head is upside down. His mop of hair has gone. Instead he's got curls on his chin and his cheeks. And a moustache like a hayrake. His face seems much, much broader. He could be a Mohammedan trader up from the south. And you, old 'un. Well, much younger for one thing. Not so much the professor type now you're clean-shaven. And the hair on your head—who knows it's a wig? A very healthy tan. Not a professional but a skilled working chap, probably a Finn. Not hungry looking, more friendly if you understand me."

We stayed in all yesterday, writing, talking, meeting messengers from Peter. Early this morning I gave Gregory, as the English say, "friendly-shake-hands" since he was staying with the Kalskes and I was moving on.

Soon once more I was at Udelnaya, freshly shaved and with a new blond wig, instructed to look out for suburban express no. 71. When I found it, I was to check that the loco was no. 293 and climb aboard the cab without hesitation, saying: "Sorry I'm late but the cat died."

When the 71 rolled to a stop, I saw out the corner of my eye Shotman taking a seat at the back next to the guard's van and Rajha taking his at the front next to the engine's tender. I walked on and, as instructed, swung aboard into the roasting oven of the driver's cab. There were two men there, which I did not expect. Both had similar open, knobbly, wind-beaten faces. Both were wearing identical blue overalls, scorched white in places and with occasional burn holes, but newly laundered. Which would be my contact, the driver Hugo Yalava?

"I'm sorry I'm late," I said to the one on the right.

"That's all right. We've got a five-minute stop here. What can we do to help?"

I turned to the other, wishing passwords were a little more conversational. "The cat died."

The second railwayman laughed. "Sounds silly, doesn't it? But I asked my old mate, Eino, to get you to say that so there would be no confusion. I'm sure our manager wouldn't mind. But your idea *is* a bit unusual and it *is* wartime. I didn't want you having to explain it to the wrong driver." He turned to his companion. "Mr. Ivanov is a writer for Gorky's paper. Wants to do a piece describing how it is being a fireman on a train. I knew you wouldn't mind lending him your overalls. You can spend the journey like a gent, smoking your pipe, with your bum on a nice soft seat."

The real fireman stripped off speedily, as if afraid I'd change my mind, jumped down and left me with Yalava.

"There's nothing to it," he said. "Except that it never stops. Since they gave up on the coal, we've had to use wood, and the bloody engine eats it a log a second from start to finish. Hope you're fit, comrade."

I was. But only just. By the time we neared Byelo-Ostrov, I was vibrating in muscles I didn't know I had, and I felt as if I had been under a shower of warm sweat. Less than six months ago, though it seems like years, as I pointed out to Yalava, I had been welcomed here by members of the party CenCom and hoisted on the shoulders of the armament workers. Somebody might remember me. Anyway, my papers as Ivanov, though superficially convincing, would not stand up to expert examination.

"Don't worry. There's never any fuss over railwaymen. If it looks as if there might be, trust me. I've got a trick or two up my sleeve. Do you know Yemelyanov? The two of us have been getting stuff backward and forward across here since '07."

At Byelo-Ostrov, it did seem as if there might be a fuss over everybody. The platform was lined with militiamen with that look in their eyes I have grown to beware. It means they've been told there'a a creature on the run nearby and they're all hot and slavering to hunt it down. Most of the pairs of eyes slipped over us as if we were bits of machinery. But when the train stopped, a couple of particularly dedicated types ignored the passengers and came strolling toward us. Police hate hurrying, or moving even. Most of them join to avoid manual labor. Their ideal state would be where they sat at a desk and suspects were brought before them, on their knees, hands tied.

They left it just a bit late in their lordly amble. I smudged my face with soot and tried to look simple-minded when the first demanded of me, in Russian—"Your papers."

Hugo did not stop uncoupling the engine but spoke to the other. "My friend speak only Finnish. Me very good Russian. Must go get water. If no water, train not go. Back five minutes." He held up three fingers and with a touch on a lever steamed gently away across slippery sprays of rails to a distant tank with a dangling funnel.

"Their boots are too nicely polished to follow us," he said and spat.

It was a good while before he finished filling up, decanting to the last exact drop like a barman in a Paris hotel.

"How long have we been?" he asked. I made a guess but my guesses are always fairly accurate.

"Nineteen minutes."

"Good. We have a twenty-minute wait."

Looking over his shoulder, teasing the lever with one hand, Hugo brought us back into dock with only the faintest of bumps. The two militiamen were still there but he delayed them again with a smile and a raised hand, leaning over to reconnect the tender. The first bell sounded.

"Now. Papers?" he asked.

But before they could reply, the stationmaster was between them and us pointing to the station clock and shouting: "Get a move on. You Finns are all slow as Tatars." The second bell.

Behind them, a general was leaning out of the window of a carriage full of ladies with flowery hats. "Officer! If you delay this train without a reason that could survive a court-martial, you'll be sorry you ever wore uniform!" The third, final bell. Yalava shrugged. "Always the way," he said and opened up the throttle.

Into Finland, by a few miles anyway, we left the train at Terioki. After returning the stoker his working clothes—he looked a little mystified at this behavior by a metropolitan journalist he assumed was carrying on to Helsinki and back—I joined Eino on horseback. We felt safe enough for the moment in Social-Democrat Finland, which had freed itself almost as much from the Provisional government as from the Tsar after the February Revolution. We could wave off Shotman and openly gallop away into the woods. I had not ridden since boyhood. To begin with it felt as if someone were standing under the saddle and continually kicking my backside. I then remembered that this was the way the *mujhik* traveled on a horse, like a sack carried by two old men. They even prefer a slow, nonstopping nag, with a back sagging like an old double bed, because it carried them farther, slower. We had been taught the English style, where you rise in rhythm with the beast. Soon I raced along as if in their Grand National Derby.

After a while, I thought to ask our destination.

"Yalkala!" Eino shouted, leaning low on his horse's neck. "To my in-laws. About nine miles."

The house of the Parvianens (Lidia's father and mother) is facing away on the edge of the village, a little back from the road. (Amazing how fashionable this ground plan is among our older party members!) Whatever plasm it is that carries hair color in families seems to favor blond, at least in this bit of Finland. Eino is mousy anywhere but Lidia glows like a lighthouse in Russia. Here, she might be less conspicuous since her father, Pyotr, and mother, Anna, are both white-helmeted, not to mention Lidia's horde of bleached brothers and sisters.

The older pair wanted to vacate half the house, turn that over to me, evidently envisaging a suite of offices and a private domain from which, like some Yankee millionaire, I will run my empire of revolutionaries.

Eventually, I convince them that neither imperial isolation nor total submersion in the rough-and-tumble of family life is what I need. Instead, my ideal is always a tiny combined sleeping-working space, like a first-class wagon-lit, separate from everyone but next door. Once sure I mean this, they turn the provision for me of the refurbished outhouse into a family project. I am forced to overcome what I see is sometimes a rather ridiculous puritanic inability to do nothing while others work. ("It's vot ve call vanity," Radek once instructed me, putting on his Viennese mind-doctor voice. "You zink only you can do anyzing right. You zink the rest of uss vill only make ze messes. In other vorts, you zink you're Gott. I zink, perhaps, cocaine twice a day and un operation on your nose should cure zis delusion. If, zat iss, it *iss* a delusion.")

I sit under a tree in silvery sunlight and read the world's newspapers newly delivered, via the Terioki stationmaster, from Helsinki and Stockholm. They are days old, of course, but they would be not be much newer in Peter. Meanwhile, the family labor gang scrub the floor, move in a desk and a bed, vases of flowers, a samovar and bright, zigzaggy curtains. I hate curtains and always take them down. Here I will have to make an exception. For the first day or two.

I can feel myself relaxing, unfolding, actually growing, like those Japanese pods that dropped into water expand into bouquets. There have not been all that many such spells in my forty-seven years of life—Kokhushkino, Shushenkoye, Capri, Archachon, the Swiss Alps, B.B.'s *dacha* at Neivola, now Yalkala. Come to think of it, not a bad list. I mustn't complain. Only one setback of a kind. I must work harder on my disguise.

When Eino introduced me as the writer Konstantin Petrovich Ivanov, old Pyotr Parvianen, his father-in-law, blew out such a gust of laughter between the gaps of his horse-teeth I thought he was going to choke.

"Sorry, *starik*," he gasped. "But I was at the Finland station the third of April. I cannot forget the features of our dear leader!" and he clasped me in a wrestler's hug and danced me round the yard with the family stamping and waving, some all smiles, some in tears. How *Latin* they can be, these Finns.

AUGUST 17   YALKALA   1917

Typical day of the last week.

Wake at dawn. Make glass of tea, go out on first-light hunt for mushrooms and other *cepes*, many will melt away as sun warms up. Make twig basket (easier than it sounds but impressive), fill with harvest, leave in shade by P.'s back door.

Work until noon, totally undisturbed, writing "State and Revolution," various pamphlets, coded letters to Nadya, some for her and Men of Confidence, others for all CenCom.

Noon. Arrival Russian papers. Read, mark, if necessary cut, file, in seat under tree. Glass of milk. Salad.

1 P.M. Expedition with children (already have made own map radius five miles) for bilberries, sour plums, other free provender. Climb trees for birds' nests. Track deer. Find lairs of foxes, pine-

martens, weasels. Or help Pyotr with mowing, plowing, hedging. Either way, end up Lake Kafi. Rowing, fishing. Then long, serious swim. Indulge myself, noting even older boys, twenty and eighteen, cannot keep up over distance, though speedier in short sprint.

3 P.M. Back outhouse, short siesta. Work three/four hours.

6/7 P.M. Main meal of day. Home-made bread, cheese, yogurt; mushrooms in batter; grilled lake fish; fruit compote with sour cream; blinis with lemon.

7/8 P.M. Work until midnight, often later.

I've never been a great food-fusser—it takes too much time. If I were going to really care about eating, I'd have to study it, test it, experiment with it, become a world's expert. It's so hard to do one thing well in this short life and for me that's being a revolutionary. But if I were to choose, so far, the best thing I've tasted I think I'd name Karelian pie—or rather, to be correct, Anna Mikhailovna's Karelian pie.

What is in it? Well, even I, who believe that everything can be analyzed—even a joke, which may be why some say I have no sense of humor—hesitate before profaning the mystery of a great pie. As soon demand the formula for a perfect sunset! It must mean something other than the usual ingredients because you can also ask—what *isn't* in it?

Certainly it contains almost every item I list above for our normal supper—cheese pastry, with herbs, made from potato flour; a creamy mushroomy, lemony sauce; a filling of every kind of local fish, in firm but juicy pieces, filleted and marinated . . . plus? Now, no one has told me this, or even hinted it, and I would not dream of hurting anyone's feelings by asking. (My triumph of diplomacy so far has been getting rid of those damned curtains without upsetting anybody.) But there must be other ingredients. Could they be amphibious—newts, frogs, toads, water snakes? Or gastropodic—snails, slugs, leeches? Vermiform—slow worms, true snakes? Or flying creatures—not just all kinds of birds, but possibly bats, large moths and butterflies? Does that sound physically repellent?

Yet *Homo sapiens* perhaps became *sapiensissimus* through being able to be omnivorous. He (she) could eat almost anything, so they survived when more specialized, daintier consumers disappeared. I do know this family collect peculiar creatures on our morning expeditions, though I instruct them, and they agree, it is cruel and perverse to kill what does not threaten you and you cannot, or do not, eat.

So is that partly the secret of the Karelian pie? I have spent long periods in false positions, in strange company, in tense situations, where the wrong word, the wrong *stress,* could be fatal, so I have developed some educated intuitions. The Parvianen family were strangely delighted when I became so uncharacteristically for me fixed on one dish. Usually, they ate it only on Saturday night, the night I arrived. Two evenings later, I pretended to be vague about the day of the week (though I was reading nine or ten daily papers each noon). "Wouldn't you say it is Saturday today, Anna Mikhailovna?" I asked.

She gave an odd smile. "Whenever you say, Ilyich." From then on, there was always Karelian pie.

Eino is here this afternoon. He advises I should move along to Shotman's next newly prepared stop because communications with Peter will be so much easier and quicker in mainline Helsinki, despite the extra distance, than here on the frontier a good gallop from a neglected minor station.

I take the point. It is the advice I would give to any clandestine party member on the run—keep changing your safe house; stay near to good communications; lose yourself in large crowds. Though I have relived some of my country childhood here in Yalkala, I realize that every day I stay multiplies the chance of damaging those protecting me.

"When the great moment comes," I asked. "Promise. You will send me a Karelian pie." We said good-byes as if I were the eldest son being dragged off in chains. It was the deepest I had ever been enfolded in another family.

Yet as Eino and I trotted the pine forests paths, I felt a kind of nursery blanket lifting from me. I was a big boy now. I had a job to do in the world—change it! My heart expanded like a bird. It was the first chapter of *The Three Musketeers.* I was on a sprightly black stallion, with a holstered carbine slapping by my knee. The adventure was just beginning.

AUGUST 20   **HELSINKI**   **1917**

Kustaa Rovio, Helsinki's commissioner of police, and my host, looks like a commissioner of police—pinky-white face covered with tiny, blond hairs; popeyes like champagne corks or organ stops outlined with kindly, crinkly marks as if many hands had screwed and unscrewed them; broad, tuba-style nostrils uptilted for easy inspection; a long, wavy mouth under a "soup-strainer" Clemenceau moustache; and a chin with a bullet-hole dimple. He reminds you of an anthropoid jungle animal in a children's book.

In other words, he looks not at all like a *real* police commissioner, but one conjured up in adventure tales, by backwoods aunties or essays by timid columnists in literary weeklies. Which is interesting since, in a way, he is *not* a real police commissioner. He is a member of the Social Democratic Party, joined in '05, a fitter and turner by trade, trained at the Aivaz factory in Peter. Yet, in another, he is as real as any police commissioner ever was. After the uprising in Finland that followed the February Revolution in Russia, the workers' Soviet elected Rovio head of the people's militia for the capital. It was a powerful, but somewhat informal post. Then, in April, the governor general and the Senate nominated, and with all due legal process appointed, him also deputy assistant to the police commissioner, Lieutenant von Schraeder. Poor old von S., as the class struggles sharpened, found himself not only daily abused by the right-wing press and politicians as the figurehead for a band of red hooligans (i.e., largely Social-Democrat militia) but also distrusted by the workers and their press as a puppet of reaction. "Also they didn't like obeying orders signed 'von Schraeder,' " laughed Rovio. "So he resigned and I got his title as well. Now I really do run the police in this city."

Kustaa is too cheerful, good-hearted, jolly a figure—especially sharing a single room, with mattresses under the tables, and only a kitchen next door. I must have told the story of my journey down from Terioki three or four times and he still laughs till he cries. "You see, a policeman, there is no one I can tell it to, even using false names," he complains. "Begin with the bit where you hang 'Out of Order' on the railway station urinal . . ."

I tell it again and again. I begin to think this is some awful punishment from which only arrest and execution will save me.

He is a policeman. He must know when there is an empty flat that I could occupy for a few weeks, or a month.

"What's the matter, Ilyich? Can't you stand me at close quarters?"

"Almost nobody, and not you, Kustaa. If I don't get somewhere I can be in solitary confinement I'll give myself up, and force you to give me a private cell in one of your lovely progressive Finnish jails."

Kustaa roars with laughter. "What a sense of humor. Say all that again. I'll need to remember it in time to come."

AUGUST 22   HELSINKI   1917

My first letter from here is not political. It is to Nadya, inviting her to come and stay with me here. Well, not exactly *here*, Flat no. 22, Hagnes Square. It is ideal for me when I am entirely on my own, which I often am since a police chief is out all day, and most of the night and this one's wife is away in the country for the summer. When Kustaa does get home, he hardly notices what the place is like except to joke about it.

"These flats," he says. "These flats. If two people of the opposite sex come inside the front door, we have to register them as married. If another person squeezes in, all three are automatically prosecuted for adultery."

However, he does see we can't very well put up Nadya as well. He is going to look for somewhere more *gemütlich*, for her visit at least.

Originally, Kustaa was worried about me starving to death up here on the eleventh floor. Like most Nordics, he is a hearty trencherman (his mouth actually watered when I told him about the Karelian pies) and all the Finns have fed incomparably better than the ordinary Russian throughout this war. He wanted to bring, or send up, a meal on a tray from the police canteen, three times a day! As if it were not risky enough to have specially chosen policemen as my postmen. If I were to allow any officer on duty (which is what would happen) to act as waiter to a supposedly empty flat . . . at best, their chief would be suspected of keeping a mistress! Kustaa has not really got the instincts of a true sleuth. As they used to say on the Volga, "A good hunter never gets caught!" I am a good hunter.

I have asked Kustaa to bring home extra food only after his day's work—bread, butter, tea, eggs. While the samovar boils for my jug of tea, I bake eggs on the lid—my one meal of the day. Bread and butter, when I pause for thought. I eat very little bread and butter!

A good rhythm of input and output has been set up. One or other of Eino's railway friends on the early morning train from Peter brings in a packet of newspapers and publicly printed matter, hidden among them letters and documents from the Party. One or other of Kustaa's police friends collects these and delivers them to me. The procedure operates, in reverse, at night when my replies, my articles and my queries are put on the late-night train back to Peter. All transactions are carried out in the open, without subterfuge, as if they were casual chores which had been going on for years. No one appears to have taken any particular notice. So I am assuming the CenCom and I now have a secure chain of communication.

AUGUST 25   HELSINKI   1917

I've done very little work at my new lodgings, 64 Fredrikenkat, though I've kept abreast by writing all through last night. I'm sitting here midafternoon at ground level in a self-contained summer-flat, large sitting room, large bedroom, glass-roofed, open-walled kitchen looking out on a high-walled secret garden. I'd chosen it from Kustaa's list of empty properties kept by the Special Branch, only to find out that the owner is a retired teacher, lapsed Party member, only too pleased to give such sedentary aid to our struggle. Teacher Usenius burbled on, recalling various episodes of '05—the last time he took an active interest in politics. Still, he has left me alone. More than I can get most of our helpers and hiders to do. He hasn't asked me whether I do the washing up!

To pass the time, I do the washing up—one tea glass and one coffee cup—then make myself another jug of tea and another flask of coffee.

The truth is this place overwhelms me rather. I find I miss the box walls I can almost touch with my fingertips standing in the center. Did I always dislike space? Does my affection for going to earth perhaps result from nearly thirty years of prison, of Siberia, of exile, of police cells adapted to become intellectual gymnasia, of round trips from bed-sitting room to library desk and back, that reproduce a convict's routine? Have I, as Pavlov would say, *conditioned* myself? Or was I always drawn to that dark box with the pinhole of light, the *camera obscura* inside which I could isolate and analyze key images picked out from history's passing picture-show? Though at Kustaa's I was a square post in a square hole, this did not stop me seeing that these pinnacles for solitary termites could easily become machines designed eventually to drive everyone in the hive to madness. I never went out, and every hour was filled, as here. Yet there I feared sometimes that the great rectangle of honeycombed façades was reverberating with unheard cries from torture chambers—the beaten wife, the abused child, the hanged man, the chained couple, the bedridden youth. I had no direct evidence of their existence, for I had never seen another tenant. But that was all the more incitement to fantasy. Certainly, these are no places, these Italianate tomb-walls, for our new socialist humanity in the world after the Revolution. *We must remember these things!* (Write it down.) Stop worrying about Nadya!

Usenius's townhouse, which obscures his rented summer-flat from almost every angle, is the address I gave Nadya, five days ago, in a letter already acknowledged. She was supposed to arrive on a soldiers' train around noon today and follow the route on my map to the front door, about ten minutes' walk. She's four hours late. I'm not really worried. No more than most husbands rendezvousing in a foreign city with their wives. But most husbands would have been able to meet them at the station with a cab. Most husbands would understand that if anything happened to their wives, it would be an accident, random, unforeseeable, with all the odds against it.

I have to consider that my wife's name, likeness, address, habits, tastes, relatives, friends, colleagues, likely places to be, are all detailed in files, held by many not very pleasant agencies. Unlike other people's wives, she is better off the fewer people there are who know where she is. She is probably safest when she is lost. That will not be easy. There are those looking for her, as a matter of urgency, all day and every day, at her *terminus a quo*, Peter's Finland station, and her *terminus ad quem*, Central station, Helsinki. There will be watchers on all the trains. If she is recognized, her fate could be multifarious, each bad for her, or for me, or for the Party, or for all of us. She could be officially arrested, held without charge, until the time was suitable for a trial. She could be unofficially detained, in secret, never charged or tried, but tortured for intelligence about me and the CenCom. She could be disappeared, vanishing without trace, to dispirit and undermine all the left.

I decided to put the best face on it. She was just lost. And so she was. I found her, she me, only an hour ago, at 4:52 P.M. In heating my letter to bring out the secret writing, she got the whole of my message but failed to notice until too late that she had burned the edges of the map. It had crumbled away what turned out to be about 100 yards from this house. While I sat here, she had been painstakingly exploring every possible exit off the page, almost within my sight. In the end, she had to ask a passerby using the only clue she could recall, the only clue I included, that my landlord was a retired teacher. He immediately replied—"What, that old Red? You're standing at his door." And so she rang.

AUGUST 26   HELSINKI   1917

Pictures of Peter under growing counterrevolution. Nadya reports that Kerensky's idea of restoring discipline in the army is to punish everyone who took any active part on the Bolshevik side during the July Days. He singled out the Machine-Gun Regiment for public degradation. She watched as they were stripped of their arms and marched in uniforms without belts, buckles, metal shoulder flashes into St. Isaac's Square. Here they were forced to stand and hear themselves sprayed with saliva from the Supreme Commander in full rant. She says: "As they led their horses away by the bridle, so much hatred burned in the men's lowered eyes, so much resentment was expressed in their stiff, slow march, it was clear no more stupid method could have been devised. I'll bet *they* will be with us, to a man, when the moment comes!"

Another petty triumph. The bodies of the Cossacks killed by Gusev's massed riflemen at Liteiny bridge were buried on the Field of Mars with full military and state honors. The arch over their graves awards the status of "revolutionary martyrs," saints of the New Russia, fit comrades for those heroes already lying there who died overthrowing the Tsar! Meanwhile, the bodies of our people, including those of noncombatant women and children, have been refused permission for any but the most perfunctory funerals. Gatherings of more than twenty at the graveside are illegal. Excess mourners have been pursued around cemeteries by cavalry with whips. This too will not be forgotten or forgiven.

Kerensky has hit on a new (possibly unique) device for protecting his precious person, and his suite in the Winter Palace. (He sleeps there in the Tsar's bed, sings snatches of opera to himself during his toilette, dresses in front of a full-length gold mirror.) Other autocrats have recruited Cossacks, Swiss Guards, Tatars on horseback (the "Savage" division), elder sons of princes, pardoned murderers, German butchers (literally) and so on. He has stationed in the Winter Palace the women combat soldiers known as "the Death Battalions." They have all publicly sworn never to disband until Germany is defeated. They are pledged to stand and defend the government (i.e., Kerensky) on whatever spot they are positioned, dying there rather than retreat an inch. Nadya thinks the idea is that even our crude, unromantic, hooligans of the Bolshevik assault squads might waver for a moment, and drop their sights, faced by these militant angels, these Joans of Arc, these virgins in arms. Long enough, anyway, to allow the Junker-cadets behind them to aim their machine guns. None of the battalions has ever been sent to the front and apparently none is now intended to operate anywhere except in Peter.

Told her Kerensky had no hope. I would personally instruct our forces that once an encounter had started no quarter was to be given on grounds of sex, age, nationality, friendship, even blood relationship, to an armed opponent. A basic rule of combat—what you are silencing is not a person but a weapon. If any of our tenderhearted need extra argument, let them remember that these Women's Battalions are shooting at you. Again and again and again, our opponents have not hesitated to gun down, bayonet and saber on the ground, leave mutilated and dying *our* women, unarmed, unprotected, untrained, innocent and peaceful. Remember the July Days!

N. laughed, and said, "Sorry, Volodya. I know it's not funny. But you should have seen them as I did. Being sworn in, being issued with uniforms, marched in one gate of the barracks as civilians, half an hour later marched out of the other as soldiers."

"They're young, mostly. A few professional spinsters. A few inverts. A lot of upper-middle-class failures, or black sheep, or misfits, or perhaps, to do them justice, girls who've never been given a chance to prove themselves.

"Once they had their hair cut, heads practically shaven, been put in trousers and long greatcoats, lined up in their hundreds, well, I couldn't tell them from the cadets.

"I said so to Alexandra (Kollontai) who was with me. She was indignant. I thought it was because she is such a militant feminist. But no. '*I* can tell the difference,' she boasted. 'The cadets are *much* prettier.' "

AUGUST 27   HELSINKI   1917

Nadya's stay has supplied a wonderful glow of warmth for an existence which is otherwise that of an intelligent machine, cold, measured, unchanging. It is like coming across a snowbound cabin in the Alps and finding that someone has left a stove burning low for the next visitor—that used to happen to us on our Swiss outings.

But Nadya has also set my mind whirring off in many new

directions. I have always seen politics clearer from afar. By questioning her, hour after hour, about Peter, little things as well as big ones, intuitions as well as facts, I have been forced to question myself. Marxism supplies us with an outline map of tomorrow. The direction of socialism, like the north, is clearly marked. But there may be, will be, many flooded rivers, many ravines, many mountain ranges, across our path that have not yet been sketched in. And new obstacles demand new routes, new techniques. I must not be afraid of original speculation so long as it can be tested against reality and found to fit.

So I have been focusing my mind into a burning beam to clear away the camouflage and discover what "counterrevolution" actually is. At first glance, this might seem the wrong way round—counterrevolution *before* revolution? Let's get power, comrade, *then* worry about how we may lose it. But, no. Not here in Russia, at least, at this moment. We have been misled by the name we gave it ourselves, *counter*revolution. It turns out on examination to be an entity in itself. Perhaps the mutation of capitalist class rule best designed to perpetuate its tyranny most effectively in the twentieth century. Just as, in the economy, competition is giving way to monopoly, protectionism to imperialism, so in the socio-political area, democracy in the old parliamentary sense will give way to the popular dictator, with his iron control of what is printed in the press, taught in schools and colleges, with mass unemployment tempered by careers in his private army, militarized labor on state projects that coin profit for private enterprise.

It is not quite clear under my lens yet. I'd understand it better—strangely enough—if I could give it a name. If anti-Semitism is the Bolshevism of fools, as Bebel said, this could be the socialism of the rich. Create an all-powerful state (but don't touch the Stock Exchange!). Let it get fat on the sweat of the workers, urged on by hunger and truncheons, then cream the profit off into your own corporations. Everybody is equal—at the bottom. To cover this crime, distract the populace with Roman shows and triumphs, constant infusions of jingoism, racism, rhetoric and lies, unity of all classes and creeds against the enemy without and the enemy within. An asylum with the most spectacular madmen in control of the drugged and cowed mass of inmates for the final benefit of the shareholders who live outside the walls. What a vision of purgatory! This may be what we must prevent getting ahead of us over the rest of the century. We on the left have spent too much time, *are doing so now,* fighting the enemies of the past. The Tsar has gone, never to return. His replacements will be republicans of humble origin. Well, I can already see *them*. Kornilov and Kerensky for a start.

Counterrevolution counts on succeeding just because the Revolution has *not* yet succeeded. Its appeal is that it will be everything the Revolution will not be. Its propagandists have a relatively easy task. Tell us what you hate and we will show it you, in the plans of the Reds. Tell us what you hate and we will promise to kill it or cure it. Workers who won't work? Soldiers who won't fight? Jews?—all the Reds are Jews! Non-Russians, Kalmuks, Tatars, Asiatics?—look at Lenin's eyes! Relics of tsarism? We'll sweep away all restrictions on free enterprise, property development, extension of modern technology to the land! *Enrichissez-vous encore, bis!*

Both Kerensky and Kornilov now peddle this line, or have it propagated in their name. Our defeat, as they see it, in the July Days whets their appetite. Already, the death penalty for disobedience has been revived in the front line. Kornilov wants it behind the lines, among the support troops, in the barracks of Petersburg. He wants all workers disarmed, all trade unions forbidden to strike, in the national interest. His opinions are passed on by industrialists, newspaper editors, politicians. Everybody knows what his opinions are, but he can always deny them if they are inconvenient for the moment. When he visited Peter, a couple of week ago, he was reportedly disgusted by the shambles of the Kerensky administration, a six-man Kerensky-appointed Directorate (shades of post-Robespierre/pre-Napoleonic France!) under Kerensky. Asked what should be done, he replied—"Hang Lenin and disperse the Soviet with a whiff of grapeshot!" We can hardly expect a clearer warning than that.

Kerensky, of course, dare not go so far. Hang Lenin—after due trial. *Re-organize* the Soviet. He has appointed Kornilov Supreme Commander, retaining himself as *Supreme* Supreme Commander. Two days ago he staged his Moscow State Conference—Moscow because it's supposedly less unruly and Bolshy than Peter. In fact, there are signs—last week's evacuation of "Red Riga," handing it over to the Germans, opening the road to the capital —that both Kerensky and Kornilov want Petersburg, and its Soviet, and its Bolsheviks (accidentally) destroyed in Ludendorff's next advance.

Moscow was rather a sickening farce. Out of 2,500 delegates in the Bolshoi, a huge reactionary majority, with only about 500 from the soldiers and the soviets. We refused to attend. My decision, reluctantly backed by our CenCom, to call the Muscovite workers out on strike was a triumph beyond even my dreams:

400,000 people refused to service the conventioneers—so no droshkies, no shops, no restaurants, no help in hotels! They had to wash up and polish their own shoes.

The squat, crude, rather Kalmuk-looking general declared he did not give a damn for government or Soviet but obeyed only his "own conscience and the will of the nation." He can pass as a son of the people, born of poor peasants, risen from the ranks, prisoner of war but maker of a daring escape, enemy of the Tsar, wanting nothing but peace on the home front and victory in battle. He made a detour to kiss the icon of the Iberian Virgin, traditionally the ritual of Tsars before their coronation. I think he was best summed up, by a fellow general, as "a simple fellow with the heart of a lion and the brains of a sheep."

Three-quarters of the State Conference would have cheered him whatever he said. It was noticed that all the soldiers, many just back from action, sat stolidly on their hands. Kerensky took a seat on stage exactly in the middle, though the "right" had long overflowed onto the "left" seats. The proportion, my agent reports, of stuffed shirts in frockcoats to unshaven faces in dirty shirts was about three to one.

Kerensky can also be presented as a sometime Tribune of the People. ("How glad I am not to have to use the word 'socialism' anymore!" he told an informant, when he had finally eased, first, the Kadets, then the SRs and Meks, out of his Cabinet.) Middle-class background, born Simbirsk, trained as lawyer—his c.v. always irritates me. I can't help seeing him as a distorted mirror-image, a black-sheep cousin. He had been eloquent in the cause of the families of the Lena goldfield miners, three hundred of whom were shot down while on strike, and they won impressive compensation. It was a case difficult to resist—the camp in the recesses of Siberia was run like some slave resort of Caligula or Nero. The workers were paid little, and had to spend that at the company store. Any protesters were not sacked—they were arrested, tortured, sometimes killed. Their employers were their rulers. No workers had any rights. Their wives and daughters had no alternative but to serve the managers and visiting shareholders as waitresses at table and as whores in bed. But then Kerensky is everybody's tribune-for-hire. He and Kornilov are parading, like those naked women on the catwalk at Folies Bergère, for the applause of their future patrons. Big business, international finance, the rising native bourgeoisie, the backers in England and France, do not care much which mask is most useful to cover their seizure of Russia. Kornilov may have more partisans in foreign countries. Kerensky probably attracts still the larger section of publishers, professionals such as lawyers, doctors, architects. He is more handsome, cleverer, eloquent on any subject at the drop of a contribution to his fighting fund.

Which will win the backing of the counterrevolution? We must not forget Boris Savinkov, another right-wing SR, professional terrorist and natural plotter, well known as author of adventure novels featuring as hero a thinly disguised magnification of himself. He is Kerensky's right hand and Kornilov's left, useful to both, suspected by both. We too have kept tabs on Boris. His latest scheme is to provoke a Bolshevik-style uprising in Peter upon the celebration of six months of revolution—i.e., tomorrow, August 28. When this has happened, or can be represented to happen, Kornilov/Kerensky will march their forces on the city and proclaim one of them Sole Ruler, second-in-command, B. Savinkov. I have made sure, so far as I can carry a wavery CenCom, that *we* will give them no such excuse. *That,* it now seems, was what they were hoping for in the July Days, but fortunately I held my comrades back then as well.

So what will happen now? It appears Kornilov is inviting Kerensky to his HQ to lock him away. Kerensky is threatening to demote Kornilov and move his troops to Peter. Savinkov is hoping to dish them both and be chosen as the one who can inherit all their support and yet seem also the choice of the non-Bolshevik left, the Meks and SRs and the Kadets—the broadest spectrum to surround a dictator so far. The Revolution is about to be born—long live the Counterrevolution!

AUGUST 29   HELSINKI   1917

Nadya has gone. I have returned to Kustaa's—how otherwise can I keep being supplied with news and eggs, my two essentials? Just as well. He woke me at dawn, having been to the office and returned in a police car with gong dinning, with a special edition of some popular Finnish daily. He reads out its headlines: GENERAL KORNILOV'S ARMY MARCHES ON PETROGRAD! OUR GREAT MOTHERLAND IS DYING! KERENSKY AIDS GERMANS UNDER ORDERS OF BOLSHEVIK SOVIET!

This is an unexpected, unbelievably sharp turn of events, and obviously calls for a revision of our attitude and a change in tactics. I had not quite understood the relationship of the two K.'s. I had thought they would keep balance, stand each other off, since they were opposing breeds of careerist reactionary. Now, I see, what I really knew, they have to be at each other's throats just because they are so *similar*. Apparently, Kerensky tried to dismiss Kornilov by telegraph. Kornilov, having been led to believe by Savinkov that the three of them were gathering forces to take power together, was furious and aghast. All the generals rallied to him, also the British and French ambassadors, also the capitalist press. He is confident he can do it alone and is concentrating his forces in a ring round Peter before launching a final hammer-blow at the capital.

The hell with security, this is touch-and-go. I must be in contact with our CenCom and I must have all the papers, all editions, from all over Europe. So I accompanied Kustaa back to his office, where I was introduced as a visiting Russian senior detective. I have even managed to get a telegraph message out, on a safe line run by Kustaa's Special Branch, giving my views to CenCom. The workers, especially *our* workers, must be armed. Kerensky has no effective force, nor does the Soviet. They will be obliged to come, apologetically, to us. The rail unions must sabotage Kornilov's tracks—no army now "marches." He will try to arrive by train. Barricades must be built in all the suburbs.

What we do is obvious enough on the spot. What we *say* is more complicated. Bolshevik policy must not become "unprincipled." We do *not* support Kerensky's government. We fight against Kornilov, just as Kerensky's residue of troops do, but we do not fight *for* him. We will fight in a revolutionary way, bringing in the masses, arousing their class feeling. Kerensky is afraid of the masses! We will set a price on our gunpower—arrest of Kadet supporters of Kornilov, dissolution of the Duma, closedown of capitalist press which undermines Soviet. We are not moving away from the proletariat gaining power. These battles will lead us to it. When it is over, all Peter will acknowledge Kerensky's feebleness, cowardice, vacillation.

While I am whistling this down the wire—the CenCom will be taken aback to get this from a direct line at the Tauride!—the Finnish colleagues of Kustaa are laying out editions of the papers. They do not look cherry for us. Every few hours brings a new, more confident communiqué from Kornilov's staff. Narva, Gatchina, have fallen. Names we all know as last-ditch fortresses against the Hun. By midnight, heavy fighting at Antropshino, twenty-five miles from Peter. Heavy casualties on both sides. Finally, as the two of us go back to our tea-chest flat, we read that General Kaledin, Kornilov's ally from the southern command, has severed both Peter and Moscow from their grain supplies. I leave still assuring my Finnish fellow cops that I know Kornilov will fail. I do, don't I?

As I get into bed in the kitchen, I search myself for fears I could be wrong. I find none. Not only will counterrevolution fail. But the threat of that counterrevolution will ensure that our Revolution is now more certain and nearer than ever. The relationship works both ways. The workers will now realize that unless they want to suffer everything *they* hate, they will have to take power now.

AUGUST 30   HELSINKI   1917

Another day at Helsinki Police HQ. Thank goodness, I have studied my enemy. I am able to tell these basically provincial officers a great deal they never knew about how we used to work in the Okhrana, and now still do in Kerensky's "Special Community Patrols."

The papers come flowing in. Still certain Kornilov is winning. But suspicious absence of detail, places, times, numbers, names of regiments. I dare not reveal how clinching all this is to any newspaperman as evidence of an attack fading out.

Around early evening, hard news starts up again, especially in the foreign press. It becomes clear that Kornilov's attempt at a *coup* has failed within four days of his riding out of GHQ on his white horse. And the workers did it. Putilov operated around the clock turning out more than a hundred field guns for the Red Guard artillery. The fleet took up a position overlooking the routes along the Gulf. The railway union that Kornilov had unwisely threatened, at the Moscow State Conference, with martial law, became his most damaging enemy. They not only uprooted track, they rerouted trains, altered signals, lost or garbled telegraph messages, in a program of creative chaos. Our best agitators drove out far into the hinterland and halted the advancing soldiers to tell them the truth about Kornilov's ambitions. As Trotsky said: "The insurrection has been rolled back, crumbled to pieces, been sucked up by the earth."

The truth was that the soldiers did not believe in their great soldier hero. He is now under arrest. The army has revolted against their Kornilovite officers in half a dozen places and lynched them.

The Bolsheviks have never been so popular. Perhaps now, not for the first but certainly for the last time, we could make a peaceful revolution? I have suggested we offer a truce. We will be loyal opposition to a broad left Soviet-backed government with free elections and free press.

SEPTEMBER 5   HELSINKI   1917

Kustaa's Russian detective friend has gone back to Petrograd. I wish his revolutionary double could do the same.

My offers of a democratic, socialist assumption of power, without use of force, by a coalition of the left, during that lull when Kerensky was at his lowest ebb, have been rebuffed. The SRs and Mensheviks imagine they can do it alone. Meanwhile, Kerensky has regained hold of the levers of power and is pursuing a reactionary, anti-working-class policy as if the defeat of Kornilov by the masses had never occurred. The general is under mild restraint, no doubt ready to escape again when the bourgeoisie need him. Savinkov, who had just taken over as governor-general of Peter, has had to be dismissed, since he was an open partner of Kornilov, but remains free. The war continues, the people starve, the peasants gradually occupy the land. The Bolsheviks are the majority in both Peter and Moscow Soviets. There is only one policy now, armed insurrection, overthrow of Kerensky's dictatorship, and seizure of power to give the people peace, bread, land.

This, from now on, is my only aim. Half the country agrees with me. I only have to convince my own Central Committee. I must get nearer to the heart of the matter. Perhaps Vyborg on the Finnish frontier, and then the Vyborg district in Peter? Let it be soon.

OCTOBER 18   PETERSBURG   1917

Eleven days in Peter, back from abroad. It is now or never. Day after day I have hammered at them the message—the time is ripe. Delay is criminal. The success of both the Russian and the world Revolution depends on three days' fighting. An armed uprising is inevitable. We must lead it and it must triumph.

I can smell it, like a whiff from a fire suddenly flaring when you think it is out, like the breath of fermenting malt in a moonshining peasant's vat. It feels as if it is searing the hairs in my nostrils. It is raising the hairs on the back of my neck—there are not many others left. It is in my blood.

Why do so few of the others feel that this is the moment? All our lives all of us have lived for Revolution. Should we not know it when we see it? How do I, who never remember not being an atheist, who never for a moment believed in luck, or intuition, or inspiration—"that man without a soul" Vera Zasulich called me— how do I know I am right, always have been right, at least the second time, learning always from my first mistake? In 1905 we got it wrong—I arrived too late. It had started without me. This time we will not fail.

How is that I can be so certain when I look around me at what are supposed to be my comrades and fellow conspirators?

Today Gorky's *New Life* carries a statement by men who call themselves Bolsheviks, Zinoviev and Kamenev, opposing our plan for an uprising. In the press! Can you imagine such infantile behavior? They might as well write to that house magazine of the international bourgeoisie, *The Times* of London, asking them to publish an announcement that the Revolution is postponed. Possibly on account of inclement weather—if wet, in the Town Hall. What do they think a revolution is—a battle of flowers? An agricultural show?

Naturally I have issued a counterstatement, denouncing both in rather mild terms, for me anyway. I call it a "grave betrayal" born of "noisy pessimism." This is a "Letter to Bolshevik Party Members"—I can hardly have copies delivered by hand to Kerensky's office.

Gorky is not much more helpful—the great, mournful, weepy ninny, with his doggy eyes, haystack of hair, and moustache that looks as if it might be wiped away with the back of his hand if he really were the horny-handed *muzhik* he imagines he is. To think of the years when he was "the stormy petrel" of the Revolution, the true voice of the people who had never spoken yet. Now he too, just as we are about, at last, to transform a sixth of the earth's surface, giving the signal to the entire world, he bleats away in his column under the heading "One must not be silent." Why not? You would think *one* could at least keep *one's* mouth shut when *one's* comrades are about to take over *one's* prison even if *one* doesn't want to escape *oneself* from *one's* comfy little cell.

It is hard to believe it. He's even got the date right, so now he's telling everybody. Let's hope the circulation is as small as I think it is.

Rumors are more and more persistently being spread that "some action by the Bolsheviks" will take place on October 20. In other words, the disgusting scenes of July 3–5 may be repeated. This means, again, trucks tightly packed with people holding rifles and revolvers in hands trembling with fear—and these rifles will fire at the windows of stores, at people, at anything! They will fire only because those armed with them want to kill their own fear. All the dark instincts of the crowd irritated by the disintegration of life and by the lies and filth of politics will flare up and fume, poisoning us with anger, hate and revenge; people will kill one another, unable to suppress their own animal stupidity.

An unorganized crowd, hardly understanding what it wants, will crowd out into the street, and, using this crowd as cover, adventurers, thieves, and professional murderers will begin to "create the history of the Russian revolution."

Maxim thinks he is part of the people, linked to them by some supernatural force stronger than nature, like an inland pool which nevertheless feels the pull of the tides of the sea. That's his kind of talk. But he could not be more mistaken about the people. He compares them to animals, it's a likeness that comes up continually, yet he doesn't understand animals either. Neither beasts nor men are vicious, callous, ruled by passions and lusts, unless society, their environment, makes them so. Their basic instincts are *not* dark.

This time, the people with rifles will no longer be disorganized, if I have my way. They will not fire at anything, but at something, at what we give them for targets. Gorky, I begin to see, is a Lenin in negative. My opposite, his blacks my whites. I do not think politics *must* be lies and filth. Our Bolshevik politics are truth, cleansing truth. Our Russian Revolution will grow from honest anger, genuine love for our fellows.

Still, his article may have done little harm. Since, in his naïveté, he thinks there will be no uprising on October 20 for the absolutely convincing reason (to him) that the Central Committee of the Social-Democratic Bolsheviks have "in no way confirmed the rumors about the forthcoming insurrection" even though we have also "not refuted them."

Nevertheless—*this is important*. I still must not ignore what Gorky writes in *New Life*, so long as it continues to be published. (Suppression of any publication must always be an option for the ruling power, especially if it turns out to be used for counterrevolutionary ends.) Few politicians, especially revolutionists, have better reasons than I to know that what is right on one occasion may not be so on the next. We must never refuse to take a path because an enemy once recommended it. Maxim is one source of light on the scene, another voice, a different opinion. To make the correct, objective assessment, I must feed his view too into my equations. I shall make a point of monitoring his paper.

OCTOBER 24   PETERSBURG   1917

Once again, I recall the Siberian wolf in London Zoo. I also thought of the legend of the lycanthrope as I saw that I had worn a path across Marguerite's French carpet, padding backward and forward along the same line, turning always at the same point. This is the sort of behavior I have noticed among disturbed children in Swiss mental hospitals, among estranged wild creatures, penned in cages. For the last five days, it is as if I were an impatient patient, a reluctant inmate in some closed institution, fighting back waves of depression, of lethargy, of impotence.

It is not the same as being entombed in tsarist cells, even deep underwater like those in Peter & Paul, cut off from all news of the struggle. Here, on the top floor of this high-tower apartment block, I hear almost too much. The rising tremors of the Revolution echo back to me from all around like rolling shock waves of an earthquake, radio signals broadcast through the ether.

I could be in a city made of glass. Observer, outsider, eye in the sky, I see what is hidden to those in the thick of it. A hovering kite, I could foretell predestined fates below—the frog about to leap into the snake's mouth, the deer backing toward the embrace of the bear, the wisp of smoke that will flare into a forest fire, the sniffing bison ready to start the stampede.

Maybe it is precisely because I cannot interfere that I also suffer the plagues of the Egyptians—shingles, insomnia, headaches, back pains, hot flushes, cold sweats, ringing in the ears, spots like meteors across the eyes. I fear they are daggers of the mind, and even Moses might have diverted the heaven-sent inflictions onto himself had his fellow-Israelites sewn him in his tent to stop him leading the Exodus to the Promised Land.

A somewhat unlikely parallel! But it kept trekking through my dreams as I lay half-awake last night. I do not like my mind to slide from rational control and I found myself stretching out a hand to M. lying as usual, arms enfolded, on her back like a Pharaoh. She awoke, instantly, without resentment, attentive to my question—was there a name to this apartment block? "Yes," she said. "Pisgah."

To someone who always came top in Religion, this did not chime on the ear as an entirely happy coincidence. Of course, I take no notice of such random patterns. An omen has no objective existence, but acquires significance from what men choose to give it. Still, the thought of dying within sight of Canaan was one I could not tolerate. Half an hour ago, I wrote a note to M.—"Gone where you didn't want me to go. Till we meet again," and signed it "Ilyich." Nobody and nothing could keep me away any longer from the fulcrum for which I have searched for thirty years, the point at which I will engage my lever to change the history of Russia, perhaps of the entire world.

Fofanova left for work earlier than usual this morning. The surname seems appropriate despite our closeness during these feverish nights. Standing there by the door, that intricate, active little body unsuspected by anybody who saw it only covered by the lady bureaucrat's uniform of blue serge, her sugared-almond face betraying no other emotion than sweet, polite willingness to serve, she seemed only (what she also was) the perfect adjutant, *aide-de-camp, chef-du-Cabinet.*

I have not been sexually involved with many women in my thirty years of adult life—perhaps six or eight. Karl (Radek) would possess that many during a summer holiday around the spas; Gregory (Zinoviev) in a working week. Yet I do seem to have the power to attract them to my service according to the strength of my need for them. They volunteer like nurses or nuns, obey without question or complaint. They clearly follow a cause that is greater than me or them—and for them, I am not so much a man as an instrument of history. They have always approached me like engineers to a machine, like surgical sisters in an operating theater. Whenever my physical desires have demanded a greater intimacy, the initiative has been mine. Apart from Inessa, where we both aim for the perfect, balanced unison of the Chenyshevskian ideal, they behaved as if what was happening was a perfectly understandable extension of the job, not distasteful but then not ecstatic. (And even Inessa, now that I allow myself to remember such things, used sometimes to complain that my dedication to equality between the sexes could fade away somewhere around the navel, as though I were following Luther's revolting dictum on women—"God made that plaster for this sore.")

So there was nothing odd about our shaking hands like the English. Or about her reminding me of CenCom's ruling that I should wear my wig *at all times,* never answer the door without checking the triple-knock and the password, always keep away from the windows, and on no account leave this flat without CenCom's *express permission.* Or about my warning her to travel warily over the five miles to the office of Devriens (publishers) on Basil Island, a wearying, hazardous journey involving two bridges across branches of the Neva, infrequent tram services, frequent street attacks by bandits, drunken soldiery, political splinter groups replenishing their coffers.

She had already been out, as usual, to fetch my newspapers. And I knew she would come back here immediately from her office if she picked up any info she felt I must have.

The day dragged on. Every bit of news reinforced my instinct that this was the day of destiny. I felt I knew what I was about to be told before I was told it. Lucky, I hope, since CenCom seem gripped by a bout of insensate security mania. As each message was pushed through the letter box, I held my breath six inches away, forbidden to signify my presence. Most turned out to be so shuffled (north for south, day night, AZ) as to baffle not only any interceptor but also the intended recipient. I relied on guesswork which, not surprisingly, ended up confirming what I was already thinking.

Telephone calls had been even less helpful. I was not allowed to speak back in case my voice was recognized—at most, grunts of affirmation or negation were permitted. I could not probe, query, ask for repetition or expansion, according to my usual method. Even worse, some compilers had obviously read books about conspiratorial techniques among the Freemasons or the Carbonari and begun giving the news in picturesque, fabular style—"The ducks have landed but not on the lake . . . we have enough wood to heat the house for a week."

Deciphering the written messages, I gathered that Kerensky had ordered the cutting of all lines to Smolny; dispatched the cruiser *Aurora* to sea; summoned back government infantry from Tsarskoe Selo and artillery from Pavlovsk; ordered the closure of *Workers' Way (Rabochy Put).* So far, only the first action appears to have been completed, not a ring all day! The success of their other measures will depend on how quickly and efficiently Trotsky's Military Revolutionary Committee can counter them. The Revolution is being forced on the defensive. As commander-in-chief, I would instantly order my forces to attack.

Around 5 P.M., Fofanova arrived back. She had left her busy office an hour earlier when her boss told her he had just been assured by a contact near to the Supreme Commander that all the bridges were about to be raised. Bourgeois, fashionable, official Petersburg would be cut off from invasion or infiltration by armed workers, the Red Guards, or mutinous regiments under the influence of the Bolsheviks. I wondered that publishers should be busy at such a time. She laughed, relighting the samovar which had gone out, piling me a plate of pickled herring from Finland she'd bought from a riverside stall.

"The more that happens, the more unexpected it is, the more people want to read about it. Books have never been so popular. The only question is—which ones? *Extracts from a Diary of the Revolutionary Year* by Sukhanov? That should do well whatever, probably in paper-covered sections. We've got quite a bit in galley proof already. Then there are banks of typesetters waiting to rush out, well, you know how it is . . . Kerensky's *How I Saved Russia* stiff blue and gold binding? *Building the Socialist Order* by Lenin or Trotsky or Zinoviev, depending on availability, black and red, pocket-size.

"My tram conductor said life goes on much the same over in the inner city. Karsavina dances tonight. Chaliapin sings tonight. Shutters are off all along the Nevsky. Tables are out under the glass awnings among the potted plants and the glowing braziers. On this side, queues for bread, for potatoes, for coal, for paraffin, for the queue to join the queue for the queue. No soldiers or Cossacks. No Red Guards. No patrols."

These Russians! Who can overthrow an empire among a people so self-indulgent? M. had to be wrong. *The bridges, the bridges, woman!*

Ah-ha! Her tram took her to the nearest, the Nikolaievsky. It was raised. The tram groaned on along the Universitetskaya Quay, across the Birzhevoysky (down), around the Kronversky Prospect of Old Peter to the Sampsonievsky (up), then finally dropped her off at the Grenardersky (down!). Just across this, on the Vyborg side, is our local Bolshevik committee rooms. Fofanova (good girl!) thought to call in here, but unfortunately they had little news and had received no instructions.

Things are moving, or at least our enemies are. I must know more. So I asked M. to go back to the Party offices, a mile south by drafty tram on a chill, dripping night, and find me *everything* they knew about the bridges—the key to any street warfare in Peter. She was pale, like someone just wounded. I took her hands, looked into her eyes, and assured her that this was the last task I would ask before we toppled the already leaning colossus. As I watched her pale, pinky-blue, icing-sugar complexion, I saw the blood spread under the skin, felt heat surge into her fingers. It was as if she had been given a transfusion. A strange effect, but one I had seen before when I willed women comrades to do something they feared was beyond their strength. Perhaps we all have it in our power to bend iron bars, lift locomotives, roll aside boulders, even if only once.

Around 6:30, while Fofanova was out, I felt a compulsion that was almost messianic (it was as if another, large iron hand had clasped over mine) to write a last letter, leapfrogging the CenCom, direct to all Party activists. The full text I have tucked away in my archives. But this is the gist of my final, long-distance appeal:

COMRADES!

I am writing these lines on the evening of the 24th at a time when the situation is critical to the utmost degree. It is as clear as can be that it is death to delay the uprising now.

With all my strength I want to persuade all of you that everything hangs by a thread, that on the order of the day are questions which are not solved by conferences, by congresses (even by Congresses of Soviets), but only and exclusively by the people, by the masses, by the struggle of the armed masses. . . .

We must not wait! We may lose everything!

Who should take power?

This is not important at the moment. Let the Military Revolutionary Committee take it. Or "Some Other Body" that declares it will relinquish power only to the true representatives of the interests of the people, the interests of the Army (*immediate offer of peace*), the interests of the peasants (*immediate seizure of land, immediate abolition of private ownership*), above all, the interests of the hungry.

It is essential NOW that all districts, all regiments, all Red Guards should be mobilized and should send delegates to the MRC, the CenCom, insistently demanding that under no circumstances should power be left in the hands of Kerensky & Co. until after the 25th. By no means!

The matter must definitely be decided this evening, at the latest during this night.

History will not forgive revolutionaries who delay when they could win this day (and will surely be victorious tomorrow) while they risk losing much tomorrow, in fact, they risk losing everything. . . .

The government is tottering. It must be given *the final push* at all costs.

Delay means death.

Fofanova returned at 9:30. At last, news of some action. All the bridges are reported in the hands of Bolshevik units under the control of the MRC. Still down and functioning, but ready to be raised whenever it is to our advantage. *Pravda* had been seized and closed, but has now been reseized and reopened by troops loyal to us. *Rabochy Put* with an "important announcement" by the MRC is promised to be on the streets only a few hours late. So far, so good. Not such good news—Trotsky as head of the MRC is negotiating (*negotiating!*) with the commandant of Peter's Military Garrison.

Fofanova now as gray as a holy man's underwear. I pumped some more blood round her system—really the last demand! Take my letter to the Vyborg District Committee of the Party. If possible, find Nadya who carries quite a lot of punch there. Above all, get my message distributed to the rank and file. It seems only they can light a fire under the CenCom and the MRC. And she was to relay my promise that if I had not by 11 P.M. been summoned to my place at the head of the column, I would consider myself released from all restrictions and take my own action.

No sooner had she gone than my old Finnish guide, body-guard and veteran companion on the run, Eino Rajha, turned up. That decided me. Now I would have company on the way. I had spent long enough, nearly a month, urging the others into battle. I would go to Smolny.

Eino gave me a typically laconic summing-up of the risks. It is dark and windy and wet out with nobody looking too closely at anybody. Vyborg district is in the hands of the Red Guards. Liteiny bridge will be the problem, this end held by us, the far end by Junker cadets. We may have to "borrow" a boat. Trams have stopped running, and it is a long walk to Smolny. If recognized on the way by any pro-government groups, I will be shot without hesitation in the gutter.

10 P.M. I have glued on the wig with a spot of flour paste. Wrapped an old hand towel round my face like a man with tooth-ache in a cartoon. Jammed on a cap. Not forgot my galoshes. Left the note for M. with this school-exercise-book volume of the diary. (If you read this far, my dear, you will know what to do with it should things go wrong.)

OCTOBER 25   PETERSBURG   1917

I write this in a new volume of the diary, a great fat ledger I found here at Smolny. It seems to have once belonged to the bursar of this famous convent school for noble girls and the first few pages are covered with his financial accounts. I have only cast my eye over them but even a nonaccountant can see he was stealing them blind!

So tomorrow should be Day One of the Revolution. I shan't feel we have taken root in history until we have passed the record of the Paris Commune (71 days). Incidentally, since leaving Peter in July and coming back in October I was away 111 days.

At the moment, Lev Davidovich and I are lying side by side on a few old blankets, sharing a pillow, staring up at an arched, embroidered roof, like a couple of down-and-outs. Sister Marya dragged this makeshift bedding out from the back of some dormitory. The whole of Smolny (a place I had never seen before) was ablaze with light from every window in the three-tier barrack block when I arrived last night. It was like a cruise ship *en fête,* and inside it could have been *Mardi Gras.* As I pushed along the corridors I kept seeing faces from the past, half-forgotten masks, as often in a bad dream. But this was like a good dream. I hardly recognized for a moment this youngest member of my own family.

As I just said to Trotsky, the jump from illegality, from being on the run, never being sure when you might be betrayed and by whom, to being the power that rules the state, balances on the pinnacle at the center, is dizzying. More in my case than in almost anyone else's. I have been so long these last months on the periphery while seeking to project myself into the heart of the struggle. "Everything is spinning," I laughed, making the gesture of a humming top. Trotsky started—"For a moment, I thought that was the sign of the cross!"

In these few crowded hours, we have had some very illuminating, rewarding talks, despite all the people shouting over, under and between us. He is often accused of flowery, over-picturesque speech and writings. True, it is very different from my public style though I wish I could come near to his vividness and immediacy when I put down words for myself alone, as here. The point about him is that the style *is* the man. He "talks like a book of psalms" (as the peasants say) because he is a kind of library incarnate. I have never heard him say anything trivial, banal, ordinary. His phrasing only makes penetrating, original remarks more memorable. True, too, his conversation is often combative. Most of us are armed only with a chair leg or a rolled newspaper against his *épée* or saber. My advice is—hide your weapon, sit down and be instructed. He has made many observations I would like to examine today. But more of that later.

To get up to date: Eino and I left Fofanova's around 10:30. We were lucky, catching the last tram back to the terminus at the bottom of Bolshoi Sampsonievsky Prospect. I huddled up in a corner, rocking my head in my hands, as if isolated in pain. Unfortunately, I had forgotten the mixture of generosity and inquisitiveness that makes up your typical Peter conductress. I had chosen the behavior most likely to attract her attention. To give her something else to think about, I made another mistake—asking where everybody was and why the tram was stopping early. She was quite intrigued now and kept bending down to look at my face. "What sort of working chap are you?" she asked. "Don't you know the Bolos are taking over tonight? Down with the upper classes! Up with the lower! Eh? Which side are you on?"

Eino, true cavalier of the streets, cut in between us. Laying on his Finnish accent, so attractive to a Russian ear, he wooed her with a mixture of mock threats, absurd compliments and comic propositions so that she was almost fainting with pleasure in his arms. How does this swaggering ease with women come so naturally to some men? Eino is rather plain, and usually dull company. I listened with admiration as he modulated a pretense at stealing her gold teeth into a declaration that she resembled a gypsy queen into an offer to give her dentistry an armed escort home, magicking a pistol into his palm from low down, as if from his fly. She got all the messages coded here without difficulty, gave Eino a hug and delicately avoided my eyes as we dropped off when her team turned into its garage, shouting out as she disappeared, "Good luck, comrades."

From the corner of Nizhegorodskaya and Botkin streets, to get to the Liteiny bridge, we had to pass several danger spots— the Finland station always swarming with plainclothes security agents; the Mikhailovsky Artillery School where the instructors and the cadets are fierce backers of Kerensky; and the guardhouse of the Military Medical Academy usually manned by pugnacious sentries with crisp uniforms and polished weapons of surgical neatness.

At any other time, I would have steered round this government island through back alleys but I dared not risk any delay. Fortunately, last night, the open spaces had been taken over by a mixed company of Red Guards and Bolshevik regulars. Camped out there, their rifles stacked like wigwams, their fires purring or gargling as the winds fanned them, the billycans boiling, the bottles clinking, they made a classic revolutionary tableau of soldiers and workers united to fight the real war—the class war—varnished with a wash of scarlets, reds, golden oranges, sunset silver, framed on the dark wall of night. Someday, I hope, we will have galleries of such paintings. Meanwhile, we skulked by, a pair of oblivious tramps.

No problems either on the Vyborg side of Liteiny bridge, held by another mixture—sailors and dockers sharing Maxim guns. Eino's pass from the MRC allowed us through without a query. Halfway, Eino stopped. "Look at the moon," he said, pointing.

I swallowed my protest. Operating underground, you must obey your guide instantly without question. Recriminations can (and usually do) come later. I admired the view.

Eino went on praising nature loudly and rather incoherently. In between, he whispered, "The cadets on the south end are having fun aiming at us. We are the only people crossing. When we get there, they'll take us apart out of sheer boredom. We must wait for company." He looked at his watch. "The eleven o'clock shift from the Renault works will be crossing any minute! We'll ride through on them." So I tried to think of new descriptions for the moon—a syphilitic eye? a grubby Chinese lantern? a saucer of germ culture? The thought of a row of spotty, reactionary kids lining me up in their sights seemed to be turning me morbid. Then, before I noticed, I was being steered by Eino into the center of a noisy crowd of workers from the northern factory going home to the Peski housing estate in the south, near the Nikolaevsky station.

They had no permits from ProvGov. They didn't need any. They had been doing this journey twice a day since the war began. No bunch of stuck-up little Kerenskys in bum-freezers and gold braid was going to frisk skilled car-builders who had been putting in twelve hours a day or night to beat the Hun while the cadets were still in petticoats. Where's your nursemaid? Get your fingers dirty. I'll stuff that rifle where you daren't show your mother. Move, move, move! We were all through and onto Shpalernaya Street.

I was just telling Eino how we all, Bolos, Menshies, Soviet leaders, guards officers, Kronstadters, armed civilians, at the Tauride Palace during the July Days, heard the thunder of hooves along this street and expected to see the Cossacks come galloping on us through the mist. Instead, there were only riderless mounts stampeding out of town after their masters had been blasted from the saddle by Gusev's sharpshooters in an encounter, yes, *on this very spot.* How quickly what happened only a few months ago becomes a piece of history, an unchangeable, irrevocable bit of the past, as distant as the fall of the Bastille, the execution of Charles I, the massacre of the Communards in Père Lachaise.

Then I heard hooves again. A mounted patrol of cadets came cantering toward us from the direction of Smolny and Tauride. "Keep close to the embankment wall," hissed Eino. "Look as if you're about to be sick over it at any moment. I'll be the other drunk."

He approached the cavalry with the fearlessness of the well-liquored. "Here, horsey, horsey, horsey," he called. "Who wants a cube of sugar? Give us a ride, Ivan. Whoa there, gee-gee! Sit!" He repeated this sort of thing over and over again, ignoring all commands to explain his presence or produce his pass.

"The man's a drunken imbecile!" snarled the cadet commander, slapping his mount's flank. They began to move off as I slid gratefully into the blackness.

"Wait a moment, sir!" called a smart lad. "He's got things in his pockets. Empty them out, you dung-ball!"

The patrol stopped and began to circle back. I knew what was bulging so noticeably under the side-flaps of his old greatcoat. How could anyone mistake the size and shape of a pair of Colt Special .45s, smuggled to him by a Finnish exile in America?

Eino looked pleased, as drunks are, not to be rejected and abandoned. "You wanna drink? Horsey wanna drink? Here, taste this. Everybody taste this."

His hands closed round the butts of the guns. I could see them distinctly in the moonlight. He was about to blast the nearest half dozen while I took to my heels in a vain attempt to outrun the rest. But the soldiers saw instead what he was inviting them to see—two hands closing round the necks of bottles. He was even tugging at them, cursing the tightness of his pockets.

"The Red traitors will not be drunk, and they'll be armed with more than bottles," snapped the commander. "Squad, ahead, *canter!*"

The suspicious cadet was reluctant to go. "Come here, piss-bed," he ordered, smiling indulgently.

Eino stared happily up, standing by the stirrup. The whip hit him sharp as a knife across his eyebrows and the blood leaped out in a row of blobs like sweat in a sauna.

Eino kept his hands on his pistols. I could see his sleeves expand as his forearm muscles clenched. He still smiled. "Horsey, horsey," he said.

The cadet stared for a second, then wheeled round and followed the rest.

I have rarely felt such admiration for courage and control. "You must have nerves of steel, my dear old friend and comrade. I promise you this will be revenged."

Eino was still smiling as he wiped his wound with a dirty scarf. "I never take prisoners," he said. "Next time, I'll not take a few more, that's all."

As we walked on to Smolny, Eino confessed that he had been dispatched by the CenCom to make sure I did *not* leave Fofanova's. I demanded to know who had given the order, but he claimed that nobody bothered to give such details to someone of his level in the movement. He had heard it was Stalin's suggestion. But then he had also heard it was Trotsky's. A racing man on the MRC had estimated my chances of crossing Peter in safety as one in three.

"Does it matter, Ilyich?" he asked. "I've got you here as you wanted. You'd never have done it on your own. To be honest, you'd probably not have done it with any other escort."

I grasped his arm, thinking of the slashing *nagaika*, the stitching of blood across the brow. I was grateful, but I was also angry. Who had forced the CenCom to decide on an insurrection? Who had insisted that they plan for every eventuality and had gone again and again over the details? Who had pressed them to set a date? Only two hours ago who had pleaded with them, in a message circulated around the entire inner circle of activists, for an immediate seizure of power. And they had left me almost alone in a top-floor flat, miles to the north of the action, not even keeping me up to date. (Had M. been part of the conspiracy?) I had to rely on my own sources, my own antennae, my own intuition sharpened by a lifetime of experience, to decide on the key moment.

"Surely they could have sent an armored car for me? I requested just a hundred of the best Red Guards. I could have moved anywhere in the city with them. I could have staged my own *coup*. Don't they know the wall is rotten and it only needs a push?"

Eino smiled, bandaging his forehead with his muffler like a Sikh turban. "Here we are, Ilyich," he announced.

Smolny was a sight that beggared description. Certainly, I could think of no comparison to anything ever seen before. I've suggested a luxury liner or a city in carnival, but that gives only an idea of the excitement, the whirl and bustle, the sheer joy of activity, something virtually unknown in Russia, except perhaps at a gypsy wedding. How to convey also the consciousness, on all sides, that this is more than pleasure, more than business (at times I was reminded of Paris and the brokers howling on the Bourse), that this is *revolution*? So there is a whole military side. Smolny has always been a working palace (as a girls' school). But now it is frogged with barbed wire; blockaded with walls of loose timber; bristling with machine guns on the roof; field guns in the porticoes;

almost hidden by armed men with bayoneted rifles, ringing the walls. You need only glimpse it from a distance to recognize that it is a great hive of some swarm that intends to take over our little, local world by brute force. Yet you might still hesitate to imagine that this could be the famous, long-awaited Russian Revolution because you could not help asking yourself—then how dare they do it so publicly? With searchlights everywhere, pointing inward as well as outward. With couriers on bikes, horses, motorbikes, speeding in and out. With disciplined platoons, marching and countermarching in the quadrangle. With armored car and troop carriers being serviced, washed and polished.

Never in history have the insurgents, the rebels, the new class, the *future*, laid themselves and their intentions so open even to passersby. Victory must be really assured.

Here we were, like Buttons and Cinderella at those wonderful Alhambra pantomimes in London, being barred from the ball. For Eino's white pass no longer admitted him "with friend." Since he had left to visit me, it had become a red pass. Eino had been through a lot and I feared for the lives of dumb, young sentries who shook their heads at his claim that he was here with a member of the CenCom and the MRC. "Trotsky or Lenin couldn't get through without a red pass tonight," repeated one. So we argued, and objected, and blocked the door, using every authority except my name. (I now wanted to see what was going on before I was known to be on the premises.) And, as I hoped, the people behind became so furious at having to wait in an ever-growing queue that a ripple of frustration surged through the anteroom and its peristaltic squeeze popped us in, without the red pass.

I told Eino to find a first-aid room. If my advice had been taken, Smolny should have its own ambulances and medical staff as we had in the July Days. As for myself, I was lost. Looking in one of the full-length mirrors which faced one room (ballet classes?) I wondered whether anyone would want to find me. Long gray hair, chubby, many-layered figure, plain-glass, beady spectacles, an expression somewhere between insanely cheery and fatally weary, I must be Mr. Pickwick's unfortunate elder brother.

I found a room with a long refectory table and a lot of plush leather chairs which must very soon attract to itself (this is Russia) a committee. (Radek used to say that Martov obeyed one rule— "Never commit yourself, committee yourself.") I was sorting my thoughts when in came some Meks I recognized, especially their leading organizer, Dan. (This is another odd thing about Smolny.

Because the MRC is officially the organ of the Soviets, and not any particular party or fraction, its GHQ is open to all kinds of anti-Bolsheviks and non-revolutionists.) Dan must have thought there was something familiar about me, or perhaps I looked like someone who could not afford to eat, for he offered me a piece of cheese in a bread roll.

I said nothing but shook my head very slowly. Even more slowly, as if all his bodily processess were running down, Dan gradually recognized me in painful, delayed stages—his eyes winching open, his mouth dropping like a drawbridge, at last the sandwich sliding, sliding from his hand. Then he switched to the opposite gear, was up and away and out of the door, almost smelling of alarm, like a pickpocket who finds he's hoisted a time bomb.

Somebody passed on the word. For the next arrival was a messenger from Lev Davidovich welcoming me and inviting me to the MRC in Room 100. When I got there, I was still laughing about Dan and so perhaps seemed a stranger to nonadmirers of Pickwick. Trotsky came across with hand out but the others just sat talking, giving only a cursory glance.

"Here I am at last, comrades," I said, giving the words an ironic twist. And I raised my cap.

I do not know what reaction I expected but it was not what I got. They paused for a second, then their eyes lit up like so many matches struck together and they laughed. And they laughed. And they laughed.

I looked at my very ordinary, boring worker's cap. It was festooned with my old gray curls. Automatically, I raised my hand to the crown of my head and encountered the dirty bandage. The whole sequence must have resembled a bad routine in a cabaret. First, the Ancient Mariner of Dingley Dell, then a balding *babushka,* then a beardless Vladimir Ilyich, like a badly cleaned portrait, with a face smeared with actor's makeup, plain dirt and a strong fifteen-o'clock shadow.

I could see it was *quite* comical. So I played that up a bit, throwing away the wig and the bandage, and calling on them to witness I would never need them again. After all, the Revolution was over, *wasn't it?* If there had been an undernote of embarrassment in the laughter during the first burst, there was now a lot of unease in their chuckles. "Otherwise, how did I get in here without a red card and without being announced?" I asked.

Lenin the headmaster was back, and not before time. I took my place, without allowing for any other possibilities, as leader of the Party. And I began to run through my question list, checking that what was to be done was being done. Jump to it, I thought. And as though they had heard me, they did.

OCTOBER 26   PETERSBURG   1917

I have already issued a proclamation to "the Citizens of Russia" announcing the fall of the Provisional government. This is a fact, yet various awkward inconsistencies make it hard to prove it in a way that would convince an academic historian. Especially if he is writing years later and thousands of miles away. How is it, then, the Winter Palace has not been occupied? I ask this all the time and have already collected half a dozen convincing, yet contradictory, excuses. In the end, I thought I should literally explode, or at least spontaneously combust. At 2 A.M. this morning, its occupation was finally confirmed and a gaggle of unimportant personages found there were carted off to spend the night in prison. It has all gone here anyway (I hear there is heavy and bloody fighting in Moscow) with incredible ease. If I had known revolutions could be made like this I'd have started one in April, straight after arriving at the Finland station! For real excitement, armed workers on the march, street fighting, blood in the gutters, cavalry charges, machine gun duels, speeches and speeches and the roar of the crowd, it cannot compare with the July Days. Yet when the official version is produced (by us, I hope) I know it will be October that is the stuff of legend while the long, dangerous climb to the pinnacle of power will get little space on the page.

This evening I appeared at the Congress of the Soviets. Even I, who care little for pageant and ceremony, wondered whether this battered old suit and the trousers I tread at the heel would not be seen as a sort of insult. I should have been ashamed to underestimate the victorious comrades. I had toyed with various eloquent, or anyway elaborate, openings. But in the end it came out flat, simple, unadorned. I had to wait several minutes for the great rolling, building, multiplying roar of the ovation to stop— there seemed no reason why it ever should so long as this great multi-piped organ had bellows to power it. Then it stopped as at a conductor's baton. Into the silence my voice, small, hoarse, dry, fed the words, *"Comrades, we shall now proceed to construct the socialist order."* The voices had only been in a pause, the cheers now fell like an avalanche. I was buried alive in noise. For a moment, I was afraid at what I had done.

MOSCOW

VI

1917-1924

So. Our Revolution will go down in the annals as the most peaceful ever. Anything less spectacular it would be difficult to imagine. I have to confess, in a funny way, it makes me feel almost a fool. I was right on several counts, on almost all. I was right to insist that we should mount an armed insurrection, that it should be *now* because delay was fatal, that we should act alone without seeking allies to left or right, that our slogans should be land, bread, but above all, *peace*. And yet I was wrong in thinking that we would not succeed unless we worked to a detailed plan, using dominating force, at the precise, vulnerable joints of the government. In other words, I have to say I was politically correct but militarily confused. Imagine a communist uprising seizing control of the capital city of a vast empire in the middle of a war on the twenty-fifth of the month. Then finding next morning, the twenty-sixth, that the right-wing papers, that is virtually all of them, appear on the breakfast tables of that city without even a paragraph describing the event! It almost defies belief. No wonder many of our opponents, particular those leftists who regard themselves as extra-orthodox Marxists, put our "revolution" in quotes. It was, they say, a back-stairs *putsch, a coup d'état* in the inner circle, a matter of a handful of hands swapping over on the levers.

One of the tests is usually blood. Take the Easter Rising of 1916 in Ireland. It tended to be not just the poets, the mystics, the romantics, but also the proletarian leaders of England's Poland, even Connolly and Larkin, who crooned on about the terrible beauty of death and martyrdom, the sacred intoxication of slaughter. Indeed, I have often speculated that the present "Great War"—though the fancy is difficult to reconcile with Marxism—was partly precipitated by an appetite for the lanced vein among the feverish, high-pressured, overrich young, a whole generation of the officer class across Europe, without occupation or ambition, for whom death seemed an awfully big adventure.

I have never thirsted after blood, but then, I have never allowed the thought of shedding it to make me flinch. One of the Menshevik objections to a revolution in wartime had been that it must result in "rivers of blood" being spilled. And I replied more than once that no victory is ever won without cost. Our overthrow of the government might spill rivers. This was nothing to the tidal waves of blood daily thrown up by the imperialist war. At least, our dead would die to end the butchery, not to prolong and intensify it. I do not withdraw the argument, but it comes as a bit of an anticlimax when I cite October 25 and we all see that the blood is little more than a smear as if the Revolution had cut itself shaving. The "storming of the Winter Palace" has a grandiose and thrilling sound but it was only a minor skirmish—one dead, four wounded, all on our side! In the two days of Revolution, the death toll on both sides was certainly not more than fifteen!

I am not the only observer to notice this phenomenon and look for a moral. Our old friend with the notebook, Sukhanov, has summed it up in *Novaya Zhizn* as "like the changing of the guard." Trotsky, the open and visible leader who had most to lose by any down-grading of the historic achievement, nevertheless admitted to me a week later—"It was all too quick, too prosaic, too business-like . . . I think the word might even be 'disappointing.' You're a climber, Ilyich. I imagine it is rather as if you are straining away, warning your muscles the worst is yet to come, then you take another couple of steps, and find you are up and over the summit."

I remember crossing the city with B.-B. in a tram the next day—a pistol in one pocket and the Decree on Land I had scribbled in pencil during the early hours in the other—marveling at the ordinariness. The day before, everyone agrees, had been exactly the same. Most of the soldiers stayed in their barracks. The workers left home for work, worked and came home again. There were queues to see motion pictures at the cinematographias. The theaters were open and full. My nephew, young Gora, voiced a schoolboy's bitter complaint—"You had our Revolution at last, Uncle Volodya, and I was in the classroom all through it. Our Revolution, and not even a day's holiday."

For years after '05, everybody could remember where they were, and what they were doing, on Bloody Sunday. In the years after this one, three-quarters of the population of Peter will have to admit they were here, on the spot, and never noticed this historic event occurring.

I have been musing on what all this means in the intervals of trying to organize society by giving orders to people who go away and never come back. One theory is that our physical assumption of control over the capital was so quietly, smoothly efficient that the ordinary citizen neither heard nor saw anything unusual. All those tasks I had nagged and niggled about with Nevsky, Podvoisky, Gusev and the rest in the June Days and the July Days were performed as if by second nature—bridges, railway stations, telephone exchanges, telegraph offices, ministries all ours in a single night. The weakness of this is the abundance of testimony from unordinary citizens, who knew what was supposed to be happening, that tremendous muddles and confusion developed on all sides. Take only one example. If the city was totally in our grip, how was it that the prime figure on our wanted list, Kerensky, was able to slip by our patrols in a car flying an American flag and even be saluted by sentries?

A better theory has recently started to crystallize in discussion with Trotsky. This explains why there were no monster marches or demonstrations, no gun battles on the streets, no strikes, no rivers of blood. Because they were not necessary. They would have been useless. The Revolution had already completed itself. There were in the city an estimated 300,000 men-at-arms, in and out of uniform, committed to supporting the Bolsheviks. Kerensky's government was left with only 25,000 soldiers, few of whom could see him as a cause for which it was worth risking their lives. Trotsky and Antonov-Ovseenko had almost that number (20,000) of picked, devoted men massed ready for any assault. They occupied the Winter Palace, defended by a mere 3,000, deserting by the hour. The fact that so few were involved, so little noise was made, so little damage done to people or things, is proof of its *popularity*! I had almost convinced myself that our explanation was correct. Only Lev Davidovich was to shake my belief by epitomizing the process in words that are for me just that fraction too sugary and theatrical. "Yes, yes. I see it. The social scenery shifted noiselessly as on a revolving stage, bringing forward the popular masses, carrying away to limbo the rulers of yesterday."

You can't sustain a conversation like that without feeling it should be set to music, or at least declaimed from a stage. It is no wonder that almost all those who want to get close to Trotsky are liable to find they are being forced back by an invisible barrier of thorns.

NOVEMBER 19   PETERSBURG   1917

Yesterday our delegation left for Brest-Litovsk to open direct peace negotiations with the German High Command and Foreign Office. This in itself is something of a defeat. We had hoped by the victory of our Revolution we would have established at least two beach-

heads on the far bank of the socialist future. Firstly, that my promise, broadcast to the world over the wireless, that our government
would instantly conclude a cease-fire might capitalize on the war-
hatred of all the embattled nations, arousing others to agree to
demand a peace "equally just to all nations and nationalities without
exception." And secondly, that our demonstration of what could
be achieved by a small, new, inexperienced proletariat and a backward, suspicious peasantry in a huge country without any tradition
of democracy, trade-union rights or open political action, would
encourage the older, more organized left parties in more advanced
capitalist states to be spurred by our example and soon overtake us.

What we did not expect was to be left alone so long in isolation.
None of the combatants displays any real interest in withdrawing
from the war—except the Germans. For them, it is obviously a
crucial strategic advantage not to have to fight on two fronts and
be able to transfer perhaps anything up to a million men from the
East to the West. Perhaps we are too noble, suppressing that honorable instinct for self-preservation that had led us to take power.
But we did not want the workers of Europe to think we cared so
little for them we would let their war intensify in order to damp
down our own. There have been some mutinies among troops in
France and Germany, a great deal of unrest in factories everywhere, some riots on the streets of Berlin and Paris. But both the
rulers and the ruled, in dreadful somnambulistic fashion, unite to
carry on killing each other, and us. Indeed, while the Germans
are signifying an interest in stopping their anti-Russian campaign,
the Allies have just let it be understood that they are ready—British
and Americans in the north, French in the south, Japanese at
Vladivostok—to open up a new anti-Bolshevik campaign to force
"Russia" to carry on fighting.

Still, no outside observer, I swear, would think we were struggling to survive such setbacks with something of a heavy heart if
they had seen our Bolshevik team of plenipotentiaries setting off
twenty-four hours ago. They were led by Kamenev and Joffé,
Trotsky and Radek following later. The first two had insisted that
we also appoint, as emblems of their team's representation of "the
Revolution entire," one ordinary soldier, one ordinary sailor and
one typical workman, picked at random from the Party files. It
was an interesting idea, and later today we monitored some of our
opposite number's reactions. They were, as had been intended,
thrown off balance by the contrast between their own starched,
diplomatic etiquette and the awkward, but natural and straightforward, manner of these revolutionaries and militants.

Particularly noticeable, at the social functions anyway, is one of our negotiators who goes by the name of "False Ivan"—no one has so far found any other identification. On the way to the train for the conference, somebody (nobody now can remember who) observed that they had no representative of the *mujhiks*. Just at that moment, "False Ivan" plowed out of the crowd inches in front of them, entangled himself with the luggage and the documents, fell over twice and made to carry on. Joffé, a tiny, fiery sprite always attuned to the left like a compass to north, seized the reeling "Ivan," told him destiny had selected him to walk the stage of history, issued a passport and ticket on the spot from various blanks about his person, and enrolled him as a member of the Soviet Delegation.

It would be pleasant to report that he is a natural orator, or negotiator. Perhaps, with proper training, he may become one or both. But so far, Joffé reports, he has only provoked awe among the high-living Germans by his formidable appetite for any kind of alcohol, particularly his pleasure at the sight of a wine bottle, regardless of vineyard, country of origin, date, color and apparently taste. He has not so far said a word about anything to anyone.

NOVEMBER 30   PETERSBURG   1917

American Colonel Robbins drove into Smolny this morning. The white explorer coming across feuding natives in the jungle, he instructs our guard on the gate in fluent pidgin-Russian—"Take me to your headman."

This is unfair, but not entirely so. I know more about him than he seems to know about me. Liberal/radical, businessman/philanthropist, intelligence agent/Red Cross official, he was educated in bourgeois politics under *his* headman, Theodore Roosevelt, campaigning with him on that doomed attempt at the 1912 presidency without party machine, millionaire backers or friendly newspapers. (There are some rewards for all my mornings, dictionary in hand, deciphering the world's press.) He even knows some basics of real politics, having debated on platforms with American Marxists.

I allow no glimmer of this to shine through. I realize he wants no-nonsense answers to intentionally simple-minded questions which will enlighten his masters back home without frightening them off the new rulers of Russia. Is this a democratic regime? I reply in English—my American is not so good.

"The old politicians will tell you that I am a dictator. And so I am, for the moment. I am able to because I represent the will of the mass of workers and peasants. But the next moment, when I cease to execute their will, they will withdraw their power from me. I will be switched off like a light, as helpless as the Tsar."

But I am voted for?

"I doubt whether any dictator in history has been so voted for, and against. I can enforce no decision that is not ratified by my comra—, my colleagues. I must have behind me the majority on the Central Committee of our Party, on the Central Executive Committee of the All-Russian Soviet, on the Council of People's Commissars, on the Central Committees of most city parties, and most city soviets. Since my authority, moral and physical, ascends from the people, if they come out against me on the streets, strike against me at work, I am finished. Socialism cannot be decreed from above."

Is ours a socialist state?

"Let me put it this way. We are going to challenge the world with a *producers'* republic. There will be nobody in our soviets who simply owns shares, who has only money in any enterprise. We are electing the producers. The Donets coal basin will be represented by producers of coal; the railways by those who run the trains; the postal system by those who earn their living providing communications."

Now the most difficult would be next—honesty rather than guile was called for. Would we carry on fighting the Germans?

"For us, the war is over. We have no army in the sense that you, Colonel, would recognize an army. Even if we had one, we have not the industry to support it any longer. Our former rulers locked the crew below decks and ran the ship on the rocks. When we stormed the bridge, they abandoned ship taking all the lifeboats. We are trying to refloat the *Titanic*. We look to you, another young nation born in revolution, to help salvage us. We will pay whatever price we can."

I then offered to move all the war *matériel* scattered along Germany's Eastern Front to a secure place beyond Moscow where it could not be used against the Allies. I promised to insert a condition in any treaty of peace with the Germans that they would not transfer the troops released to the Western Front. The colonel insisted on one more condition for American recognition and technical assistance in peaceful reconstruction—no release of our hundreds of thousands of German prisoners while the Central Powers are still fighting the Allies.

I agreed: subject to ratification by my colleagues, of course. But I'm sure he caught a squeak of eagerness in my voice. I changed back to Russian. It flatters foreigners if you speak their language, but when you are negotiating, you don't want any distractions. Let *them* use the strange tongue. It is just enough, even among the multi-lingual, to diffuse their concentration, and give you that edge.

I could not, inside me, despite all the decrees I had issued forbidding it, help allowing some hopes to flutter free, butterflies escaping from the chrysalis. Perhaps the bad news was that the international solidarity of the proletariat would not result in revolutions in Germany, France, England, after all. But then perhaps the good news was that the international solidarity of the capitalists would also fragment. Maybe we can play the Central Powers off against the Allies in Europe while winning the friendship of the United States?

DECEMBER 5   PETERSBURG   1917

Heard today from one of the "Friends," by name Basipetal. I cannot now remember which one he is, probably just as well. He sends bad news, but I believe, whether bad or good, it is better known than not known. At least, there is a chance to mitigate the effect.

Basipetal is part of a network of committed supporters of the Bolshevik tendency, our Party, now our government, whom we call the "Friends" (in English). I made a point of recruiting these heroic hidden workers for the cause as early as 1900, when the thought of an actual communist society, not to say such a society in the Tsar's Russia, seemed a generation, if not a lifetime, away.

They are paid no money, do not even get in return any praise or encouragement. They can expect nothing at all. Unlike the "sleepers," familiar to all intelligence organizations, who rise in business, politics, the services, of their native, or long-adopted, country and await only activation by their "control," usually in time of extreme crisis, the Friends are all "self-starters," a technical term from motorcars I believe. I chose a name for each one by stabbing a finger, with eyes closed, at a very fat English dictionary. There are only a moderate number and I fancied this would connect the person in my mind with the odd cover-name. "Basipetal," I know, means "growing from top to base." I remember that, though at random, it was exceptionally apt, but why I have forgotten. He was English and had passed top in his year into the Foreign Office where, it appears, he still is.

No "Friend" ever writes anything in his own hand. What he would normally do is get his envelope, with code-name, to me. Inside will be a copy of a document, or series of them, that he assumes I will be able to analyze and interpret. I will destroy this data immediately.

This morning an envelope was delivered to me, without a stamp or postmark, which suggested it had reached Peter by courier or through something like the diplomatic bag. "Basipetal" was in the envelope's return address, either name of house or village in England, and I almost missed it. (It is now, of course, also burned.) Inside were photographs, rather beautifully done, of two cables—one from U.S. Secretary of State (Foreign Minister) Robert Lansing in Washington to the U.S. ambassador to England, and another from U.S. Ambassador Francis in Petersburg to Washington.

The first read: "State Department authorizes loan not topping hundred thousand dollars initially Ataman Kaledin but must route via British French stop Speed essential secrecy vital as must not appear U.S. SD sympathetic Cossacks leave alone provide financial assistance."

The second was a fragment, typewritten in code in a more leisurely style, with pencil transcription underneath. Said Petersburg Ambassador Francis to his boss in Washington: "I am making a statement to Petersburg press for international papers to copy which shall forward you *en clair* denying all connection or knowledge of Kaledin movement stating your instructions are definite and emphatic not to interfere in internal affairs stating I have observed same scrupulously."

So much for Colonel Robbins's friendly questioning and my offers to assist the Allied Entente by obstructing the transfer of German troops to the Western Front before the Americans had arrived there in force. General Kaledin is Ataman of the Don Cossacks, allegedly numbering 200,000 cavalry. According to our intelligence, here and on the Don, he is raising a White counter-revolutionary army in southern Russia and intends to ride on Moscow and Peter to overthrow the Soviet government.

The new imperialist giant power of the twentieth century clearly recognizes the danger to international capitalism of a small insecure communist regime. This is the first step of intervention by outsiders into Soviet Russia, while war still rages in Europe, and we have not even agreed to peace terms. I see that the wolves will all soon be gathered howling round our frozen sled. We have lighted the way ahead for the proletariat of the world. They must come to our aid before we collapse from terminal inertia.

Nevertheless, thank you, Friend.

JANUARY 1   PETERSBURG   1918

Midnight plus one minute. Our first Soviet New Year. N. and I have just come back from a week's compulsory leave in Finland, a sanatorium like a crystal, folktale mansion, in the woods just across the border. How often Finland has provided me with rest and recuperation, with a feeling, quite extraordinarily intimate and physical, of tangled lines being cut, of clogged channels being cleared! It is as if I were some modern, supercharged torpedo boat, say, that would drift, without power, doomed on the flow of a stream to be broken up at the rapids, unless the dirt in the oil filter, the weeds wrapped round the propeller shaft, could be blown out and cut away.

We are guests of honor at a party in the Vyborg district— another haunt of friends and protectors from the old days—held in the huge hall of the Mikhailov Artillery School. As is my custom on such social occasions, I make only a short, inspirational speech—what Trotsky says, from his time in America, is called "a pep-talk"—full of congratulations, optimism, promise for the future. Who needs a detailed balance sheet, a full-length look in the mirror, at a time of holiday? Our people are celebrating an achievement without parallel in the history of the world—never before have working people, the bottom layer of the pyramid, taken over the entire running of a continental empire, already the largest area ever ruled by a single authority, and dared to administer it all themselves. The thought can be quite dizzying. Of course, I have continually laughed off the perils and problems. And the point that always goes down so well at mass rallies—if the Tsar could keep the machinery going through 30,000 capitalists, why shouldn't we do it with 240,000 Communists?—remains valid. But when you begin to think it through in detail, listing the actual things desperately needing to be done in the real world . . . well, never mind. The central justification for being a leader is that you must carry on and on and on letting problems tramp through your brain, convicts on a chain gang, at a time when others are free to forget them. More than any other workers, except perhaps their co-equals from Putilov, the inhabitants of the Vyborg district are the ones who gave, and will continue to give, their scraped-together kopeks, their beaten and wounded bodies, their magnificent courage and confidence, to the cause of Revolution. I know how hard, how much harder, on them the coming years will be than even those that have gone. This is their peak, in ways they cannot suspect, possibly for the decade.

N. times the ovation for me—not for vanity, but as a political fact. They put me on a chair and carry me round the floor. When I am freed, we slip away. Almost every one of them will be happier without thinking my eyes will be on them. But also, according to my custom, I talk in a more serious, detailed, pragmatic way with those comrades around the hall who have real questions, worthwhile arguments, crucial propositions. These are the unlucky ones, like me, who cannot deceive themselves with utopian visions of the world reflected back to them, as in fairground mirrors, by their own vanity, timidity, ignorance, naïveté, sentimentality, even their good-heartedness. They are the ones I respect and recognize, and once recruited them as my Men of Confidence, and am now encouraging to join the Soviet apparatus. I stress to them, that not only must they reject utopias, of course, but they must adjust to accepting that the society we construct, and inhabit, will for several years remain more jerry-built, more uncomfortable, more deprived, packed with fuller danger, starvation, regimentation, than any in the past.

It says a great deal for the maturity, the moral toughness, of our militantly committed comrades that, even on New Year's Eve, some were determined to take the opportunity of my presence to ask questions about government policy and the direction of the Revolution. They were not too concerned over material problems close to home—the shortages of food, the lack of housing, the failure in supply of clothes, boots, bedding. They did not even raise the subject of peace or war, though many of them were deserters from the front or workers who had refused to be conscripted. No, they were concerned about the wider issues, affecting them possibly only at one remove—the suppression of a bourgeois newspaper, say, or the arrest of SRs accused of counterrevolutionary sabotage.

I gave them my usual encapsulated reply, after pointing out that when we had released the capitalist ministers, agitators from right or left of the "socialist" spectrum, even tsarist generals, like Krasnov, on their word of honor, they went underground and were later found in league with armed bands attacking our Soviet power.

"When a revolutionary class is fighting the propertied classes that offer resistance, that resistance must be crushed. And we shall crush the resistance of the propertied classes using the same means as they used to crush the proletariat—*no other means have been invented.*"

In Vyborg, that is not enough. They want to know the theoretical, the Marxist justification for our authoritarianism. Have we Bolsheviks, after October, not perhaps pushed beyond extremes the concept of the dictatorship of the proletariat? What would Engels say? Would Plekhanov have approved? Why was Martov now denouncing us? On a bitter winter night, here were people (women as well as men) with teeth falling out, hair thinning, skin hanging loose, clothes in holes or mended like patchwork quilts, boots gaping like clams, ignoring their ration of vodka and pickled herring to worry . . . about what? About what might be happening to former exploiters, to compromised intellectuals, to cashiered officers, who had breached our socialist principles of working democracy. *Formidable!*

JANUARY 14   PETERSBURG   1918

Two nights ago, on the way back to Smolny, after making a speech on "How to Organize Competition," I was attacked on the back seat of the car by my old friend and comrade, Fritz Platten. I was in mid-sentence when he grabbed my head and forced it to the floor. He then fell on top of me and I could feel blood trickling down into my eyes. I knew it was blood because I could taste it.

The driver accelerated and we rolled about under the seats as he screeched round the corners. By the time we had returned to normal speed, and I had enough breath to ask, "What the hell do you think you are doing?" I already knew what Fritz had been doing. He had been saving my life.

Fritz had seen back and to the right of us a flash he knew instantly was a rifle being fired. Presumably, it went high because he had time to put his hand on my bald head, and depress it, before a bullet holed the window and creased his knuckles. Our driver did the rest.

Back in the flat, I had an exceptional buffalo-grass vodka and Fritz had his usual quarter-bottle of cis-Alpine grappa. Over the drinks, I remarked on how odd it was that in such an emergency many people (like Fritz) were unable to say anything, even "Watch out!" He had a good answer. "You would have been dead if it hadn't been for my mime," he said. True. Still, *I* would have spoken *as well.*

"Since you were asleep during the key point of my lecture," I said. "I will repeat myself. Far from extinguishing competition, socialism, on the contrary, for the first time creates an opportunity for employing it on a really wide, and on a really mass, scale. We must get rid of the despicable prejudice that only the so-called 'upper classes,' only the rich, and those who have gone through the schools of the rich, are capable of running the state. They can't even produce a decent assassin."

This is exactly how the two of us reacted to the attack. Of course, it was serious, and frightening, at the time. But afterward, we talked of all the tight corners we had been in, how many friends had died in their dozens, how many people we didn't know had died in their hundreds of thousands. So somebody blamed me, and happened to have a gun (as who hasn't these days?) and he loosed off a couple of rounds. If he hadn't had the gun, he might have written a letter to Pravda or perhaps to *Novaya Zhizn.*

Not many people took our rather frivolous view, I'm afraid. *Pravda,* the next day, had a screaming headline on its editorial— *"Beregites!"* ("Watch out!") Just what I'd complained Fritz hadn't said. But then it went on, in crude, false, yellow-press style to warn the bourgeoisie: "For each of our heads, a hundred of yours!"

That was pretty awful and I sent a note telling them so. But then what about *Novaya Zhizn?* The day after that, Gorky also writes an editorial. He denounces me for encouraging *Pravda* and all over an incident in which "a certain joker or bored idler had punctured with a penknife the body of an automobile used by Lenin." This was, if anything, worse as it seemed to suggest that I had made up the whole episode. I sent Gorky a note as well.

What would it be like if I had not drawn the fangs of the capitalist press, and had to deal with the lies of really trained shit-stirrers?

JANUARY 19   PETERSBURG   1918

We are a coalition government. The Left Socialist-Revolutionaries hold the portfolios of Land, Law, Local government, Posts and Telegraphs, State Property and one or two more. They are not what I call Socialists. In France, they could sit in the same seats in a bourgeois Cabinet. In England, they could stand as Lib-Lab radicals. After all, the Right SRs were in the Provisional government. But they are comfortable enough partners for the present.

The first political problem (there have been plenty of economic, social and military ones) we faced together was the Constituent Assembly. Now all revolutions have had to have a Constituent Assembly, ever since 1789. The calling of this body was in our Party program. As it was in the programs of the Kadets, the Trudoviks, the Mensheviks and the SRs. None of them did anything about it when they were in power, though they had plenty of opportunities. So we can take credit for being the first Russian government since the fall of the Tsar to actually carry out their pledge on this.

One of the first decrees we issued was a proclamation of elections for the Assembly in November. It was a mistake, I now see, to invite the nation so soon, in a secret ballot on universal adult suffrage, to choose any sort of parliament. It was being unfair to ourselves for a number of reasons, the main one being that, apart from taking power, we had not yet had time to put more than outlines of a few of our policies into effect.

We had rushed into the thing so quickly that Left and Right SRs were still standing on a united ticket, though most of the candidates were from the conservative wing. Their slate attracted twenty-one million votes, against nine million for us, one and a half million for the Meks and four and a half million for various organizations still representing the bourgeoisie.

Now, there are all sorts of powerful arguments against regarding this ballot as representing the true voice of the people. For instance, that our government partners were submerged by *their* partners and never able to put to the voters the difference between their two platforms. It was significant that here, in Petrograd, where the SR Left had their own list, they and we together won 576,000 votes, giving us an absolute majority over all the others combined (363,000). In the north, center and west of European Russia, we could point out, we got 43 percent of the poll. I am confident that, given the time for a national campaign, say after six months of power, we would have been given the mandate of an absolute majority everywhere. After all, we already had this in the soviets, a body with superior claims to true democracy since every member is elected by those who know him or her personally on a farm, in a factory, on a housing project, etc. where they all work together. But all such pleas sound too like sour grapes.

The Soviet government was ready to accept, in another version of dual power, a sharing of authority with a chamber which had 421 SRs, 183 Bolsheviks and 120 others. All we required was that they should declare support for our joint statement of intent as government, "the Declaration of Rights of the Working and Exploited People." It did not seem much to ask.

I sat in a box in the Tauride Palace for the opening session yesterday. Very soon it was clear that this was an organization dominated by our enemies and they had no intention of making the slightest gesture of conciliation. Sverdlov asked the Assembly as its first act to ratify the Working and Exploited People's Declaration. They refused with scorn, and some amusement. Then there was the election of the Speaker. Maria Spiridonova, the clever, daring, beautiful Left SR who had probably fought and endured more than any other revolutionary under the Tsar, was rejected in favor of the machine-politician Victor Chernov, from the SR's far reactionary past. The Assembly then proceeded to pass a resolution ordering us to give up power and hand over to our opponents. It shows how much they understand about politics, people, realities of the state and the government, that they actually seemed to think we might do so!

It then degenerated into an empty contest of parliamentary rhetoric—for example, a long rallying duel between Bukharin and Tseretelli. This is not our style of running a country. Around four in the morning Sverdlov rang me to say he had sent in a handful of Kronstadt sailors to tell the members that the chamber was to be cleared because "the guard was tired."

This morning, the doors are locked. This afternoon, I have issued a decree dissolving the lot. We were a little uneasy that there could be violent, or at least noticeable, protests from the citizenry. But even the dispersed members have to agree, the populace has taken the news without the slightest stir of interest, let alone concern. In the words that Trotsky used to dismiss the protesting Martov (he thought our takeover was "irregular") on the first day of the Revolution, they have gone to "the rubbish dump of history."

FEBRUARY 23   PETERSBURG   1918

This day, the Red Army is born. "Born" is the exact word for once. It remains weak, uncoordinated, just learning that its various senses and organs exist. But it is a prodigious child, like Hercules in his cradle, growing all the time. The old Russian Army has melted away. "The peasants have voted against any more war," said Radek last weekend, waking me in my camp bed in the Kremlin Office. He had papers in his hand, so I put on my spectacles—"Excuse me, *voted*? How?" He laughed. "With their feet, Ilyich. With their feet. The best way to vote. They've gone home and they're not coming back."

The same weekend the Germans let loose the most tremendous attack from the Baltic to the Black Sea, outflanking Petersburg. While our reps at Brest-Litovsk under Trotsky had begun to clown and posture and rant and coin phrases, the enemy were getting ready to act. Now they could not only tear off all the land they could swallow, but in the process they could squash those troublesome, subversive Communist-Anarchists, and do even the English, French and Americans a favor.

At Pskov, the invaders encountered the defense in depth of new-formed regiments, recruited from factory guards and village defense units. Former soldiers of the Tsar and Kerensky, they had walked away from a front line near the borders of a country too big for them to imagine. They had come home on their own, bringing their weapons with them, to work on the lands the Revolution had released. But because they did not want to fight where the generals put them, that did not mean they would not fight where they had settled themselves. When the front line caught up with them, they formed themselves into another army, the Red Army, and fought back. And because they knew their ground, they fought in a different way, without trenches and parapets, barbed wire and fixed lines of communication. They were like a cloud of bees waiting to swarm. When the Germans came their way, they scattered into distant, individual targets. When the Germans turned back, they descended from every side in a dense, stinging mass. They repeated the maneuver again and again, until the invaders stopped out of sheer, bored frustration. But the point was—they stopped. First at Pskov, then north and south, all along the line.

Gusev is there at Pskov. He telegraphs, in clipped Caesarian sentences, that it isn't a famous victory. We won no battle. But the Germans will not push any further east. Our fighting men, unscathed, watch them from a distance, like Indians on the American plains. When the Germans leave, half of the Russians will go back to the factory and the field. But half will stay on in this new, mobile army, the Red Army. Gusev says the military discovery our troops have made is—"improvise"!

It is a discovery our politicians will have to make too. The Germans will not leave without a price being paid. The negotiations begin again at Brest-Litovsk, if they can be called negotiations where one side dictates not only the offer but also its acceptance. Our regime, our country, the Revolution, they need time and space. We have little time, but lots of space. I must buy the first at the cost of the second. If we had struck a deal earlier, we should not have had to pay so high a price.

MARCH 10   PETERSBURG   1918

Thought in the night—the absolute truth is that without the revolution in Germany, we shall perish.

MARCH 12   MOSCOW   1918

Never have I had such need of whatever props, whatever tools, whatever disciplines, can sustain me and us on course. Like Columbus, like Moses, like Noah, like Galileo, I have to keep saying—yet it *will* move, yet the floods *will* sink, yet the promised land *is* there. I think more sympathetically of the great leader than once I did.

Examples of national renaissance in history are not so rare as one might fear. At the beginning of the last century, much of Europe had to suffer defeats as total and flattening as we have done. The leaders of Prussia, for example, signed a treaty with Napoleon which was as ignominious and despoiling as Brest-Litovsk. This was the peace of Tilsit in 1807. To their contemporaries, the Prussians appeared to have suffered the final, utter humiliation. But the progressive statesmen of the day (von Stein and Gneisenau) used the breathing space afforded them for revitalizing and reshaping their stricken country, building up a new army, preparing for revenge. They knew how to wait, to endure steadfastly the yoke of the conqueror. When it seemed to them the time had come, they made war again. But again were defeated, again signed a treaty, this one even worse than Tilsit. The next time the moment seemed ripe, they rose once more, made another war and *liberated themselves at last*. Where was their former conqueror? On an island in the Atlantic, lord of a few square miles of rocks, being bored to death by his English captors.

I have read the letters and the journals of these Prussians. They resisted as long as they could the logic of their predicament. But in the end, they had to accept that if you have no army, you cannot fight. You make whatever agreement you must. And then you concentrate on building a nation and a society that will not be defeated. They thought it might take a generation, but they achieved their ambition within a decade.

The masses gave us power six months ago in order, above all else, to stop the war. They refused to fight an hour longer for anyone, Tsar, bourgeois government, Soviet or Kerensky. I do not believe this refusal is final. When our new people's state is under deadly threat, they will flood out again on our side. Pskov proved that. But *not yet*. I see this so clearly I can hardly credit that I am in such a minority on CenCom. Who could have forecast that it was only my threat to resign from all jobs, made before today's secret session at the Tauride, which stopped a Dantonesque Trotsky from linking with our ultra-lefts Jacobins to remove me from office?

The Revolution should always be grateful to him for reacting thus to my only trump. The war faction certainly assumed that his ego, his ambition, his theatricality would be thrown into the same balance as his courage, his optimism, his conviction. That here he would proclaim he was right and I was wrong. Why then did he refuse the leadership offered him on a plate?

I am convinced he made this sacrifice entirely out of selfless dedication to the Revolution. That is his only law. So he remains unshakable in his support of me and the peace faction despite enemy moves in the days since the signing—the German seizure of Kiev and most of the Ukraine; the Austrian entry into Odessa; the Turkish occupation of Trebizond. The Germans are determined to rub our noses in the shit. They have ordered me to recognize their puppet government in the Ukraine. They have threatened even deeper invasion of our territory if we support our comrades (mainly peasants) who are being rounded up and executed there. Here Trotsky still urges me to resist, warning that there are more dangers than opportunities in a policy of appeasement.

The Congress falls silent at a most piercing, heart-stopping note. This is the unthinkable in the lexicon of any Marxist theoretician. But Trotsky challenges the worst interpretation head on. If the Soviet republic is so weak that it cannot defend our Ukrainian brothers, then ought we not to admit a frightful possibility? That *"we have come before our time?"* That *"this false spring"* is really another winter? That we should hand over to the Liberals, the Mensheviks, the SRs, the whole ragbag of Constituent Assembly in other words, and go underground to fight our partisan war for yet another decade?

I had to explain again and again (bearing in mind that, though secret, our proceedings could easily be leaked) what would happen if we sent our troops across our borders. *We would lose them,* and help no one else.

If the war faction *had* won, I would have been removed from the leadership of the Party. Trotsky made this clear to the delegates when he explained his decision: "We cannot wage a revolutionary war with a divided Party. A split would be too high a price to pay."

But I really knew how nearly the unity of the Soviet government had been preserved by a hair's breadth when Radek took me aside in the corridor as if for an informal gossip. Smiling in that moony, misshapen way that is so winning, he said, "If I could have found five hundred courageous men in Peter this last week, I'd have imprisoned you and invaded Europe!" I smiled back.

"I know. I had a private room in a Cheka rest home all ready for you under the name of Anacharsis Cloots. You'd have been in it before you recruited your second insurgent." Anyone watching us might have thought we were sharing some tremendous joke.

He squeezed my forearm and hailed another delegate. Karl knows his French Revolutionary characters as if he spent an hour every morning having coffee with them in his favorite Paris café. He did not need to be reminded who Cloots was: the leader of that Commune jointly suppressed by Danton and Robespierre, when he tried to invade Europe in defiance of Jacobin policy.

Outside the palace, a light rain is falling upon the few pieces of our luggage, piled there by the commissars and their assistants. Now the foreign policy is finally agreed, our planned, but unannounced, move to Moscow can begin. The general mood is resigned, but level-headed. We all appreciate that the conflict which must have raged inside Trotsky was based on genuine, opposing theorems. He had dramatized the dialectic inside himself. "With a weak country behind us, with a passive peasantry and a tired proletariat, only a decision that unified the Party was possible," he summed up.

I applauded this time right out in the front where I could be seen, exhibiting real admiration and gratitude. I was even thankful for one warning barb that penetrated deep—"Lenin must still beware that we do not sacrifice the one thing that makes life worth living for the sake of merely carrying on being alive."

What nobody says, what many do not know, what those who do know cannot bear to say to themselves, the dreaded open secret upon whose temporary lid I sit, keeping it closed with my weight, is this—*we* have no troops! We have a defense force which will protect its own patch so far as its eyes can see. But as for an ARMY, an offensive fighting arm that will surge out to meet an enemy halfway, we Reds have barely the blueprints.

MARCH 15   MOSCOW   1918

It is three days since we moved the seat of government here to Moscow—a change that makes nobody happy, but everybody approves enough not to oppose. The decision is full of ironies.

Delegations of workers came to Smolny to protest against the transfer. I couldn't deny that we had denounced Kerensky for just such a plan, arguing it meant handing our capital city to the Germans. They mentioned rumors, which *they* didn't believe but *others* might, that this was part of an agreement with Kaiser Wilhelm to allow him to occupy the cradle of the Revolution. I maintained that by being in Moscow we would help ensure not just the safety of the government but of Peter itself. The Germans might take risks to capture the capital *and* the government, but what would they want with an enemy Bolshevik city, full of hungry mouths? It was not a very reassuring argument (for obvious reasons). And I saw that it too might have been made by Kerensky.

The CenCom were hardly easier to convince, though some of their objections were almost certifiably eccentric. I could understand Zinoviev, newly elected chairman of the Peter Soviet, feeling that he had been demoted overnight from a metropolitan, into a provincial, boss. But Lunacharsky! Only days after the Revolution, he *resigned* in protest at a planned elimination of St. Basil's in Moscow which had never been planned. Now he says that he is reluctant to leave Smolny: that "symbol of the people's accession to power."

My first close look at the Kremlin. Could be a combination armory and harem designed by Genghis Khan. Scarcely seems the place for the first workers' and peasants' government in history. But then Smolny had been a boarding school for noble girls.

Even what we eat here is a sort of a paradox too. I don't think about food much so I hadn't really noticed what Lev Davidovich keeps denouncing (we share a small dining room)—that the flour,

rice and barley all have sand in them. Now I look it does seem
odd we are served red Ket caviare, sometimes twice a day. T.
laughs: "Speak to our Commissar for Foreign Trade. Russia hasn't
exported a jar since '16. It's your revolutionary duty to consume
as much as you can to save on pig's trotters and salmon heads for
the masses."

MAY 28   **MOSCOW**   **1918**

Passed before my eyes, for possible publication next month, an
essay by the poet Alexander Blok, *The Intelligentsia and the Revolution*. B.-B. has marked this passage:

> We Russians are living through an epoch which has had few things
> to equal it in grandeur. Our aim is to remake everything. To build
> everything anew, so that our lying, dirty, boring, monstrous life
> becomes a just and clean, a joyous and beautiful life. The Russian
> Revolution aimed at embracing the world. A true revolution can-
> not wish for less. . . . "The peace and the brotherhood of the
> people"—that is the symbol under which the Russian Revolution
> is taking place. It is of this that its torrent is roaring. This is the
> music which those with ears must hear.

What can I say? *Nihil obstat*—no objection. But then who am I—
the Pope? I must discourage people from sending me things like
this as if they were nervous about my reaction. As if they might
countermand whatever instructions have been given should I show
some hint of disapproval or irritation. I must get it clear—I have
no intention of interfering in the publication of cultural works.

Well . . . that is not entirely true. I must not deceive *myself*!

Of course. I do reserve a right to interfere. But if any work
is recommended by reasonable, trustworthy comrades, whose taste
nevertheless may be different from mine, I would never try to
stop it being printed. What I might do is *suggest*—no more—that
the print order be kept around 5,000 rather than 50,000. Those
who want such stuff, so long as it is not openly counterrevolutionary, ought to be able to get it. Perhaps after a bit of searching and
trouble . . . why not? Almost nothing should be banned completely.
But nor should almost anything be issued in an edition of a quarter
of a million which some rather overexcited executives in publishing
seem to have convinced themselves is normal.

Myself, I am not able to succumb to the peristaltic waves of admiration for Blok's October poem, *The Twelve,* which appear to have gripped (*griped?*) the gut of the public and the commentators alike.

It is as if the truffle-hunters of culture feel surprised and embarrassed about the Revolution ever having actually happened. So they are grateful for any convert to the cause who proclaims that it is a genuine step forward for humankind. How wonderful! *Imagine!* A Symbolist poet, writing in Russian, someone taken seriously by the cultural élite of Berlin and London. Above all, admired hero of that sophisticated city where even the sewermen and market porters juggle with *les images,* Paris. He has been able to find us crude Bolsheviks a fitting subject for his subtle verse.

The Twelve is effective enough most of the way—a passably vivid picture of a platoon of Red Guards, earthy, vulgar, tough, patrolling through the Petersburg night; white snow, black sky, yellow flashes of gunfire, red stains of blood. I remember this too, creeping through the fog and mist, hiding in doorways, sliding and slipping on the ice, a phantom world where friend and enemy might swap over from street to street. I make no objection to Blok's soldiers, though their conduct is more probable than admirable. He wrote his poem in January this year, within months of the events. I even savor the irony of highlighting a floating banner proclaiming "All Power to the Constituent Assembly" within days of the Bolshevik Party having dispersed it. We are not ashamed of what we did, however the undercover bourgeoisie and their left-sounding allies whine. But what I definitely do not appreciate is Blok's finale—the twist in the tale that apparently has made it notorious.

> Onward still the Twelve go striding;
> In their rear—a starving cur;
> And with bloody banner leading,
> Hidden from the howling storm,
> Safe from human hurt or harm,
> In a chaplet of white roses,
> Stepping through the pearly snowdust,
> Shrouded in the snowy mist,
> In the distance—Jesus Christ.

Who needs Jesus to elevate our Revolution to its proper place as one of the great cleansing, liberating, noble events of modern times? Blok has already said as much in his essay. Rather too much, to my mind—I hate this gushing rhetoric, this religious sentimentality. All right, it's more or less true. Say it once, and that's enough. Anyone can mouth "Revolution." What we have to do is live it.

I don't see that Jesus is really good enough to march at the head of our column. We've got plenty of heroes and martyrs of our own. Do these poets and their admiring critics know the first thing about Jesus? I wish, first of all, they'd stop tagging on Christ, as if "Christ" were a surname—"Jesus Godovitch Christov." It is based on the Latin for "anointed," i.e., the Messiah. Since he isn't our Messiah, it is misleading and rather silly for us to keep awarding him the title. Like liberal republicans who urged the abolition of the monarchy but fell over themselves to repeat "Your Royal Highness" when they met a minor princeling. You can still find them in Britain and France. And Jesus, we can be fairly sure, was a name no one among his own people ever called him. In Palestine, he would be known as Yeshu, translated by us as Joshua. "Jesus" happens to be the Latin equivalent. But what did Jesus ever do? Not much. What did he preach? Not a lot. (I can never get over him, God's only son, not having written a book.) But it is exactly the things he didn't do, and didn't say, that tell us the sort of hopeless ally he would be for us. He didn't raise a hand against the Romans, cruel, greedy, alien, colonial exploiters of his people and occupiers of his country. He kept clear of the national struggle for independence as much as he did from the class struggle. There are traces in the New Testament texts that have come down to us, heavily edited and rewritten, which suggest he may once have been a much more militant figure—selling your cloak and buying a sword and so on. But in the received version, he's a pacifist, a conciliator, a nonactivist, almost a Menshevik.

And what does he say that is positive, specific, progressive, giving us radical guidance in our daily life? No denunciation of slavery as an institution. Nothing about the exploitation of servant by master, or laborer by landowner. No demand for equality for women, or the end of their use as beasts of burden or objects of sexual abuse. Not even a condemnation of cruelty to animals. No improvement, really, on the morality of the Jews. In the Talmud, it is written: "Do not do unto others that which it would be disagreeable to you to suffer yourself, that is the main part of the law; all the rest is only commentary." And even this can also be found, before Jesus, in Sextus, in Isocrates, in Lao-tse, in Buddha.

No, I do not think I want Jesus as an advance scout of any Red Guard platoon I am in. Better than his essays, better than *The Twelve*, I like Blok's latest work, *The Scythians*. It tells me nothing

I did not know, but it warms the fire in the belly. In days like this, when there is little else in our bellies, it's welcome. What about this for an opener?

> You are but millions. Our unnumbered nations
> Are as sands upon the shore.
> We are the Scythians! We are the slit-eyed Asians!
> Try to wage war with us—you'll try no more!
> You've had whole centuries. We—a single hour.

I've suggested we set that to music and then get our bands playing it. We need a new "Marseillaise."

JUNE 25   MOSCOW   1918

When we were an underground, conspirational party, I never cared much about the moral constitution of any valuable comrades. I did not want to know how they behaved toward their lovers, what they did with money, how many weaknesses of character they were hiding. I was much attacked for this neutralism, but I think I was right. The point was—could this person do that job? Was he, or she, true to the Revolution? Our aim was to move, advance, attack, subdue. I did not want the best man to win—I wanted our man to win. The good loser is still a loser, perhaps invariably a loser. The bad winner nevertheless wins. You don't halt your fire chief, or distract the pilot of your airplane, to take his confession or audit his books.

After the Revolution, everything is reversed. We have occupied the territory through the looking-glass. Every kind of corruption is everywhere. The internal life has become central. Power is no longer fleeting, insubstantial, easily acquired and lost. It has turned solid, real, lasting, inheritable, transferable, buyable and sellable. It is crucial now that we who ride the juggernaut are not easily flattered, seduced, suborned.

Napoleon made his brothers kings, his marshals princes. Some created dynasties that long outlasted his emperorship. I make sure I am not tempted. I know my family's worth better than anyone. My two sisters are exactly where they should be according to talent and experience. Who challenges Manyasha's place on the editorial board of *Pravda*? She is almost too educated as a communicator. She has studied in Russia, Belgium, France and Switzerland. She speaks half a dozen languages as effortlessly as Mother did. Her medical knowledge outweighs that of most doctors—I even forgive her joining up as a nurse on the outbreak of war.

Anna—Anyuta—is different, very much an acquired taste. She unnerves people, puts them off but also puts them on their honor. In her presence, it is hard to exaggerate, to boast, to retell the story in a way that puts you in a better light. These is something about her of the *tricoteuse* at the guillotine, of the *chatelaine* and the *concierge,* the lady at the cash desk, but in a most superior, intellectual establishment. You want to give her a title in French. She has been enormously useful to me, even more than Nadya. Sometimes I feel I have stood in her way by forcing her to be my "stand-in" (as they say in the theater).

Trotsky suggested as much to me once. (When? I ought to have written it here.) I think it must have been one of those long, strained nights at the end of October. "You know, Ilyich," he said, "gender is to women what class is to men, what color is to races. Biology is biography. If your Anna had not been always condemned to have first Sasha, then you, as the dominant male in front of her, *she* might have been Lenin!"

Certainly, she has been the true editor of everything I have written. If I give my profession as "publicist," Anyuta is the one who taught me the subtle technicalities of the art. Time and again, she persuaded me to doctor my language, to clarify my ideas, to restrain my *rages,* to target my propaganda from afar with an exactitude my enemies could never explain. She was the explanation. Ever since that first tussle over the letter at Kokushkino just after I was expelled from Kazan U. (I know I described it in my diary at the time).

Now she has a middling job in the Commissariat of Education. Below her capacity, because everyone knows she is Lenin's sister. Her husband, Mark Elizarov, is a stolid Bolshevik, one of the few with experience of business, first in marine insurance, then in Volga steamboats. He had been made Commissar of Transport— we need experts we can trust. But no one who knows them both would doubt his wife's superiority in sheer brain-power and originality of thought, grasp of *things as they are.*

What about Mitya, the handsome doctor for whom the phrase "bedside manner" might have been invented? My own experience, using him as a consultant on family health, has not been very happy. So far I have vetoed all attempts to give him some prominent government role—until yesterday. Sverdlov rang, one of the few, like Anyuta, who answers questions I do not have to ask.

"What do you say to your Mitya as Director of Recreation and Rest Homes?"

"What recreation?"

"Who knows?"

"How many rest homes have we?"

"None."

"Fine, Yakov Mikhailovich. You have my vote."

JULY 17   **MOSCOW**   **1918**

I received a report by telegraph direct from Ekaterinburg that the regional Soviet has executed Nicholas Romanov, former Tsar, his wife, his son, his four daughters. I gave no orders for this act, having left discretion on the matter, depending on circumstances, to our people on the spot. Nevertheless, I approve without reservation. I would have done the same without hesitation.

I have always had a reluctant admiration for Nechaev, a revolutionist much slandered and scorned by milksop revolutionaries. People forget that Sergei Genadievich had a unique imaginative talent, an ability to invent special techniques of conspiratorial work everywhere, even from a solitary confinement dungeon. Above all, he developed the power to give his thoughts such startling formulations that they remain forever imprinted on your memory. Instantly there comes back to me the words of one of his catechisms. Replying to the question—in 1870, the year of my birth —"Which members of the reigning house must be destroyed?" he gave the brisk answer, "The whole Great Responsory." This formulation was so simple and clear it could be understood by everyone living in Russia at the time. Then the vast majority of the people, in one way or another, for one reason or another, attended the Orthodox Church. And so everyone knew the Great Responsory which listed all those members of the Tsar's family, to the furthest degree, whom we were *commanded* to love, admire, obey and give thanks to God for. The most unsophisticated reader then, asking himself which of them on the great day of liberation should be destroyed, would see the obvious, inevitable answer at a glance: "Why, the entire house of the Romanovs." They were the ones who chose to write themselves onto our list. It was an instruction simple to the point of genius.

I would not have complained if the telegram from Ekaterinburg had included the whole Great Responsory.

I am only sorry that our summary revolutionary justice was

obliged to fall also on Nicholas Romanov's physician, cook, cham-
bermaid and waiter. Possibly they could have been retrained and
educated to serve the people in some less revolting fashion.

JULY 18   MOSCOW   1918

This afternoon in the middle of a discussion of the Council of
People's Commissars—*Sovnarkom*—about the new public health
decrees, Sverdlov entered and sat down beside me. Commissar of
Health Semashko was in full windy flood, so I was happy to break
in and request the floor for S. to make an important announcement.

"I wish to announce," he said, in his announcing voice, "that
in Ekaterinburg, in accordance with the decision of the local authorities, Nicholas has been shot. They report that he had been
making plans to escape and the Czech Legion was within striking
distance of the city. The presidium of the Central Executive Committee have already decided to register their approval."

Knowing the news already, I preserved impassivity, looking
at each Sovnarkom member in turn.

The Tsar has a hiding-place in almost every Russian soul. They
have been brought up with the Little Father's eye on them from
morning to night. Despite what their reason tells them, deep down
in what Lev Davidovich says psychologists now call the "unconscious" they cherish childish feelings of awe and loyalty. After all,
even our tough, rude, crude Joseph Vissarionovich confessed to
me once that he often has dreams of the Tsarina cradling him in
her arms, and suckling him, like a babe. My own roots were torn
out, and the wound cauterized, when Sasha was hanged. I saw that
all those round the table were moved to some degree. And I knew
that a discussion would serve no purpose, only the release of unhealthy emotions.

I have always sensed as a practical agitator and propagandist
(what the theoretical evidence is, I do not know) that the best time
to hit your audience and get them moving in the direction you
want is when they have just been shocked and aroused by some
unexpected event. What that is scarcely matters, even whether
rationally it is to your benefit or not. It can be an outburst of
violence (gunfire, hand-to-hand fighting), or simply noise and lights
(say, an explosion, a fire, a thunderstorm), or news (triumph or
disaster will serve equally). When your listeners are off-balance,

you brand yourself upon them as fiercely as you can so that all their free-floating emotions, now broken loose, then unite and home in on you. Today could have been an occasion for an attack on the Tsars *à la* Nechaev. I thought not. Rather an opportunity for sardonic, callous, soldier's humor.

Sverdlov was standing by the door.

"I will officially release the news that the former Tsar has been put to death. But the others?" Everyone waited. "In *Izvestia* tomorrow," I said. "I suggest the form of words—'*Nicholas Romanov's wife and children have been sent to a safe place.*' " There was a rattle of laughter running round the room like a Chinese firecracker, or a succession of machine gun bursts. I raised my hand to stop it almost before it had begun.

"Thank you, comrades. Now, Commissar Semashko, I think you were explaining Clause 5 . . ."

I knew I now had them firmly at my side, on the Revolution's side. None of them could later say that he had protested, or even disagreed in silence, after that laughter. We were all bonded together as chuckling regicides. And why not?

After all, as I had argued long before we had come near to getting our hands on the levers of power, "If in such a cultured country as England, which had never known a Mongolian yoke, the oppression of a bureaucracy, or the arbitrary rule of a military caste, it was still found necessary to behead one crowned brigand in order to teach kings to be 'constitutional' monarchs, then in Russia we will be forced to behead at least one hundred Romanovs."

It seems I exaggerated a trifle.

JULY 23   MOSCOW   1918

Today tele-message from Belobdorov, executive chairman of local Soviet—REGRET INFORM YOU EKATERINBURG OCCUPIED WHITE GUARDS AND CZECH BATTALION.

SEPTEMBER 7   MOSCOW   1918

TROTSKY RECOVERY PROCEEDING EXCELLENTLY LENIN. Those are the first five words I have put on paper since August 30. I hope they are true. Everybody tells me so. But in the end I must know best.

It is really very interesting, from the point of view of the scientific observer, being shot, twice.

I had made several strong, passionate speeches that night. Before the Revolution, I rather despised rhetoric. I went for facts, argument, logic, realism. Now, I'm afraid, that approach doesn't work quite so well anymore. Our situation is frightening—our borders are reduced to the Old Russia of the seventeenth century; everywhere there are plotters, SRs, tsarists, foreign intelligence agents, bourgeois bureaucrats; everywhere there are invaders, generals like Kolchak and Denikin, with French, British, Japanese and German money and arms; production is forecast for the next twelve months as at best one-quarter of 1913. I could go on. But I cannot say this to my factory audiences. What they see themselves is horrifying enough. I dare not pass on bad news they have so far been spared.

All I can do is acknowledge the defeats we have already suffered and published, gathering what comfort there is from pointing out that it has not happened here. "It could be worse!"—not the best of slogans. But it works. What has happened in the Ukraine, the Volga, Siberia, the Caucasus? The Soviets have been driven out by the counterrevolutionaries, by other nations' armies. And the result? The aristos have taken back their land. The workers' unions have been suppressed—no more eight-hour day. The factory owners have recovered their mills and works. The proletariat is forbidden not just to strike, but to complain, to negotiate, under penalty of being fined, locked-in, locked-out, ridden down and beaten, by the returning police and Cossacks. "That's your choice—a new Tsar or a new world. There is no in-between. Victory or Death!"

The last time I ended on those words, at the Michelson Works, I glared as I said them in order to distract from any lack of conviction in my voice. And I was looking straight at a couple three or four ranks back. As the applause rolled deep and throbbing round the factory yard, I saw these faces, pale as suet, like people about to be executed. There was something dreadfully wrong here. I was nearly asphyxiated with the stink of danger. Yet I ignored it, against all the lessons I had learned. I was hurrying to the exit, relieved that the speech was going down so well, anxious not to face any too-awkward questions.

I actually made my way toward the pair as the man (Novikov, it seems he was called) cleared a path for me toward the woman (Fanny Kaplan, like her companion, a right-wing SR). I could not have arranged myself as a better target if I had rehearsed the whole thing. She brought out a revolver from under her coat and fired three times.

I watched like a child. Heh, that's funny. Bang! Nothing! Has it missed or is it a blank? Bang! Ouch! That hurt, like a punch on the arm. This could be serious. Bang! Another punch up around the neck. The crowd were scattering like dropped marbles. The ground and sky were tumbling round and round and I was on my back on the cobbles.

I knew then, well, I knew all along, even before the gun appeared, that this was an attempt to kill me. "Victory or Death!" What a jest! Yet all I could think was how awful the woman looked, pasty, sallow, sullen, sour.

Afterward is now a blur. I'm told I insisted on being taken to my flat in the Kremlin, not a hospital. I would not be deterred from walking up the stairs. I kept telling the doctors, "It's nothing. You're getting worked up over nothing." Nadya came and I said she looked tired and ought to lie down. I seemed to want to take over and run the whole show.

I remember nothing else—no pain—until two days later when I woke up feeling really very well. My body is still tough and resilient, even carrying its extra load of lead. It's my mind that seems to be slowing down in its intake. Who can blame it? Almost nothing behaves the way I envisaged. The brain is not geared to facing a new challenge every hour, eighteen hours a day. What we have won, it turns out, is only the first battle of what will be a very, very long war.

OCTOBER 23   MOSCOW   1918

Who would believe such twists and turns outside one of those spy "thrillers" so popular in the West by authors like E. Phillips Oppenheim and William le Queux?

For three days, I now learn, a man with white hair and beard, and what veterans call "a shrapnel face," has been presenting himself at Smolny and insisting on being taken to the CenCom (no longer there, of course). He gave his name, but no one recalled having heard it before. Eventually, he was arrested as a nuisance and turned over to the Cheka. One of the smarter ones rang me direct—"Malinovsky is here again!"

I asked that he be sent straight to Moscow and allowed no contact with anyone until delivered for interrogation at the Lubianka.

NOVEMBER 1   MOSCOW   1918

After nine days of close examination in the cellars of the Cheka, Malinovsky is today produced before the High Revolutionary Tribunal of the All-Russian Central Executive Committee of the Soviet in the Kremlin. I could not stay away and yet I could not take part, either as witness or judge.

The prosecutor is Krylenko, friend of Bukharin and Troyanovsky (possibly also the new lover of Elena Rozmirovich Troyanovskaya, if Gregory's gossip is correct) and former assistant to Malinovsky at the Duma. He does a good job, parading witnesses from both our side and the former government's. Most impressive are testimonies in the box of Dzhunkovsky, Vissarionov, Popov and Malinovsky's wife, Stefania.

Malinovsky himself made a six-hour speech, staring at me from time to time in a most disturbing way. I looked at my cap and listened. He admitted his treachery but blamed it on blackmail. He said he left the Duma on impulse and without being instructed by anyone. He asserted, repeatedly, that when he came to me in Poronin I must have known of his role as police agent! He exaggerated his contribution to the Revolution by his activities in the POW camp. He protested that all he expected was the death penalty, but he wanted his comrades above all to know the truth.

If he was not shot, he believed that, as someone converted to Bolshevism before Trotsky (ha!), he could serve the first socialist state in the world in many honorable ways. Afterward, some of the Tribunal told me that they believed him. I expressed no opinion but left them to deliberate through the night.

NOVEMBER 2   MOSCOW   1918

Woken at 6 A.M. by a call from the Tribunal. M. has been found guilty and the sentence is death by shooting. I register this decision but avoid comment.

7 A.M. Further call. Roman Vatslavovich Malinovsky, age forty-two, has been executed in the Kremlin gardens by a bullet in the back of the neck.

I slept very late.

NOVEMBER 12   MOSCOW   1918

I have authorized—as is now usual *after the event*—the shooting by the Cheka of a number of enemies of the Revolution. Today's figure is eight hundred. It is not a statistic that any enemy of tyrants and oppressors, any opponent of policemen and executioners, can register without a twinge of unease, a flutter of self-doubt. Their Terror could not crush us, Rosa Luxemburg argued; why do we think our Terror will crush them?

As I pointed out to her, there is little logic in that proposition. Where is the law of history that says that what has not happened will go on not happening? True—*we* were not crushed by Terror. But not because we were so adamant, sincere, courageous, well-organized. Our opponents can also be unflinching, fanatical, brave and disciplined. We survived uncrushed only because their Terror was not powerful *enough,* not sustained, not repeated, not ever-growing, all-reaching *enough.* We shall not make that mistake! A mistake made not just by their side, by the Tsar, by Charles I of England, by Louis-Napoleon of France, not just by the forces of reaction and absolutism, of feudal lord and bourgeois boss, but also a mistake made by our side, by Cromwell, by Robespierre, by the Paris Commune, by Garibaldi, by the leaders of revolution, by the creators of socialism.

Terror's nature is such that it does not operate like a sniper's rifle, or even the hosing stream of bullets from the barrel of the machine gun. So long as it is directed by rational decision, according to information provided by the naked eye, the telescopic sight, or the information of spies, then it can be avoided. The more important the enemy figure to be neutralized, the more likely he is to keep out of sight of sharpshooters, to doff his officer's epaulettes or (as in Shakespeare) his kingly crown. What our victim (he or she—our Terror must be as sexually impartial as our Welfare) cannot anticipate, cannot avoid by planning, by disguise, by counterintelligence, is random Terror, mass Terror. Terror instituted not just by Soviet authorities, or by secret police, or Red Guards, or by militant unionists. But Terror, boiling up out of the ground, pouring through the holes in society like lava from a volcano.

We are battling against the forces that run, as they have always done, every state in the world, except ours. They have a planet to lose, the loot of a thousand years. In Marx's phrase, we are storming heaven. To stay where we are, we have to mobilize a tidal wave of Terror that frightens even us. Eight hundred counterrevolutionaries is a tiny skirmish in the class war. After all, think of *their* Great War. It had lasted (when it ended yesterday) 1,561 days. It was fought only for greed, the new young burglars against the fat, old fences. Was there a single day when so few as eight hundred were slaughtered? Their dead were people who had committed no crime, except obeying the command to take arms against other people who had also committed no crime. In the front line have always been the poor, the ignorant, the gullible, the exploited. During 1915, Russia lost one million men on the Eastern Front. The Turks deported 1,750,000 Armenians to Middle Eastern deserts where 600,000 died and another 600,000 just disappeared. In the Dardanelles, the British, and their colonial dupes from Australia and New Zealand, sacrificed a quarter of a million men between April and December. The Battle of Verdun lasted nine months—281,000 German casualties, 315,000 French.

And what were *you* writing then, my dear Rosa?

The finest, the most intelligent, the best trained forces of international Socialism . . . the Workers of Great Britain, France, Germany and Russia, are being slaughtered in masses. That is a greater crime by far than the brutish sack of Louvain or the destruction of Rheims Cathedral. It is a deadly blow against the power which holds the whole future of humanity, the only power than can preserve the values of the past and carry them on into a newer and better human society.

I agreed with you then, when we were alone and unsuccessful. I still agree now, when we have captured one of their citadels. Those masses are at last rallying to our side, on every side.

Can you not see that our petty Terror is not even near to approaching the awesome, unparalleled, apocalyptic scale of theirs? By the time the capitalist powers called a halt—probably temporary—to their mass slaughter, ten million human creatures had died in Europe and Asia. Thirty million were missing or wounded. Now millions more are dying of influenza. Millions more will soon fall to famine, plague and yet more warfare.

We have taken Russia out of the war—the first nation with the first government to lay down its arms. How dare those gentlemen reproach us with Terror? As for Rosa, well, she is a woman. But what am I saying? I have learned in my years of struggle, especially since the war began, that my truest, my bravest, my least opportunist comrades, even if I do have to give them the flick of the ringmaster's whip now and then, have been women—Nadya, of course, Inessa, Rosa, Tver, Sandra.

One of the key mistakes of all past revolutions has been—not to shoot too many, but not to shoot enough. What about such as General Krasnov released on word of honor to cease fighting? We shall see.

FEBRUARY 6   MOSCOW   1919

I have few illusions about the peasants. I do not think they are wiser, nobler, more heroic, more in touch with reality, than I am. On the contrary, what I fear is that it may be their prejudices, their lusts, their fears, their fantasies that our Soviet state will have to indulge and rely on for survival. I have set aside Fridays at my Kremlin office for visits from them.

Today there was a delegation from Penza, Kursk, Smolensk and Samara—some of them places in which I once lived. They hadn't expected to meet the Chairman of the People's Commissars in person. I could tell from the mingled excitement, bravado and satisfaction in their voices next door without being able to distinguish a word. I determined I should speak to them with absolute candor and precision, but if possible spend more time listening. I need to hear what they have to say more than they do what I have. The result turned out to be a bit of a surprise. I have to say it—very *Russian*.

They were carrying the usual great bundles, bags and sacks, so odd-shaped that it might be a good children's party game guessing what can possibly be inside. A stuffed octopus with two wooden legs? An easel and blackboard? They unloaded them in the waiting room, blocking me off from the rest of the world—a convenient way to set up an assassination attempt. (Must tell B.B. to keep an eye on such apparently accidental setups. I have had several warnings from Central Security that they are picking up whispers of an approaching attempt on my life. It is a strange feeling. I wonder how Nicholas liked it?)

They filed in, stood in a line in front of my desk. They were not, I was glad to see, at all overawed, but rather skeptical. As if being shown a new machine that city-folk claimed would change and improve their lives, but might, instead, give off a puff of blue smoke and seize up forever. They were on the watch for corruption—signs of luxury, vanity, autocracy, laziness, pride, pomposity. All the things they had learned to associate with their rulers, lords and masters.

I saw them clocking up the number of telephones—five in all. Three on my desk, one fixed to the wall, another on the window ledge. On the landing, beyond the other doors leading off the waiting room, there are half a dozen instruments and a switch-board. Our Army Signal Corps set this up—a brilliant fellow! He also arranged that my telephones do not startle with that tooth-jangling ring but just softly purr. When I am working late into the night, even this can be too much of an assault on the nerves. So the telephone nearest my right arm, its number known only to a few key comrades, never sounds at all. It just glows with a faint golden light (my patent).

Just after these were installed, I had a visit from Karl Bern-hardovich. He was on his usual intelligence-gathering round. At a subcommittee I had set up about possible technical advances in the transmission, and publication, of news to the mass public, while others speculated about the future of talking motion-pictures, shortwave radio, photographs via telegraph, and the rest, Radek interrupted out of turn—"You want the quickest, most efficient means? In my experience, *gossip!*" On this occasion, he examined, as he always did, each new acquisition, particularly the telephones. He laughed—"Leo Tolstoy would have claimed his prophecy was coming true."

I was not intended to understand, so he went on. "Don't you remember? When the telephone first came to Russia all your rich country gents were scrabbling for this new toy. The press said it would shrink the country to European size. Only Leo Nikolaevich issued a mysterious warning to the old world. 'Beware of the Genghis Khan who will rule through his telephones!'" What would the old fraud have said if he could see, not just the switchboard, but the banks of Hughes teletype machines which fill the corridor? This is the latest bourgeois American technical wizardry. Across the Atlantic, they use it only for business. Here it supplies the ropes of my governmental web with which I can daily envelop more and more of Russia. Already the telegraph gives me permanent, safe, *instantaneous* links with our soldiers, our major cities and railway junctions, the Cheka.

But the peasants. Ten of them, as I manage to count when they stop changing places, pushing each other forward and back-ward, seem impressed by the Head of the Soviet State's array of governing equipment. They hardly glance at my two socialist icons on the wall—an enlarged photograph of Marx and a bronze plaque with a bas-relief of Khalturin. They recognize neither. They take little notice of my wall clock which never keeps time. No country-man has any idea of Moscow time. He regards it as a kind of metropolitan pretension with little relevance to *true time*. This, as everyone knows, is regulated by sun and moon and can only be observed in the country.

They nudge each other at the number of my pencils, every one sharpened to a hypodermic point. These are the tools of my trade, as they see it. (I sometimes wonder if they are not the in-struments of my addiction.) An ambitious peasant is graded by his neighbors (the only people whose opinion he gives a damn about) according to the number of spades, billhooks, plow blades, scythes he can muster. Clearly, I must be equivalent of a lord among landlords. My pencils are flanked by stacks of pens; at least two pairs of scissors; a careless scatter of paperknives; several desk calendars in different languages; an elaborately decorative inkwell with twin lamps; an ashtray with its own lighter device. (*Never* used for smokers, who must instantly extinguish in here—but for burn-ing sensitive papers.)

What rivets most eyes, I notice, is my bronze statuette of the Ape with a Skull. It dominates the desk, and appears in almost every one of the publicity photographs that B.-B. insists be taken when I have famous or influential visitors. The ape is about ten inches high, hardly a flattering portrait of anyone's ancestor. Outsize ears, a wide, slack mouth, long arms with giant hands, and an expression of puz-zled idiocy. It is sitting on a pile of books, more or less in the posture of Rodin's *Le Penseur*. While it strokes its dropaway jaw with one set of fingers, it holds up for examination a skull rather bigger than its own, a parody of Hamlet in the graveyard.

I like it. It starts off in my head several apocalyptic fantasies which come as a relief from the endless detail of government. In one, I see a next-century earth, devastated by some global calamity, perhaps natural, perhaps human, possibly the result of a revolu-tionary war which ironically has obliterated the future of mankind. We will no longer need to worry about tomorrow because we will not have even today. The ape sits on books, for which it can have no other use, and wonders where this advanced creature, *Homo sapiens*, has gone. The question, I imagine, is—"Could the pattern start all over again?"

Pretty banal stuff. But it is surprising what old romantic bol-sters of rags and patches the mind will rest on when it needs a change from the strains of confronting reality.

More instructive is how visitors react to the object. Most ordinary people, simple folk, peasants, the typical worker, assume it must be a famous masterpiece of great art. Mostly, they do not warm to it themselves, but they are used to having their taste corrected, ugly objects foisted on them as beautiful, by superior persons. Then there are upper-class, international sophisticates, familiar with Europe's best stores and galleries. (I do get one or two of these.) They hate it but imagine it must be handmade, possibly an original, created specially for the President of Sovnarkom. They also assume I admire it.

The only visitors who would recognize it for what it is never come to see me. They are the self-made, philistine social-climbers who fence themselves in with endless possessions to give their empty personalities a ballast of would-be comfort and culture. They often, at least, actually like my ape. Many of them probably have it. They would have picked it up at a souvenir stall or a tourist shop.

I am one of the few who see that it is crude, cheap, harmless *dreck*. But it pleases me because of that, not despite that. It also carries a commodity not very common in my life—"sentimental value." Inessa bought it for me at a little seaside flea market, near St. Jean de Luz, after much kulak (or French housewife) style bargaining. It was several months before I discovered there was a piece of paper pasted underneath it in her handwriting. It was a quotation from someone who was once known as "Russia's first philosopher," Vladimir Sergevich Solovyev. It is still there, and reads: "The Russian intelligentsia produced a faith based on a strange syllogism—We are descended from the apes, therefore we must love one another."

What does that mean? I ask. After all, I am supposed to be a little bit of a philosopher in my own way. She laughed. It was like a cat running along a piano keyboard. "It means nothing," she said. "That is why it is so impressive. Almost nothing means nothing. I want you to remember it. It will be our secret."

What did *that* mean? I knew better than to ask. I kissed her hand.

FEBRUARY 7   MOSCOW   1919

Hughes's message from my roving "snapper-up of unconsidered trifles" (Is everything from *Hamlet*?) Ozerov's dispatch shows how

different the real feet-in-the-cow-shit experience of the construc-
tion of socialism is from what is churned out in official reports,
propaganda speeches and library pamphlets.

He visited a village near Mogilev, almost at the limits of Soviet
control, choosing one at random. He used "caution." That is tel-
egraphese, I know (having seen him in operation), for sticking
fairly near to the armor-plated, converted delivery van he travels
in. It involves walking with a crouch so as to get the more quickly
at the pistols in his knee boots. But the peasants were very friendly
when they heard he was a Bolshevik. They showed him how they
had divided up the landlord's acres into nice reasonable plots. It
seemed like a model cooperative farm. Just as he was leaving, the
village elder shook him by the hand and said: "Tell them in Moscow, we are all behind you Bolsheviks. You needn't worry. If the
Communists ever come here, we'll trounce them. Those Reds have
no supporters among Mogilev people."

Ozerov was naturally taken aback, but kept his face straight.
He asked what was so good about one and so bad about the other.
The elder replied: "It's easy to see you know little about country
politics, comrade, no matter how clever you are in Moscow. There's
no comparison. The Bolsheviks got rid of the Tsar, stopped the
war, and gave us back our land. The Communists are the ones
who have set up their own Great Responsory. They want us to
fight in new wars, and they are taking our land for the government."

This is real country politics. This is the sort of intelligence I
want to hear—not stuff about capitalist conspiracies and SR plots.
I can leave all that to the Cheka. Ozerov confirms what I have
often thought but hesitated to admit, even to myself. In fighting
for the Revolution, the peasants were our natural allies—"Peace,
Bread and Land!" They have believed since time immemorial that
all the earth of Russia belongs to them, not to Tsars or landlords
or even village councils. So in building socialism, the peasants are
our natural enemy. They do not want social ownership. They do
not believe in equality. They do not give a pig's fart for the proletariat, or any other town-dweller. The most radical peasant would
usually rather starve on his own patch, keeping secret his income
and expenditure, than be given the best salary, the most generous
share of the communal profits. This must be studied very carefully.
Looking back, I see I never finished reporting the Gogolian tale
of the peasant delegation from Oblomovia. Which also has a moral.

After having examined my room, the peasant deputation bowed
to me. I came round the desk—these symbols of authority are

worse then useless in such meetings—and sat down on a stool
among them. I waved them toward the leather chairs, that sofa
rather battered from many nights spent on it when too tired to go
home.

I asked each his full name, and where he came from. I am
able, through a simple system of mnemonics, such as are used by
market auctioneers, commercial travelers and the like, to retain,
and regurgitate later, most patronymics or hometowns. I suppose,
when I first started agitating in Peter in '95, this was a conscious,
demagogic device. But now it is second nature. Indeed, I regard
it as offensive *not* to do so. The intelligentsia, who pride themselves
on their memory for scrolls of useless facts, are the worst at recalling the names of real people they have just met. You cannot
tell me this does not reveal something about their priorities in life.
And so I returned the peasant bows.

So what was wrong? A very large figure with the face of an
old stud bull, graying curly locks on a solid bone forehead, big,
girlish, boiled-egg eyes, and an elastic mouth that could have swallowed my arm up to the elbow, stepped up into the free space.
Like many peasants, he would have to act out his story. (I could
not help thinking of the Italian Socialist group that came here last
December during the lowest temperatures below zero for twenty
years. Radek claimed that none of them said a word to any of us
because it was too cold for them to take their hands out of their
trouser pockets.)

First, however, our peasant tried to thrust upon me the details
of his complaint written on the back of an old grain bill. Words
on paper have a magic power to the near-illiterate. They seem to
think I only have to read it, repeat it, possibly backward, and like
some priestly trick in church, it will cast a spell. I gestured toward
the left-hand side of my desk.

It is always piled high with every sort of written document in
no particular order. I tried to have each one graded according to
urgency and importance. But soon I found no one person's estimate agreed with another's. Soon I was only reading what somebody alleged to be "Most Important" and "Extremely Urgent," and
missing all the rest. Now I neither pick nor choose, so my colleagues
never know where I will intervene. I find the chatter of the telegraph or the ring-ring of the telephone reaches out, touches people
like a probing finger, in a way no letter ever can.

The big fellow started to describe his grievance. But his friends
kept interrupting, correcting: "It's about the government . . . no,

about the land . . . about us being oppressed . . . no, about the grain quotas . . . no, about us being insulted."

"Please," I said. "Igor Gregorevich, from Penza. What about our government? Isn't the Soviet government the best system in the world?"

"Well," he said. "You see, we had the elections."

"Well, elections are good."

"No, but the citizens we elected to our local soviet. Once they were in power, they took away all our weapons. Then they were the only ones with guns. They began to oppress us. We have no freedom now. It is worse than under the Tsar."

"Wait a minute," I said. "*How* do they oppress you?"

"Every day in every way. There is no escape, day or night. Those of us from the Penza district had to come here in secret, in disguise. If they knew we had talked to Comrade Lenin, they would throw us into prison when we got back."

"Steady on. Nobody is going to lock you up. You are under Comrade Lenin's protection. You come from my province. I was born in Simbirsk. I was an attorney-at-law in Samara. If anybody touches you, he will be squashed like a bedbug. Tell me, *what* does your soviet do to you?"

"They come into our houses and take everything. They fine us for breaking this regulation and that. They are always registering amounts of flour and salt and seeds. Then they take them away. They never bring them back. You complain, and *whumpff*, you're inside."

"How is this possible?" I asked, striding up and down, increasingly disturbed. Were such corruptions of power really becoming commonplace?

"Surely, you elected these people. They are your people. You knew what they were like. In a village, everybody knows who can be trusted. Surely these were the good, the honest, the best. They must give justice."

"Yes and no, Vladimir Ilyich. They *are* our people, right enough. But there is no justice in them."

"Why not, you great boobies!" I shouted. "Do you want to be exploited and cheated all your lives? Who are these tyrants who rule by popular vote in Samara province? You *did* elect them, I suppose?"

The giant was now nervously pacing my floor with me, while the others patted and prompted him. "They are all horse-thieves, drunks, cheats, gamblers. Everyone a jailbird. We elected them because they were used to being locked up and wouldn't mind it so much as we would."

There was a murmur of agreement. "Yes, we did the same." "Us too." "Same in our village." I thought I was going mad.

"Why on earth should the representatives of the Soviet authority, freely chosen by universal suffrage, need to be used to jails? Who is going to lock them up?"

There was a silence. The spokesman stopped in front of me, kneading his old cap, staring at his felt boots.

"To tell the truth, Vladimir Ilyich. That is it. We never believed ordinary peasants would ever be allowed to have their own government. We thought that they couldn't last more than a few months. Then the Cossacks would come and those who had been on the soviet would be the first to be arrested and thrown behind bars. We thought they should be people who were at home there. Us, we're farmers, family men. We work round the clock. So we elected the horse-thieves and the rest . . . And now they rule the village like little Tsars and they oppress us."

"Oppress us . . . oppress us . . . oppress us," they wailed. It was not a normal peasant word. I expect they had picked it up from our Bolshevik propaganda, and thought it would appeal to me.

I had meant to stay calm, and logical, and decisive, *whatever* they said. But I could not help smiling. Every time I tried to be serious, I thought of the craftiness that had landed them with King Stork. And I started again. Just the sort of scheme my Samara brother-in-law, old Gorcheeza, would have dreamed up. Igor Gregorevich was sitting down, his chin in his hand, staring at his cap—a bit like the Ape with the Skull . . . ? No, no. Just a thought.

"You were wrong," I said eventually. "I don't blame you. You have been fooled so often. But Soviet power really must be the power of the people. I don't have to tell you now. You should have elected the best there is into your soviet. You see what happens when you do not trust the Bolsheviks. We freed you from the Tsar, the landlord, the Cossack, the moneylender, all the oppressors."

"You are right, Vladimir Ilyich," groaned Igor Gregorevich. "But what can we do now? The horse-thieves will be there forever." He perked up. "Unless you squash them like bedbugs."

"I cannot do that," I said. "But you can sprinkle a bit of flea-powder among them. How long have they been in office? Three months? Well, delegates to any soviet must offer themselves for reelection every six months. You can get rid of them in June."

They left like schoolboys promised an extra holiday.

I see that the future of Soviet power is going to depend more and more on us learning how to deal with the peasants. I rang for B.-B. and told him to check the villages they had come from, and put on the wire to their local soviets a suggestion from the President of Sovnarkom that the current members might care to opt for early retirement and a new election *at once*.

FEBRUARY 10   MOSCOW   1919

In our speeches, and in our newspapers, in all our propaganda, we lay the blame for the two years of undeclared war against our government and nation on the insatiable anti-Bolshevik madness of such as Churchill. I have not really had a chance to think about this dreadful, incessant, multimillion-pound crusade. But I see at once when I put my mind to work that it is very un-Marxist to assume that such a vast enterprise can be understood in terms of personal feelings and political ideology. Economics must be at the bottom of the filthy conspiracy.

As I process this thought, aptly comes to hand a cutting from the *Bulletin* of the Federation of British Industries, the toffs' trade union. It comes, without a stamp, in an envelope from England —return address ends . . . Basipetal, Kent. In a recent speech at a banquet of the British-Russia Club, before an audience of politicians and financiers, Sir Francis Baker, European manager of Vickers, remarked:

> We wish success to Admiral Kolchak and General Denikin, and I think I cannot do better than raise my glass and ask you all to drink to the health of Admiral Kolchak, General Denikin and General Yudenitch.
>
> Russia is a great country. You all know, because you are intimately connected with it in your business, what the potentialities of Russia are, whether it be from the point of view of manufacture or the point of view of mineral wealth, or any other thing, because Russia has everything.

He then raised his glass again in another toast.

> Siberia, the most gigantic prize offered to the civilized world since the discovery of the Americas! The whole country with market possibilities such as even the most optimistic dared not dream of.

Russia! The granary, the fishery, the lumberyard, the coal, gold,
silver and platinum mine of the world!

I can almost hear their mouths watering.

JULY 1   MOSCOW   1919

> From the office of
> the Chairman of the
> Soviet of People's Commissars
> Moscow, the Kremlin
> July 1, 1919

Comrades:
    Knowing the strict character of Comrade Trotsky's orders, I
am convinced, so absolutely convinced, of the correctness, expe-
diency and necessity for the success of the cause, of any order
given by Comrade Trotsky, that I unreservedly endorse this order.
> V. Ulyanov/Lenin

There was a certain amount of consternation, a dash of an-
noyance, perhaps envy, at today's meeting of the Politburo as I
picked up a piece of our most impressive official paper, seal and
all, and speaking the words aloud dashed off this authority, in red
ink with a scratchy pen. I took no notice.

"If you want any more blanks like this," I said to Lev Davidovich, "you only have to ask."

Nobody spoke while Trotsky folded the permission to do what
he willed and with a triumphant smile put it in his tunic pocket.
He had been threatening to resign, having been overruled on the
appointment of commander-in-chief. I wanted to show despite that
disagreement, and in front of the others, in the most memorable
way, that he retained my complete trust. Only half an hour later,
it was clear that I had anticipated the unanimous judgment of the
Politburo. Ten minutes after that . . .

But, for the moment, only Kamenev broke a disapproving
silence. "I thought only the Pope, or Ivan the Terrible, handed
out bits of authority like that. It's Lev Davidovich's use of the
powers he's already got. Life and death. Capital punishment with
or without trial. That's what I wanted to bring up. We are *civilians*.
The least we can do is dress like civilians."

"Not all of us," I interrupted. Kamenev was pointedly looking at Trotsky's well-cut, impractically pale uniform (rather reminiscent of Kerensky, to be honest), all the more impressive for having no badge of rank, with the lovely doe-skin pistol holster slung low over his genitals.

"Remember our late-lamented Yakov Mikhailovich Sverdlov, the hub, the spindle of the Revolution. Remember his black leather outfit? The *blouson* jacket, the polo-player breeches, the high jackboots, the belt with the silver buckle. He dressed like a commissar before we invented commissars."

Everyone laughed, except Kamenev.

"Yes, well, exactly. Like the rest of us, he never acted like the military. We are responsible to our staff, to each other, to the workers. We arrive at our decisions by free vote. You, Ilyich, you don't command, you don't order your comrades around. You, quite often, don't get your way. We stand together for active, revolutionary democracy. But Comrade Trotsky, why, he's like a little Emperor, a Tsarevich. Some of us may have a car, when it works, and a driver. Lev Davidovich has a whole train, with two locomotives. A personal bodyguard—talk about leather! They swagger about in great puffed-out greatcoats with specially minted medallions on the left sleeve. They each carry a portable machine pistol. On this train, he's got a garage of armored cars and bulletproof limousines. His wireless transmitter can reach the Eiffel Tower. Then there's a telegraph machine. A printing press. A restaurant. A boutique full of tinned food, underwear, washing and medical things. Field telephones, binoculars, radios, watches, compasses, maps and other soldiers' gifts. An electric-power generator. A library. A bathhouse. Even, they say, a folding airplane. It is the traveling palace of the Bolshevik warlord. He's got more power than anybody but you. And with this permit perhaps more than you. Did Karl Marx give you *carte blanche* to be his vicar on earth?"

I'd never known Lev Borisovich to be so critical about me since the July Days. This was interesting. He made a mistake, though, challenging us both. Trotsky alone was equal to the whole lot of them and I could see he was ready to rise to his feet and perform. Even leaders of a revolution have to be allowed an occasional bit of entertainment, some on stage, some in the *fauteuil*. I folded my arms and sat back.

Lev Davidovich walked round the table, like a medium or a mind reader, and stopped behind Kamenev. He reached over and picked up a pile of papers that lay there, glanced at them in a dismissive way, like a teacher recognizing schoolboy pornography. Then he tipped them straight into an open stove. While he had his audience off-balance, he went *wham!* into Kamenev's unstated complaint.

"So, Lev Borisovich, it's the commander of the Fourth Latvian Regiment, isn't it? It's Trotsky's liquidation of the heroic Communist soldiers of Svayzhsk? The mutinous Balt has been in prison a year. Fancy that. Which of *us* has not been in prison for a year? Do his friends think it is an act of tyrannous autocracy to keep him there?"

Lev Davidovich then told us about the famous train. Yes, it did have everything Kamenev had claimed. And more. But didn't his "Old Bolshevik" comrades in arms (a touch of sarcasm there since he didn't become a new Bolshevik until August 1917!) realize that this steaming armored chariot with slogans and pictures, was the epitome of the Revolution, "the Marseillaise on wheels"? It panicked the enemy, heartened our troops, wherever it arrived, hooting and trumpeting. ("You forgot to mention we have a small brass band, every player a sharp-shooter!")

The odds and ends distributed from stores were nothing, chicken feed to our exchequer. But everything to the soldiers, "all boys at heart." His "bodyguard" were dedicated young Communists, the best fighting men in Russia. They could match the British Guards, the American Marines, and they poured out charging head on at the enemy. "Each time the train halts, I lose half a dozen of my friends." Trotsky slapped his breast with his open palm. Still, there was no shortage of replacements. Lads from the college, the factory, the farm, many who'd never even seen a fowling piece. Within 500 miles they became trained killers. Their reputation paralyzes an enemy who only have to recognize the uniform to shit themselves. ("I copied the style from Sverdlov's.")

Trotsky then turned to the time and the place when he was supposed to have exceeded his power in *summer 1918*. Our country invaded, occupied, exploited, without a real army of its own. German rule in Poland, Lithuania, Latvia, Byelo-Russia, the Ukraine, a lot of greater Russia beyond Pskov. On the Volga, France, England finance the rebellious Czech Legion. To the North, Americans, English in Murmansk, Archangel, striking down to Vologda. White guards (Savinkov) pushing north to join Czechs via Vologda. On the Don, the south, General Krasnov an ally of anyone who paid. Civil war, a noose tightening round Moscow. Simbirsk has just fallen.

Trotsky commandeered a special train, roughly equipped it,

steamed down to protect Kazan. Though he did not know this, it had already been seized. *Svayzhsk,* forgotten before and since, then the limit of the rail line, by a bridge over the Volga. In the air here hung the miasma of defeat. Every group fought for itself alone, organized itself only for flight. The Soviets appear doomed. The fate of the Revolution, as everyone stares into everyone else's eyes, is about to be decided on this spot. A feather can tip the balance.

The first troops T. met were the Fourth Latvians—lying in the mud, under the rain, refusing to fight, begging to be moved to a safer place. Their commander, and their political commissar, sent a joint ultimatum—either agree to our demands or there will be *"consequences dangerous to the Revolution."*

That caught every one of us around the table. No one here, no one in any authority anywhere in our Soviet Russia, could ignore a direct challenge, an open threat, uttered in such terms.

T. carried on in Arabian-nights style, unrolling the colorful carpet of his story, always reaching down to extract another glittering ornament. (No wonder Gusev, my man on the Volga Front, dubs Trotsky, not entirely in admiration, Haroun al-Raschid with pince-nez).

T. invited both commander and commissar onto his train and then drew his gun on the mutineers. The rest of his troops were already in action trying to hold the bridge. So he handcuffed the couple to the rail. As soon as he could muster a field tribunal, he put them on trial. The verdict was guilty and both were sentenced to five years' imprisonment.

Before he finished, we were all on his side. I could feel the spread of blood to my face. I knew my voice would sound hoarse. "Let them rot!" I said. "You were too soft to begin with."

But T. had a few more rolls of carpet yet.

It was even worse down by the water. A torpedo boat was standing by to evacuate the senior officers. Further downstream, a river steamer had been seized by a runaway regiment which wanted to escape north to Nizhny-Novgorod and then desert. The enemy were only a mile away. Shells were bursting, "like peas from a pod," all along the banks. T. announced that he was commandeering the naval vessel. But its captain only grinned in his face: "Our engine has a curious weakness, Comrade Commissar for War. When we withdraw, it works perfectly. When we have to advance, it goes on strike."

Trotsky had only two weapons on his side, the gun in his hand and the one carried by his communication officer. Here was his chance to prove that the pen really was mightier than the pistol. The two of them started up the printing press, running off copies of this message:

> I hereby give warning that if any unit retreats without orders, the first member to be shot will be the political commissar, and next the military commander. Brave and determined soldiers will be appointed in their place. Cowards, dastards and traitors will not escape the bullet. This I solemnly promise in the presence of the entire Red Army.
>
> Signed: L. D. Trotsky, Commissar for War

The Fourth Latvians distributed the leaflet all round the army and to all the ships.

T. returned to his torpedo boat, its engine now purring sweetly. He wiped the smile off the captain's face, reducing him to the ranks.

He appointed his own favorite sailor, the dark, silent Markin, whose nerves of steel in October had saved T. in many tight corners. With a mere twenty leather-coated submachine gunners, Markin docked the torpedo boat alongside the mutinous steamer, climbed aboard alone and arrested Commissar Panteleev and Commander Zalutsky. Their troops stood silent by, watching, everyone with Trotsky's leaflet in his hand. As Markin was leaving with his two prisoners, about twenty of the steamer's crew swarmed up from below with carbines and cutlasses shouting "Death to the Bolsheviks! End the War!" But Markin's marksmen had every one of them covered. They too were put under arrest.

"What should I have done?" demanded Trotsky, glaring round our hot, dark, airless office. "It was only my death threat that had disarmed the disaffected. If a shot had been fired, the middle mass of the soldiers would have stampeded toward the defeatists, the counterrevolutionaries, the enemies within, instead of rallying to the Revolution, the fighters, the Men of Confidence. But now I must show I meant what I wrote. So I paraded every man not absolutely needed in the firing line. I explained the situation without hiding any facts or minimizing the danger.

"I told them our solidarity had been grievously damaged—a red-hot iron had to be applied to the dangerous wound. The indictment was read. And not denied. The guilty men, some of them, begged for mercy on their knees. I had them all shot in full view of their comrades. I would do it again today. I may have to do it again, tomorrow. Those who are now alive in prison may count themselves lucky."

He sat down to a low growl of approval. I could sense that the others itched to applaud but thought this might seem frivolous. I took the opportunity of asking for their unanimous backing of my blank order. It was given.

I thought it appropriate, as I now frequently must, to make clear some theoretical lessons from this practical demonstration.

"Comrades, I should not need to say we Bolsheviks do *not* consider human life sacred. Many more human beings are condemned to die before our Revolution is safe. Very probably, some of us here. In all wars, it is essential to have death behind, as well as ahead, of the army. Capital punishment will never be enough to guarantee discipline among those who do not wish to fight the war—Kerensky learned that. But we cannot allow deserters, traitors, cowards, to escape their duty without some punishment. And there can be only one punishment a soldier fears. We can ignore the rebukes of our enemies, hypocrites all. They have slaughtered millions upon millions over the centuries, for the benefit of a few. We kill for *mankind*, for the future, for a new world. Nobody will condemn, as an immoral act, Comrade Trotsky's execution of twenty, or two hundred and twenty, or even twenty thousand. There is only one test—was it necessary to preserve our socialist republic?"

If Trotsky has an outstanding fault, it is his inability to release any parcel without tying a large bow on it. He would have been wiser to have remained silent—the center of a focus of admiration, almost hero-worship, such as sedentary bureaucrats must inevitably feel for the man who strides in smelling of cordite, mud, engine oil, aviation spirit, hospital dressings, sweat . . . and blood. Instead, he rose again.

"Only one thing could have dragged me away from that battle. You will all recall, comrades, what it was. It was the assassination attempt on Comrade Lenin. I rushed back, sickened, poisoned by vague, free-floating fears. What did I see? Ilyich sitting up almost as healthy and vigorous as he is now. I was paraded before him as the Macbeth of Svayzhsk, with bloody hands, the butcher of commissars. I brought him a present—do you remember what it was? A telegram from Tukachevsky, impressively laconic: ORDER FULFILLED STOP SIMBIRSK RECAPTURED STOP WHAT NEXT QUERY. Our *Starik* here lit up like a lighthouse. He gripped the arm of Gorky, who was grizzling through his moustache as usual, and he said: 'Show me another civilian who can organize a new model army within a single year. Who wins the respect of military experts all over the world. We have such a man. That means we have everything. We shall work wonders.' When Comrade Lenin had extracted from my mouth, like a backwoods dentist, every useful piece of information, he pushed me away, almost rudely: 'Go, Lev Davidovich. Work us more wonders!' Did I hear any of you complaining I had exceeded my powers *then*?"

This coda was a mistake. I could hear the others thinking— "Oh! So *that* is how Ilyich manipulates *him*! How about us?" Trotsky is the most able man in the country. But could he look after himself should another Fanny Kaplan learn to shoot straight? He can dance with crowds but treads on the toes of individuals. I tried to help by asking him to tell us the story of his part in Raskolnikov's torpedo boat attack on Kazan. He did so. And it is still marvelous, particularly his phrasing. My heart always leaps at the moment when one of his shells hits a fuel store and the whole river is lit up, revealing Lev Davidovich's little boat . . . "like a fly on an empty plate!" The Politburo enjoyed it too. But I saw they had put him back again into the box labeled mountebank actor, the teller of tales, the Jewish entertainer. Pity!

AUGUST 18   MOSCOW   1919

Ours is a new morality. Our humanism is absolute, for it has as its basis the desire for the abolition of all oppression and all tyranny. To us everything is permitted, for we are the first in the world to raise the sword not for the purposes of enslavement and oppression but in the name of liberty and emancipation from slavery. We do not wage war on individuals. We seek to destroy the bourgeoisie as a class.

OCTOBER 10   MOSCOW   1919

Vorovsky. One of those comrades who, even while you are still on the long uphill struggle, keeps looking down, trying to footnote every step of the way. It's as though he will not be able to believe that he was there, that anybody was there, that there was any "there" to be, unless it is recorded in some book. The result was that, in the old days, he was always taking notes of what anybody said, sometimes returning the next day to make sure he'd got the phrases right. Taking notes was never a very popular activity among revolutionaries—unlike bourgeois politicians we sometimes had to literally eat our words as the police broke in.

Now, Vorovsky, whom I have made head of Gosizdat (State Publishing House), still apparently cannot believe that the revolution has arrived until he has every scrap pigeon-holed in his historic museum of Bolshevik memoranda. I've told him that I do not want my collected works published. (Anyway, not while I am still alive.) But he is nevertheless engaged, I suspect, in doing so. He interrupted a committee meeting this morning to ask if I would repeat something I had said about Chernyshevsky's *What Is to Be Done?* to him *in Geneva in 1904!*

He seemed a bit taken aback when I told him to go to hell and not bother me with such nonsense. Then just as he was leaving I called him back. "Never mind about 1904," I said. "What about 1919? What about this pamphlet on the Comintern I have here in front of me? Gosizdat would be better employed making sure that what is written about today makes sense. Look at this. It has been printed and edited appallingly. A complete bugger-up. No table of contents. Evidently some illiterate moron, possibly half-squiffed, has gathered together the materials, shuffled them, then published them as they were dealt, all out of sequence."

I made a small pause.

"Who could that person be?"

Then I left a nice long pause. (It was during a warming-up break at Sovnarkom when they are all trying to get a good place by the stove while pretending to be making room for some one else.) I could feel the other comrades growing interested, and turning to listen. I raised my voice. "I am here and now issuing instructions—our GenSec will confirm them—instructions that the person in charge of this abortion will, when found, be immediately locked up in solitary confinement, and left there until he has pasted the corrigenda slips into every copy."

Vorovsky went white and left. No doubt he is even now making notes, possibly in invisible ink, about the Mad Monster in the Kremlin. He was never much good at recognizing a joke. I'm not so sure it was a joke. In these temperatures, even the blood circulates like embalming fluid. There are not many smiles on the faces of the walking dead.

FEBRUARY 2   MOSCOW   1920

Alexander Alexandrovich Ozerov was originally a research assistant here. He is brilliant, learned, original, tireless—but almost useless, owing to a temperamental infatuation with irrelevance. He could never keep to the official topic for more than five seconds. If you sent him to look up one fact, he came back with six others. If he were dispatched to the archives to find out about pig iron production last year, he wouldn't come back until I sent a guard after him. Then he'd enter, positively possessed with excitement. "Here!" he'd cry. "Do you know how many pairs of drawers each dancer in the Imperial Ballet got through each year between 1910 and 1914?"

One of the key maxims of dialectical materialism can be translated as—always turn your weaknesses into strengths. (Easier said than done.)

So I have made Alexander a wandering investigator, empowered to poke his nose into everything that nobody else has thought to ask about, and instructed him to report only to my private office. His latest dispatch was read this morning by my chief secretary, Fotieva. She seemed upset. Skimmed of the meringue, the nut is this. Here am I in Moscow, rightly proud to tell congresses of working women that this is the first state in the history of the world that has given them freedom and equality. Out there, beyond the sight of our campfires, the noise of our speeches, it might often be another planet. He has encountered two happenings which suggest that much of our country is still in the Dark Ages, if not even more primitive times. (1) At Vladimir, just over 150 miles from here, he arrived too late to stop an old peasant woman being' burned alive as a witch. (2) About another 150 miles to the east, just outside Nizhny-Novgorod, he arrived in time to witness six naked virgins being harnessed to a plow, about to drag it round the village to create a barrier against a typhoid epidemic. Somehow these are more profoundly depressing glimpses of the barbarism inside modern man than the undeniably authentic examples he sent me last month of cannibalism being practiced just over the hill from the Trans-Siberian railway.

FEBRUARY 8   MOSCOW   1920

I ask that a sample of all intelligence arriving at Security Center be sent to me *in its raw state*. I cannot, of course, even at my speed of reading, physically cast an eye over more than one item in a thousand. But it is essential that nothing is deliberately kept from me that might later be seen to have been of crucial importance. I want never to hear the excuse: "We did not think it important, or important enough for *you*, Comrade Lenin." This, of course, also means that I have only myself to blame when it turns out—as it does from time to time—that we have all missed some important clue, some key sign, illustrating what is about to happen around us, at home or abroad.

But it is a risk I am willing to take. I know how to delegate. I have picked, to assist me, comrades whose minds follow mine, like sparring partners, complementing the movements of my thoughts. B.-B. and Fotieva, and even my driver and bodyguard, spend any time when I am not actually using them (the first of them two hours before I arrive in the morning; the latter when I am safely desk-bound) going through the ever-growing files. They watch out for the large as well as the small. Sometimes things are too obvious and overwhelming to be noticed by somebody like me who must always keep his nose to the grindstone. Nevertheless, what I want are just these tiny items, the oddities, the rumors, the bits people tell each other over a drink but usually forget to put in official reports.

This morning, for example, everybody in the city knew that the White Guard rebel chief Kolchak had finally been defeated. The admiral had been arrested aboard his armored train with 663 million of our gold rubles and was shot yesterday by our Revolutionary Committee in Irkutsk. It was assumed I must have heard the news independently, at home during the night. So it was never mentioned. Or rather only mentioned when my driver chuckled and said; "Listen, boss. I like this, just come in, a song of the Siberian Red Guards.

> "Uniform British,
> Epaulettes from France,
> Japanese tobacco,
> Kolchak leads the dance.
> Uniform in tatters,
> Epaulettes all gone.
> So is the tobacco,
> Kolchak's day is done!"

He sang it to a very odd, jerky, catchy tune, though where *that* came from I'll never know. I can tell immediately it is the kind of ditty that workers love to sing in taverns, soldiers on the march. I wish I could get Mayakovsky or somebody to turn these out by the dozen. This is true proletarian poetry.

FEBRUARY 18   MOSCOW   1920

How little many political pundits and thinkers know of what actually happened in the history of their own countries. Yet they still
come here to preach moderation, tolerance, fair play, democracy,
and the rest of the liberal claptrap, to me, a revolutionary who is
in the middle of a revolution. A typical mixed bag of them toured
the Kremlin this morning. I had to stop important work, decisions
left untaken that might affect the lives of thousands, actions unauthorized that could alter our future, to listen to a lot of preachers,
whiners and pedants.

One of them, Fossard by name, a French Communist of the
most theoretical sort, was worried by our Terror. They all are.
The very word makes them wet themselves. Halfway through a
question which was really a sermon, very badly translated by an
ancient wisp of an expatriate Russian exiled in Paris since '97, I
interrupted. In French. I was word-perfect. As I should have been
since I had been practicing the remark with B.-B. the evening
before, recommending it as the stock response to be sent by him,
on behalf of Soviet power, to any Gallic lefties who felt their consciences itch when enemies of the people bit the dust.

I said: "A Frenchman has nothing to denounce in the Russian
Revolution, which in its methods and in its procedure recapitulates
the French Revolution."

An American socialist then put his head above the parapet.
He argued, in broken Russian, that this might be all right for our
French supporters who had after all had their own Revolution plus
their own Terror. But it was not an argument that appealed to
American workers for whom such traditions were alien. I wiped
the self-admiring, Holy Joe, piousness off his face, reminding him
(in English) that his country too had been born in revolution, and
its leaders had supported the French. Thomas Jefferson could
hardly be regarded as a radical extremist. Yet what had he said
about the Terror? Naturally, the old, half-educated pragmatist had
no idea. My English was running out a bit, so I quoted from a
piece of paper I keep in my top right-hand drawer just for this
purpose.

Jefferson said: "In the struggle, which was necessary, many
guilty persons fell without the forms of trial, and with them, some
innocent. These deaths I deplore as much as anybody and shall

deplore some of them to the day of my own death. But I deplore them as I should have done had they fallen in battle. It was necessary to use the arm of the people, a machine not quite so blind as balls and bombs, but blind to a certain degree."

I couldn't, and haven't, put it better myself. I advised him to print it in a box once a week on the back of the Party paper.

How is it these creatures come here and presume to advise us on how to make a revolution? We have already begun. But how many of them ever ask for our advice on how to start one in their own countries?

APRIL 22   MOSCOW   1920

My birthday—the fiftieth. Whenever I see a publicity photo of myself, and our Party publicists somehow manage to keep on taking them despite my prohibitions, I see a picture of my father. To be correct, I see a picture of someone who looks more like my father's elder brother! I have inherited the family looks and build, father's energy and insistence on doing everything himself. If I have also had passed down to me his medical history, which seems likely, I have four years left.

Of course, we have done tremendous things in the last four years. Just to take power was an achievement. Almost nobody outside our Party believed it possible. Very few inside believed it probable. Then to hang on against a world in arms, hated by the rich everywhere, feared by the middle class, only occasionally supported and remembered by the workers of other countries. Yet here we are.

It being my birthday, a little introspection may be permissible. Though we have many physical, basic, blood-and-guts problems (keeping alive, no less) that would overawe Hercules, I think the key to our survival may be moral. This is not a proposition easily put over to our Party *en masse*, let alone to the general public. But those few hundred of us at present ruling from the top know what I mean about being "true to the Revolution." This is not an appeal to any abstract virtues; it is severely practical politics. If we betray the aims of the future, we will lose control of the present. We are always accused of being ruled by the doctrine that the end justifies the means. In one sense, we are. What else can justify any means, if not its end?

But even the most pacific, vegetarian, quietist contemplative, self-exiled in his hermit's cell, uses *some* means to his end. And every means has the potential of being dirty and dangerous. And no means, however obviously dirty and dangerous, not the taking of life or the threat of it, not starvation, kidnap, blackmail, imprisonment, torture, terror, lies and so on and so forth, has ever been totally rejected *in extremis* by king or pope, president or general, philosopher or bureaucrat. Our Marxist's problem is to discover the means that will *not* abort the end. Throughout history, the oppressed masses and their tribunes have been far more often the victims of deception, extortion, exploitation, slaughter, slander, mutilation, rape and organized class terrorism than have their rulers and masters. In history's double-entry account book, we the people are owed a much greater sum total in revenge than we will ever, or could ever, demand be paid in kind.

The real temptation to acquiesce in the use of the wrong means is more subtle. I feel it occasionally very strongly as the lure of the role of benevolent autocrat. I have often been right, entirely on my own. At those times, I have felt this certainty on my tongue, prickling along my veins, like the gulp of pepper vodka. But (I have to remember), I have (less often, but often enough) felt this and yet been wrong. At tonight's Party celebration of my birthday (resisted by me, probably not determinedly enough) Stalin said, as if remarking on a miraculous quality in a Bolshevik: "Comrade Lenin has never been afraid of acknowledging his mistakes!!!" I could have kicked him. Is there no way of convincing my old comrades and friends-in-arms that I really do find this kind of thing *revolting and perverted*? I would as willingly endure such Asiatic leader-worship as go off to a brothel. No, no, I'd *prefer* a brothel, even a male brothel.

How slyly they bait the hooks! The *Collected Works of Lenin* in various different bindings—why not? I absolutely forbid it. I looked through the MSS and cuttings they had amalgamated. I read out some bits. "How stupid we were then," I remarked. "Who needs these dead disputes?" But then they worried that the Mensheviks abroad, or here, might be publishing their own distorted, falsified versions. For example, what I had said about Trotsky, and he about me, in the year before the Revolution. This could be used to split our Party, undermine our solidarity. Would it not be better to have the true texts, checked by me, put in context, set in their historical background, a school of training guaranteed to identify compromisers, traitors and cowards for those who come after us? So, reluctantly, I gave my *imprimatur*. I fear I may be wrong.

That is another temptation—to be the person who stamps permission to print or not to print. I felt right to accept this power of *nihil obstat* over my own works. But I have to resist the push I feel around me inviting me to become a dictator by universal consent. I expect a certain amount of personal authority based on the strength of my arguments; based on a record of more successes than failures; based on the visible fact that I am the leader of a Party that runs on rationality, scientific concern for objective truth, the unity of theory and practice, a position achieved not by force, by money, by inheritance, but after fierce open competition.

But I do not expect to have my way without dispute. Indeed, as a Marxist, I know that no true decision is ever made without surviving a battle against error. You only know you are right when all your alternatives are shown to be wrong. My authority has never been, and must never be, absolute. That way I would never acknowledge my mistakes, because I would not know what they were.

Four more years and I shall be like many of our other Old Bolsheviks—unable to realize that new problems need new solutions. The regular citing of old parallels, former examples, even from the holy writ of Marx and Engels, is not enough. Every day, I encounter opposition, disagreement, challenge, resistance, up to and beyond the door of this office. Naturally, I try to hit it head on, to scatter it and then reassemble it, turn it facing my way. The better I am at this, the better I am at my job. I have always been good with the waverers, the doubters, the foot-draggers, persuading them that my way is the *only way*. (I have made it my way *because* it is the only way, and not vice versa.) But I will never swell my ranks by threats of expulsion or gagging.

What, then, about Party discipline? This is a difficult subject —how far is the free debate, essential before the majority decision, still permissible *afterward*? Should it be allowed to every individual but forbidden to groups? As in any martial organization, the severity of punishment must vary with time and place. What may be allowed on a battleship in harbor will not be condoned in a lifeboat in midocean. What is advisable the day after victory may not be so the evening before a crucial battle. But what I have insisted upon, and hope *all of us* will always insist upon, is that the same discipline as applies to the others applies also to me. Neither I nor any one of us must ever have such a formal preeminence, such hierarchical superiority, that alive or dead, our position becomes unchallengeable by any minority, unalterable by every majority.

The machine of myth-making rolls on, seemingly under its own impetus, grinding out stories about how the Revolution was made. The nearest parallel is the spreading of the tales told by the supposed apostles about Jesus. It is sickening to have to record that I am the focus of many of them. I find the process sickening. But every time I protest, I am assured that the masses yearn to believe that at the top of the state is someone larger than life, a semi-divine figure. Each legend, they tell me, has been calculated to be worth an extra ration of bread a week or the like.

How can this be? Why should ordinary people want to be told that I have thick, red, curly hair, when everyone who comes within half a mile is dazzled by the shine on my bald head? Why should they need to be assured that every morning I am at my office by 8, some say 7:30, when it is notorious among the thousands who work in and around the Kremlin that I get up at 10 and reach my desk by 11? Would it not be better to tell them the truth, that afterward I work until 4, have dinner exactly at 5, then Cabinet meetings until midnight. Sometimes work at home, perhaps until 5 or 6 in the morning. I would prefer to drive in a car without a bodyguard—I'd walk everywhere alone, given the opportunity. But the same people who insist on bulletproof glass, armed protectors, fast driving through crowds, are the same ones who insist that we must pretend not to be doing exactly that. Instead it is whispered that I frequently "mingle unrecognized among the people" like a prince from the Arabian Nights. Celebration of my fiftieth birthday, two days ago, staged by the Moscow Committee of the Party, gave me the opportunity to put a little dent in the cult of personality. I conspicuously absented myself from the eulogies, on the grounds of: "If you can't beat them, at least don't join them." Then I appeared for a moment only when the massage of the ego, the sound of vanity, was over. Without seeming too ungrateful, I said as flatly as I could: "I must thank you for two things. For today's greetings. Even more, for excusing me from listening to today's greetings."

You cannot win. Now they will go around saying "What modesty!" and "How self-critical!" They do not seem to understand that any true Bolshevik finds it physically revolting to hear any person endlessly licked and groomed as a super-being, even more so if it is himself. After all, the eulogies on the tombs which cover the reputations of the great leaders of the past—Alexander, Genghis Khan, Charlemagne, Caesar, Napoleon, Cromwell, Garibaldi or whoever—might flesh out a skeleton of truth. I was not there to test them against the standards of such heroic Socialist rebels as Herzen, Bakunin, Chernyshevsky, Marx, Engels. But I do know *who* I am, *what* I am. I do not seek adulation for doing what has to be done.

Even Bonch-Bruevich, secretary, helper, fixer and friend during twenty years of exile, cannot, or will not, explain to me what is happening.

"What is it all for?" I demanded, looking at today's papers. "It is getting so I cannot bring myself to even read the headlines. Wherever I turn, they are writing about me. Surely they know that this completely un-Marxist emphasis on a single person is extremely harmful? And these portraits. Everywhere! What is the purpose of all this? I do not need an election campaign. Is there a Napoleon in the wings—the general in the white tank—waiting to rumble in and take over? Is all this a buildup for the one who comes after, the hidden Imam who will inherit my mantle, my seat, my power and now my transferable near divinity?"

But B.-B. is better at doing what he is told than at telling what he is doing. He reads out to me a questionnaire prepared by the Comintern which must be completed by all top Bolsheviks. Do you speak any foreign language? he asks. *None,* I reply to him (in English). What are your specialties? *None,* I repeat *Nichts! Niente! Nix! Rien! Nada!* Do you have any other comments or suggestions? Yes, I would like the comrades who compiled these forms to see me immediately when I will be able to tell them something to their advantage. I will show them how to occupy their time usefully in furthering the Revolution and strengthening Soviet power. There are still vacancies in the Red Army.

MAY 12   MOSCOW   1920

I have now settled into a routine of executive work, heavy but satisfying. There are no free periods, which is the way I want it. I need to face each new crisis, dilemma, problem, head on. Then everything seems possible. It is when the brain tank is allowed to sink low that the fears crowd in.

So. Once a week, since March last year, I have convened a

working session of the five-member Politburo, a team picked from, and by, the Supreme Council for Labour and Defence.

On Wednesdays and Fridays, there is a meeting of the Communist Party Central Committee, elected by the Party Congress. It is made up this year of Stalin, Trotsky, Kamenev, Bukharin and me. I am the chairman. We start at 6 P.M., and intend to adjourn at 10 P.M., but often carry on until midnight. Then there is the Cabinet (Sovnarkom) which meets every Tuesday, sometimes for an extra session on another day as well, from 6 to 10, also with an occasional extension to midnight. I chair this as well. I spend what's left of the days of the week, Monday to Friday, from 11 A.M. until around 4:30, in my own office dealing with whatever turns up. What's left from what turned up gets worked over during the weekend.

To begin with, the other members of STO and Sovnarkom were often late—a bad Russian habit, typical of all backward, undeveloped nations. Well, no more. I made it a rule that we began on the dot. Even if I was the only member present, as I was a few times in early days. Every late arrival was recorded in the minutes. This, and a beady glare or an annoyed jerk of the head, was usually enough to persuade the defaulter to become a good timekeeper. There were, however, a few regular backsliders. For them, I instituted, in addition to an entry in the minutes, for the second offense, the fine of a day's pay. For the third, the final deterrent —a reprimand printed in the press. Within weeks, there were no more late arrivals or unjustified absences. And that is the way it will be while I'm in the chairman's seat.

Another wastage of resources, so familiar none of the comrades noticed it until I pushed it under their noses. The way all kinds of outsiders queued up in the anteroom waiting to be called into STO or Sovnarkom. This, of course, was a hangover from tsarist days when the concept of waste (certainly waste of *time*) did not exist. If you lingered day after day in the corridor outside the office of some minister—that was just another kind of work. For professionals, it could become a way of life. For amateurs, the start of a bad habit which might rot away most of a lifetime.

As soon as I heard that all sorts of valuable officials, who needed to bring us reports, provide evidence for our decisions, or be instructed on how to handle our projects, were in the waiting room, I paid them a visit. There they were—playing chess, reading books or newspapers, gossiping, sleeping, sharing out food, drinking, and smoking, smoking, smoking until you could fancy they were all kippered. I went in there like Jesus among the money changers in the Temple. I told them they could be charged with "dereliction of duty by misuse of scarce material"—i.e., themselves. They were to get back to the place from whence they came, whether office or home, and find some useful occupation until summoned by the telephone or messenger.

I insist that everyone always use *the telephone* rather than write letters. Once something is written down, it automatically creates its own bureaucracy. A letter has to be acknowledged, answered, filed, copied, indexed. It soon grows a companion archivist in constant attendance. Correspondence, like marriage, can often develop without any of those involved having any idea of how it began.

When these outsiders were summoned, I gave them five minutes. It cleared their brains with amazing speed. Afterward, all of us permanent members would frequently be able to remember what had been said even months later. Writing something down —especially getting someone else to write something down for you—is the best way of forgetting it. You fool yourself the paper is doing the remembering and digesting for you. Anyway, we have almost no paper.

JUNE 4   MOSCOW   1920

Interviewed by two correspondents of Japanese newspapers—R. Nakahira of the Osaka *Asahi* yesterday and K. Fusse of the Osaka *Mainichi* and the Tokyo *Nichi-Nichi* today. As an old newspaper man retired upstairs, I dare say I am a bit out of touch. But I always thought that bourgeois papers—basically a medium for entertainment, rhetoric and gossip rather than education and enlightenment—were in fierce rivalry, always trying to get in ahead of a competitor, searching for "scoops." As myself now a provider of, rather than a dealer in, news headlines, I see that journalism in a capitalist economy obeys the same laws as any other service industry. It may start with a series of hard-fought sprints by a large variety of small entrants of roughly equal size and capabilities. But very soon, through undercutting, merging, rationalizing, the race is reduced to an amiable amble by two or three semi-monopolies. Open competition is replaced by board-room deals. The employees follow the example of their proprietors. They only pretend to be cutting each other's throats in search of an exclusive story.

This sprang to mind when I noticed in my appointments book

that these two Japanese correspondents, still somewhat rare birds since their government continues to finance all kinds of bandits, adventurers and propagandists on our soil, seemed to represent papers in the same city. And yet were proposing to quiz me jointly.

I asked B.-B. to reschedule this pair a couple of days apart so that each could get a slightly different angle. Perhaps the truth is that the press no longer find me quite such a height that I have to be scaled alone—"I Question Lenin . . ." or do they feel safer in pairs? Anyway, they actually *complained* about being separated!

Both seem sincere, pleasant and honest reporters, only rather dull and a bit limited. Even not in each other's presence, their interests turned out to be more or less identical. I thought the most rewarding part (for me) of each interview was when I questioned them. I learned a lot about Japan from slight, but often striking, differences in their separate answers.

I keep a shorthand note-taker within earshot these days after some rather bad experiences. In order to avoid alienating the foreign correspondents, I try to make his presence not too obvious. Extraordinary how journalists *hate* to be quoted, even when their remarks are agreed to be on the record. However, I have never met one who refused to accept the offer of a transcript if his own jottings later proved rather meager.

In my view, the only interesting news for their readers was my answer to Fusse's question—"Where does Communism have more chance of success, in the East or in the West?" They sound such apparently simple, neutral propositions. But when you are spokesman for the ruling body of a great national state, also simultaneously spokesman for the ruling body of a great international ideology, there are bigger problems than might at first be apparent. There are always far more groups you are certain to insult than you are likely to please. If the local CP is happy with my "quotes," then you can be sure I will have made even more bitter enemies among the government, the bankers and financiers, the patriotic press, all other parties, and the permanent civil servants. (And, of course, vice versa.) In 1917–18, I would have said that was the way it should be. In 1920, I'm afraid, our Soviet society depends for its survival more on bankers and financiers, bourgeois governments and the rest, than on the militant, international working class.

There are even small obstacles hidden in such flat queries which can badly stub a toe, possibly break a leg. Fortunately, B.-B. and I do our homework thoroughly. We anticipate most traps. For instance, you might foresee little truble in the request for a prognosis for Communism, East or West. How many realize that when a Japanese says "East," he means everybody beyond, say, ninety degrees longitude west of Greenwich, except himself. The Japanese do not think of themselves as Orientals any more than the English think of themselves as Europeans.

Both countries regard themselves as independent, individual entities, unconnected with any other on the globe, possibly dropped here eternities ago from Mars, and only moored offshore, beside an alien continent, by the most crass, meaningless accident. They see their neighbors rather differently, however. The English look down on the Europeans as people, regarding them as immoral, humorless, superstitious, and racially inferior, but nevertheless are learning to respect their talent for heavy industry, high finance, the manufacture and use of armaments. The Japanese rate Russia lower than their other country next door, China. Both are seen as ripe pickings. Russia a semi-colonial dependency, an undeveloped emergent territory like a gargantuan Alaska, until 1917 in the pocket of French and English money lenders, and today ranking on the scale of global importance just above India, possibly coming level with Turkey. China is a once royal grandfather grown senile, in some ways the Greece to Japan's Rome but in others the South America to Japan's USA—anyway Japan's to rule against the pink, big-nosed barbarians by "manifest destiny." So my reply was aimed at almost everywhere in the Orient (except Japan).

Here is our note of my words: "So far, real communism can succeed only in the West. But it must be remembered that the West lives at the expense of the East. The imperialist powers of Europe grow rich chiefly at the expense of their Eastern colonies. But at the same time they are arming these colonies and teaching their inhabitants how to fight with up-to-date weapons. By doing so, they are, I am happy to say, digging their own graves."

I went on, with both reporters, to recommend that in future they should not try to get their copy out of such as Lenin, but instead talk to the people in the factories, in the armies, in the fields. I offered to give them free travel warrants to anywhere the Soviet writ runs. What about a trip on the Trans-Siberian railway to somewhere like Lake Baikal? Just a little further on they would find the territory of the Bolshevik-hating Cossack ataman, Grigori Semyonov. A constant whine in the reports on Soviet Russia in the foreign press condemns the ruthlessness with which we supposedly carry out our policies. Why did not M. Fusse and M. Nakahira sample (at a safe distance) the methods of this self-appointed Nero?

Semyonov is a genuine monster. He has to start the day killing someone with his bare hands the way others have to begin with a cup of coffee. I do not vouch for this. But I do know, from all too many firsthand testimonies by refugees, that he cruises our eastern rails, along some 900 miles of the Amur and Shilka rivers, killing and torturing, mainly for pleasure. Last winter, he executed his prisoners by pouring water over them, transforming them into statues of ice, a method he found convenient because it allowed him to break off limbs and keep them as souvenirs. This January, at Kyakhta, just our side of the Chinese border, his demonic aides murdered 1,800 captives in five days. They used a different means each day to avoid the work growing tedious. Day one, poisoning; two, beheading; three, shooting; four, suffocation; and finally, five, burning the remainder alive.

Both correspondents, on different occasions, politely examined my invitation, then declined it. They explained that their readers would not stomach such dreadful, unnecessary details of human degradation. Why should Lenin think the civilized Japanese public needed to be exposed to this? Each time, Lenin was able to reply: *"Because it is the civilized Japanese public which is paying the taxes which permit a civilized Japanese government to subsidize Cossack Semyonov."*

I wonder how much of *this* appears in the Osaka *Mainichi* and *Asahi,* or the Tokyo *Nichi-Nichi?*

JULY 10   MOSCOW   1920

"We have an advantage over the rest of the world . . ." Even as I hear myself say it—it is my message this month—I wonder whether I can carry on and complete the proposition.

What is our advantage? Last winter it would have been hard to imagine anyone dreaming up the phrase. I can hardly believe now, even the memory. All Russia stopped. Still as a photograph, framed in snow, glazed with ice. Nothing moved. Transport was only a word, a boy's train set in the display window of a closed store. There were the locomotives, glued to their rails. There were the granaries, heaped with immovable food. Denikin's White Army held the Don and the coal stayed below in the white ground. Our enemies occupied Baku, and the oil was stuck in the well. The Volga was frozen, the logs on it embedded like sausages in batter. Our marvelous Russian weather—as ever—betrayed our people. Seven feet of snow fell in one single storm, a world record, blocking roads, railway lines, rivers, burying whole provinces.

Our cities had no heat at all for weeks. In the Kremlin, our commissars sat in rooms from which all the furniture had been taken to feed the now-dead stoves. We huddled away from the broken windows, wrapped in fur hats, coats and gloves, and still frostbitten. Birds fell dead from the air. What food there was we kept for the children. And the Red Army. Who knew whether it would ever end?

Abraham Lincoln used to tell the story of the Oriental emperor who summoned all his wise men and asked them to pool their brains until they could discover for him one truth that would always remain true, whatever the circumstances. After years of consultation, they appeared before him and gave their conclusion—"This, too, will pass." I must have repeated it to myself, silently, once a day throughout that winter.

Today it was John Reed, the American journalist and socialist, to whom I gave the message. He is no fool. His faith in our ultimate victory has never wavered. He traveled thousands of miles across the Soviet territory and saw how winter imposed a worse dictatorship than any human could ever inflict. Now he tells me that things have enormously improved—he is so optimistic I cannot believe him. For example, he says he has just come back from Estonia, a bankrupt and speculator-ridden country where "fields lie unplowed and factory chimneys stand smokeless" and where "the ragged people run alongside the train, begging." After this, to cross the frontier into our Russia, he says, is like "entering a rich, well-ordered land!!!" His book, *Ten Days That Shook the World,* for which I wrote an enthusiastic few lines of foreword during the worst of that winter of 1919, has been marvelous propaganda for us everywhere. But now he seems to be so overdoing it I have flashes of wondering whether he may not be some kind of double agent.

Anyway, I told him the Abraham Lincoln story which I saw he had known since childhood but was too courteous to tell me so. I went on to explain what our great advantage was over the rest of the world.

His eyes lit up.

"We can experiment. We can try any schemes we please. And if they don't work, we can change our minds. We can try something else. The workers know we are fighting against capitalist exploitation for their benefit. They trust us." He copies it all down. Newspapermen love a "quote." It hardly matters what it is, so long as somebody has said it. So long as it is a trifle more interesting than what they could make up themselves. Reed is an honorable, dedicated, courageous man, somewhat naïve, with that fat, rolled-meat look all offspring of the American bourgeoisie seem to retain all their lives however little they later eat. Who can resist someone who gives you a copy of his book with written across the title page "Lenin—the locomotive of history"? I do not like to tell him that the phrase is Trotsky's. Only he applied it to . . . War! Still, not bad. Sometimes I think I have been waging the same war for fifty years.

OCTOBER 12   MOSCOW   1920

I cannot say there was never a day since we met that I did not think of Inessa. That would have been weak, foolish, indeed criminal. Increasingly, across that decade, I have been involved, night and day, in one of the most colossal, sustained crusades ever mounted by man. Often, I was, still am, a key figure, a decisive element, the fulcrum on which a whole huge balance rests. Again and again, I have cried out for more time, for release from the dictatorship of sleep, from the necessity to eat and drink. Even now, when many of our first objectives have been reached, I often wake from a dream where I have grown six heads. And I almost weep that it is only a dream.

I have trained my body and brain to bear as much as any leader in history. Like Julius Caesar, I can read, dictate, write and listen, all at the same time. I do not complain. I hope that my comrades, the Party and the people, never realize I might have anything to complain about. I regard myself as a machine, to be well serviced and maintained as long as it operates economically. But once it has become more trouble than it is worth, then scrapped and replaced. The longer I live, the more pitiful do I find the pretensions of the individual, the more noble the movements of humanity.

Yet, whenever I have disengaged my mind from the struggle, Inessa is the first name, face, lips, smell that floods in the gap. Is this how the truly religious think of their Christ? She has always been my inspiration. Of course, the real Inessa has been around too. She has never ceased to be a worker for the cause. Sometimes, well, probably only once, she has opposed me. She took the side, at the time of Brest, of those who wanted revolutionary war, willing to go down banners flying, guns firing, bands playing, handing on the torch to another generation, another proletariat. That would appeal to her gallant, inspirational nature—a pity the right decision, my decision, had to be so grim, so sordid, so lowering to the spirit! *Surrender!*

Since then she has shown that she does not scorn the dreary, workaday bureaucratic tasks on the Moscow Executive Committee, the Russian Red Cross, the Woman's Page of *Pravda*. But of our old loving intimacy, our white nights of talk when ideas and feelings flowed back and forth through our very skins by osmosis, there have been no more than two or three opportunities since October. We made that Revolution so that the people of Russia, we hoped, then, very soon, all the peoples of Europe, could have their rightful share of happiness here and now. By doing so, I cut myself off from the one person who could have given me lifelong happiness.

Only last month, I came upon Inessa, by accident, in a corridor of the Kremlin. She had always been severely, unflatteringly dressed—as Nadya, of all people, was first to point out in Paris in 1911. "Didn't you notice, Ilyich?" she demanded, a slight gleam in her eye. "You who are the Argus among revolutionaries?" It was true, I hadn't. All I saw was that she always had a bright red feather in her fur hat—probably very un-*chic*. This time, I did notice. Inessa was dressed like a patient in a madhouse—ill-matching coat and skirt, threadbare blouse, holes in gloves and socks, not even sensibly protected against the autumnal chills. She also looked half-starved. Her nose pinched, more vulture now than eagle, her lips bloodless, her great eyes even greater but dulled almost to that grape bloom I had seen only in moments of desire. My heart leaped. I once might have said, leaped as if a bullet had hit it. But as I now know, a bullet is barely noticeable in comparison.

I squeezed her hand, but had to hurry on. My reward was a smile that seemed to rise from her lopsided shoes. I have it with me still. Is it all that I have?

Perhaps I should have done more. At that time, it seemed quite a lot. As soon as I was back in my office, I grabbed the bank of telephones and got on to the Cheka—the best people for any job needing imagination and initiative. (I can highly recommend them to anyone.) I said Inessa Armand, address unknown, was immediately to be given a hamper of food, a selection of the best-made, most attractive and *warmest* clothing, an open ticket for two (soft-class) train berths to our vacation sanatorium in Kizlovodsk in the Caucasus (I knew the name because the CenCom are always trying to send me there) and an official direction from the Chairman of the Council of People's Commissars ordering her presence there within the week.

A week later, I checked. The Cheka had done all I asked, even adding a couple of bodyguards, discreetly lodged in the next compartment. Unfortunately, none of us could have foreseen the White General Wrangel advancing through Georgia. Inessa had to be evacuated northward within days. But she was safe, and active as usual, nursing sick children who were on her train. I telegraphed supplies of food and medicines to the next major stop, Vladikavkaz, and requested that I be kept in touch.

Five days ago came the news which has struck me like a cerebral hemorrhage. Inessa has died in Vladikavkaz from typhus contracted from those she was looking after. Her body was being brought back in a cast-iron bath of ice. Today was her funeral. She was buried, as of right, in the wall of the Kremlin. I do not remember anything of the ceremony. I put my hat over my eyes and walked like a blind man all the way, one hand on the coffin which was closed because of the danger of infection. I believe that Sandra (Kollontai), another beautiful, fearless woman, top-full from head to toe with pure revolutionary ichor, Inessa's friend and confidante, made a speech that had everyone sobbing like babies.

I am now back in my office. Sitting alone at my desk in a darkened room. I must have looked terrible, a walking basilisk, for no one has ventured to approach me, say a word, send a message. What is wrong with them? We must win the war in which Inessa battled so indomitably.

If I speed up peace negotiations with Poland, I can release an enormous train of artillery to blast Wrangel out of the Crimea. It is time the last White Army on our Soviet soil was liquidated, and we became masters of our own land. I had ordered that enemy officers who surrendered were to be given safe conduct. Still, the ghastly Bela Kun is our man in charge down there. He never takes prisoners. Good.

"I have supped full with horrors."

NOVEMBER 15   MOSCOW   1920

When bourgeois visitors visit me—industrialists, philanthropists, philosophers, newspaper publishers, writers, out-of-office politicians—they gradually come round to complaining that we Communists remain dedicated to what the English press called, when it was practiced by the Germans, *frightfulness.* I no longer bother to dispute with them. Once I used to confound the American, the French and the English, all of them from states founded on revolutions they now would rather forget, by citing occasions in their history when they too, threatened by enemies at home and abroad, used measures they would also now not care to remember. I would point to the map of Russia and cite the number of White generals backed by foreign powers, or foreign armies without even the pretense of including Russian nationals, who had invaded our soil since October 1917. All in all, there have been *nineteen* of them.

Now, I simply invite them to consider the career of Winston Churchill. Will they point to any equally bloodthirsty warmonger among our leaders? Not just because his handsome porker face, his fur-collared tail-coat, his dress hat and cigar make him resemble the traditional cartoon of the Capitalist Beast in our socialist press. I'm told—we are getting some very useful sources in London's Whitehall—he rejoices in the discovery that he can read every message Bolsheviks send to each other since his secret service possesses the key to our codes obtained from the defeated Germans. If so, he should also realize that we have long borne that fact in mind. But does he know who supplied us with the information that his own wife, in a recent bout of argument at home, rebuked him for being "a Mustard Gas fiend, a Tank juggernaut and a flying Terror"? No one can deny that Churchill *is* obsessed with the machinery of mass destruction—chemical weapons, armored vehicles, air-bombers.

His wife's description is rather more carefully phrased than Churchill's usual frothing abuse of us. His description of me as "a bloodstained monster on a throne of skulls" is not much more than fetid hot air, the familiar flatulence of a political careerist who eats and drinks too much. I will not attempt to analyze the so-called "psychological" significance of the images he repeats so often— Radek claims they reveal "an infantile homo-erotism" that Churchill dare not acknowledge. Secretly, he envies our ability to smash the entire defenses of the class-enemy's state. It may even be that he is in love with *me*! At least, according to some of our Marxist-Freudians. Most of that stuff is so much poppycock. But when I show my visitors what Churchill does actually say, few can deny its curious nursery malice, its total lack of adult control.

Take his fixation on zoological comparisons, particularly from the Monkey House. (How many fruitful hours I've had arguing with comrades as we ambled round the zoo in Regent's Park!) "The babboonery of Bolshevism" was his first attempt. That so pleased him he went on to elaborate it to his prime minister, Lloyd George. He was outraged that civilization should permit the Russian Commu-

nists "to hop and caper like troops of ferocious baboons amid the
ruins of cities and the corpses of their victims." When Lord Curzon
proposed to treat our trade delegation like lepers, he was ordered
by Lloyd George to instead "be a gentleman." Churchill reproached Curzon afterward. "Did you really shake hands with those
hairy-arsed baboons?" His postwar policy he summed up as: "Kill
the Bolshie! Kiss the Hun!" And even the most healthy-minded observer may find something unpleasantly intimate in this equation:
"One might as well legalize sodomy as recognize the Bolsheviks."

Churchill seems totally unable to put himself in anyone else's
position. What was his policy in Ireland, while repressing the legitimate aspirations of the Irish people, but Anglo-Saxon Terror?
He praised the brutal murder squads of the Black and Tans, encouraging and authorizing their savage reprisals against the civilian
population. He even proposed that open-air meetings of men,
women and children, unarmed and peaceful, should be bombed
and machine gunned by planes—an Irish "Bloody Sunday"!

But the clinching illustration is surely Churchill's positive love
of poison gas as a weapon of war. Shortly after he became minister
of war in January 1919, he turned his mind to anti-British movements in the Middle East and along the Indian frontier: "I am
strongly in favor of using poison gas against uncivilized tribes. The
moral effect should be so good. Loss of life should be reduced to
a minimum. It is not necessary to use only the most deadly gases;
gases can be used which cause great inconvenience and would
spread a lively terror. . . ." He had wanted to gas the Turks during
the Dardanelles campaign in 1915 and later that year begged to
be allowed to use it against the Egyptians. The Afghans were another nation on his list for the civilized treat of chemical warfare.
Near the front of the queue throughout, naturally, had been the
new, young Soviet state. Here I tend to pass round some photographed pages of a War Office file on the future possibilities of
poison gas. Here Churchill observes—"I should *very much like* the
Bolsheviks to have it."

My visitors who have followed me so far, without dispute, tend
to express doubts here. After all, Britain is an imperial power and
has to hit hard at various dark-skinned, barbaric natives, but Russians, even Red Russians, are white men, Westerners (well almost)
and very near to Europeans. Am I sure this is not some forged
document, devised to stir up animosity?

I can assure them that Churchill not only wrote it, he has done
it. In the first two weeks of September last year, the British Royal
Air Force flew eleven sorties over our sovereign territory of Ar-

changel. They dropped a total of (at least) five hundred gas bombs on the Red Army. Even against the Bolshevik baboons, this would rank as a war crime, except that it was committed in time of peace. News of the operation has been carefully kept from the world public. We can document it in detail. I myself have questioned eye-witnesses. But who wants to hear our official protests? After all, as the capitalist world well knows, only the Bolsheviks use Terror.

Some day a socialist Britain will open up the archives of White-hall and reveal evidence of "frightfulness" beyond anything we now imagine. Until then, Winston Churchill will do as a prize exhibit. No government which includes him can ever accuse us of an appetite for atrocities.

JANUARY 15   MOSCOW   1921

Sverdlov shared an exile's hut for a while in Siberia with Stalin and he used to say that the Georgian was more many-sided than any of us suspected. For instance, in those days, he was fond of word games and quite intellectual ones too. There was "Sermon" where you are given an object, say a toothpick or a bootlace, and asked to improvise a homily showing how this demonstrates the goodness of God. Stalin had been educated in a church seminary and could be very funny at this. Then there was "Proverbs" where you had to invent a convincing peasant saying. Stalin was good at that as well. Yakov always remembered one of Joseph Vissarion-ovich's winning entries—"There are people with gloves who have no fingers."

I wonder if Stalin is still playing the game? Only yesterday we were interviewing professors competing for some job, and we had before us an archetypal armchair radical whose enthusiasm for revolutions increased with distance. He had written books applaud-ing socialism in the abstract, in the future, but he didn't like the often violent and arbitrary way it worked in practice. Stalin leaned over and breathed on him—"If you can't stand smells, don't use our shithouse."

I used another metaphor a couple of years ago in *Pravda* and came across it by accident while quizzing the professors. It is in-teresting to read today when we no longer need analogies. Our case is made, *en clair*, everywhere you look. I argued:

> They have heard, and admitted "in theory," that a revolution should be compared to an act of childbirth, but when it comes to

the point they take fright, make an excuse and leave the room. Let us accept the comparison. Take the descriptions of childbirth given in literature, when the authors aim at presenting a truthful picture of the severity, pain and horror of the act of travail, even with modern anesthetic and pain-killers. Human childbirth remains a function which can transform the woman into an almost animal, bloodstained mass of flesh, tortured, tormented, driven crazy by agony. Yet what sort of booby would it be who could see *only* this as the means and end of love? Would you classify as a human someone who then renounced all love, all sexual passion, all responsibility for procreation, all pleasure in parenthood, for *this* reason?

I see now it smacks a little of the childless innocent who'd seen more books then babies. It wasn't universally popular, on our side anyway. Sandra Mikhailovna (Kollontai), our leading apostle of free love, argued that I had got my example the wrong way round.

She came into Sovnarkom, sat on the arm of my chair to the scandal of some of the company, and complained: "You should have compared the intellectual riffraff who're afraid to jump in the deep end to *men*. They are eager enough at the moment of conception. But they regret they cannot be sure where they will be, and how they will feel, nine months later. And there's no alarm clock to remind them of the appointment. It's the women who are the Bolsheviks of the sex war—we will the means, we will the ends. We carry our alarm with us. We *have* to be there when the time comes. We *are* the time."

I find it hard to refuse Sandra almost anything for old times' sake. She was Inessa's closest friend. And I never forget that she may have been the only one at the Finland station who both knew what I was saying and backed me to the hilt. She wavered a bit over Brest-Litovsk. But then so did Inessa. It's the romantic in them—urging us to fight on, crying: "If our Soviet Republic perishes, others will carry the banner!" Now she's the heart of the Workers' Opposition. She'll have to be squashed for the moment, though there is a lot in her critique. If our Soviet institutions really want to get rid of the red tape that ties them hand and foot, and strangles them with a bow at the neck, then, as she says, "the Party must ruthlessly kick out its own bureaucrats."

All history is struggle. No struggle has ever succeeded in history, except through violence. And these three years since the October Revolution only confirm this truth. Don't our enemies know we all of us dearly wish it to be proved false?

We would like to picture progress the way the German reformists and revisionists have always done—as a Nordic express
train gliding with peaceful, quiet, smooth orderly pace up to the
buffers at the terminus. And a sedate conductor opening the door
of the carriage to call down the corridor: "Social Revolution Station! *Alle aussteigen!*" For a while just before, just after October,
we fancied it might just be possible. In countries where the bourgeoisie did not put up such a savage resistance, we thought they
could begin the march to socialism without such bloodshed, treading the human way. Alas, this remains a pipe dream. Here, where
revolution merged into class war, civil war, capitalist intervention,
the reactionaries attacked us in their hundreds of thousands. We
soon saw, even in Germany, our most hopeful example, that the
choice remained brutal. Either be hunted down by uniformed
killers such as murdered Karl Liebknecht and Rosa Luxemburg,
the legal massacre of the best leaders of the workers, or mount an
armed uprising to suppress the exploiters. There is no middle way.
Those who pretend there is, today, can really be our most harmful,
threatening enemies.

What can we produce to match the White Guard terror on
behalf of the old ruling class, everywhere across the globe? The
Americans collect colonies in South America, in the Mediterranean, in China and the Philippines—"from the halls of Montezuma
to the shores of Tripoli!" The British hang on in Ireland, shooting
the wounded leaders of the rebels roped to their chairs, condoning
the Cossack pogroms of the Black and Tans. The British in India,
the slaughter at Amritsar, nearly two thousand men, women and
children killed and wounded in an atrocity worse than "Bloody
Sunday"—even the Tsar would not permit the general who gave
the order to profit from a national fund to the tune of 26,317
pounds, 4 shillings and 10 pence, including a tenner from Rudyard
Kipling. "Kornilovism" rises again in the new force of "fascists" in
Italy, their *Freikorps* imitators in Germany, the Hungarian nobles
hunting down democrats like game. Either them or us. There is
no third choice, no neutral course, no peaceful alternative—nor
can there be!

JANUARY 20   MOSCOW   1921

Message from B.-B. reporting on his visit to P. A. Kropotkin, the
heroic old Anarchist, who must be nearly eighty by now. I recall

I visited him, some time in May 1919, I think. I know we had a marvelous ding-dong about the state, about bureaucracy, about authority and liberty.

I had been searching everywhere yesterday for B.-B. and was becoming enraged by his absence. It is not that I think everyone should always be within reach of my yell. In fact, I continually advise colleagues to take short breaks, even long holidays. When I see they are disintegrating under my nose, I point out that it is a criminal offense to waste and misuse "government property." Trying to carry on in a way that damages yourself is a form of sabotage. I give them the choice between the rest home and the cellars of the Cheka! But I do insist on knowing when someone is likely to be absent. We are all links in a chain. The least you can do is give enough notice for another link to replace you and take the strain.

I suppose B.-B. thought I might stop him. What sort of person do they think I am? Kropotkin and I are about as far apart as two revolutionaries can be, but we are still the same breed. We are united in determination to smash the old system. Where we differ is in what should replace it—he seemed to think you could walk straight into the Garden of Eden. My vision was of something more resembling Purgatory. Still, I have never forgotten what he said to the deputation of creepy liberal-left tossers from abroad in the summer of 1920. They came, hoping to hear the venerable patron saint of Anarchy denounce Lenin. Instead, he handed them a long letter addressed to "the workers of Western Europe." He wrote that "the toilers of European countries and their friends in other social classes must persuade their governments first to abandon the idea of armed intervention against Russia, in whatever form, open or masked, and renew relations with the Soviet state."

B.-B. reports: "I went yesterday together with (Health Commissar) Semashko and other consultants to see Kropotkin. The old man was very moved by our solicitude. The state of his health is grave and he is suffering. *Angina pectoris,* of which an attack may last four to six hours, makes him choke terribly and gives him a pain in the heart and in the left arm. This is aggravated by quite severe, though so far localized, pneumonia. His temperature is 38.9. His pulse is normal. The doctors warned that in view of his advanced age one can expect anything. We must provide Kropotkin with proper nourishment. He should not eat black bread, but there was no white flour in the house at all. He needs semolina, potato flour for making *kisel* (a kind of nursery pudding), and so on. I am enclosing a list of what is needed. They have no kerosene, consequently no light. (Yesterday we got just a little with difficulty.) He must have milk; they do have a cow, but there is nothing to feed it and the animal is half dead. Fodder must be provided. All this can be arranged, because the quantities are ridiculously small. We should also take over the cost of wood and the cost of delivery—they just had to pay 67,000 rubles for bringing in wood: this is quite beyond their means, and they were obliged to sell their last treasures."

As soon as I read this, I instructed the Cheka lieutenant who grows outside my office door to uproot himself, collect all the things on the list, and take them personally on a special train to Dmitrovo and put them in the hands of the Kropotkin family. I checked every item myself and stamped his instructions with the highest priority.

JANUARY 21   MOSCOW   1921

I asked B.-B. this morning how it was that K. could have been allowed to get into such a shameful state. I thought we had settled all that when he chose, with great courage, to come to Moscow in 1918 and be with his fellow-Russians in the first days of the Revolution. I was shocked by what B.-B. told me.

When he got to Dmitrovo, B.-B. said, he and Commissar Semashko and the doctors found the local party officials attending them at the station. There was a bit of mixup on the platform, nobody knowing where to go, or who to lead the way there. It turned out that the top men in Dmitrovo were mystified at a visit that was so obviously arranged by highest authority—two extra trains to avoid a long delay at the junction, two cars ordered in advance to meet us. (How B.-B. did all that without consulting me I decided not to ask.)

When they learned that the whole thing was laid on because word had reached the Kremlin that someone called Kropotkin had become very ill, they were amazed. They thought him not only a bore, a nuisance, a trouble-maker, but also probably an enemy of the people. They had never heard of him as a political philosopher, a great writer, a famous revolutionary Anarchist. All they knew was that he was a former prince. He lived in the house of a former landlord. From time to time, they observed that he was granted a few tiny special privileges. This only irritated them more. They could not make out what he could be doing to deserve them.

And Peter Alexevich, a man of uncompromising honesty and outspokenness, did not spare them from his criticisms. Who knows what went on in this backwater during the turbulent years of civil war and intervention? B.-B. believes that the local bigwigs not only dislike K., but may actually have been persecuting and hounding him over the last year or so.

"They looked very uneasy when they stood whispering together as we drove off in our cars to his bedside," mused B.-B.

"I'll give them something to be uneasy about," I said, feeling a wave of rage, not untinged with a few staining drops of guilt at having left him so unprotected. "You know this is Self-Education Month, and the slogan is *Renew Your Revolutionary Roots!*?"

"That was December, last year," B.-B. said. "This month is actually Self-Discipline Month and the slogan *Cultivate the Middle Ground! . . .*"

But I swept such equivocations aside. In Dmitrovo, they hardly knew December from January. They were probably still painting up *All Power to the Soviets!* I told him to get onto the Hughes telegraph machine and rattle off an urgent message to our Cheka lieutenant through whatever is the nearest police post to that nest of philistines, Dmitrovo. This should read: "As part of national Self-Education campaign on Our Revolutionary Traditions Dmitrovo has been picked to organize a pageant on the Legacy of Anarchism to be staged on the 20th of February in honor of Peter Kropotkin, first citizen of their commune."

FEBRUARY 8   MOSCOW   1921

I was working late. And in the early hours of this morning, around 3:40, the telegraph awoke with its usual wild castanet clicking. A cable from Dmitrovo: "P. A. Kropotkin died peacefully at 3:10 A.M. Cause of death: drastic weakening of heart activity."

B.-B. asked to be allowed to arrange the transfer of his body to the great Hall of Columns in the House of Trades Unions. I suggested it should lie for three days so that the people of Moscow, unlike those benighted Dmitrovites, may be able to pay their last respects. His emphasis on "mutual aid," which so smacked of petit-bourgeois compromise *before* the Revolution, may now, as we build the Soviet state, be more central to our philosophy, and benefit from a well-publicized airing.

FEBRUARY 15   MOSCOW   1921

Trotsky and I both keep a beady eye (one each—ha!) on the Western capitalist press. It is not a pleasant task. What we are trying to do is to find out what is happening in countries we once knew well. Between us, we are familiar with most of them.

The problem is—how far can we trust what we read? Do the hirelings have one standard for news about their home country and other lands of which they approve, and another for Soviet Russia? Certainly, most reports they carry of happenings within our borders (almost invariably datelined Ankara, Warsaw, Berlin, Helsinki, Vienna—almost never Petrograd or Moscow) are complete fantasy.

However, occasionally there is a story about us, untrue at the moment of printing, which gives us a useful warning of what they hope, or they are plotting, will happen. L.D. reads his foreign papers himself as soon as they arrive—he likes to browse among book reviews, cultural news, pieces on philosophy or finance. I rely on a polyglot assistant trained to sniff through international stories, then gut and concentrate them for me the next day. So it is that Trotsky often uncovers the "time bomb" item first, and passes it around.

This morning he drops me this (copy to C.-in-C. Baltic Fleet, Admiralty, Petrograd): "*Le Matin* (Paris) issue February 13 carries report dated February 11 (Helsinki) announcing uprising Kronstadt base, Kotlin Island, Gulf of Finland, sixteen miles due west Petrograd, also cruisers *Petropavlovsk, Sevastopol*. Few details except sailors demanding democratic freedoms and 'Soviets without Communism.' " Naval authorities advised be on alert and confirm degree of truth. Trotsky."

This afternoon, he drops a copy of C.-in-C. BaltFleet's reply: "All quiet Kronstadt, *Petropavlovsk, Sevastopol*. Have warned Commissar Kuzmin nevertheless be on alert. Please inform. Why this among many lying provocations from abroad need concern Trotsky/Lenin?" And he has added in his own hand at the bottom of the carbon—"Purely as matter of intuition suspect this item different from others. Possibly same category July 1920 foreign press report of Chernov-Spiridonova armed uprising Nizhny-Novgorod."

I remembered the occasion. Again L.D. had singled out for

further investigation the most sober among hundreds of firsthand
accounts of fictional attempts to overthrow us. Then too, our people on the spot assured us that this news story was totally without
foundation. And so it was, *then*. In *August* 1920, however, a *coup*
was attempted in the names of Chernov and Spiridonova in that
same city. It was quashed only with some difficulty. It would seem
that, among all the inventions spewed out by imperialist scribblers,
an occasional genuine forecast, disguised as accomplished fact, is
slipped in. Quite what the purpose can be remains debatable. L.D.
inclines to the theory that it is the trigger signal for agents to
activate an actual plot. I am doubtful—foreign papers are hardly
the easiest commodities available here, certainly not in N.-N. I
incline to the view that these particular clairvoyances are designed
to nudge us into a denial which is then shown to be worthless when
the event occurs. We shall see.

FEBRUARY 22   **MOSCOW**   **1921**

Is there anything greater than Beethoven's *Appassionata*? Inessa
used to play it for me. I could listen to it every day. It is astonishing,
superhuman music. While I am listening, I feel I want to murmur
sweet, gentle banalities. I would like to pat the heads, stroke the
faces, of people who can live in this dirty hell of a world and still
create such beauty. Perhaps there was a time when this was possible, permissible. But today it is unwise to put out your hand to
stroke or pat—you will get it bitten off! Most of your energy had
to be spent beating heads, thumping them without mercy, battering
them in if necessary, even though in our ideal, our new socialist
world, we would forbid the use of force against people.

Duty is hellishly hard.

FEBRUARY 28   **MOSCOW**   **1921**

This evening I addressed a gathering of activists called by the
Party's Moscow Committee. I spoke to them candidly and soberly,
among equals, giving them those unwelcome figures (and more!)
I noted on New Year's Eve. I explained, what they already knew,
that their government had made many gross, crass errors. We
misjudged the grain deliveries, promising an increase this year.

The truth is we will have to reduce the bread ration, and may not be able even to guarantee that. Kulak rebellions in Siberia are cutting our supplies ever lower and we have no stocks. The uprising in Armenia seems to be subsiding but not in time to compensate. This is sad news. We can do nothing but face it.

We are, for the moment, *in a deteriorating situation,* I told them. Spring is on its way, but that also means that the SRs abroad, and their imperialist friends, will revive their dreams of overthrowing Soviet power. Fuel has almost reached vanishing point. I have not got the figures so I cannot even make a useful guess at the cause. I ended by pointing out that they were as much at fault as we are. I had detected widespread feelings of distrust of the Party, now seen by many ordinary workers as a club for careerists, egoists, bullies and bureaucrats. "We are up to our necks, comrades, in a flood of discontent. This must be drained from below, through the Party apparatus, as swiftly as possible, as tactfully as possible. Otherwise, it will have to be suctioned off from above, through the state apparatus, by means that may need to be brutal and painful."

There is one possible weapon we can all share—the New Economic Policy. I gave them its outline, which caused a buzz so strong I felt I could see it, like a man-size tornado, spinning round the room. The comrades sprang apart into instant, opposing camps. I asked them to keep the discussion among themselves until I can present the proposed change of direction, in detail, at the Tenth Party Congress opening on March 8.

MARCH 2   MOSCOW   1921

For the only time I can recall, the door to my Kremlin office has been barred all day. My disconnected banks of telephones, like black, metal daffodils, stand stiffly silent. Even my emergency line, number known only to a dozen intimates, personal and political, remains quiet though still plugged in. I have cut myself off to plan our regime's first retreat. Oh yes, tactical, temporary, limited, ordered, pragmatic, of course! But still, a step, a giant step, back in order to prepare for a small leap forward. Instead of head on assault we must adjust to a slower method, the siege.

I have always been pleased by one quality I possess—realism. It is among the rarest of the gifts handed out to the newborn in the cradle, and one of the unluckiest. The realist will never have a happy life. He is hated if he is wrong, even more if he is right. To be popular, it is better to be a fantasist, a liar, a romantic, a salesman of heavenly caviar, witness the endurance of Christianity. Even though paradise on earth never arrives, you get credit for believing it is on its way.

This view may seem odd coming from me. As a Marxist, I too have promised a new, pure society inevitably growing inside the pregnant, corrupt old world. Even though I warned that the birth pangs could be cataclysmic, I remained confident that afterward the people would be easily able to govern themselves. "Every cook should rule the state." I favored open democracy in the soviets, in the Party, in the factories and the farms. I encouraged argument, disputes without fear or favor, a search for truth, among those who remained always comrades in arms.

I considered then that this was a rational, realistic summing up of the prospects. I still think today that I was making a correct appraisal on the basis of the facts *as they appeared then*. No one could know that every alternative chosen by history would turn out to be exactly the wrong one for us. I have never believed in "socialism in one country." Well, Switzerland perhaps, but not giant, back- ward, defeated, exploited Russia. But still I never expected that we would so soon stand alone, deserted by our obvious allies, at- tacked by unexpected enemies.

For us to continue existing against all these odds is one of the greatest achievements in history. We lost the bet on the German revolution, on the workers' overthrow of their oppressors across Europe and into the Orient. On Wilhelm settling for a reasonable deal as a price for Russia making peace instead of insisting on the rapacious dismemberment we suffered at Brest-Litovsk. On the Allies withdrawing from our territory once the German war was over instead of invading ever deeper, backing the White Guard generals, continuing to subsidize terrorists and bandits even after they and their client armies had gone. On the dreadful effects of plagues and famines, rundown industry and ruined agriculture, mankind preying upon itself in endless slaughter and torture, so that large parts of our miserable land have been whipped and starved back beyond even the Middle Ages to the fringes of the Stone Age.

This *via dolorosa* is littered with abandoned hopes, ideals, il- lusions sacrificed to realism. Step by step, we have had to renounce many of the freedoms of the February Revolution. We could not afford to allow our enemies to publish newspapers, to organize parties, to infiltrate our organizations. We were obliged to institute or reintroduce capital punishment, trial by courts-martial, shooting of prisoners, prohibition of strikes, forcible appropriation of surplus production. The dictatorship of the proletariat was an actuality, not a metaphor.

We were not facing mild, liberal, constitutional rivals for the hand of a virgin populace. Our opponents were engaged in assassination, kidnap, bombing, sabotage, armed insurrection, pogroms, larceny, obscene libels, mass poisoning. The only way to fight them was with Red Terror, much of it introduced at the demand of the workers and peasants themselves, rather than by the wish of the Party. Almost all of us in the leadership shrank from such devices at first. But then we understood that the privations the nation had suffered had burned out such intellectual tendernesses. The masses had been robbed, beaten, raped, wounded, threatened, starved, deceived and disillusioned. Unless we outreached our enemies without hesitation, they did not believe we could be serious.

Now that peace has come at last, I long to be able to announce a general relaxation. Few of us at the top here are happy with Russia as it is, an embryo workers' state crippled by many hideous bureaucratic deformations. And yet, I will have to tell the Congress as I introduce NEP, that just because this is a retreat, as in any army, discipline must be ten times more severe than during an offensive when everyone is moving forward. The new system should soon afford more food, greater choice, more initiative, increased output combined with less rationing, fewer forms and permits, the withdrawal of the official hand on every knocker.

Much of this I had jotted down in note-form for my speech. I have not been feeling well lately. The familiar steel cap round the head growing tighter and tighter. But as I looked forward to the injection of at least a little pleasure into the national bloodstream I felt the band unwind. Until the telephone rang.

It was Trotsky. "*Le Matin*'s crystal ball seems to be in working order."

Two days ago, a fortnight after the Paris daily reported it, there began an anti-government manifestation in Kronstadt. First, the sailors on the cruisers *Sevastopol* and *Petropavlovsk* held meetings denouncing what they called "the excesses" of our regime. Since "the present Soviet government does not represent the will of the workers and peasants," they demand that "new elections be held immediately by secret ballot."

At the end, they announced a mass demo in Kronstadt's Anchor Square for yesterday at which they planned to elect their own local soviet. (Not by secret ballot then?) It seems that those involved are almost all sailors, and almost all sailors are involved. The rest of the islanders, the shore-based staff of the forts, the people of Oranienbaum, have remained—choose your own term—"impartial," "apathetic," "uncommitted" or "wary."

Zinoviev, chairman of Peter Soviet, final authority for the NW District, has followed a quiet, unprovocative line. He pointed out that the current Kronstadt Soviet has only weeks to run so there will be an opportunity soon to replace any unsatisfactory members. Until then, he suggested, the sailors should listen to their resident commissar. (Kuzmin? If so, the speech, as the peasants say, will be "sharp and short, like the devil's prick"). In addition he offered them our Head of State, President Kalinin, as mediator, and possibly hostage. Trotsky was not sure whether the "old fox," Mikhail Ivanovich (never quite so cunning as he thinks he is) quite understood his dual role.

What happened next is also not entirely clear. The sailors raised the banner of the Third Revolution with the slogan: SOVIETS WITHOUT COMMUNISM. They then put forward a manifesto with fourteen clauses. From what I could make out—rather a bad line—it embodies no coherent political philosophy but is rather a pig's breakfast of random demands mostly to the "right" of Bolshevism but some to the "left." These included freedom of speech, press, assembly. Abolition of single-party control of government, legalization of left SRs and anarchists as candidates. Right of peasants to keep own cattle. Return of small businesses to private enterprise. Disbanding of Communist shock-brigades in factories, on farms, political officers in the Navy and Army. Ending of special rations for any groups. Arrest and trial of senior officers of Cheka. But most often repeated, an end to the barrier units (*zagraditelnye otryady*)—those armed detachments we have unfortunately found it necessary to ring round our cities to intercept workers smuggling out unauthorized factory goods in exchange for black-market farm produce.

Kuzmin made no comment on the manifesto. He appealed to the famous loyalty of the Kronstadters. The Soviet government would certainly listen to whatever they had to say. But they must remember their country was still threatened—by forces inside and outside, by forces human and impersonal, by forces over which the government could have no control as well as those over which it must have complete control. There was more to survival than compiling lists of what you would like for Christmas or resolutions you'd make for New Year. (Sounds like a good speech!) Among the threats, he cited Pilsudski's French-armed Polish army occupying territory newly stolen from us and Gerasim Antonov's Menshevik republic in Tambov hogging the grain intended to feed the rest of us. Worse even than famine was plague. He ended by warning that utopian wishful thinking was easily exploited by enemies abroad, especially today the French. General Wrangel had been defeated in the field, but he still commanded an army of between 70,000 and 80,000 men sulking in Turkey. If they could link up with the remnants of the tsarist Black Sea Fleet, now off Tunisia, Kronstadt might find itself an unwilling base for an invasion flotilla launched to divide up Russia among the imperialists like a second Africa.

There were cheers at this! (According to our informant.) And the short-fused Kuzmin (understandably) lost his temper. "Forget this foolishness," he shouted, "and so will we. But do not imagine that Bolsheviks will hand over power on request. If you want a fight, you can have it. We will protect our Soviet democracy to the bitter end."

Trotsky wonders whether this approach was mistaken, too peremptory and militaristic, almost tsarist. It was certainly a deviation from Zinoviev's softly-softly policy which would have promised everything, and then when the hubbub subsided, and the insurgents were emotionally disarmed, have disarmed them physically. But, I pointed out, this too was a tsarist tactic. In my view, Kuzmin had behaved as one always should when in doubt, honestly and straightforwardly. In the Kronstadt of old, they would have carried him on their shoulders round the fort. Yesterday, they tied him up and rolled him into a dungeon.

MARCH 3   MOSCOW   1921

More from Kronstadt. Unlike Kuzmin, our man on the spot (needless to say, perhaps, Kalinin) escaped across the ice in his motorsleigh. (He had never left it, pleading a sprained ankle.) But he stuck out long enough to be able to assure Trotsky, in a signed report, witnessed by his driver, that Kuzmin's speech was not the reason the commissar was seized along with all his staff. In fact, his speech seemed to have succeeded. The sailors were drifting away when somebody pushed their way from the back through the great crowd, shouting that fifteen armored cars, full of Red Army sharpshooters carrying machine guns, were on their way from HQ Northern Group at Konnaya Lahta to disperse the demo. Simultaneously, one of the officer delegates on the platform began whispering to the front rows that the Bolshevik military cadets on the island had joined with the other *kursanty* from the mainland in a raid to blow up the arsenal and spike the artillery. It was these rumors that fired the sailors into aggressive action, the detention of all loyalists, the armed occupation of the island, the fortress of Kronstadt, and the two cruisers for the moment locked in the ice.

As of tonight, the mutineers have not attempted to attack any government troops (there aren't any) between Kronstadt and Peter, nor to spread the rising to other towns or cities. So long as they contain themselves, our best policy may be simply to contain them.

MARCH 4   MOSCOW   1921

Mixed reports from Kronstadt. The North West District (i.e., Zinoviev) does not emerge very well from this emergency! Z. failed to take seriously, even for a moment, Trotsky's message about *Le Matin* and so never passed it on to Kuzmin and the Kotlin Island command. He was (Trotsky says) besotted by the sailors and they have until now been his greatest admirers, always ready to applaud his speeches, echo his slogans and march about Peter in shiploads giving the rest of the inhabitants the impression he is the most popular Party leader in town.

Lev Davidovich, who had been involved in some rival jockeying without their support, is not so keen. He points out, I'm sure quite correctly, that they are no longer the legendary, fearless giants we knew as "the pride and glory of the Revolution." Throughout the civil war, as commissar in charge, he would send for a detachment of Kronstadters whenever his soldiers had their backs to the wall. Until the end of 1919, he said, they never failed him. Then, in 1920, his generals began to complain that they were getting an inferior breed of fighting sailor, often more trouble than he was worth.

Last year, Trotsky visited them and was quickly disillusioned. I could not help but chuckle as I listened to him spitting his contempt down the telephone line, revealing an undertone of vulgarity and cattiness most untypical of him.

"They're all *boys*"—it was between a hiss and a crackle—"Revolution's just a word in a book . . . if they've read a book. For them, a slogan is an intellectual achievement. . . . Sons of peasants,

Ukrainian peasants, Ukrainian middle peasants, the most reactionary, nationalist, anti-Semitic, God-fearing, Tsar-adoring dirt-collectors east of the *Champs Elysées* . . . They show letters from home, all nagging . . . how can you fight for these Communist robbers? Yet what do they do? Nothing! Who do they fight? Nobody! They take in each other's washing, pressing and bleaching their bum-tight bell-bottoms. They give each other sporty haircuts . . . obscene tattooes . . . *they dance together*! They want for nothing. Because they're a tongue locked into the orifice of the West, Grigory bribes them with extra rations. After all, as one said to me: 'I can *skate* to Finland or the Baltic States. . . .' " No wonder every sailor hates the barrier units. The *zagraditelnye otrayady* report they catch more Kronstadt boys in blue dealing in state property than any other citizens. Then they have to let them go because they are part of our protective shield against capitalist attack. . . . If you ask me—today the Kronstadt sailor *is* the capitalist attack."

I must say, this enjoyable outburst has relaxed the chain around my chest. I had still been thinking we might have to suppress, before the eyes of the world, the heroes of October. How un-Marxist of me to forget that everything has a history, nothing remains unchanged! Opposites interpenetrate, *yin* becomes *yang*, thesis—antithesis—synthesis. It is a very crude error to assume that because the name stays the same so does the essence. After all, to ensure the future of socialism, humanity's freest state, I myself am about to allow its dreaded predator, capitalism, out on a leash. If the Kronstadters would only wait—and I have given hints galore—what they really want will be largely granted, without need of threats and disorders.

Remember Marx's unique insight, unsuspected by psychologists or sociologists of his day—you cannot judge people, or parties, or societies by what they say about themselves! All over the world, liberals and laborites, academic radicals and milk-and-water socialists, are writing and passing resolutions asking why our government cannot agree to these nebulous proposals—"freedom," "freedom to trade," "workers' emancipation," "soviets without Bolsheviks," "genuine elections," relief from "Party tyranny" and so on and so forth. If they had learned anything from Marx, or from history, they would know that only the most childish now take these honey-sweet idealizations at their face value. We have to interpret such words according to the class bias, the social composition, the past record, the future aims, of those who use them.

Even the most romantic theorist will hardly credit an island of sailors setting up an independent regime in the name of a barrage of abstractions. Like their leader Petrichenko (twenty, petty officer, parents medium farmers Ukraine, no combatant service, trained admin, stores—I have his Cheka file in front of me), they want the specific, tangible relaxations of War Communism that will benefit them and their families—peasant rights to keep private plots, slaughter own cattle, deal directly with town bag-men plus the counterbalance of career servicemen's rights to deal directly with country, buy own homes, receive promotion purely on seniority, technical merit regardless of political maturity, intellectual status.

The history of the class struggle in Russia has been between the vanguard of the new urban proletariat and the pioneers of new finance capitalism to dominate that majority of middle and small peasants without whom no regime can survive—the petty-bourgeoisie. In 1917, we won. In 1921, we are paying the price of wagering most of our stake on the city and the workers. Concessions are essential for small businesses and medium farms. *This does not mean we can permit organized parties whose sole political aim is to strengthen and advance the petty-bourgeoisie!*

Trotsky and I have issued a press statement on the Kronstadt affair indicating these considerations for advanced comrades but for mass newspaper readers underlining rather more demagogic points. These include: the significant advance notification by the reactionary rag, *Le Matin;* the rapid rise in price of pre-1917 shares in Russian factories and tsarist state bonds on all Western stock exchanges; the gathering in Finland, along the shores of the Gulf and just across our northern borders, of growing numbers of SR terrorists, Menshevik publicists, White Guard officers, imperialist secret agents; the advocacy in Western parliaments and editorial columns of Allied financing for General Wrangel, and the fleet off Bizerta, in a seaborne invasion through Kronstadt; the role in the sailors' takeover played by Commander (formerly tsarist general of artillery) Kozlovsky, who has been urging (so far in vain) the bombardment of Petrograd forts and seizures of the half-empty, three-quarters-starved, lightly-defended city.

This should have some effect on the Kronstadters or I'm no newspaperman!

MARCH 5   MOSCOW   1921

The Kronstadt sailors, in an unexpected, rather unnerving fashion, continue to glower down their gun barrels, neither venturing out nor giving in. Until now, I must say, I had thought them more a propaganda than a military danger, a peripheral embarrassment about as likely to unbalance our Soviet state as the Irish Republican Army is to bring down the British Empire. Any student of war and revolution could easily find more convincing threats to our supremacy in 1921—I would nominate the declaration of independence by Antonov, the Right SR, in Tambov; or the anarchist Makhno's declaration of a Third Revolution, under the banner of his insurgent Peasant Army, in Kiev. Yet these, and several other such, are ignored by a world that insists on categorizing Kronstadt as the fiercest challenge so far not only to our stability, but also to our honesty and sincerity, since it comes from rebels of our own kind.

Trotsky stresses that, in terms of battle capability, the sailors are by no means negligible. In all, the island now holds about 16,000 determined critics and objectors to our *status quo*. At least 10,000 of these are trained combat troops, well-supplied fighting men skilled in the use of close-quarters weapons—rifles, bayonets, grenades, and pistols. In addition, Kozlovsky has amassed some 68 machine guns and 135 pieces of artillery, his specialty. Whether by luck or cunning, the two ice-locked gunboats and the cannon-stuffed fortress form a triangle which commands a withering arc of firepower in every direction and a range that reaches well beyond the banks of the Gulf.

As I pondered whether or not we should hang on a few days longer before confrontation, prowling up and down my Kremlin office, I realized my ears had been picking up a cheery, chuckling sound without realizing what it was. The icicles that fang the gutters above my window are starting to melt.

I knew then that I was fed up with all sailors, but especially ours. Apart from the Cossacks, no men in uniform here exude such a swaggering contempt for civilians, such a high regard for themselves. Whatever assistance they had provided in '17, they are worse than useless today. No match for the British Navy in the West and the Japanese Navy in the East, their Baltic Fleet, the only one we have left, remains bottled up outside Petrograd, a floating academy of dandyism and self-indulgence. Their warships might as well be sunk as barriers to enemy vessels, or sold off as scrap metal on the international war-surplus market. And as for the boys in blue, I wonder how they would react to being remustered into labor brigades, shipped off to work those old family plots they love so much, whipped along by the old boys they left behind???

Sovnarkom endorse my assessment of the situation. With the

Neva ice about to melt like our Moscow icicles, we must not risk
waiting to see if the thawed-out cruisers will stick where they are,
or steam into the old capital and hold it for ransom. Our commissar
for war, Lev Davidovich, is to replace Zinoviev, take over the North
West District and order the Kronstadters to submit or be eliminated. We cannot afford any other outcome.

MARCH 7   MOSCOW   1921

Trotsky's ultimatum, issued in Peter March 5 1400 hours, brisk
and to the point: "Only those who surrender unconditionally can
count on the mercy of the Soviet Republic. . . . Simultaneously with
this warning, I am issuing instructions to suppress the rebellion
and the insurrectionists by force of arms. . . . This is the last warning."

It is countersigned by two of our former tsarist staff officers,
General (Sergei) Kamenev, now Red Army c.-in-c., and General
Tukachevsky, commander Seventh Army. It has taken some days
for them to mobilize our forces against Kronstadt since Zinoviev
had allowed the NW District border guards to run down, assuming
(not unreasonably) that Kronstadt *was* our best border guard. According to Kronstadt's surprisingly powerful transmitter, boosted
via Radio Helsinki, Trotsky also threatened the sailors that he
would "shoot them down like partridges."

The partridge is a tricky target and I'm sure L.D. did not use
any such phrase on the record. But it does sound a bit like him,
feet up and buttons undone. I hope it sends a shiver through the
rebels. We want no bloodshed, no *more* bloodshed perhaps I should
say. I am not on the spot, like Trotsky, but it seems to me, so long
as the ice remains solid, the sailors are more like sitting ducks.
Only two reactions so far. At 1500 hours, the entire cadet force,
kursanty, marched out, unhindered, to support the government.
Then at 1600 hours (so the radio alleges) one quarter of the island's
Party members resigned and declared solidarity with the rebels,
complaining that the Revolutionary brotherhood had degenerated
into "a club for careerists, egoists, bullies and bureaucrats."

Telephoning me the last development, Trotsky made his voice
sound very puzzled. "Not a bad phrase . . . I wonder where they
got it from."

Late this evening, while I was still at work on the Congress
program, the Hughes telegraph began to chatter: our long-range

guns in Kosa Tarkhovskaya from the northeast and Krasnaya Gorka from the southwest have begun to shell Kotlin Island.

MARCH 8   MOSCOW   1921

The Tenth Congress assembles just before noon—990 delegates speaking for 732,521 card-carrying Party members. These three-quarters of a million activists, agitators, opinion-makers, law-enforcers, risk-takers, shock-brigaders can make or break our Politburo's New Economic Policy.

I am always conscious that the more scarred and flea-bitten our comrades are, the less they will be likely to applaud any change of direction. At best, I expect them to accept this one as a lesser evil. The delegates I do not trust are those who will hail it with enthusiasm.

Often in politics, what appears, as it approaches from one side like a flaming arrow, to be a disaster turns out, after it has passed through the target and shot off on the other side, to be a triumph. That is not to say that it was never disastrous or triumphant but that what it was depended on when it was where it was.

Not long after dawn, as I slept in my Kremlin cot, that tireless chanter of news, the Hughes, nagged at my ear. The cannonade at Kronstadt had ended two hours before daylight. Then Tukachevsky, who was in charge of front-line operations, led an encircling attack in person across the slippery, snow-powdered plain as the sun rose. He had chosen as his assault wave the best and freshest soldiers available, mainly the young who think themselves immortal—almost all the *kursanty*, volunteers from the Red Army and the Red Guards, a backbone of veterans, Letts, Asians, Chekists.

He dressed them in white sheets, painted white all their equipment, the wheeled guns, the ammunition sleds, even the stocks of the rifles. They had reached within shouting distance of the island before a sharp-eyed lookout in a crow's nest spotted these rolling snowdrifts, advancing line abreast. It was a brilliant piece of soldiering. Except that it was a catastrophe.

They should have stormed the fortifications (all well known to the *kursanty*) with the advantage of being shapeless, forewarned attackers picking off surprised defensive cutouts lined up along the parapets. It was a maneuver worthy of Cesare Borgia or Garibaldi. But someone on the other side (Kozlovsky?) also had a stroke of genius. Instead of concentrating their packed fire power on an enemy it was difficult to see clearly, the Kronstadt gunners directed their shells either downward, just offshore of their own beaches, or lobbed them, howitzer-style, over the heads of our besiegers, between us and the far banks. The foot-thick ice was ruptured along two lines, before and behind, like perforations on a tear-off coupon. Whether they advanced or retreated, our troops slid down the tipped slabs and vanished into the black depths, frozen solid inch by inch as their grip gave way.

Tukachevsky's special force has lost almost a third of its members. Much, much worse—though only those who fought there have the right to say it—was that half of these were deserters to the rebels who waded ashore at prearranged spots using prearranged passwords.

The only consolation that our two generals and commissar for war could find for themselves, when I talked to them over the direct wire, was that the bravest, most loyal troops turned out to be the young: the cadets, the new recruits to the Army, the student members of the Red Guards. The new generation's record was even better than that of veteran Chekists. I joined with them in gratitude that Lincoln Steffens, the great American radical muckraker, was right. He said in October, "I have seen the future and it works!" Here are those who will be our future, and they work!

I pointed out another unexpected benefit. As the news of the setback on the Kronstadt ice circulated, the opposition to NEP melted away. The substitution of later cash taxes and charges instead of immediate seizure of surplus in kind was seen as the easing of a long-standing complaint by middle and small peasants. The delegates cheered my assurance that no new class of NEPmen would be able to take political power to match their economic power nor would it be possible for them to pass on any privileges to their families. This is a purely temporary, technical adjustment.

MARCH 12   MOSCOW   1921

Three more attacks on Kronstadt by Trotsky's assault force have proved indecisive. The ice is getting thinner. A thaw is predicted within four days. This is our most vulnerable spot, an open mouth or perhaps wound, through which our enemies can pour. There must be no more delay.

I do not know who floated the idea of a crack commando of

dedicated, motivated revolutionaries to lead the next assault, but three hundred delegates from the Congress, almost a third of the total, have volunteered to do so. They left Moscow this afternoon and should be fighting on the Neva by tomorrow morning. When you consider that the 990 Party stalwarts here include many like me who are getting on in age, or not in the best of health, those willing to risk being killed for their convictions in what we had been celebrating as the first year of peace may be nearer nine-tenths of those available. It is a heroic gesture.

MARCH 13   MOSCOW   1921

The Tenth Congress "regiment," with Tukachevsky again leading from the front, braved the creaking, buckling surface of the great Neva just before dawn, determined to show that history cannot be mocked, nor the Revolution bartered and bargained over like a dirty deal between Imperialists. Quite un-Marxist, of course, but magnificent nonetheless.

Trotsky quips over the direct line he has had linked to the riverbank: "If it works, then it is Marxist, only we didn't realize it."

Two hours later, he taps out the message: "It has worked." It wasn't just naked courage, determination, unconquerable will. Tukachevsky is a commander with many original techniques. The center of the channel, as the defenders knew, has already turned back into a liquid corridor at least fifteen feet wide. There was no way we could cross this, so we would not attempt to. But there was, and we did. Taking advantage of the fact that his latest recruits were combatants trained to an inner discipline, who yet knew how to take individual initiative, the general dished out some new equipment. Not just the white guns and cloaks, but white ladders thirty to fifty feet long, white tarpaulins with roped corners that could cover a city street. On their bellies, advance scouts used these to breach the great gaps in the ice. When a barrage of star shells and Very lights blinded the islanders, the fittest delegates swarmed across on the ladders, balancing like acrobats, while the others scrabbled and slid forward on the bouncy, artificial parade ground, flailing like wrestlers, never firing a shot. By midday, they had led the other troops on to the beaches of the island which they continue to hold, pinned down by fire. It will not be easy. Indeed I foresee massacre and counter-massacre if they have to fight house to house.

MARCH 17   MOSCOW   1921

Early yesterday, all resistance collapsed on Kotlin Island. The fortress of Kronstadt surrendered. A struggle, door by door, roof to roof, at close quarters, guaranteed the heaviest possible casualties. Hardly a combatant on either side escaped without some wound, often quite serious. There is no doubt that the enemy were in the end as highly dedicated, driven by as powerful motives, as we were. "Like wild beasts," says Tukachevsky.

Perhaps they thought that we would execute all our prisoners as counterrevolutionary traitors. If they did, they may yet be right. I cannot interfere in Peter. The anger of our survivors there, particularly those soldiers in mufti from the Congress, glows at white heat. It will not easily be denied the satisfaction of cauterizing this corruption from the living flesh. Anybody found with, or near, a warm weapon has been put in chains and thrown into the Peter and Paul dungeons. Zinoviev is eagerly soliciting the approval of those who fought by advocating that those captured should be shot in batches.

Thousands escaped from the northern side of the island into Finland. There, bourgeois paymasters, loaded with subsidies from the European rich which arrived too late, are rewarding them with money and praise. Kronstadt's leaders are being interviewed by the world's press and their views broadcast by radio across the water to us. I'm afraid what they say, or are said to say, will not much help those left behind in our hands.

Commander Kozlovsky is quoted as complaining that the sailors' leaders would not take his advice. They should either have delayed until the channels were open and the cruisers could sail straight into Peter or invaded across the ice as soon they had seized the guns, surrounding and silencing the other forts. The insurrection remained too long, he said "a passive revolution." Petrichenko, the petty-officer instigator, blames himself for not immediately executing all active supporters of the government, locking up the rest, and refusing to let anyone leave. The harsher and crueler the losers tell us they ought to have been, the harsher and crueler they are going to make the winners.

APRIL 3   PETROGRAD   1921

I came to Peter today for Trotsky's victory parade of the loyal troops, just in case there was any danger of people believing we were not united on our policy of "submit or be destroyed." I issued a statement stressing that we had no real choice—from October onward, the only alternatives have been dictatorship of the proletariat or tyranny of capitalism. I pointed out that the few reasonable suggestions they put forward were already being canvassed *before* they took over Kronstadt. They were being ratified by an overwhelming majority while they tried to kill the very delegates who had passed that vote.

After the initial confusion of left-right, utopian-sensible, silly-clever ideas, the Kronstadt rebellion decayed rapidly into the reactionary poison. I passed around issues of their own *News* (*Izvestia*) with articles which would have disgraced the Black Hundreds. Our entire leadership is denounced as "an autocracy of Soviet Princes," living in luxury, dressed in silks and jewels, waited upon by beautiful girls (though some prefer boys), traveling everywhere in *de luxe* trains, surrounded by armed guards. We are all mongrel foreigners—favorite alien taint: German or Georgian!—but preferably Jewish. Gregory is "the evil genius, fat-boy Zinoviev" and Lev Davidovich "the monster Trotsky, knee-deep in workers' blood."

We may have made mistakes dealing with the rebels of Kronstadt. We certainly have made mistakes, plenty of them, ever since we took power. But is that any reason to tamely hand over a key position to our rabid, capitalist-imperialist enemies? If Petrograd falls, the road is wide open to Moscow. Also *our* Revolution remained passive too long. At last we have cracked and shaken off the external lice that fouled our Russian linen. Now we must search out and squash the home-grown lice still lurking in our body-hair. We must no longer be afraid, as a sovereign nation, of striking first, at home or abroad!

Trotsky's speech, dripping with praise for "our boys," is thought a little too fulsome by some of the Politburo who accompanied me from Moscow. I think it about right—this was, after all, an incredibly savage and horrific encounter in which perhaps 30,000 died. No one who took part is ever likely to forget the sights he saw. We, who did not, are in no position to query a few adjectives. L.D. pays a genuine tribute to the insurgents—"our blinded sailor-

comrades"—misled and duped. And he cites me as agreeing with
him that history will record our triumph here only as a "tragic
necessity."

Some Social-Democrat visitors from abroad remain uneasy
about what was, in the end, a minor event. As if we had chosen
to kill Soviet citizens in a staged battle, for obscure ideological
reasons, without taking note of what European sympathizers might
feel! I do not care if they throw Kronstadt in our faces forever. It
illuminated reality like a flash of lightning. And now nobody who
examines the facts can doubt that we only did what we had to do.

I will register just one piece of evidence in addition to what I
have already put down about this story: Paul Milyukov's comments
from Paris. P.M. was always the most able, realistic Kadet leader
in Peter between the two Revolutions of February and October.
He is a kind of Marxist inside-out, never deceiving himself, always
carefully analyzing the workings of the class structure, and deciding which movement most favors his class and his cause.

When the sailors took over and spawned the manifestos, Victor
Chernov argued they were a revival of the SRs; Julius Martov
counterclaimed it was the resurgence of Menshevism. But Milyukov assured his friends on the Stock Exchange, in Whitehall and
the Quai d'Orsay: "It does not matter whom we support, be they
anarchists or any variety of soviet supporters, as long as the Bolsheviks are overthrown, as long as there is *a shift of power;* it does
not matter whether the move is to the right or the left, to the
Mensheviks or to the anarchists, so long as it is *away from the Bolsheviks.* The rest will take care of itself." Here you have the objective
truth, the class truth. This is what happens in all revolutions. Look
at history! The narcissistic Chernovs and Martovs talk. The White
Guards and Milyukovs act. And so do we.

JUNE 5   MOSCOW   1921

I cannot find out who it is who spreads this mania for questionnaires, personal forms, the whole cult of the curriculum vitae. But
when I do I shall set him memorizing the maiden names of all the
maternal grandmothers of the first 5,000 members of the CPSU
(B). Some of our foreign comrades assume that this is part of some
Leninist dictatorship of the proletariat. They are amazed when I
point out that the ramshackle tsarist state kept trace of any and
every citizen who gave the *slightest* sign of not being identical with

his neighbor, from the cradle to the grave, a total running into millions. For example, one of our particularly archive-loving Old Bolsheviks (I fancy it must have been Vorovsky) came to me recently with some reports filed by the Kazan Okhrana during the eighties and nineties. They contained the address of every house in which I, and every other member of my family, passed an evening from the date of my brother's execution to our departure from the neighborhood around the turn of the century. In those days, I was not a very important enemy of the state. But on occasion, they listed places I had visited where I thought I had taken such exquisite care not to be followed. This was rather shaming.

Before me now I have yet another of those personal histories to fill in. I cannot refuse. Clearly it has been properly authorized. And I have no desire to require exceptions to the law made in my favor. Still, I am tempted to answer such items as: "State the name, occupation, class and address of your paternal grandfather" with some such reply as: "I do not know anything about my grandfather." Not strictly true. But I make the habit of blotting out trivial information that clutters up the brain. So I can say, truly, I no longer *do* know anything about any grandfathers. Also (I am reminded) Anna has been giving lectures about the Ulyanovs, entirely against my instructions, assuring provincial audiences that our father's father was "lower-middle-class."

I can hardly call her a liar. So I will avoid commitment by a manly, firm "Don't Know."

Future collectors of my laundry-lists and penciled notes on envelopes will have to do without the help of this diary which Nadya swears she will burn, or bury, on my death.

Strange woman, though one with whom I have shared most of the best, and all of the worst, of my life. I want no one to read this, except her. And she does not want to read it. What, I wonder, does she expect to find here that she does not already know, only too well?

Radek just dropped by, that misshapen face, like an old candle-end, as usual bulging with mischief and jokery. As ever, he started to read everything on my desk, while talking away, nineteen to the dozen, to distract attention from his entirely automatic snooping.

Then he became so interested in my personal history he forgot to pretend he wasn't reading it. "Ho, ha, hum, well, well," he said. "Paternal grandfather *not known*. How interesting! Quite mistakenly I imagined him an Astrakhan tailor, therefore probably a Mongol, or Chuvash, or Tatar. Certainly a non-Russian, ex-serf. Maternal ditto—funny name, Blank. The kind they gave to Jews as a practical joke when accepting them as Christians. But I see you know nothing of this?"

I wasn't really annoyed. But I enjoy giving Karl Bernhardovich a flick of the whip occasionally.

"Are you suggesting I'm telling lies or suppressing the truth?"

"Oh no, Comrade Chairman of Sovnarkom. I'm sure it's meticulously correct. I mean, like this answer here to 'Where have you lived in Russia?' "

"Well?"

"I see you say, almost apologetically: 'Only on the Volga and in capital cities.' "

"Well?"

"If you say so, Comrade Chairman. Of course. It's only I was sure you were like the rest of the Old Bolsheviks. At sometime or other, exiled in Siberia. Shushenskoye, I'd heard. From 1897 to 1900, wasn't it? But, naturally. If you'd rather it didn't get around . . ."

I felt as if I had just discovered an extra room in my brain. How could I have missed out Nadya's "enchanted kingdom"? (That reminds me, she should have said *"republic."*) All those—what?— seventeen years of bolting backward and forward across Europe, waiting for the bell of revolution to ring, I had always been sustained by a vision of two places. They were my Oblomov's dream—Kokushkino and Shushenskoye. Yet one of them had been sealed away inside my head. Are my brains going porridgey at fifty-two?

I started to ask Karl Bernhardovich. But he'd gone. I could still hear his tongue clacking along the corridors and the other Sovnarkom members, aching for me to stop working so they can go home, greeting his rallies and quips with—if there is such a thing—disapproving laughter.

What sort of man forgets he spent three years in Siberia?

JULY 7   MOSCOW   1921

Michelet said that *chaque époque rêve la suivante.* It is a persuasive thought, echoing in the mind like a phrase of music, giving a sheen and a shine to visions of the future. But is it at all true that each era dreams the next that is to come?

It seems to me even in Soviet Russia, that most people barely register the present. Asked to name what features of life around them will survive and expand in the years ahead, they almost invariably cite those that are the essence of the past and already on their way out. Generals fight the last war. Rulers repeat the mistakes of their predecessors. The inventor, the innovator, the pioneer rarely profits from his own insight and courage. The money is made by those who commercialize the devices at second, third, fourth hand when they no longer alarm and baffle the public. Most ordinary people live out their lives facing backward, like Volga boatmen. Their idea of success is when they surpass their *parents*, preferably in money, rank, education, comfort. Possibly just in age. It is thought unpleasant, near perverted, to compete with your children's generation.

That is almost a definition of the reactionary—someone whose golden age is always in a past that never existed. In this sense *chaque époque rêve la précédente*, and most people feel it natural to be reactionary. Even those at the compressed base of the pyramid—perhaps especially those, for example, the peasants— dream of a time when they ruled Eden like a race of Adams. Our *muzhiks* cannot be budged from the conviction that once they owned all the land. The Tsar was only holding it for them, as Little Father, in paternal trust until they came of age.

This is a reactionary view—*that* goes without saying. Yet I was able to turn it to radical account by showing the peasants that they would never get back their patrimony, their God-given inheritance, through any process of piecemeal reform. Such a colossal theft could only be righted by a colossal act of expropriation. And only the Bolsheviks were extreme enough to attempt it. This may not have turned out quite as the peasants thought. But then dreams are never carbon copies of reality. That is why they are dreams. This is something our opponents, even our rivals, never grasped. They would tell us—hypocritically, if they were liberals, briefed to appear for the capitalist bourgeoisie; or sincerely, if they were Mensheviks or SRs, peddling their own roads to Socialism—that we should be more moderate, more realistic, more conventional if we wanted to win over the masses. Yet it was precisely *because* we were so outrageous, so intemperate, so insanely sure of our- selves, that we won the allegiance of workers and peasants, soldiers and intellectuals. It was like Pascal's invitation to humanity to make a bet on God's existence. He argued that the rewards of being right were so much greater than the debits of being wrong. In '17, all Russia was falling through a hole in the planet Earth. It seemed as if society would be sucked out into space and explode. In their hearts, the vast majority of our countrymen suspected that nothing could save them. Only the Bolsheviks claimed to be able to operate in an environment where all orthodox science, history, political theory and practical economics, above all any common sense, were against us. We boasted we could defy gravity, exist without oxygen, turn black into white. People were grateful that we thought plain survival was even imaginable. That we promised in addition a brave new world, the first true golden age, hit them like vodka on a long-empty stomach.

This ability to apply a form of philosophic jujitsu to life, to use the power of our enemies, real or abstract, to our advantage and against them, is what we Marxists call dialectics.

Outsiders regard the dialectic as a form of fairly sophisticated magic, a theological proposition that confirms their view of Marxism as a thinly disguised religion, based on faith, not works. Yet the principle has been known since humanity first began to make generalizations from experience. It is Yin-Yang—no blessing is unmixed; all growth springs from decay. It is the law of thermodynamics—for every action, there is an equal and opposite reaction. You find it in the most basic, pragmatic crafts, such as warfare. Clausewitz, the Machiavelli of the battlefield, demonstrated that with commanders of equal talent, and armies of equal strength, more casualties will be suffered when attacking than defending, by advancing not retreating. Logically, this should mean that the aggressor was always defeated, the winner always lost. And this is ridiculous. Or is it? Who won at Brest-Litovsk?

The great rational dreamers have always been on our side. Marx explained the workings of a new machine, like a clock in a glass casing, that most of his contemporaries hardly realized was more than a painting on the wall. Indeed, in many parts of the world, such as Russia, it was not yet ticking. And today, in countries like India, China, the Middle East, it has still not developed beyond the blueprint. This was clairvoyance on an heroic scale, comparable only to Copernicus or Darwin. When he died in 1883, he was considered largely a failure. This political philosopher, economic historian and revolutionary analyst was buried seventeen years before the end of the nineteenth century. Only seventeen years after the beginning of the twentieth century, there was born a state aiming to rule a sixth of the world's surface, dedicated to Marx's (so-called) dogmas.

Yet without disrespect, as an exact chronicler of the epoch yet to appear, no one can equal Engels, the Nostradamus of Socialism. Somewhere in these pages, I have included his forecast of the

European World War, and its aftermath, now still unfolding in all its ambiguous intricacies at this moment, some forty years later. I have copied out, and tucked away in my archives, several other frightening glimpses of what lies in wait for us as he plucks down volumes of diaries yet unwritten. Today I turned out this and enter it here without comment. I hope that I shall reread it in ten (no! five) years with less of a gripe in the guts and dabble of sweat along the almost vanished hairline. Engels wrote:

> The worst possible fate that can befall a leader of an extreme party is to be compelled to take over the government in an epoch when the moment is not ripe for the domination of the class which he represents, and the realization of the measures which the domination of the class requires. . . . Thus he inevitably finds himself impaled on a dilemma. What he can do contradicts his whole previous position, his principles, and the immediate interests of his party; and what he *ought* to do cannot be done. . . . Whoever finds himself in that precarious position is irrevocably doomed.

MARCH 3   MOSCOW   1922

An awful fug, an air of staleness, deadness, a whiff from the tomb hangs around me. I feel ill, but, even worse, I feel stupid. It is as if I had halted on a railway journey because the train was stuck in the station for reasons not at all uncommon in Russia today—no more rails! I want to lie down on a bench and sleep away the year to come. But the journey is not over. The passengers must not rest. They must get out and dig their own way ahead, lay out their own track. As I write this, I see it all very vividly as if it were a memory of an actual experience. It must have been a dream at some time because only in dreams could I feel that I am not just the passenger lying on the bench, not just the driver of the engine or the leader of the laborers putting down the rails, but also the locomotive *itself*! (I said I was getting silly.)

So I have declined to lead our delegation to the international conference in Genoa. The bourgeois press, taking the hint from some of our own people, explain that this is because I am afraid of being assassinated outside our Soviet borders. If only they knew! The way my brain feels today, sunk like a frog in mud, I could be killed tomorrow and not be missed, even by myself.

MARCH 26   MOSCOW   1922

The Eleventh Party Congress begins tomorrow. There have been times recently when I have wondered whether I would survive it. I realize I have been operating on between half and three-quarters brainpower since last summer. How easy it is not to observe what you are doing, a kind of self-censorship of unwelcome symptoms. It was not until others, mainly someone in my marvelous all-woman secretariat, began saying things like "You've been standing still holding your head for five minutes. . . . You're hanging on to the furniture like a drunk, Ilyich. . . ." that I realized I must be a damaged man.

This has set me reading medical books. Too many lay people are afraid of them—after all, what are doctors but simple souls with a gift of total recall who have read more medical books than we have? I have warned myself and my colleagues that I am marked down for a stroke. I don't want it to come as too much of a shock to anybody. It also gives me a certain sardonic pleasure to brush aside their uneasy denials, based on no evidence whatsoever, and insist—"Remember my words!"

The news has spread that I have been ill and telegrams pour in from all over the country, begging me not to be disabled, or incapacitated, or die on their hands, apparently assuming my own life or death can be decreed by a simple "yes/no" on a form. They are often signed by hundreds of people, by entire factories and housing estates. Who arranges such things? Can they be in any sense spontaneous? I incline to believe they are nothing but somebody's exercise in agitprop. If they are genuine, then I incline to think less of those who organize and support them.

I intend to cut down my participation in the Congress this year, confining myself to fairly brief opening and closing speeches, avoiding participation in the debates in between or the behind-the-scenes hammering out of resolutions. Are there any other parties in the world whose policy-making ruling body has an open forum, day after day, where orations can be heard (fifteen minutes each) that range so confidently across the whole landscape of human thought—politics, economics, history, literature, science, art—yet always return like a nesting eagle to the knotty, messy problems of survival here today? I would back it against the Roman Senate, Cromwell's New Model Army, the Conventions of revolutionary France or America, the Paris Commune. The parliamentary cretinism of bourgeois talking-shops is no comparison.

My whole thrust these days is toward saving our society from being sucked into a foul swamp of bureaucracy, a molten bog of rotting paper. We have built a sort of gnomes' wonderland where misshapen clerks squat on their red tape mushrooms tapping out decrees and decisions, stitching together new departments, electing each other onto commissions. *Perestroika*—"reconstruction," "reorganization"—is the favorite new game. Anything so long as it's not work. They are playing with their own shit like children. Decisions, decrees, commissions, departments—they're all shit. All that matters is getting the right people, setting them real tasks, then making sure they do the tasks. By telephone, by telegraph, by summons to my office to be inspected, by dispatch from my office of new inspectors, without leaving my desk I sweat at smoking out the gnomes' parlors, burning away the dry rot, sealing off the rising damp. Two priorities: (1) search for personnel; (2) check on achievement. Everything else is fiddling with yourself. *Glasnost,* "openness," "candor," is my slogan. It is a wound that itself can heal the very wounds it may inflict.

APRIL 2   MOSCOW   1922

Our system still runs according to a sort of Dual Power, a hangover from the days of the February Revolution, when the Provisional government consisted mainly of bourgeois ministers who could only issue orders when they were countersigned by the CenExCom of the Soviet. Our two arms are different, but similar. The governmental side, which runs the various commissariats with their thousands of civil servants, is represented by the Soviet, VTSIK, and what would in England or France be the Cabinet is Sovnarkom. I am the chairman of Sovnarkom, with two deputy chairmen and eighteen commissars. The nongovernmental side is the Russian Communist Party which elects its CenCom (twenty-seven members) which in turn elects its Politburo (expanded to seven this time). I am the chairman of this also, Stalin is the GenSec, and, as of today, the others are Trotsky, Zinoviev, Kamenev, Tomsky and Rykov.

Which is on top at any period depends on circumstances. At the moment, I would say the Politburo, though neither seems to be doing much of a job, judging by the state the country is in.

One bonus point to the Party is the way it has purged and

cleansed itself (almost literally). I think I can claim to have been the enema that flushed out the waste. This time, we had 522 delegates speaking for a Party of just over half a million. In the last six months, it has slimmed away an impressive 169,748 members, almost a quarter of those registered at the Tenth Congress, for offenses that include political illiteracy, careerism, laziness, drunkenness, corruption, personal unpleasantness (rude and crude attitude to spouse, offspring, neighbors, workmates) and the like. Bravo!

Typical example of the gnomes at play—full reports of all that was said is, of course, in the papers or the archives—concerns the Moscow Consumer Association and the meaty chunks from France. It really needs to be told, as I did in my opening address, rather slowly and with significant pauses. It had them crying with laughter and fury.

But in precis, it remains a moral tale. The salesman brought fifty tins with him, and the picture on the label was enough to make your mouth water. He offered umpteen thousands more within two weeks at a price that made the MCA whistle—I think it was 160 billion rubles. I'm a bit vague about the figures because *they really do not matter*! The rubles were paper. They cost us almost nothing—if necessary, the figure could have been overprinted on one single note. And the Frenchman would have to spend them here. Here where we fix the prices. There the tins were real. And many thousands of Moscovites were as near to starving as you can come and still wake up tomorrow. How could the MCA hesitate? How? Very easily! Their board decided they needed a second opinion, a conference, a commission, consultation with as many others as possible, presumably so that if the meat in the tins turned out to be rotten, say, then so many people would have been involved in the deal that no individual could be identified for punishment.

The gnomes at MCA did not even presume to open one tin and pass it round. They put half of them aside and sent the rest to Commissar for Foreign Trade Krassin. Now Leonid Borisovich is an old friend, chairman of our first Bolshevik Congress in '05, one of the greatest engineers in the Russian Empire. He ran the famous underground printing press, Nina, in Baku. He made the bombs that blew up Prime Minister Stolypin's villa. I wonder what happened to that promise that he would one day produce an explosive the size of a walnut that could flatten half Petrograd. Anyway, even he wouldn't open the tin of meaty chunks.

Leonid Borisovich took a sample tin along to a member of the

Politburo, Kamenev, *Lev* Borisovich, another seasoned revolutionary. He also found himself unable either to open or to authorize the import of these tins of meaty chunks. Naturally, he had to call a full meeting of the Politburo of the CenCom of the Russian Communist Party. We have 4,700 responsible, key officials in our government offices in Moscow, most of them active members of the Party, and they cannot find a quorum to import some tins without taking the decision to the very top.

I was not in very good health at the time and so I was not present at the famous Politburo deliberation on the "Meaty Chunks Question." But when I heard about it, as I told the Congress, I wrote to the CenCom saying that in my view every bureaucrat who was a Party member in Moscow should be locked up in the most uncomfortable Moscow prison for six hours, and that all the officials in the Commissariat for Foreign Trade, Party members or not, should be locked away for the weekend. (The Congress cheered and hooted.) I wish I thought this was the end of such moronic blunders. Any capitalist sales manager would have signed the contract, or turned it down, within hours. Yet, here we are in Soviet Russia, the state that is going to advance the world by its example toward mankind's noblest ideal, communism—and 99 percent of our Party members cannot execute a simple business transaction.

I admitted to the Congress, rather shocking the ideologues and the theorists, that many a worker or peasant came to my office and asked me a question I could not answer. Typically, they would say, "Tell me, in simple words, *Starik*, how it is that in the old days the capitalist supplied us with things we wanted? Yes, he cheated us, he insulted us, he exploited us, but he provided something for us. Can you do it? No, you cannot. You come preaching communism. He never preached capitalism. But he bought and we sold, he sold and we bought. You bring us nothing."

The whole point of the New Economic Policy is to learn from the shopkeeper, the peddler, the market-woman, the financier, the commodity-broker—yes, the profiteer and the gambler. We must rediscover money. We must learn the value of gold. I have always said that someday I would like to give Moscow a new sewage system, building the pipes and bowls of its public lavatories with gold. That time is not yet. We are hemmed round with hungry monsters and we must feed them with their favorite food—profits.

I also rebuked those communists who saw NEP solely through abstract words and in classic terminology. Even Marx and Engels had no expectations to fit our present situation. It is useless asserting that we are running a system of state capitalism (which we are) and this must be reactionary and counterrevolutionary because we are against capitalism. I had to lead such comrades through a Socratic questionnaire. Who ran the state under previous periods of state capitalism? The capitalists. Was this, then, capitalism using the state to benefit the capitalists? Of course! Who runs our state and for whose benefit? Oh, the Party on behalf of the workers and peasants. Would you say that the workers and peasants are at last beginning to benefit from NEP? Yes. Then is this not state capitalism *on behalf of the people* and not the capitalists? Yes, though the little capitalists are also benefiting. Agreed. But did not some of the workers and peasants some of the time benefit under *capitalist* state capitalism and did this make it *socialist* state capitalism?

Not everybody was convinced and the debates were fiery, eloquent, hard-hitting with even a Homeric quality about them, as can be confirmed by anyone who reads the verbatim reports. It is not only in epic poetry that warriors can speak wingéd words—there was Antonov-Ovseyenko, who stormed the Winter Palace, denouncing me for optimism, denying that the capitalist countries cannot afford to give up our trade, sounding the dreadful warning that our Revolution may have been premature.

One speech I did enjoy, though it undermined my best comic passage and turned the laughter against me as I sat on the platform steps making my notes, was by Vladimir Kossior. He pointed out that the meaty chunks story could be told in numerous versions. In his experience, he said, rolling his great melancholy bull's head, the Politburo might easily have *insisted* on being consulted even about an order for tinned food. In the trade unions, it was always interfering in the most piddling local appointments, "many of them not worth half a plate of tinned French beef."

Trotsky spoke out for me. I did not really seek this, but the steadying, helping hand is always welcome, perhaps even more so when it is stretched from affection rather than from necessity. He has always praised my ability to isolate and exhibit, not theories, not wishes, but *"what is."* He is growing his own microscopic/telescopic eye. My closing speech became a kind of bridge to him, especially one passage which the majority received with mystified apathy.

Trotsky had performed an autopsy on War Communism, showing how it was, though possibly wrong from the abstract, economic standpoint, then our only hope politically. The middle-size businesses were then still in the hands of private enterprise. Their managers and directors were probably the best people to run them but they were also certainly our enemies, active units of world counterrevolution. So they had to be removed. But it would be silly to pretend that this desperate decision was a socialist step. Even before the civil war was over, Trotsky had campaigned for a policy almost identical to NEP. Our people had to learn to *manage*. If we had followed him, we would have saved a year. This is what I said:

> Something has happened rather like what we learned in our history lessons when we were children: one people subjugates another. The subjugator is then the conquering people and the subjugated a vanquished people. This is true enough, but what happens to the culture of these two peoples? The answer is not so simple. If the conquering people is more cultured than the vanquished people, the stronger imposes its culture on the weaker. But in the opposite case, the vanquished country may impose its culture on the conqueror. Is this not what has happened through NEP in the capital of our Soviet state? Have not 4,700 (almost an army division) of the best Communists, our best administrators, been submerged by an alien culture? Should we reach the conclusion, then, that the culture of these vanquished ones is at a high level? Not so: it is wretched and insignificant. But while it works and ours does not, it remains superior to ours.

APRIL 7   MOSCOW   1922

Power must be flowing from government to Party. Otherwise why would Joseph Vissarionovich have resigned his two state appointments (Commissar of Rabkrin, the Workers' and Peasants' Inspectorate, Commissar Nationalities) for the rather boring workhorse post of GenSec of the Party? Could it have anything to do with Professor Klemperer being flown in from Berlin along with Dr. Foerster, a Breslau neurologist, by the Politburo to give me a "general checkup"?

At first, I refused. It would have shown more *glasnost* to have consulted me first. I am not, after all, just a piece of national property to be handed round and held up to the light by visiting experts. But it was put to me that I was a valuable investment and that I must obey as a matter of socialist discipline. I agreed, so long as it took place in my office. Afterward, Klemperer told me I'd been given a marking of A2 in almost every area. I took his telephone number (a routine precaution) and forgot about the whole business.

That visit was on April 3. Now, I have *twice* seen Stalin, our new "endlessly busy" GenSec, lurking about in the corridor between my sitting room and Trotsky's. Senior Kremlinites sometimes drop in here to read the foreign papers. I asked my staff if JVS had been after any issue in particular and was told he had been trying to book the April 6 copy of the *New York Times*.

I am sorry to say the story he had presumably been after was not on the front page. It was an interview with Professor Klemperer (he told the capitalist press more than he ever told me!) that can be boiled down to this:

> Lenin is a man of strong physical constitution and great working energy who has for a long while worked intensively fourteen to sixteen hours a day. Recently, his capacity for work has diminished, and he and his friends resolved to ascertain just what was the matter with him.
>
> We examined Lenin and found only a moderate neurasthenia, the result of overwork. Of more serious complaints, such as an infection of the nervous system or internal organs, there was none. Apart from a few general prescriptions regarding exercise and diet, no medical advice was necessary. We recommended that Lenin should take care of himself for a while and go on a vacation.

I did my own translation (Stalin knows barely a word of English) and had him sent a copy, with my compliments. I can't see it gives much comfort to our, or indeed just my, enemies, or, for that matter, to me. I'm fed up with being urged to take vacations, particularly a long, long way away, particularly in the Caucasus, particularly by those who were born in the Caucasus but choose to live here. First, it was Stalin himself, then his great chum, Ordzonikidze, then, of all people, Stalin's one-time bandit boss, the cross-eyed Kamo.

I don't want to be in any place where "getting back to Moscow" presents a huge problem. Baku, Tiflis, Sochi and the rest are three days by train at the fastest. So I've written them all the same letter—"the last thing I need for a nerve cure is fatigue, boredom, bustle, hustle, hassle and squabble." Then just to give them something to research and waste time over, I have explained that I must know the exact height above sea level of each property recommended, citing Nadya's weak heart and its intolerance of high altitudes. Compromise on "holidays" in Gorki, "the Little Hills," twenty-five miles from the Kremlin.

APRIL 22   MOSCOW   1922

So far this year, I have been awarded an exceptional six weeks "holiday" (Jan./Feb.), then another extra three weeks (March 6—March 25). All are intended to throw off these dreadful strait-jackets of disabling illness. I feel rather guilty trying to persuade my comrades that their remedy has been successful. I do not fool them. It must be obvious to any observer that I always feel less sick working than resting. My physical symptoms do not change much but on the move it is easier not to think about them. For example, if I read and write and talk through the night, this can be classified as overtime, going without sleep for a purpose. If I go to bed and stay awake, following the same thoughts round and round, then that must be classified as insomnia, going without sleep for no purpose. Who can doubt which is preferable?

There is no point in lying down before fate gives you its fatal punch. I hope I shall die, like Macbeth, with my harness on my back. Like father, come to think of it, drawn pen in hand, wing collar up!

One real worry about these sneaking, subversive assaults by the body on the mind. It makes you wonder whether you are still getting the correct signals through your nerve endings. Just recently I have felt a curious impression run through me every time I make contact with the state machine and attempt to move it my way. I suppose those who drive cars or fly planes (things I have never done) will know what I mean. It has happened to me only once, around forty years ago, when I led a group of Simbirsk lads in the takeover of an abandoned Volga barge. While they rowed, I took the tiller. I became quite tipsy with power as each small pressure grew and multiplied until I was levering the great hulk around every spreading river bend.

Then, as the others began agitating to take a turn, I felt some force wrench the boat away from me and point it somewhere I had not chosen. The long hulk no longer responded to the tiller. Instead, it began to hurl itself at a large rock, known as Pugachev's Head, about half a mile from either bank. "Jump!" I ordered. And the six of us escaped only seconds before the crash.

I have uncanny intimations (no, not uncanny, *morbid* perhaps?) that Russia too is pulling hard to escape being steered by me. This may be an illusion, but I do not think so. My antennae are picking up the influence of some invisible planet, some submarine current, possibly some person rather than thing, some faction rather than some trend.

That I am not yet easily imagining things was proved this morning when I came to the Sovnarkom office unexpectedly early. I have always liked the rather juvenile game of playing the great detective. It's amazing how many educated people are awestruck by logical deduction and would prefer to believe you have occult powers than that you put two and two together.

So I looked at that old buffer Semashko, various shifty members of the Politburo, some of my embarrassed staff gathered at my desk, and I said: "Why are you inviting Klemperer here again? Don't you believe what you read in the *New York Times*? I could take one of those bullets out with my pen-knife and a shaving mirror."

Then I indicated the progression from Semashko (commissar of health); the telephone number on my desk I recalled being Klemperer's; the well-known fact that my personal telephone had the best connection with Europe, especially in the early morning; the folder in my secretary's hand, one of the day-to-day diary series I started in October '17, and which carries a date, read without much difficulty upside-down, that I do not easily forget—August 30, '18.

APRIL 23   **MOSCOW**   **1922**

I learned yesterday that Klemperer, contradicting what he had told me, the press and the Politburo earlier, now believes that my headaches are caused by lead poisoning from the two bullets fired by Fanny Kaplan three and a half years ago! I have rarely heard such tripe. Probably one in five Old Bolsheviks has been wounded by a revolver or rifle shot, and thousands of them still carry a bullet inside them. I've never come across one being damaged by the metal itself, nor of a bullet giving headaches unless it hit the head.

This morning I asked Semashko for his professional opinion, but got only a lot of "ohs" and "well's" and "you see's." His assistant, Dr. Rozanov, not having risen so far in the medical establishment, was more outspoken. He'd been a field surgeon at the front in the German War, operated one of our mobile operating theaters during the July Days, served with Trotsky in the Red Army. He'd never heard of lead poisoning (except as a joke) from gunshot wounds. I watched Klemperer's *locum*, the imported Professor Borchardt, very closely as he questioned Rozanov in broken Russian. When he was informed about his colleague's recommendation of an operation, and then the reason why, his professional reserve was shaken. *"Unmoeglich!"* I heard him mutter beneath his breath. "Impossible!" indeed. Yet it was clear the three of them were nerving each other to go ahead, Borchardt because his fee had been guaranteed, Rozanov and Semashko because political instruction took precedence over medical expertise. After being prodded and probed, I left them muttering among themselves.

When I turned up at the military hospital, accompanied by the posse of bodyguards my secretaries had foisted on me, the three sawbones were edging toward a compromise. Dr. Semashko, being a commissar, kept an open mind. Doctors Rozanov and Borchardt agreed: (1) the bullets were packaged in little bulbs of tissue, isolated from the rest of the body; (2) there was no metal contagion; (3) the bullet buried in the left shoulder could only be retrieved by major surgery; (4) the bullet just under the joint in the neck was removable with minimum trouble; (5) since neither caused me any problems, the best course would be to do nothing.

And that was that, apparently. Except that I have never warmed to the concept of "doctor's orders." My view is that you hear their advice, then decide whether or not to take it. (Perhaps having the baby of your family, sweet, dim Mitya, become a doctor disillusions the older ones.) I knew that getting out the neck bullet could not be much harder than skinning a banana—I could have pinched the flesh and it would have jumped out.

"All right," I said. "We'll extract the easiest one. It'll stop people pestering me about it."

This took them rather aback. There was a lot of after-you, no-after-you, about who should hold the knife, and who should hold the dish. "Look," I said. "There's no point in taking this to the Supreme Soviet. Professor Borchardt must operate. Otherwise why waste our scarce foreign currency bringing him here?"

Rozanov injected a solution of novocaine. I had that weird sensation of someone inserting instruments into a part of you that has become immaterial, made of ectoplasm, visible but nonexistent, a trick of genuine magic. Then it was over. Or almost. The physicians disagreed for once. The Russian said I could leave. The German said I must stay overnight. Semashko was neutral. Manyasha claimed bullet was a dumdum but only she could see the notch.

Borchardt was not used to our hospitals. All the wards were

full, some two to a bed. The only free bed was in the women's section. I gathered my strong-arm squad and left.

On the steps, Rozanov gave me another piece of great clinical advice: "Have a vacation."

"No," I said. "*You* have a vacation. Go back with the professor here and see what Germany is like. And this nurse. *She* must have a vacation. This is *my* prescription."

Rozanov said he preferred Riga. The nurse asked if she could take her adopted son with her to the Crimea. Holding a bandage to my neck, I scribbled instructions that these arrangements were to be made. Then I gave the papers to Commissar Semashko and told him to report without fail on their fulfillment within three days. Medically, this has been a pointless exercise. Actually, though, I feel really well for the first time in months.

MAY 20   GORKI   1922

The bullet therapy had not lasted long. I toss fitfully in a long trough of ill health. I kept my eye on the Genoa Conference from my sofa here. A good job I could not go, though invited by name. As I suspected, it was basically an exercise in manipulating public opinion by those two mountebank poseurs, Lloyd George and Poincaré. All the decisions had been agreed between them on the golf course at Cannes. But at least it gave an opportunity for the two pariahs of Europe, Germany and Russia, to sneak off to Rapallo and make an agreement for mutual help. Quite a stroke by Krassin. Since then I have not been able to contribute much except a stream of criticism from the backwoods. It has its effect. Almost every other member of the Politburo or Sovnarkom is too busy to look out of the window and see what is happening in the real world. I have nothing else to do but look out of the window. I may be a long way off. But my telescope is strong. My telephone snakes in everywhere.

So there have been ricocheting round the country Leningrams containing detailed suggestions with a barb in the tail. My Praetorian Guard of secretaries keep potted details in a great book, entered up every day. No better end to an evening than some fried mushrooms followed by a nip of vodka and than a browse of my own prose. Those Kronstadt sailors hardly begin to find words for that worst of sights, a Communist gone rotten: "adventurers and rogues . . . boastful loudmouths . . . climbers and creepers . . . parasitic worms." The émigré press in Paris is tame by comparison in its picture of a society teetering on the edge of a precipice: "tsarist thrones covered with a flaking Soviet veneer."

MAY 26   GORKI   1922

We used to argue in the old days that capitalism meant all sorts of superfluous persons making a living out of useless fribbles whose only purpose was to flatter those richer than themselves. This has now all been abolished. Any assertion to the contrary is an émigré lie.

Then why do I get this morning from the dreadful Luna-charsky an abstract of a project many paid functionaries of the Education Commissariat have apparently been beavering away at in semi-secret? Of what possible value to our socialist-oriented society can this be?

They are sorting through everything I have written and spoken, or am believed to have written and spoken, since 1895, counting the frequency of every important word. It is scarcely an operation to be encouraged anywhere at any time, hardly in our siege economy, certainly never when the subject is alive. Does Lunacharsky know something I don't know about me?

For what it's worth, it seems I have a vocabulary of 37,600 words, not to mention 4,000 I apparently have invented, often Russifications of Western European terms. ("Opportunist," "idealism," "on a commercial basis.") Of existing native words, "bureaucratization" comes high, just ahead of "discipline," *glasnost* forty-six times. A few coinages from Soviet life—"NEPman" and "Chekist" for petty profiteer and security police agent. At another time, though condemning the waste of effort involved here, I might have learned something about myself, though I doubt even that. One quite illuminating citation: where the rest use *perestroika*, "reconstruction," to mean endless worrying about new methods and forms of organization, I use it to mean, "the practical application and testing of every idea *in real life*." If my colleagues, now I fear increasingly to be classified as my successors, get that through their skulls, this academic exercise may not be entirely wasted.

MAY 29   GORKI   1922

This is the first bell. My speech is not very good. Write that down. Write down everything. Even write *that* down. You can understand quite well what I am dictating if you do your job properly and listen. Take no notice of the way my face flaps and lisps. Pretend I have just been to the dentist. Forget one half of me is discon-nected, flattened, like a . . . like a what? Like a tree trimmed down one side. I promise you I will recover. For a while. I shall be angry if I find you have not written what I am saying. The first bell. Do you understand that? It's on the train in the station. It is the warning you ignore. Only the first bell. Then the second you have to hurry. Then the third. It is too late if you hear that and you are not on board. The third bell is death. I have another one to go. I know about trains. I was a fireman crossing into Finland once.

I have begun to rely on this diary though it is not the same, not quite, when I do not write it by hand. Writing was important to me. My writing changed with my mind. Got better, bolder when I was interested, excited. Now I have only half a mind. Still I want to put that down. How many days was it. Two? Three! May 26, then, You see I am improving as I speak! Like a village idiot, like a drunk, like a man being sick. Sick. Sick. It began with vomiting. Manyasha, volunteer nurse, thought it was bad fish. Food poison-ing. Then how could I be the only one vomiting? Manyasha does not think like that. Telephoned Rozanov in Kremlin. They came out in two large cars. Get it right: Dr. Roz., old Semashko, my brother the Dr. Mitya, a few non-names. Who did I have here? After vomit, Dr. Levin. He mouthed "Paresis." I already knew the word. Doctors do not know everything. Usually only words. I was, am, partially paralyzed, right leg, right arm. Dentist's mouth. "OK" as the Yankees say. Rozanov tells me "slight, temporary, nonsig-nificant setback." Take a vacation, Rozanov! It *is* the first bell.

JUNE 5   GORKI   1922

No point in dictating more of the stuff I did the last ten days. Lydia Alexandrovna! I am going to speak of *you*. You look at me as no woman would look at a man were he just a lover. Yours is a transcendental devotion. As if you would swallow me with your eyes, nurse me cradled inside your head. What ridiculous things I say, too Dostoievskian! I disgust myself. But believe me, I do appreciate that you and my prickly, beautiful rose garden of girl secretaries have epitomized me as the atomic epicenter of the Revolution. You are protecting not Lenin but October. My dear Fotieva, without you (plural) I should be a basket case, a roll of old carpet, sometimes on a bench, sometimes in a wheelchair, a relic that has no voice. You will outlive me. (Not a difficult task!) But will your name be in the indexes of the histories, the biogs, that will surely flood out from our runaway presses, every chairman of a Publishing Co-op being by nature a sorcerer's apprentice? Keep your notes! Attend to your diary! Hide away your memoirs under the floorboards! Some day my successors will ache to have you to tell them about these first five years of the Russian Revolution—what really *was*, who-whom, where-when, why Lenin for one did what he did, said what he said.

Second thoughts. Can you have second thoughts if you do not have first thoughts? Maybe you should delete my advice—read it back! Yes, you should. If things fall apart, my words may point too dangerously to you, frustrating the point of the exercise. I know you have not set down any of the other wandering dream-talk I have jabbered since my stroke. But now I feel I could be coming up from the cellar, emerging from the tunnel. Thanks to you, I know Klemperer has landed in Moscow and will be here soon. We all want to please our doctors. Even if it means lying to them, telling them we are much better than we can possibly be. Be our guest, Professor!

JUNE 26   GORKI   1922

Felix—how distant Europeans seem with only one *prénom* and no patronymic!—Klemperer has become quite a friend. The professor had never understood that Marxism is as scientific as medicine, well, let's say, as *psychology*, where Germany leads the world. When I told him—well, after I told Lydia Alexandrovna, and *she* told him—that our socialist intellectual technology was formed from German philosophy, English economics, and French politics, he became rather unnervingly enthusiastic. I think he was overjoyed to find such a bargain, a Holy Trinity, three for the price of one, on the cheap!

Anyway, Klemperer, who stayed here with me until yesterday, was full of what you need from your medical adviser. That is, not a lot of words you have to nod at, then look up afterward, only to find they never mean the same in another language, let alone your own. Instead, he gave detailed, practical information about how this soft machine works in detail, here and here and here, *now*. With his assistance, I have serviced my own body. From a vantage point up behind my eyes, one of them not much more than a barnacled old porthole, I have sent electrical messages to muscle after muscle, alerting each one to twitch occasionally, then regularly, then in series with others, then as part of the (almost) total circuit. Judged by the standards of Vladimir Ilyich of twenty years ago (twenty-five press-ups morning and night!) I am a valetudinarian convalescent. Judged by the condition of V.I. of exactly one month ago, I am a miraculous renovation, verging on a Lazarus. (Christian apologists never mention that the Emperor Vespasian, near contemporary of that rabbi-revolutionary Yeshu, Latinized for us as Jesus, also raised people from the dead in front of many more eyewitnesses. Why was Vespasian not the Son of God as well? I see I *am* getting better! Ha!)

Must not overdo writing, i.e., dictating. I *can* move—I am, as the Yankees might say, *auto-mobile*, self-propelled. I can talk so that I do not hate myself. I remain as intellectually endowed as most bourgeois philistines. In the House of Commons or the Reichstag, I might pass as the next prime minister but three. But here is Professor Felix Klemperer, internationally renowned surgeon who once thought I was getting headaches from lead poisoning, speaking yesterday in Berlin to the world's press. (We have got beyond just the *New York Times*.)

> The evening before I left Moscow I walked in the gardens of provincial Gorki with Lenin and he said he felt, and he certainly seemed, relatively well. He is not capable of concerning himself with brain work for an extended period. He cannot read very long either, because if he reads a book, magazine or newspaper he gets a headache. . . . Lenin's present indisposition (!) has absolutely no connection with his former wounds. . . . For the last thirty years of his life, he has worked sixteen or more hours every day. No man can undertake this load and not expect his body to protest. . . . I categorically deny that Lenin is suffering from any form of progressive paralysis. . . . He will get better, not worse.

It would be marvelous to be able to rely on every word of that, or even most of it. Unfortunately, I cannot forget that I myself suggested several of the phrases. What a pleasure self-deception must be, so long as you don't know you are doing it.

JULY 12   GORKI   1922

Lydia Alexandrovna! This will give you a surprise. And you can congratulate me on a step, behind your back, to recovery. Proof? This handwriting. I have made a try or two before but none of you could read it. Now, I fancy, it *begins* to look quite human.

So! Start preparing the following selection of books for me (and send me the list). (1) Scientific: the latest, theories, speculations, discoveries, by materialist thinkers. No technical abstractions, no toshy idealism. Includes psychology, sociology. (2) Novels: you know what I like, adventure, achievement, outdoor action, optimistic, about real people. (3) Political: factual, historical, strong feel for economics, how things can be run. (But leave delivering these until last as they are still prohibited by the cabal of Politburo medics.) When task fulfilled, report back, then paste this, as an entry, into my diary. Yours, Lenin.

P.S. Years ago in Capri, I told Bogdanov he should give up trying to smuggle God into Marxism and go back to novel-writing. I believe I even gave him a theme—how the sharks of capitalism have robbed the workers of our planet's future, wasting away the last resources of oil, iron, timber and coal. Now he's chairman of the Supreme Council of the National Economy and busy with the Arnold Hammer concession in the Urals. But I hear he wrote one H. G. Wells-type fantasy (I don't know when) about Martians circling the Earth in a "space-ship" looking for a superior example of Earthman to take back home for further analysis. After much sorting of names, they had almost agreed on "Lenin" when it occurred to them that my disappearance might jeopardize the success of any proletarian revolution. What a hoot! They could take me now, gladly. If you can find this work, it might quite amuse me these days. Anyway, it could provide a curio for those shelves of "Leniniana" you do not think I know you keep.

V.I.

JULY 13   GORKI   1922

My improvement has not gone unnoticed outside Gorki, it seems. Stalin and Kamenev turned up for a visit today.

There are two views about Stalin among our dozen or so leading comrades. The majority think him efficient, talented, hard-working in a boring way, the perfect "number two" to any of *them*. Trotsky sees him as bureaucracy incarnate and therefore a genuine threat to Soviet democracy—just as Louis-Philippe in France was the first citizen king, with an umbrella for a scepter, so Joseph Vissarionovich could be the first desk-bound dictator, with a paper knife for an ax. This is Trotsky's theory. When he actually has to be in the same room with Stalin, L.D. finds it difficult to believe this crude, leathery, southern mountain-man, pugnacious but oddly placatory when punched back, could really attract any following. Radek regards Stalin as a comic monster from Gogol, a cardboard cutout from a toy theater, with power to frighten only those who believe he is real. Bukharin takes him seriously both as ally and as opponent, but only for practical tasks, handicapped as he is by ignorance of theory. Only fiery Pyatakov, almost Bukharin's twin, though even more to the wild Left, has been heard to prophesy that Stalin will be the "gravedigger of the Revolution," the new Napoleon. Myself, I think he is more various, more solid, more capable of moving, like a chess queen, in directions the rest cannot imagine. That he should provoke so many different assessments already marks him as someone exceptional.

Certainly, Kamenev was like the head-boy on an outing with the headmaster. I tried to fish some items of current affairs out of him without success.

So I determined to provoke Stalin a little by raising the subject of the future of the other peoples now gathered within our Soviet borders. In another age, another world (1912? 1913? in Krakow) I commissioned a youngish Georgian worker to write a pamphlet on *Marxism and the National Question,* sending him on to Vienna's libraries where his guide was an even younger intellectual—they were thirty-two-year-old Stalin and twenty-four-year-old Buk-harin! B. thought only the working class deserved independence, not whole countries which would contain capitalists and nobles. S. agreed with me that we must throw open all gates to the Tsar's "prison house of nations." Every colonial serf was our ally. But now I hear these two are uniting in a move away from the federation I have always backed, whose members would be truly autonomous, and toward a binding union, where the central authority (naturally run by the Greater Russians) would permit the lesser breeds only limited internal powers.

"So, this 'Nationality business.' You're turning into a Greater Russian chauvinist."

He smiled, and said something in Georgian. I do not understand the language but decided to act as if I did, making a guess
that it must have been some variant of "But I am a Georgian."

"Those are the worst kind," I replied. "You even said you
were a Georgian with a Russian accent."

He squirmed a bit on the infernally hard chair Lydia Alexandrovna always gives visitors to encourage them to keep their
stay short. Now I had started thinking about the qualities of leadership available in a future without me, I was observing everyone
very closely. I peered for a second inside his skull and saw he was
thinking that the old man had a while to go yet before you could
fob him off with phrases. He rallied immediately and I had to
award him a five in almost every department of political salesmanship.

He appeared (almost) convincingly hurt.

"Ilyich! What can you mean? These nations will be conquests
for the Revolution, recruits to socialism. No arguments. Yet who
was it who gave self-government to the Bashkir Republic in 1918?
To the Tatars in the spring of 1920? To the Kirghizes in the
autumn? Who constituted a republic of Daghestan, another for
the Karelians, and another for Yakuts? Who made Tatar the official language co-equal with Russian? Our Commissariat for Nationalities, on which I had the honor to serve. Now, I would not
hope to fob you off with political salesmanship. Between us it is
true they are not *absolutely* independent. In theory, they could leave
our federation tomorrow. But we mix up all the connections so it
would take years. And let us be realistic, *Starik*. We are still surrounded by enemies. You can't have bits of the country suddenly
drifting away whenever they feel like it. Think what we've given
them. Er . . . civilization. Irrigation. Hydro-electrics. Liberation of
women. Like your father, my commissioners have opened up thousands of schools where there were only a handful, and those only
for the rich. We are prodding them into the twentieth century."

I said: "That's the same argument the British use in India."
But my heart wasn't in it. He'd done well. He was partly right, and
so was I. That's what I call a political chat between old comrades.
Nothing like it. But it was enough for the day. I pressed the bell
push hidden under my Scotch rug and pretended to be surprised,
and a little annoyed, when Fotieva appeared and said that that was
enough for the day.

JULY 15   GORKI   1922

I feel like an actor reading the reviews. A good write-up from J.V. in *Pravda*! Put it in the cuttings book.

I remind him of a front-line soldier who had been sent to a rest-camp far behind the lines after surviving battle after battle. He quotes me as saying about my regime here: "I am not allowed to have the newspapers. I am forbidden to talk politics." Then apparently I get up and mime my morning routine. "I make a careful detour around every scrap of paper on this table in case it turns out to have newsprint on it for then I would be guilty of a breach of party discipline."

He goes on to report that he gave a hearty laugh. "I laughed because though I praised, rightly, the typical, steel-hard self-discipline of Comrade Lenin, we both knew it was ridiculous of any doctors to think that old professional activists, meeting together after an absence, could avoid talking politics."

It is only two days ago. Perhaps my mind is having blackouts. But I do not recall any of this. I do not even have a table outdoors. I keep all my papers tucked down the back of the sofa. But I must admit it *sounds* quite like me. Is *Pravda* employing short-story writers now to give their reports those fictional details that are so more convincing than fact? But no. Look here. Fotieva has entered, as per my rules, the names of each day's visitors: "July 13, afternoon. Kamenev and Stalin. Stayed twenty-five minutes."

No mention in *Pravda* of Kamenev. Perhaps Stalin wants it to look as if only he cares about the stricken Lenin. Has it come to this? These are the stratagems and tricks of the Sultan's harem. If Stalin employs such devices on a casual level, then maybe he is the man in the white armored limousine we all see in our nightmares. Must keep in touch with Trotsky about these thoughts.

AUGUST 5   GORKI   1922

Another visit from Stalin. Nadya has never liked him. I have noticed most women find him disturbing, vaguely threatening, even when he is being attentive and polite. Perhaps then especially so. There is something very crudely male just in the way he sits and smokes his pipe, the hard peasant father, the tough proletarian head of the household. Women sense he will get his way, a prospect that can be all the more exciting for being frightening.

As he comes in, Nadya says: "Back again so soon, Joseph Vissarionovich? You will be happy to see Ilyich is almost entirely recovered, won't you?" And she leaves.

You would have to be much thicker-skinned than J.V.—and behind the man-of-steel mask he is as responsive as a fish to changes of pressure around him—not to notice the sarcasm in her words. Almost every one is given some kind of italic accenting. I see his yellow eyes light up, like those warning bulbs on the control panel of the latest automatic machines we are importing from America. Their glow signifies that some part inside is undergoing a dangerous stress. But then the light subsides. He has made an internal adjustment to spread the load and thus avoid the threat of an explosion. For the minute.

He will not get his way with me. I appreciate his enormous talents, his energy, his ingenuity, his sheer capacity for work, but I know this is combined with a crudity and roughness, a callous determination to succeed on his own terms, that weakens his value as a comradely member of a team. He has persuaded the rest of the Party leadership that he is somewhat stupider, slower then they are. He will do the boring jobs, he will take the middle road. It is as if he were the carthorse with a back broad enough for anyone, any two or three, to ride. It is an entirely false picture, but it suits him even more than they think it suits them.

Besides, I have never forgiven him for losing us Poland. That is odd. I am writing this just after he left. And that feeling about Poland—one I never knew I had—flashed into my mind from nowhere as I watched him wreath himself in smoke like incense, a self-adoring god, a dictator sitting for a bronze statue of himself. Can it be that that "unconscious mind" I am beginning to believe in is nudging a message past my conscious defenses? Surely, whatever his strengths, Stalin cannot hope to outmaneuver operators like Zinoviev, Bukharin, Radek, especially Lev Davidovich?

After sitting for a while, puffing, J.V. says with an almost insulting lack of genuine concern—"My pipe does not bother, I hope?"

"Not at all," I reply, giving him a double-edged glare.

"I have been deprived of sensual pleasures of every kind, since before my stroke. Since before my operation. If you were to get drunk, eat half a pig and dance the gopak, I'd enjoy seeing someone living the full life."

His brow wrinkles. He does not understand whether he is being reproved, mocked, or invited to share a joke between friends. As a compromise, he puts the pipe out.

"Well, then," I go on to say, giving him a job while still off-balance. "Haven't you brought me something? I did ask for the supply of books to start again."

"With respect, Ilyich. You seem to have mountains of newspapers, magazines and books from the library all over your bed. Do you really need more?"

I'd had my eyes closed when he came in but I was watching him just the same. After five attempts on your life, you get just a little bit wary about the next person who pushes in close. And I'd seen that Stalin was carrying a green cloth bag, with a drawstring at the top, containing rectangular objects that could only be books. Or if not books, what? There was something about those "books" that made him uneasy.

"Well, at least let me have a look at the ones you have there," I said, gesturing with my left hand. It smacked a little of persecution mania. But I slid the right hand under the side pillow where, warm and strong like a well-loved toy, nestled my Browning.

Stalin moved ever so slowly, limbs reluctant, to the bag by the door. But as he came back with the books he looked triumphant. They were superb. I could see that even from a distance. I held all three in turn in my hands savoring the candid, soft white of the paper, the strong, dark outlines of the print, the sturdy flexibility of the covers. They had all been made to standards our publishing houses could no longer afford. Yet . . . Yet they were in Russian. *Emigré works!*

I adjusted eye and brain to the speeded-up, out-of-gear style of fast-readings, leaping down the page a line at a time. Within minutes, I had taken in what sort of works these were and sampled several examples of their style. Stalin looked eager for praise. Now he was a dog, a really savage dog nobody would tangle with. Yet one that yearned to be rewarded for bringing back the stick its master had thrown.

I rang the bell for Nadya.

"Comrade Krupskaya, please be witness to this comrade's replies to my questions," I said. "Comrade Stalin, who chose these books for me to read?"

"Why, I did."

"And so you know the nature of the sentiments they contain?"

"Well, yes. Of course."

"I see," I went on, turning to Nadya who had caught my tone

and was keeping a straight face. "Comrade Krupskaya, please invite in the two trusted executives from the Cheka who are in the outer room. Meanwhile I will read to Comrade Stalin the sort of writings he thinks appropriate to bring to the bedside of the convalescent chairman of Sovnarkom.

"Item, a novel, published under the auspices of White renegades, by Yevgeni Chirikov, a Populist expelled with me from Kazan University in 1887. Now proclaimed an enemy of the people subsidized by bourgeois, foreign governments.

"The subject of the novel, as you know since you chose it, is me, Vladimir Ilyich Lenin. I, it appears, have long been noted for 'pathological vanity and readiness to take offense.' If this is true, how unwise to bring this fault to my attention. In this fictionalized biography, young people in Simbirsk talk to each other about me as a boy—'His hands are always damp! And yesterday, he shot a kitten . . . then grabbed it by the tail and threw it over a fence.'

"That one at least hides itself as a work of imagination. But next we have the memoirs of Vodovozov, a radical deported to Samara for a year's supervision. I often debated with him there in the nineties. Rather too successfully perhaps? For he testifies strongly to the 'immoralism' which he claims is 'an inborn trait' in my character. He says I was notorious for my—here, let me read it out—my 'crude behavior, my coarse gestures, my acrimonious remarks, and there were many'—that's still him talking—which 'greatly shocked Maria Alexandrovna'—that was my mother, as perhaps you know—so that often she couldn't help saying 'Oh, Volodya, Volodya, how *can* you!'

"Are they writing about *you* yet, and *your* mother, Joseph Vissarionovich, in their memoirs? I'm sure you'd appreciate that.

"How about *your* appearance? Do you find deserters from the cause think it worthwhile to describe it in some detail in books published in other countries?"

(I knew I had a point here. Stalin, though handsome in a kind of cocky, fairground cheap-jack, riverboat-captain fashion, is known to be touchy about his pockmarks. Somebody—was it Radek?—said his face looked as if etched on a muffin.)

"This is what Vodovozov thinks of my appearance. Listen. 'He startled one by an odd mixture of cleverness and crudeness. I would say he showed a sort of animality. One's attention was drawn to his forehead—intelligent but sloping. A fleshy nose . . . something stubborn and cruel in these features combined with undoubted brainpower.' Well, well, that should pick me out in a crowd. Wait a minute. Don't go."

Stalin got up and prowled as far as the door where Nadya stood, flanked by a pair of armed giants, a duchess supported by her footmen. Actually they weren't from the Cheka, but from my Lettish bodyguard regiment. They were, naturally, Bolsheviks— at least I hope so. For they had also constituted themselves my Praetorians, devoted themselves to me beyond normal dedication. To everyone's alarm, particularly mine, they would advise each other: "Shoot first, ask questions afterward." Stalin sat down again and lit his pipe.

"Just one more question, Joseph Vissarionvich. From the third book you chose for me. Another half novel, half autobiography. Not a very satisfactory form, do you find? I seem to cross the pages only incidentally, so far as I can make out from a quick dip. But someone, presumably you, has marked one passage I might have missed. Apparently Lenin has green eyes . . . 'like a monkey.'

"Thank you, Joseph Vissarionovich, this has made my day."

Stalin stood up and made a signal to the Letts. To my surprise, they nodded and went away. I could see he was going to play the old-soldier card. He grinned in a slightly overdone way.

"I'll strangle the bastard!" he said. "I might have known there was a trick in it. I didn't choose the books, it was . . ."

"No," I interrupted. "I think Nadya and I know who it must be. Right, all together now." And all three of us in unison said— "*Radek!*"

And all three laughed and laughed.

Stalin has his rough edges. And when you bump into him, they bruise you more than they do him. But underneath, the tough one is 100 percent with us.

SEPTEMBER 20   GORKI   1922

To the astonishment of everybody, doctors above all, though considerate callers make an effort not to look *too* astonished, I am almost completely recovered. I alone seem able to take this in my stride, itself only faintly hampered by a limp of the right leg. I have had to learn nearly every bodily process over again from the beginning. It was a challenge I rather enjoyed, to tell the truth. All my life I have pushed my body to its limits, awaking, parading, drilling muscle by muscle, so that when a big push was needed I could alert them all in seconds. This training has enabled me this year to reassemble myself from a thing back into a man.

"I told you so" is not a phrase anybody, except the speaker, likes to hear. But I cannot resist it. After all, it was not so long ago that I could not tell anybody anything. Now I am poking my finger in everywhere. And, I should record, I do find myself, wherever I make a test, in general agreement with our GenSec Stalin. More than any other member of the Politburo, or commissars in Sovnarkom, he keeps in touch with me and keeps me in touch.

He called this afternoon. "Our warrior chief ready to mount again, eh, Ilyich?"

"I told you so."

"And I told *you* so. I wrote it in *Pravda* after my last visit. But, I forget, you don't read the papers anymore."

He laughed, shaking all over like a dog being sick. My dog, Aida, shook itself and snarled.

"I see in the foreign newspapers, the capitalist scribblers already have you dead and buried. Perhaps we should publish a series of photographs of you down here. A Day in the Life of . . . sort of thing. I'll see what *Pravda* can do along those lines."

"Certainly not. It's clear you never read that trash for yourself. Else you'd understand that would be just the stuff to convince them I've cashed all my rubles. Lenin on a bench. Lenin under a birch tree. Lenin with his dog, his wife, the local child, the statutory peasant. It has all the signs of a fake testimonial. No, let the capitalist *smerdi* lie and enjoy themselves. Their whole social system is about to come to its end. We shall bury them. You should not deprive the dying of their last consolation. Anyway, I don't intend to remain down here anymore in Siberian banishment at Gorki. I am coming back to Moscow. The beginning of next month at the latest."

I moved my leg to ring Fotieva's bell, a feat roughly equivalent, with my present physical equipment, to performing a handspring when I was a student. Stalin was watching.

"Don't bother to ring," he said. "I'm going. Do you know the Tsar wanted to put an electric fence all the way round Russia in 1916? It is in the Royal Archives. Nice dog."

Off he went, bandy-legged, head cocked, right hand giving his withered left a Masonic grip, like a old farm hound retiring to its kennel. Aida followed him, walking tall, protective, arrogant, my personal, incorruptible guard. As he turned to wave, he cuffed her, hard, under the chin. She reared, then cowered, belly in the dust, licking his boots.

SEPTEMBER 24   GORKI   1922

Bike rider—shades of poor old Sverdlov!—all leathered up, black and glossy, a conveyor-belt Gucci commissar, skids to a racing stop up by the gate.

Early edition of our very first *Pravda* picture supplement, what Radek in a Yankee drawl calls the "rotagravure," has to be exciting, almost whatever its content. The Germans were the pioneers here, even before the war. I remember whenever I crossed their frontier I'd rush out and buy one. Pages of news pictures always have a certain cheap allure, like food eaten hot on the street from a paper bag, especially to someone who has spent so much of his life working on the *blatts*. Young people, and many foreigners, seem to think I was solely a cellar conspirator, amassing weapons for an uprising. I have to explain that I have always been first a propagandist, then an organizer, one supported the other—I built our Party, that overthrew an Empire, upon a newspaper!

The acidy, sour-fruit smell of the ink—the cauliflower-melon sweetness of damp paper—the baked-pie, pastry warmth of the presses—the aromatic gum and salady oil . . . doesn't this create a seductive dressing that, for an old pro, makes any message preferable to a white space?

NO!

Not when the copy, as in this souvenir extra, is a dreadfully sensationalized mixture of sentimentality and hero-worship, religiosity, childishness, masquerading as socialist emotion and revolutionary passion.

WE WANT HIM BACK! screams a headline. "Please do not leave us, Comrade Lenin!" runs a plea, in various phrasing, across reams of letters, interviews, resolutions. Marooned every few inches in this dark, Sargasso Sea of print is an island of sepia photography—me on a bench, me in a deck-chair, me reading, me picking mushrooms, me with Nadya, me with my sisters, my secretaries, with Stalin, him standing, me almost lying down, uncle and nephew pose.

I have had myself to plant a concealed message behind a formal one too often to miss the significance of the iconography. Clearly, this Lenin is an aging, retired invalid. This Lenin is no longer handling the levers of power. I can understand the bourgeois press, and émigrés, preferring such a picture of me, even to one of me smirking in my coffin. (Father had a curious, smug smile on his dead face as I walked round the corpse.) It reads in invisible ink—Lenin is gradually fading away . . . just like Communism.

But why do the editors of *Pravda* publish such things? I hate all of it. I would like to have no portraits of me anywhere. If this *drek* is necessary to keep the Revolution turning (as they always pretend when I hunt them down by telephone) then *we must have made the wrong revolution.*

It is all so . . . so . . . so *American!*

Back to Moscow, to show I am not a superannuated heirloom.

DECEMBER 7   GORKI   1922

In country once again after busy spell in city. Took back several key files. I am determined not to be starved of the oxygen of information that keeps my brain turning over between bouts of getting coked up like the engine of my hiccupping, old, official Rolls-Royce. This evening, for example, I telephoned the secretariat at Sovnarkom with precise instructions on how its business was now to be run in my absence so that I can bring myself up to date as quickly and easily as possible whenever I return. (The details are registered, with all my other communications, even the oral ones, in my office diaries.) But typical piece of procedure that it ought not to need me to insist upon—all documents forwarded to me must be numbered, entered with short summary in telegraphic form not more than three lines, in a special volume, kept in two copies.

Later still, this evening, I telephoned Moscow again and laid down the rules for the functioning of the Politburo. Meeting every Thursday, 11:30 A.M. until *not later than 2 P.M.*, agenda to all members before noon Wednesday; written data should accompany; new subjects added to agenda on day of meeting *only in emergency* in writing, and if all members concur; leftover business dealt with at added sessions, Friday, Monday, but basic rule—*action this day!* And so on.

Russian officials, tsarist or Communist, eventually do what they are told, but *only* what they are told, and if something is not mentioned, they assume it is either impossible or forbidden!

Also roughed out letter, to be dictated to Fotieva tomorrow, about the tasks appropriate to Tsyurupa, Kamenev and Rykov, my three deputy chairmen at Sovnarkom. I put all my authority, moral, personal, official, historical, into showing them that their task is to scrutinize, correct and improve the function of our state. It is not to sit around chattering with commissars and assistant commissars—their previous method of running the country. The trio must "descend to the depths," get down to the seabed and the coal-face of real administration. They must personally, and without warning, burst in upon the *apparatchiki* in action, high and low. urprise the bastards! Demand explanations for everything! When they leave, they must order that whatever investigations are necessary be summary and immediate, results produced in writing, circulated to *all* departments.

This is what Stalin's old ministry—he gave it up just a few months ago—ought to have done and didn't. Rabkrin, the Workers' and Peasants' Inspectorate, should live up to its name and be the hands and eyes of the people. So far it begins to look like nothing so much as a club for Stalin's veterans of Red Army days—old soldiers, I fear, instead of being knot-cutters and takers of short cuts, actually love red tape.

DECEMBER 10   GORKI   1922

I have been off and on back in the Kremlin, in my old office, trying to carry out my old job, from the first of October until a few days ago. It was rather like treading water in a whirlpool. I stayed afloat. But I'm not sure how far I got anywhere. Everybody kept telling me I was doing a fantastic amount and had completely recovered. It's easy to believe what you want to believe. To be certain I am not fooling myself. I asked Fotieva this morning to show me the official records she keeps of my work load, later circulated round the Politburo.

It turns out that in the last 70 days I have dictated 224 letters or memoranda, received 171 official visitors, presided over 32 sessions of Politburo or Sovnarkom, made 3 major political speeches, and spoken at 4 congresses.

Not bad, even by my standards. Especially considering I have continually refused to become a figurehead, a quasi-royal dummy on wheels. I cannot help involving myself up to my elbows, or possibly eyebrows, in anything I touch. Still . . . too many things are eluding me. I can't get this nationality business straight. I will not permit the first state ever to be captured and run by the oppressed to be oppressing others because they are minorities.

Georgia is the *locus classicus* here. This was the one part of Russia where the Mensheviks seemed genuinely popular, genuinely proletarian, genuinely revolutionary. (Proof in itself that nationality is not an artificial, unreal invention of the bourgeoisie to divide and rule—only Georgians could breed Menshies like that!) I later sanctioned our Red Army invasion because I believed that Stalin's chums, the Georgian Bolsheviks, were even more representative of the people's feeling, people as workers, people as Caucasians. Now I hear that Sergo (Ordzhonikidze) and Koba (Stalin) and Kamo (Ter-Petrosian), the whole Georgian Camorra here, are kicking out the local Bolsheviks, their own people, and imposing a centralized, colonialist regime upon them, operated from Moscow. Non-Russians are always the worst Russifiers. I have asked Felix Edmundovich (Dzerzhinsky) to find out what is going on there and I should have his report in a couple of days.

There is also the question of the monopoly of foreign trade. It seems obvious to me that this must be kept a monopoly, and kept in the hands of a ranking commissar in the Politburo. Otherwise, we shall have Western bourgeois millionaires and their bagmen creeping around, buying up ex-tsarist bureaucrats, planting their own agents on our sales directorates. Then . . . life corruption, political and economic power becoming interchangeable commodities, all the moral decay of a backward country being exploited by insidious money influence instead of open military domination. Here again I find it hard to unearth the facts. Not even the latest figures for officeholders in the civil service! Trotsky is on my side. Everyone else is evasive. And again, Stalin! He haunts the Kremlin. Always floating past at the end of the corridor, just around the corner, a presence signaled by the flapping door in the empty documents room, the spoor of pipe-smoke in the double-locked filing cabinet.

DECEMBER 12   MOSCOW   1922

Back again in Kremlin. Two-hour meeting of Sovnarkom directorate. Some routine stuff from Tsyurupa and Kamenev. (Tsyurupa does not look well—I told him to take two weeks off by the Black Sea, otherwise, my old joke, I would have him arrested and charged with damaging property belonging to the state!) I thought I might learn something about what is happening in Georgia from Rykov. But he only looks shifty, and repeats that he has made a joint

report with Dzerzhinsky, and it would not be "correct" to anticipate it.

I spent the afternoon in what Inessa used to call one of my
"ratty" moods, that is tugging and tearing away at what others have
just done up into neat parcels and giving a nasty nip to anyone
who tries to distract me. This time, they were beautifully typed,
laid out, sleeved and tied up (with red tape! Ha!) Rabkrin cases
from Joseph V.S.'s day. Every one a cover-up, a long short story,
an imaginary investigation of an imaginary injustice solved by
imaginary means—Arthur Conan Doyle could not have done better! I sent each one back to its individual inspector with an accompanying sheet, signed by me, saying only "Not good enough, try
again." Typed, at the bottom I had put "Copy to local branch of
Cheka"—(*Most secret*: it does not go to the Cheka, but it does no
harm for whitewash experts to think it does.)

At last, Felix Edmundovich turned up at 6:45. Dzerzhinsky is
a great man. Some say, though in my vocabulary that is hardly
praise, a *saint*! "Yes," quipped Radek the first time the claim was
made, "Saint-Just." It was a jest that set off an immediate response
round our circle, all of whom can recite the events of the French
Revolution by heart and talk about its leading figures as if we had
known them. Comparisons, even self-comparisons, are common.
I have been likened to Robespierre by Plekhanov, by Martov, I
think by Trotsky, and of course, since our Revolution, by every
petty scribbler in the West who has access to a biographical dictionary. Saint-Just and Felix have many traits in common. Both
steely, uncompromising, hard-liners, men of the left extreme, who
respond to the call for blood and sacrifice, preachers of liberation
by war. Saint-Just was Robespierre's most loyal supporter and Felix
has always backed me, especially when I have been in a minority,
as during my campaign to advance the timing of the October
uprising. He was against me over Brest-Litovsk though, convinced
we could carry socialism into Europe on the tips of our bayonets.

I would mark him far above Saint-Just myself, a real thor-
oughbred, forever keyed and ready for the race, prancing and
curvetting to be released. Not a saint, but a fanatic in the best
sense. Much reviled, not only among the bourgeois slanderers, as
the "Red Hangman," he is internally coiled spring upon spring,
not easy to explore. Like an infernal machine, he'd explode before
he revealed his secrets. His enemies would jeer if they knew, as I
do, of his affection for children, his quite amazing ability to tame
and attract animals, his tender concern for ordinary people. Everybody knows that when the Cheka, the Extraordinary Commission

for the Struggle against Sabotage and Counterrevolution, was being set up, he *asked* to be made its head. What few realize is that this was not because he feels drawn toward the inevitable killings, beatings and other brutalities he would have to witness and authorize. He hates the idea of the Cheka with all his being. But he realizes such "dirty work" must be done and he never shrinks from the inevitable. Felix is more "Bolshevik" than all of us rolled together. He always wants 110 percent: total support or total opposition—a great strength, but sometimes an unfortunate weakness.

Would I say that if he had emerged on *my* side over Georgia and the dispute about the role of nationalities in the new constitution? Maybe not. I thought he would at first, his report was so damning of Stalin's strong-arm brigade in the Caucasus, even to Ordzhonikidze using his fists to strike fellow comrades. Absolutely unpardonable behavior! But I forget, Felix is a Pole and a Polish nobleman. He knows the power of patriotism, love for the land and the people, and he fears that this may override commitment to socialism, and the first worker-peasant state. "If they are given a real right to secede, and create their own piddling principalities, they will," he says. Also his time at the Cheka has made him obsessive about security just as his other job as commissar for transport, succeeding poor dead brother-in-law Mark, has made him a stickler for centralization. He openly confesses he will be my implacable opponent on this and several other matters, eyes blazing, lips curled in a Satanic sneer. What he does not tell me is whether this also means he is backing Joseph Stalin as, not just a *primus inter pares,* the sort of first among equals I have been, but a Mussolini-style Roman dictator.

It is a great blow. I feel I have lost a right arm. At the moment I can't afford a finger.

DECEMBER 13   MOSCOW   1922

What a blow indeed! The second bell? Time may be growing short. If I don't catch the train, it could leave without me. Even worse, without me, it may never leave at all.

The physical and mental, the emotional and organic, have always been peculiarly intertwined inside me. I see now—our scientists could use me as a guinea pig to investigate this unexplored area—that a history, a chart, of my illnesses would also be a history, a chart, of my successes and failures as a professional revolutionary. Place one on the other and they would exactly coincide. Now there is an extra irony. Every time I suffer a wound to my health, I am shifted another step away from power. Every time I am shifted another step away from power, must I suffer a wound to my health?

Around 3 A.M., as I lay in bed digesting the hard, bitter lesson of Felix's defection, I felt as if I had been struck again by Fanny Kaplan's bullets. It was a pain which removed pain, leaving behind a frozen emptiness. I had been shot in the head, but from inside the head. Then I was seized by an attack of nausea such as I would never have believed possible, a seasick passenger tossed in a wet sheet of sail over a boiling ocean.

I vomited into my washbasin, coughing up jagged projectiles. I had the ridiculous schoolboy terror, hangover from some feeble fairy tale, that I was getting rid of my ration of days, gobbet by gobbet.

There is no question of keeping your bodily needs secret at the top in the Kremlin. Within minutes of my giving the final heave and falling into bed like a casualty in a field hospital, bodyguards were pounding along the corridor. Aida was making her last stand against them at the door. Then various doctors squeezed in. Then the personal assistants of all the various commissars, chairmen and general secretaries. Do they all sleep across my doormat, like the sons of the Sultan?

I watched this through a screen of haze, as from inside a clouded goldfish bowl, hearing only atomized fragments. When all but the medics were cleared out, I rose like a puppet and acted out another bout before their eyes. That time, when I toppled back into oblivion, I heard Dr. Auerbach say—"Two cerebral thromboses within one hour . . ."

Today has seen nothing but authorized visitors advising me to not do this or that—being translated *give it up.* "All work must stop" seemed a popular comment, since they repeated it to each other.

So first I got rid of everybody including Fotieva and her team in order to put down this entry. I don't know how much, if any, will survive of this account, kept going, intermittently, since I was sixteen. But, if they edit out all the largely irrelevant personal stuff, it may prove useful to historians of our state and those who seek to make such another. Nobody thinks I can be writing, because the ink has been removed and will only be produced on demand. But baggy, ill-fitting suits have an advantage. There is plenty of

room for concealed weapons—mine is a "fountain-pen" given to
me by H. G. Wells. Portable reservoirs of writing power may be
common in the West. Here they are not even suspected. The diary
pad fits unnoticed in a back pocket. I can put my thoughts on
paper whenever I want—a wonderful boon!—though this suspi-
ciously jumpy right hand may be a sign of worse to come soon. I
must hurry, hurry, hurry! Second bell!

DECEMBER 17   MOSCOW   1922

I'm keeping my strategy just—I almost wrote "one jump" . . . that
would be a joke, ha!—just ahead of my brain and my body. Fortunately, I was able to get rid of all the busybodies and the informers and even the doctors, whose interest often seems political
rather than clinical. I have been dictating round the clock like a
power-driven mincer, the girls leaping in, one after the other, to
spoon up the flow, package it and dispatch it.

I cannot sleep. Ice-picks of pain puncture my head every few
minutes. I have never worked so hard, ever. I have put my views
to Stalin on a wide range of subjects. If he emerges as a would-be
Bonaparte, which of course he will present as the epitome of "Len-
inism" (his coinage), he will never be able to quote me verbatim
in support of his present policies. (Copies have been kept and filed
in several safe places.) Basically, my strategy boils down to more
power to Rabkrin and other independent inspectorates; no agreements with agents of foreign powers except at top level after open
discussion and majority decision. The CenCom, at twenty-seven
members far too small and easily dominated, far too full of pen-
pushers and gun-toters (i.e., bureaucrats and police), must be expanded to include fifty, or preferably one hundred, genuine workers. No more bullying and repression of national feelings, e.g., in
Ukraine, Caucasus, Baltic states . . . I have done the same with
Trotsky, asking his support for them in any future struggle over
policy. I have written to all other leading comrades, stressing the
need for new means to deal with new problems, for reliance on
the energy, the invention, the courage of the rank and file, while
summarizing my messages to Stalin and Trotsky. I want to show
that I am not in exile, not a voice from afar, not a retired convalescent pottering about the woods with his dog and his mush-
room basket (as in the *Pravda* supplement). While I am alive, and
can move a finger, even flick an eye, I will keep up my barrage
on the Kremlin.

But *that* is the question. How alive am I? Last night I came again under attack from the enemy within. Once more, I felt what amounts to a curious absence of feeling—the numbness that follows a gunshot wound—creeping across the left-hand side of my brain, drooping over the eye which went blank, looping round the ear which went deaf. It lasted for exactly, by my admiral's watch, thirty-five minutes. When it was over I again vomited like a machine gun. But this time, when I collapsed on my camp bed, I realized that the opposite side of my body, the right-hand, was almost completely paralyzed.

Four days ago, the doctors had accepted my plea that I must have a couple of hours each day to "wind up my affairs." Now, they blame themselves for allowing me to continue working. What the most able of them, Dr. Foerster, calls this "cat-and-mouse game" must stop, they decree. I am to do *nothing*!

DECEMBER 26   MOSCOW   1922

Three days ago, I started to dictate a Letter to Congress, a sort of political Last Will and Testament. Whether I will circulate it now, or leave it to be read out after my death, I have not decided. I may have no choice. The first attempt, I had to give up after four minutes.

I have kept trying to put down how I feel about the comrades who will carry on after me. Today, it is finished—well, the first installment. I have always tried never to deceive myself even when forced to deceive others. I know that I cannot have more than a year left, if that much. Let's say New Year's Day 1924—the seventh year in the life of the Soviet Union.

The manuscript rests with Nadya. She will guard it well—I have taken her views into account throughout, possibly tilting rather more than I earlier intended against Stalin, for instance, since she reports lately some almost incredible coarse abuse and threatening insults whenever she has mentioned that I am still reading the papers and studying the Party memoranda.

I include here a shortened version:

> The stability of the leadership will depend on cooperation between Stalin and Trotsky, by far the most experienced revolutionaries available.

> Comrade Stalin, having become GenSec, has concentrated

enormous, almost unlimited, power in his hands. I am not sure he always knows how to use that authority with sufficient caution. Stalin is too crude and domineering, and this fault, while tolerable among veteran Communists, becomes insupportable in such an office as GenSec.

Therefore I propose to the comrades that they find a way to remove Stalin from this position and appoint to it another who differs from Stalin only in his superiority as a person—that is, more patient, more loyal, more polite, more receptive to other comrades, less moody and willful, etc. . . .

On the other hand, Comrade Trotsky is distinguished not only by his exceptional ability—personally, he is without any doubt the most able man on the CenCom—but also by his too far-reaching self-confidence and a disposition to be too much attracted by the purely administrative side of affairs.

As for the others. Well, Bukharin is not only the most valuable theoretician in the Party, he is everybody's favorite across the membership. Personally, I have the greatest reservations about how fully Marxist he is, since there is something rather scholastic about him. Has he ever really learned and understood that the dialectic is not a philosophical concept but a practical guide to action?

Everyone knows the outstanding talents, and the long service, of Zinoviev and Kamenev. I have to say that their behavior in October was not, of course, accidental. But the past is past. Their actions then should no more be held against them than I ever have the pre-1917 non-Bolshevism of Trotsky.

How much better do I feel having got that off my chest.

Perhaps I will be able to pass on what I have learned, particularly *my mistakes,* before I go. I have in mind a farewell lecture to be called "Better Fewer, but *Better!*"

JANUARY 4   MOSCOW   1923

I have added to my "Testament." After much sniffing of the wind, listening to the sound of treads on the forest floor—the hunter's (or hunted's) instinct reviving?—I recommend that Stalin should be demoted. But not now. The change would be a shock to the system that could only be endured if the whole country could see that this was somehow a natural, obvious time for a reshuffle at the top. When would that time be? There is only one answer, I'm afraid. I'm glad to find I can face this fact with a certain amount of humor. It is, of course, on my death!

When I murmur such things to Nadya, she devises displacement activities not to listen. Not difficult, since my speech remains rather blurred. Oddly enough, this does not seem such a handicap with outsiders as I would have thought. Once people have elevated you into an eminence above them, they begin to imagine that you are and that you are saying what they want to believe. I only have to respond with *"Tak!"* or *"Vot!"*, favorite exclamations of mine, well, I suppose of anybody's, for them to go away having blown up my "So!" "There!" and "That's it!" into approval and support for whatever they were proposing.

If she does hear more than *"Tak!"* or *"Vot!"*, and I get the impression that my dear, marvelous wife is doing her best to deny the reality of my decline, step by step, plateau by plateau, she snaps at me: "Don't be morbid!" But I am being, on the contrary, extremely *healthy* and *natural*. I am adjusting to my inevitable disappearance from the surface the way the higher animals do, without pointless protest, fuss and general outbursts of "how-can-this-happen-to-me?" I want to go as rationally and modestly, yet realistically, as any Roman stoic.

MARCH 4　　　　　　MOSCOW　　　　　　1923

Victory! Of a kind. I find you learn to adjust to scale. But still quite impressive considering where and what I am and who and what *they* are. In the old days, I only had to threaten resignation from the leadership to break their nerve. Now it is the threat of not obeying "doctor's orders"—yesterday I took all the medicines and threw them into the pond. An hour later there was a call to say that after all I would be shown the documents about the Georgian business, the foreign trade monopoly, and anything else I wanted. I said: "Publish 'Better Fewer, but Better!' in *Pravda*." And here, today, it is.

Trotsky rang to congratulate me and give his personal thanks. We are closer now than ever, perhaps than I have ever been with anyone. (Politically, that is, for he is now my only hope for perpetuation of my policies. Personally, he still worries me. On the outside overambitious, glory-loving, hungry for power, but actually inside not half as ruthless, selfish, cunning as he needs to be to outmaneuver Stalin.) He says, as a joke—well, I hope as a joke—that my article hit the Politburo so hard, and they were so apprehensive of the effects of its publication, it was even suggested they suppress the piece but *publish a false one-off edition of the paper to fool me!* I'm flattered. So it was as good as that! Almost certainly my last contribution in thirty years as a newspaperman.

What it boils down to is this. I'm fed up with hearing Lunacharsky and his poets and publicists dilating about "proletarian" culture. I'd settle for a mild dose of the real bourgeois culture, even serf culture. Too much of a hurry is one of our big mistakes. Let's start with most people being able to read and write and *count*. Measurement is the beginning of all control of the world around you, all science. The first poems mankind composed were about animal husbandry, care of the crops, records of the weather.

Then, our state apparatus is deplorable, not to say wretched, rooted in the past. Five years is a breakneck speed from tsarism to Sovietism. I do not think more than a tiny minority have realized in themselves yet the true *goodness* of our social system. We must be skeptical, avoid boastfulness. The people will never believe what we promise for the future if our promises in the present are seen to be hollow.

This is the bit I wanted in italic capitals:

> In order to renew our state apparatus, we must at all costs set out first, to learn, secondly, to learn, and thirdly, to learn, and then see to it that learning shall not remain a dead letter, or a fashionable catchphrase, as so often. Learning must become part of our very being.

For this we must have a complete overhaul of Stalin's old power base, Rabkrin, Workers' and Peasants' Inspectorate. It must be run by the most advanced workers, really enlightened elements for whom we can vouch they will not take the word for the deed—the Bolshevik's greatest temptation—nor *utter a single word that goes against conscience*.

No more bustle masquerading as actual achievement. Among all people, at all levels, better fewer but better. More study of management. Send our most conscientious people to study it abroad, Germany, Britain, most particularly the USA. We must root out the rogues. We must study, not just in classrooms but out in the real world, shaking each other up, making jokes, producing some really sharp, biting *satire*. We must stop being prim, staid, dropping what the French call *pruderie*. Openness is all. We have made a revolution yet we stick to the mustiest rituals. We have made a great leap forward yet we show amazing timidity at the slightest change in office routine. We must get rid of theory for the moment.

Our historical duty to humanity is—survive! Hang on until the Socialist Revolution is victorious in more developed countries. The capitalist powers, partly deliberately but also partly unconsciously, utilized the civil war to spread ruin across our country. They could not overthrow our Revolution, but we must admit they have strongly hindered our progress toward socialism.

We must display extreme caution, at home and abroad. Thrift is the watchword, no extravagance. But does this mean a regime of peasant limitations? No, thrift will make for savings, for accumulated capital which we will spend on large-scale machine industry, electrification above all. These are lofty tasks I dream of for our Workers' and Peasants' Inspectorate (new, improved version). But everyone must get behind it, especially the Party and its leadership.

Enough for one article. I have written so much. Will the readers, inured to endless exhortation, sense this is different?

MARCH 6   MOSCOW   1923

Everybody now knows that I have taken the necessary steps to make permanent my retirement. I quite see leading comrades cannot run the ship if the former captain, supposedly in his wheelchair in an old sailors' home, keeps leaping aboard a tug to halt them in mid-ocean and correct their navigation. In a way, I wish Nadya could give out that I'm dead and gone, then I could read my obituaries and, much more vital, see who fills the vacuum I've felt.

I've done my best, though feeling increasingly awful, these last few days to leave as little as possible to chance. I have written a really smoking letter of red-hot criticism to Stalin about his bullying treatment of Nadya and told him he has to go. I have written to Trotsky, confirming the basic agreement of our views, and asking him to speak in both our names on the Georgian and other questions. I have written Mdivani and the other Georgians emphasizing that Trotsky and I are on their side against Stalin. I have asked Nadya to convey personally to Kamenev that I expect him and Trotsky and my former colleagues to use my authority to the utmost in the struggle to suppress Stalin. If he can carry on, after all these attacks, then he is another Rasputin.

MARCH 8   MOSCOW   1923

I do not know how long I can go on dictating a diary. Already it
is only my closeness to Fotieva—dear creature who has to write
these words about herself—that makes it still possible. She alone
understands the words that come slurred and broken from my
lips, like vomit from an empty stomach. On stage it would seem a
magic trick, or even a show of occult power. Today I make it easy.
She is to copy two passages from many that N. has collected, who
knows why or when, in a tin box labeled "Tributes." Most are
nonsense, some rather sickening. But two I believe say something
about me I would want said. I indulge this last little vanity.

N. herself has scribbled (quite recently?):

> In the course of this last year when I have stood so often by Ilyich's
> bed while he slept like a dead man, I have covered in my mind
> our whole life together. And this is what I would want to say to
> the nation. He loves with a deep love all the workers, all the
> oppressed. He himself never said this, never would have said this.
> Nor would I. I never would have even thought of this except at
> such a solemn moment.

And then, also in her own hand, she has recorded a fragment
to which Alexei Maximovich (Gorky) has put his signature. Is it
something he said to her, here, on that last visit? I see they are
both a kind of obituary.

> I have never met in Russia, the country where the inevitability of
> suffering is preached as the only road to salvation, nor have I
> ever known, any man anywhere who hates, despises and loathes
> so deeply and strongly all unhappiness, grief and suffering as
> Lenin did, *does*.
>
> He is particularly great, in my opinion, precisely because of
> his burning faith that suffering is not an essential and unavoidable
> part of life, but an abomination that people ought to, and are able
> to, sweep away.

Of the two I prefer the latter. That is the most important
message of life, my life. Yes, struggle. Marx's dying word. But
suffering, never.

AUGUST 10   GORKI   1923

No, I have not quite gone, though a lot of bits of me may have done. Positively the last appearance!

Two days after my last entry on March 8, the third bell sounded for my third stroke. I was found in bed in the Kremlin flat a corpse with rolling eyes. I could not move my right arm or leg, or speak, or understand much. I recall it vaguely, as if from inside a smoky ball. I was not frightened, or in pain. Mild irritation, perhaps, as you would if temporarily locked out of some big store behind a thick plate-glass door.

The next two months are like memories of childhood, vivid but fragmentary, and seemingly random. I seemed forever staring at the ceiling with occasional side glimpses of a distraught Nadya. I do recall her weeping and shouting something like "They have put him among the living dead!" *Merci!* as somebody I now can't remember would say.

In mid-June, I see from the calendar kept by my devoted secretaries, I moved to Gorki. Here I half-remember getting very nervous and excited, occasionally even twitching—a bad sign in health, but a good one in sickness.

Today, August 10, I have been given permission, out here at Gorki, to write small, short personal notes, no politics, no articles. I have taken the opportunity, left alone in the sunshine on a bench in the woods as requested, to put down what will definitely be my last words.

I have not much time, or space, or energy.

Collective leadership seems to be working quite well in the Kremlin with no bids for single power. What was my real, historic mistake? I do not have any absolute answers, so many results lie still in the future. But there is a strong case for arguing that I should have started the New Economic Policy as early as 1918. We then had the peasants, newly endowed with land, on our side. We could have avoided grain requisitioning with armed city-bands raiding the countryside and removing crops and cattle at gunpoint and substituted a reasonable tax in kind. We could have allowed some limited free trade and private enterprise. Parvus might have been a help—instead I rejected his offer as "dirty hands." City people still had things to sell that the country folk wanted. We alienated the peasantry. We also made the workers take the hardest, the almost unbearable, burdens—they starved, they froze, they worked tsarist hours for money which bought no tsarist necessities, *they* fought and died as both militia and Red Army soldiers. Who gained? The question I also asked. Nobody! We had the world against us and we almost defeated ourselves.

In 1918, I made the basic mistake of assuming we must keep to the strictest rules of socialism. I did not realize that "capitalism" is just a word like any other. NEP has made our enemies enrich us in order to enrich themselves. I had thought Soviet power too weak, and too disorganized, to face an explosion of free enterprise. I think I was wrong. Socialism will survive NEP and learn from it. Tomorrow must extend freedom, not reduce it.

But the comrades will march over the hill and into the sunny uplands without me.

[Lenin lived on, able to hear and understand, but unable to speak or .write, until his health suddenly deteriorated on January 21, 1924. He died at 6:50 P.M.

Stalin outmaneuvered all his enemies and rivals, to become dictator of the Soviet Union. Kamenev and Zinoviev were put in the dock in 1936 in the first of Stalin's show trials, found guilty and executed. Bukharin was a defendant in later show trials of 1938, found guilty and sentenced to be shot. Krupskaya had a token role as "Lenin's Widow" and survived under Stalin's eye until 1939. Kollontai became ambassador to Sweden and lived abroad until she died peacefully in Moscow in 1952. Trotsky was defeated by Stalin, deported in 1929, murdered by an agent of Stalin in Mexico in 1940.]